# Renault
# 9 & 11
# Owners
# Workshop
# Manual

## John S Mead

**Models covered**
All Renault 9 and 11 models, including limited/special editions, 'Electronic', Broadway, Automatic and Turbo
1108cc, 1237 cc, 1397 cc & 1721 cc

*Does not cover Diesel engine variants*

(822-8U6)

ABCDE
FGHIJ
KLMN

2

Haynes

THE
BOOK ®

**Haynes Publishing Group**
Sparkford  Nr Yeovil
Somerset  BA22 7JJ  England

**Haynes Publications, Inc**
861 Lawrence Drive
Newbury Park
California 91320  USA

## Acknowledgements

Thanks are due to Régie Renault, particularly Renault UK Limited for their assistance with technical information and the provision of certain illustrations. Thanks are also due to Champion Spark Plug who supplied the illustrations showing spark plug conditions, to Holt Lloyd Limited who supplied the illustrations showing bodywork repair, and to Duckhams Oils who provided lubrication data. Sykes-Pickavant Limited provided some of the workshop tools.

Special thanks are also due to Bride Valley Motor Company of Winterbourne Abbas, Dorset for the loan of project cars, to Westward Motors of Bath, Avon for their assistance in providing a vehicle for photographic purposes, and to the staff at Sparkford who assisted in the production of this manual.

© **Haynes Publishing Group 1992**

A book in the **Haynes Owners Workshop Manual Series**

Printed by J. H. Haynes & Co. Ltd, Sparkford, Nr Yeovil,
Somerset BA22 7JJ, England

ISBN 1 85010 844 7

**British Library Cataloguing in Publication Data**
A catalogue record for this book is available from the British Library

We take great pride in the accuracy of information given in this manual, but vehicle manufacturers make alterations and design changes during the production run of a particular vehicle of which they do not inform us. No liability can be accepted by the authors or publishers for loss, damage or injury caused by any errors in, or omissions from, the information given.

# Restoring and Preserving our Motoring Heritage

Few people can have had the luck to realise their dreams to quite the same extent and in such a remarkable fashion as John Haynes, Founder and Chairman of the Haynes Publishing Group.

Since 1965 his unique approach to workshop manual publishing has proved so successful that millions of Haynes Manuals are now sold every year throughout the world, covering literally thousands of different makes and models of cars, vans and motorcycles.

A continuing passion for cars and motoring led to the founding in 1985 of a Charitable Trust dedicated to the restoration and preservation of our motoring heritage. To inaugurate the new Museum, John Haynes donated virtually his entire private collection of 52 cars.

Now with an unrivalled international collection of over 210 veteran, vintage and classic cars and motorcycles, the Haynes Motor Museum in Somerset is well on the way to becoming one of the most interesting Motor Museums in the world.

A 70 seat video cinema, a cafe and an extensive motoring bookshop, together with a specially constructed one kilometre motor circuit, make a visit to the Haynes Motor Museum a truly unforgettable experience.

Every vehicle in the museum is preserved in as near as possible mint condition and each car is run every six months on the motor circuit.

Enjoy the picnic area set amongst the rolling Somerset hills. Peer through the William Morris workshop windows at cars being restored, and browse through the extensive displays of fascinating motoring memorabilia.

From the 1903 Oldsmobile through such classics as an MG Midget to the mighty 'E' Type Jaguar, Lamborghini, Ferrari Berlinetta Boxer, and Graham Hill's Lola Cosworth, there is something for everyone, young and old alike, at this Somerset Museum.

## Haynes Motor Museum

*Situated mid-way between London and Penzance, the Haynes Motor Museum is located just off the A303 at Sparkford, Somerset (home of the Haynes Manual) and is open to the public 7 days a week all year round, except Christmas Day and Boxing Day.*

# Contents

*Spark plug condition and bodywork repair colour pages between pages 32 and 33*

**Renault 9 TSE**

**Renault 11 TSE**

# About this manual

## Its aim

The aim of this manual is to help you get the best value from your vehicle. It can do so in several ways. It can help you decide what work must be done (even should you choose to get it done by a garage), provide information on routine maintenance and servicing, and give a logical course of action and diagnosis when random faults occur. However, it is hoped that you will use the manual by tackling the work yourself. On simpler jobs it may even be quicker than booking the car into a garage and going there twice, to leave and collect it. Perhaps most important, a lot of money can be saved by avoiding the costs a garage must charge to cover its labour and overheads.

The manual has drawings and descriptions to show the function of the various components so that their layout can be understood. Then the tasks are described and photographed in a step-by-step sequence so that even a novice can do the work.

## Its arrangement

The manual is divided into twelve Chapters, each covering a logical sub-division of the vehicle. The Chapters are each divided into Sections, numbered with single figures, eg 5; and the Sections into paragraphs (or sub-sections), with decimal numbers following on from the Section they are in, eg 5.1, 5.2, 5.3 etc.

It is freely illustrated, especially in those parts where there is a detailed sequence of operations to be carried out. There are two forms of illustration: figures and photographs. The figures are numbered in sequence with decimal numbers, according to their position in the Chapter – eg Fig. 6.4 is the fourth drawing/illustration in Chapter 6. Photographs carry the same number (either individually or in related groups) as the Section or sub-section to which they relate.

There is an alphabetical index at the back of the manual as well as a contents list at the front. Each Chapter is also preceded by its own individual contents list.

References to the 'left' or 'right' of the vehicle are in the sense of a person in the driver's seat facing forwards.

Unless otherwise stated, nuts and bolts are removed by turning anti-clockwise, and tightened by turning clockwise.

Vehicle manufacturers continually make changes to specifications and recommendations, and these, when notified, are incorporated into our manuals at the earliest opportunity.

**We take great pride in the accuracy of information given in this manual, but vehicle manufacturers make alterations and design changes during the production run of a particular vehicle of which they do not inform us. No liability can be accepted by the authors or publishers for loss, damage or injury caused by any errors in, or omissions from, the information given.**

# Introduction to the Renault 9 and 11

Available with a choice of three engine sizes and a variety of trim and equipment options, the Renault 9 was introduced in the UK in March 1982 and was voted that year's car of the year by a panel of 52 motoring journalists. In July 1983 the Renault 11 was launched in this country as a three- or five-door hatchback version of the Renault 9. Apart from the obvious bodywork differences, altered facia layout and the choice of an additional larger engine, both the Renaults 9 and 11 are mechanically identical.

The cars feature independent front and rear suspension by MacPherson struts and trailing arms respectively, four or five-speed manual or three-speed automatic transmission with front-wheel-drive, 1108 cc, 1237 cc or 1397 cc overhead valve engines and, on the Renault 11, a 1721 cc overhead camshaft unit.

All models in the range have been designed with the emphasis on economical motoring, with a high standard of handling, performance and comfort.

6

# General dimensions, weights and capacities

*For information applicable to later models, see Supplement at end of manual*

## Dimensions

Turning circle (between kerbs):
    Renault 9 ................................................................. 9800 mm (386 in)
    Renault 11 ............................................................... 9750 mm (384 in)
Wheelbase ..................................................................... 2477 mm (98 in)
Overall length:
    Renault 9 ................................................................. 4063 mm (160 in)
    Renault 11 ............................................................... 3981 mm (157 in)
Overall width:
    Renault 9 (with side protective mouldings) ................. 1668 mm (66 in)
    Renault 11 (with side protective mouldings) ............... 1660 mm (65 in)
Overall height ................................................................ 1406 mm (55 in)
Ground clearance .......................................................... 120 mm (4.7 in)
Track:
    Front ....................................................................... 1395 mm (55 in)
    Rear ........................................................................ 1357 mm (53 in)

## Weights

Kerb weight – Renault 9 models:
    C and TC ................................................................. 840 kg (1852 lb)
    TL, GTL and TLE ..................................................... 860 kg (1896 lb)
    GTS and TSE .......................................................... 880 kg (1940 lb)
    GTX ........................................................................ 900 kg (1984 lb)
    Automatic ................................................................ 885 kg (1951 lb)
Kerb weight – Renault 11 models:
    TC ........................................................................... 830 kg (1830 lb)
    GTL (3-door) ........................................................... 860 kg (1896 lb)
    GTL (5-door) ........................................................... 870 kg (1918 lb)
    Automatic ................................................................ 905 kg (1995 lb)
    TSE and TXE .......................................................... 900 kg (1984 lb)
    GTX ........................................................................ 910 kg (2006 lb)
    Turbo ...................................................................... 915 kg (2018 lb)
Maximum roof rack weight ............................................ 60 kg (132 lb)

## Capacities

Engine oil (refill with filter change):
    1108 cc, 1237 cc and 1397 cc engines (except Turbo) ...... 3 litres (5.3 Imp pints)
    1397 cc Turbo engines ............................................ 3.7 litres (6.5 Imp pints)
    1721 cc engines ...................................................... 5 litres (8.8 Imp pints)
Oil filter capacity:
    1108 cc, 1237 cc and 1397 cc engines ................... 0.25 litre (0.44 Imp pint)
    1721 cc engines ...................................................... 0.5 litre (0.88 Imp pint)
Manual gearbox:
    Four-speed units ..................................................... 3.25 litres (5.7 Imp pints)
    Five-speed units ..................................................... 3.4 litres (6.0 Imp pints)
Automatic transmission (refill after draining – approximate) ........ 2.0 litres (3.5 Imp pints)
Cooling system:
    1108 cc, 1237 cc and 1397 cc engines (except Turbo) ...... 6.0 litres (10.6 Imp pints)
    1397 cc Turbo engines ............................................ 6.9 litres (12.1 Imp pints)
    1721 cc engines ...................................................... 6.7 litres (11.8 Imp pints)
Fuel tank ....................................................................... 47 litres (10.3 Imp gallons)

# Buying spare parts
# and vehicle identification numbers

*For information applicable to later models, see Supplement at end of manual*

---

### Buying spare parts

Spare parts are available from many sources, for example: Renault garages, other garages and accessory shops, and motor factors. Our advice regarding spare parts is as follows:

*Officially appointed Renault garages:* These will be the best source of parts which are peculiar to your car and are otherwise not generally available (eg, complete cylinder heads, internal gearbox components, badges, interior trim etc). It is also the only place at which you should buy parts if your car is still under warranty; non-Renault components may invalidate the warranty. To be sure of obtaining the correct parts it will always be necessary to give the storeman your car's vehicle identification number, and if possible to take the old part along for positive identification. Remember that many parts are available on a factory exchange scheme — any parts returned should always be clean! It obviously makes good sense to go straight to the specialists on your car for this type of part as they are best equipped to supply you.

*Other garages and accessory shops* — These are often very good places to buy materials and components needed for the maintenance of your car (eg, oil filters, spark plugs, bulbs, fan belts, oils and greases, touch-up paint, filler paste etc). They also sell general accessories, usually have convenient opening hours, charge lower prices and can often be found not far from home.

*Motor factors* — Good factors will stock all of the more important components which wear out relatively quickly (eg, clutch components, pistons, valves, exhaust systems, brake cylinders/pipes/hoses/seals/shoes and pads etc). Motor factors will often provide new or reconditioned components on a part exchange basis — this can save a considerable amount of money.

### Vehicle identification numbers

Modifications are a continuing and unpublicised process in vehicle manufacture quite apart from their major model changes. Spare parts manuals and lists are compiled on a numerical basis, the individual vehicle numbers being essential for correct identification of the component required.

When ordering parts it will usually be necessary to quote the numbers on the oval plate under all circumstances and often those on the manufacturer's plate. If engine or gearbox parts are being ordered the engine plate or gearbox plate numbers will be needed. The paint code may be required if the colour of the car is not easily described. All these numbers with the exception of those on the gearbox plate are located in readily visible places in the engine compartment. The gearbox plate is affixed to the transmission housing.

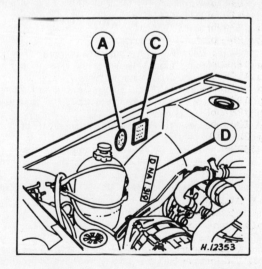

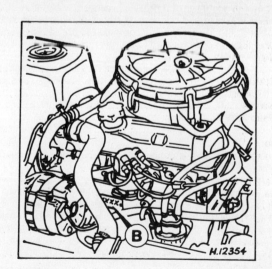

**Vehicle identification number locations**

*A  Oval plate*       *B  Engine plate (1108 cc and 1397 cc engines)*       *C  Manufacturer's plate*       *D  Paint code*

# General repair procedures

Whenever servicing, repair or overhaul work is carried out on the car or its components, it is necessary to observe the following procedures and instructions. This will assist in carrying out the operation efficiently and to a professional standard of workmanship.

## Joint mating faces and gaskets

Where a gasket is used between the mating faces of two components, ensure that it is renewed on reassembly, and fit it dry unless otherwise stated in the repair procedure. Make sure that the mating faces are clean and dry with all traces of old gasket removed. When cleaning a joint face, use a tool which is not likely to score or damage the face, and remove any burrs or nicks with an oilstone or fine file.

Make sure that tapped holes are cleaned with a pipe cleaner, and keep them free of jointing compound if this is being used unless specifically instructed otherwise.

Ensure that all orifices, channels or pipes are clear and blow through them, preferably using compressed air.

## Oil seals

Whenever an oil seal is removed from its working location, either individually or as part of an assembly, it should be renewed.

The very fine sealing lip of the seal is easily damaged and will not seal if the surface it contacts is not completely clean and free from scratches, nicks or grooves. If the original sealing surface of the component cannot be restored, the component should be renewed.

Protect the lips of the seal from any surface which may damage them in the course of fitting. Use tape or a conical sleeve where possible. Lubricate the seal lips with oil before fitting and, on dual lipped seals, fill the space between the lips with grease.

Unless otherwise stated, oil seals must be fitted with their sealing lips toward the lubricant to be sealed.

Use a tubular drift or block of wood of the appropriate size to install the seal and, if the seal housing is shouldered, drive the seal down to the shoulder. If the seal housing is unshouldered, the seal should be fitted with its face flush with the housing top face.

## Screw threads and fastenings

Always ensure that a blind tapped hole is completely free from oil, grease, water or other fluid before installing the bolt or stud. Failure to do this could cause the housing to crack due to the hydraulic action of the bolt or stud as it is screwed in.

When tightening a castellated nut to accept a split pin, tighten the nut to the specified torque, where applicable, and then tighten further to the next split pin hole. Never slacken the nut to align a split pin hole unless stated in the repair procedure.

When checking or retightening a nut or bolt to a specified torque setting, slacken the nut or bolt by a quarter of a turn, and then retighten to the specified setting.

## Locknuts, locktabs and washers

Any fastening which will rotate against a component or housing in the course of tightening should always have a washer between it and the relevant component or housing.

Spring or split washers should always be renewed when they are used to lock a critical component such as a big-end bearing retaining nut or bolt.

Locktabs which are folded over to retain a nut or bolt should always be renewed.

Self-locking nuts can be reused in non-critical areas, providing resistance can be felt when the locking portion passes over the bolt or stud thread.

Split pins must always be replaced with new ones of the correct size for the hole.

## Special tools

Some repair procedures in this manual entail the use of special tools such as a press, two or three-legged pullers, spring compressors etc. Wherever possible, suitable readily available alternatives to the manufacturer's special tools are described, and are shown in use. In some instances, where no alternative is possible, it has been necessary to resort to the use of a manufacturer's tool and this has been done for reasons of safety as well as the efficient completion of the repair operation. Unless you are highly skilled and have a thorough understanding of the procedure described, never attempt to bypass the use of any special tool when the procedure described specifies its use. Not only is there a very great risk of personal injury, but expensive damage could be caused to the components involved.

# Tools and working facilities

## Introduction

A selection of good tools is a fundamental requirement for anyone contemplating the maintenance and repair of a motor vehicle. For the owner who does not possess any, their purchase will prove a considerable expense, offsetting some of the savings made by doing-it-yourself. However, provided that the tools purchased meet the relevant national safety standards and are of good quality, they will last for many years and prove an extremely worthwhile investment.

To help the average owner to decide which tools are needed to carry out the various tasks detailed in this manual, we have compiled three lists of tools under the following headings: *Maintenance and minor repair*, *Repair and overhaul*, and *Special*. The newcomer to practical mechanics should start off with the *Maintenance and minor repair* tool kit and confine himself to the simpler jobs around the vehicle. Then, as his confidence and experience grow, he can undertake more difficult tasks, buying extra tools as, and when, they are needed. In this way, a *Maintenance and minor repair* tool kit can be built-up into a *Repair and overhaul* tool kit over a considerable period of time without any major cash outlays. The experienced do-it-yourselfer will have a tool kit good enough for most repair and overhaul procedures and will add tools from the *Special* category when he feels the expense is justified by the amount of use to which these tools will be put.

It is obviously not possible to cover the subject of tools fully here. For those who wish to learn more about tools and their use there is a book entitled *How to Choose and Use Car Tools* available from the publishers of this manual.

## Maintenance and minor repair tool kit

The tools given in this list should be considered as a minimum requirement if routine maintenance, servicing and minor repair operations are to be undertaken. We recommend the purchase of combination spanners (ring one end, open-ended the other); although more expensive than open-ended ones, they do give the advantages of both types of spanner.

*Combination spanners - 10, 11, 12, 13, 14 & 17 mm*
*Adjustable spanner - 9 inch*
*Set of Torx type keys or socket bits*
*Engine sump/gearbox/drain plug key*
*Spark plug spanner (with rubber insert)*
*Spark plug gap adjustment tool*
*Set of feeler gauges*
*Brake bleed nipple spanner*
*Screwdriver - 4 in long x $\frac{1}{4}$ in dia (flat blade)*
*Screwdriver - 4 in long x $\frac{1}{4}$ in dia (cross blade)*
*Combination pliers - 6 inch*
*Hacksaw (junior)*
*Tyre pump*
*Tyre pressure gauge*
*Oil can*
*Fine emery cloth (1 sheet)*
*Wire brush (small)*
*Funnel (medium size)*

## Repair and overhaul tool kit

These tools are virtually essential for anyone undertaking any major repairs to a motor vehicle, and are additional to those given in the *Maintenance and minor repair* list. Included in this list is a comprehensive set of sockets. Although these are expensive they will be found invaluable as they are so versatile - particularly if various drives are included in the set. We recommend the $\frac{1}{2}$ in square-drive type, as this can be used with most proprietary torque wrenches. If you cannot afford a socket set, even bought piecemeal, then inexpensive tubular box spanners are a useful alternative.

The tools in this list will occasionally need to be supplemented by tools from the *Special* list.

*Sockets (or box spanners) to cover range in previous list*
*Reversible ratchet drive (for use with sockets)*
*Extension piece, 10 inch (for use with sockets)*
*Universal joint (for use with sockets)*
*Torque wrench (for use with sockets)*
*'Mole' wrench - 8 inch*
*Ball pein hammer*
*Soft-faced hammer, plastic or rubber*
*Screwdriver - 6 in long x $\frac{5}{16}$ in dia (flat blade)*
*Screwdriver - 2 in long x $\frac{5}{16}$ in square (flat blade)*
*Screwdriver - 1$\frac{1}{2}$ in long x $\frac{1}{4}$ in dia (cross blade)*
*Screwdriver - 3 in long x $\frac{1}{8}$ in dia (electricians)*
*Pliers - electricians side cutters*
*Pliers - needle nosed*
*Pliers - circlip (internal and external)*
*Cold chisel - $\frac{1}{2}$ inch*
*Scriber*
*Scraper*
*Centre punch*
*Pin punch*
*Hacksaw*
*Valve grinding tool*
*Steel rule/straight-edge*
*Allen keys*
*Selection of files*
*Wire brush (large)*
*Axle-stands*
*Jack (strong scissor or hydraulic type)*

## Special tools

The tools in this list are those which are not used regularly, are expensive to buy, or which need to be used in accordance with their manufacturers' instructions. Unless relatively difficult mechanical jobs are undertaken frequently, it will not be economic to buy many of these tools. Where this is the case, you could consider clubbing together with friends (or joining a motorists' club) to make a joint purchase, or borrowing the tools against a deposit from a local garage or tool hire specialist.

The following list contains only those tools and instruments freely available to the public, and not those special tools produced by the vehicle manufacturer specifically for its dealer network. You will find occasional references to these manufacturers' special tools in the text of this manual. Generally, an alternative method of doing the job without the vehicle manufacturers' special tool is given. However, sometimes, there is no alternative to using them. Where this is the case and the relevant tool cannot be bought or borrowed, you will have to entrust the work to a franchised garage.

Valve spring compressor
Piston ring compressor
Balljoint separator
Universal hub/bearing puller
Impact screwdriver
Micrometer and/or vernier gauge
Dial gauge
Stroboscopic timing light
Dwell angle meter/tachometer
Universal electrical multi-meter
Cylinder compression gauge
Lifting tackle
Trolley jack
Light with extension lead

## Buying tools

For practically all tools, a tool factor is the best source since he will have a very comprehensive range compared with the average garage or accessory shop. Having said that, accessory shops often offer excellent quality tools at discount prices, so it pays to shop around.

There are plenty of good tools around at reasonable prices, but always aim to purchase items which meet the relevant national safety standards. If in doubt, ask the proprietor or manager of the shop for advice before making a purchase.

## Care and maintenance of tools

Having purchased a reasonable tool kit, it is necessary to keep the tools in a clean serviceable condition. After use, always wipe off any dirt, grease and metal particles using a clean, dry cloth, before putting the tools away. Never leave them lying around after they have been used. A simple tool rack on the garage or workshop wall, for items such as screwdrivers and pliers is a good idea. Store all normal wrenches and sockets in a metal box. Any measuring instruments, gauges, meters, etc, must be carefully stored where they cannot be damaged or become rusty.

Take a little care when tools are used. Hammer heads inevitably become marked and screwdrivers lose the keen edge on their blades from time to time. A little timely attention with emery cloth or a file will soon restore items like this to a good serviceable finish.

## Working facilities

Not to be forgotten when discussing tools, is the workshop itself. If anything more than routine maintenance is to be carried out, some form of suitable working area becomes essential.

It is appreciated that many an owner mechanic is forced by circumstances to remove an engine or similar item, without the benefit of a garage or workshop. Having done this, any repairs should always be done under the cover of a roof.

Wherever possible, any dismantling should be done on a clean, flat workbench or table at a suitable working height.

Any workbench needs a vice: one with a jaw opening of 4 in (100 mm) is suitable for most jobs. As mentioned previously, some clean dry storage space is also required for tools, as well as for lubricants, cleaning fluids, touch-up paints and so on, which become necessary.

Another item which may be required, and which has a much more general usage, is an electric drill with a chuck capacity of at least $\frac{5}{16}$ in (8 mm). This, together with a good range of twist drills, is virtually essential for fitting accessories such as mirrors and reversing lights.

Last, but not least, always keep a supply of old newspapers and clean, lint-free rags available, and try to keep any working area as clean as possible.

## Spanner jaw gap comparison table

| Jaw gap (in) | Spanner size |
|---|---|
| 0.250 | $\frac{1}{4}$ in AF |
| 0.276 | 7 mm |
| 0.313 | $\frac{5}{16}$ in AF |
| 0.315 | 8 mm |
| 0.344 | $\frac{11}{32}$ in AF; $\frac{1}{8}$ in Whitworth |
| 0.354 | 9 mm |
| 0.375 | $\frac{3}{8}$ in AF |
| 0.394 | 10 mm |
| 0.433 | 11 mm |
| 0.438 | $\frac{7}{16}$ in AF |
| 0.445 | $\frac{3}{16}$ in Whitworth; $\frac{1}{4}$ in BSF |
| 0.472 | 12 mm |
| 0.500 | $\frac{1}{2}$ in AF |
| 0.512 | 13 mm |
| 0.525 | $\frac{1}{4}$ in Whitworth; $\frac{5}{16}$ in BSF |
| 0.551 | 14 mm |
| 0.563 | $\frac{9}{16}$ in AF |
| 0.591 | 15 mm |
| 0.600 | $\frac{5}{16}$ in Whitworth; $\frac{3}{8}$ in BSF |
| 0.625 | $\frac{5}{8}$ in AF |
| 0.630 | 16 mm |
| 0.669 | 17 mm |
| 0.686 | $\frac{11}{16}$ in AF |
| 0.709 | 18 mm |
| 0.710 | $\frac{3}{8}$ in Whitworth; $\frac{7}{16}$ in BSF |
| 0.748 | 19 mm |
| 0.750 | $\frac{3}{4}$ in AF |
| 0.813 | $\frac{13}{16}$ in AF |
| 0.820 | $\frac{7}{16}$ in Whitworth; $\frac{1}{2}$ in BSF |
| 0.866 | 22 mm |
| 0.875 | $\frac{7}{8}$ in AF |
| 0.920 | $\frac{1}{2}$ in Whitworth; $\frac{9}{16}$ in BSF |
| 0.938 | $\frac{15}{16}$ in AF |
| 0.945 | 24 mm |
| 1.000 | 1 in AF |
| 1.010 | $\frac{9}{16}$ in Whitworth; $\frac{5}{8}$ in BSF |
| 1.024 | 26 mm |
| 1.063 | $1\frac{1}{16}$ in AF; 27 mm |
| 1.100 | $\frac{5}{8}$ in Whitworth; $\frac{11}{16}$ in BSF |
| 1.125 | $1\frac{1}{8}$ in AF |
| 1.181 | 30 mm |
| 1.200 | $\frac{11}{16}$ in Whitworth; $\frac{3}{4}$ in BSF |
| 1.250 | $1\frac{1}{4}$ in AF |
| 1.260 | 32 mm |
| 1.300 | $\frac{3}{4}$ in Whitworth; $\frac{7}{8}$ in BSF |
| 1.313 | $1\frac{5}{16}$ in AF |
| 1.390 | $\frac{13}{16}$ in Whitworth; $\frac{15}{16}$ in BSF |
| 1.417 | 36 mm |
| 1.438 | $1\frac{7}{16}$ in AF |
| 1.480 | $\frac{7}{8}$ in Whitworth; 1 in BSF |
| 1.500 | $1\frac{1}{2}$ in AF |
| 1.575 | 40 mm; $\frac{15}{16}$ in Whitworth |
| 1.614 | 41 mm |
| 1.625 | $1\frac{5}{8}$ in AF |
| 1.670 | 1 in Whitworth; $1\frac{1}{8}$ in BSF |
| 1.688 | $1\frac{11}{16}$ in AF |
| 1.811 | 46 mm |
| 1.813 | $1\frac{13}{16}$ in AF |
| 1.860 | $1\frac{1}{8}$ in Whitworth; $1\frac{1}{4}$ in BSF |
| 1.875 | $1\frac{7}{8}$ in AF |
| 1.969 | 50 mm |
| 2.000 | 2 in AF |
| 2.050 | $1\frac{1}{4}$ in Whitworth; $1\frac{3}{8}$ in BSF |
| 2.165 | 55 mm |
| 2.362 | 60 mm |

# Jacking and towing

To change a wheel, remove the spare wheel and jack, apply the handbrake and chock the wheel diagonally opposite the one to be changed. On automatic transmission models, place the selector lever in P. Make sure that the car is located on firm level ground and then slightly loosen the wheel bolts with the brace provided. Locate the jack head in the jacking point nearest to the wheel to be changed (photo) and raise the jack with the spanner provided. When the wheel is clear of the ground, remove the wheel bolts and lift off the wheel. Fit the spare wheel and wheel bolts and moderately tighten the bolts. Lower

the car and then tighten the bolts fully. Note that on some models the spare wheel and tyre are of a different design and construction to that of the main wheels and is intended for emergency use only. Do not drive the car for prolonged periods with the spare wheel fitted. With the spare wheel in position, remove the chock and stow the jack and tools.

When jacking up the car to carry out repair or maintenance tasks position the jack as follows:

If the front of the car is to be raised, position the jack head under

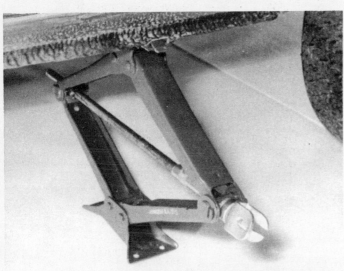

Ensure that the jack is properly located under the appropriate jacking point

The jack is located in the luggage compartment

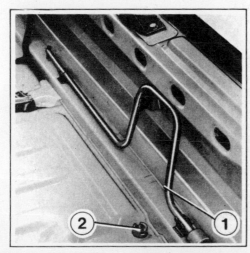

To lower the spare wheel use brace (1) to undo nut (2)

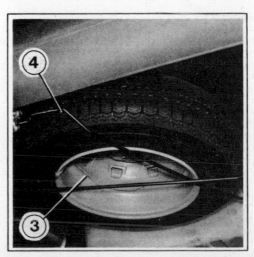

Remove the spare wheel (3) after unhooking the cradle by lifting the handle (4)

Slacken the wheel bolts using the brace

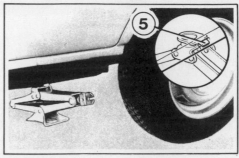

Ensure that the jack head engages properly in the jacking point location (5)

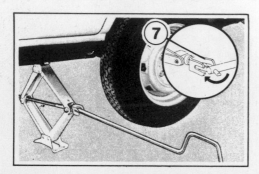

Raise the jack using the other end of the wheel brace (7)

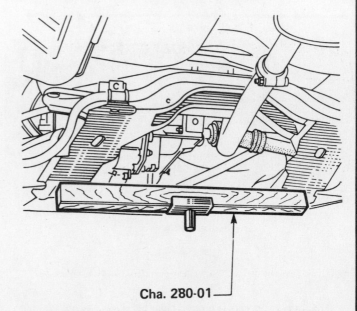

Cha. 280-01

To raise the front of the car for service or repair tasks, position the jack head under a stout wooden beam placed between the sides of the subframe

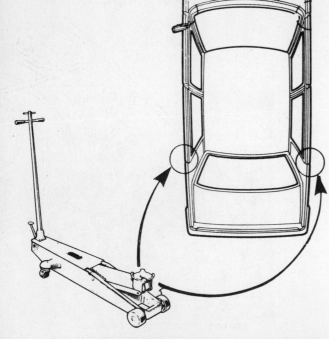

To raise the car at the rear jack up each side in turn at the load bearing underbody members

Position of jack and wooden block for raising the side of the car

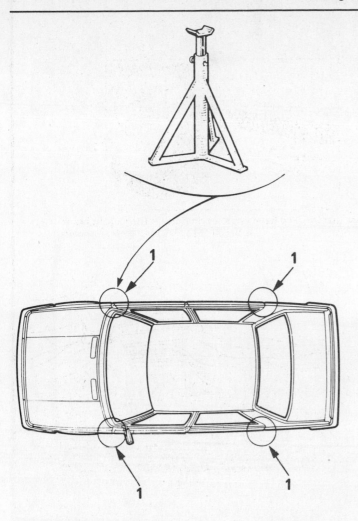

**Always support the car on axle stands positioned as shown (1)**

FRONT

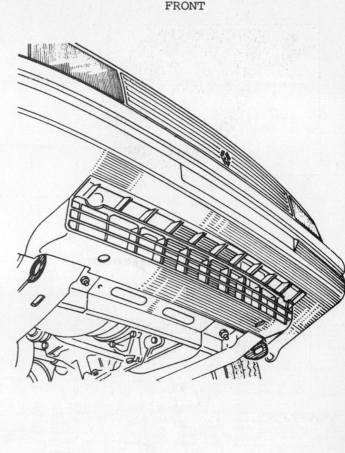

a stout wooden beam placed transversely across the underside of the car and in contact with the front subframe side rails. Supplement the jack with axle stands which can be placed under the subframe or under the load bearing members of the underbody.

To raise the rear of the car, jack up each side in turn with the jack head positioned under the load bearing underbody members just forward of the rear axle trailing arms. Supplement the jack with axle stands positioned in the same area.

To raise the side the car place a block of wood under the side sill and located centrally under the front door. Place the jack head in contact with the block and raise the car. Shape the wooden blocks as necessary to avoid damaging the sill edges and supplement the jack with axle stands positioned as described previously. Never work under, around or near a raised car unless it is adequately supported in at least two places with axle stands or suitable sturdy blocks.

The car may be towed for breakdown recovery purposes only using the towing eyes positioned at the front and rear of the vehicle. These eyes are intended for traction loads only and must not be used for lifting the car either directly or indirectly. If the car is equipped with automatic transmission the following precautions must be observed if the vehicle is to be towed. Preferably a front end suspended tow should be used. If this is not possible, add an extra 2 litres (3.5 Imp pints) of the specified automatic transmission fluid to the transmission. The car may now be towed for a maximum of 30 miles (48 km) at a speed not exceeding 18 mph (30 kph). The selector lever must be in the N position during the tow. Drain off the surplus transmission fluid on completion of the tow.

REAR

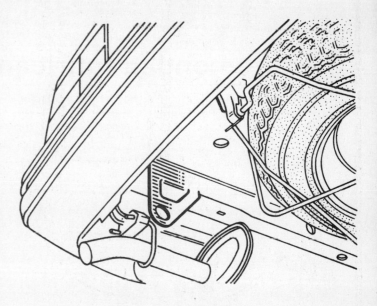

**Front and rear towing eye locations**

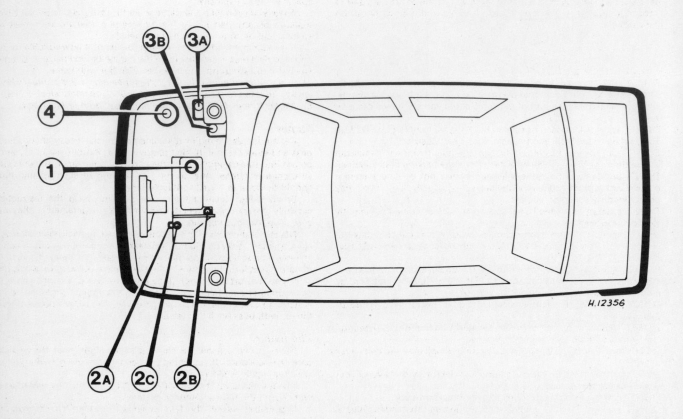

H.12356

# Recommended lubricants and fluids

| Component or system | Lubricant type/specification | Duckhams recommendation |
| --- | --- | --- |
| Engine (1) | Multigrade engine oil, viscosity SAE 15W/50 | Duckhams Hypergrade |
| Manual gearbox (non-Turbo models): | | |
|   Later type (2A) | Hypoid gear oil, viscosity SAE 80 EP | Duckhams Hypoid 80S |
|   Early type (2B) | As above | As above |
| Manual gearbox (Turbo models) | Gear oil, viscosity SAE 75W/90 | Duckhams Hypoid 75W/90S |
| Automatic transmission (2C) | Dexron type ATF | Duckhams Uni-Matic or D-Matic |
| Brake fluid reservoir (3A or 3B) | Hydraulic fluid to SAE J1703 F, DOT 3 or DOT 4 | Duckhams Universal Brake and Clutch Fluid |
| Cooling system (4) | Ethylene glycol antifreeze | Duckhams Universal Antifreeze and Summer Coolant |
| General greasing (unless otherwise specified) | Multi-purpose lithium-based grease | Duckhams LB 10 |

# Safety first!

Professional motor mechanics are trained in safe working procedures. However enthusiastic you may be about getting on with the job in hand, do take the time to ensure that your safety is not put at risk. A moment's lack of attention can result in an accident, as can failure to observe certain elementary precautions.

There will always be new ways of having accidents, and the following points do not pretend to be a comprehensive list of all dangers; they are intended rather to make you aware of the risks and to encourage a safety-conscious approach to all work you carry out on your vehicle.

## Essential DOs and DON'Ts

**DON'T** rely on a single jack when working underneath the vehicle. Always use reliable additional means of support, such as axle stands, securely placed under a part of the vehicle that you know will not give way.

**DON'T** attempt to loosen or tighten high-torque nuts (e.g. wheel hub nuts) while the vehicle is on a jack; it may be pulled off.

**DON'T** start the engine without first ascertaining that the transmission is in neutral (or 'Park' where applicable) and the parking brake applied.

**DON'T** suddenly remove the filler cap from a hot cooling system – cover it with a cloth and release the pressure gradually first, or you may get scalded by escaping coolant.

**DON'T** attempt to drain oil until you are sure it has cooled sufficiently to avoid scalding you.

**DON'T** grasp any part of the engine, exhaust or catalytic converter without first ascertaining that it is sufficiently cool to avoid burning you.

**DON'T** allow brake fluid or antifreeze to contact vehicle paintwork.

**DON'T** syphon toxic liquids such as fuel, brake fluid or antifreeze by mouth, or allow them to remain on your skin.

**DON'T** inhale dust – it may be injurious to health (see *Asbestos* below).

**DON'T** allow any spilt oil or grease to remain on the floor – wipe it up straight away, before someone slips on it.

**DON'T** use ill-fitting spanners or other tools which may slip and cause injury.

**DON'T** attempt to lift a heavy component which may be beyond your capability – get assistance.

**DON'T** rush to finish a job, or take unverified short cuts.

**DON'T** allow children or animals in or around an unattended vehicle.

**DO** wear eye protection when using power tools such as drill, sander, bench grinder etc, and when working under the vehicle.

**DO** use a barrier cream on your hands prior to undertaking dirty jobs – it will protect your skin from infection as well as making the dirt easier to remove afterwards; but make sure your hands aren't left slippery. Note that long-term contact with used engine oil can be a health hazard.

**DO** keep loose clothing (cuffs, tie etc) and long hair well out of the way of moving mechanical parts.

**DO** remove rings, wristwatch etc, before working on the vehicle – especially the electrical system.

**DO** ensure that any lifting tackle used has a safe working load rating adequate for the job.

**DO** keep your work area tidy – it is only too easy to fall over articles left lying around.

**DO** get someone to check periodically that all is well, when working alone on the vehicle.

**DO** carry out work in a logical sequence and check that everything is correctly assembled and tightened afterwards.

**DO** remember that your vehicle's safety affects that of yourself and others. If in doubt on any point, get specialist advice.

**IF**, in spite of following these precautions, you are unfortunate enough to injure yourself, seek medical attention as soon as possible.

## Asbestos

Certain friction, insulating, sealing, and other products – such as brake linings, brake bands, clutch linings, torque converters, gaskets, etc – contain asbestos. *Extreme care must be taken to avoid inhalation of dust from such products since it is hazardous to health.* If in doubt, assume that they *do* contain asbestos.

## Fire

Remember at all times that petrol (gasoline) is highly flammable. Never smoke, or have any kind of naked flame around, when working on the vehicle. But the risk does not end there – a spark caused by an electrical short-circuit, by two metal surfaces contacting each other, by careless use of tools, or even by static electricity built up in your body under certain conditions, can ignite petrol vapour, which in a confined space is highly explosive.

Always disconnect the battery earth (ground) terminal before working on any part of the fuel or electrical system, and never risk spilling fuel on to a hot engine or exhaust.

It is recommended that a fire extinguisher of a type suitable for fuel and electrical fires is kept handy in the garage or workplace at all times. Never try to extinguish a fuel or electrical fire with water.

**Note:** *Any reference to a 'torch' appearing in this manual should always be taken to mean a hand-held battery-operated electric lamp or flashlight. It does NOT mean a welding/gas torch or blowlamp.*

## Fumes

Certain fumes are highly toxic and can quickly cause unconsciousness and even death if inhaled to any extent. Petrol (gasoline) vapour comes into this category, as do the vapours from certain solvents such as trichloroethylene. Any draining or pouring of such volatile fluids should be done in a well ventilated area.

When using cleaning fluids and solvents, read the instructions carefully. Never use materials from unmarked containers – they may give off poisonous vapours.

Never run the engine of a motor vehicle in an enclosed space such as a garage. Exhaust fumes contain carbon monoxide which is extremely poisonous; if you need to run the engine, always do so in the open air or at least have the rear of the vehicle outside the workplace.

If you are fortunate enough to have the use of an inspection pit, never drain or pour petrol, and never run the engine, while the vehicle is standing over it; the fumes, being heavier than air, will concentrate in the pit with possibly lethal results.

## The battery

Never cause a spark, or allow a naked light, near the vehicle's battery. It will normally be giving off a certain amount of hydrogen gas, which is highly explosive.

Always disconnect the battery earth (ground) terminal before working on the fuel or electrical systems.

If possible, loosen the filler plugs or cover when charging the battery from an external source. Do not charge at an excessive rate or the battery may burst.

Take care when topping up and when carrying the battery. The acid electrolyte, even when diluted, is very corrosive and should not be allowed to contact the eyes or skin.

If you ever need to prepare electrolyte yourself, always add the acid slowly to the water, and never the other way round. Protect against splashes by wearing rubber gloves and goggles.

When jump starting a car using a booster battery, for negative earth (ground) vehicles, connect the jump leads in the following sequence: First connect one jump lead between the positive (+) terminals of the two batteries. Then connect the other jump lead first to the negative (–) terminal of the booster battery, and then to a good earthing (ground) point on the vehicle to be started, at least 18 in (45 cm) from the battery if possible. Ensure that hands and jump leads are clear of any moving parts, and that the two vehicles do not touch. Disconnect the leads in the reverse order.

## Mains electricity and electrical equipment

When using an electric power tool, inspection light etc, always ensure that the appliance is correctly connected to its plug and that, where necessary, it is properly earthed (grounded). Do not use such appliances in damp conditions and, again, beware of creating a spark or applying excessive heat in the vicinity of fuel or fuel vapour. Also ensure that the appliances meet the relevant national safety standards.

## Ignition HT voltage

A severe electric shock can result from touching certain parts of the ignition system, such as the HT leads, when the engine is running or being cranked, particularly if components are damp or the insulation is defective. Where an electronic ignition system is fitted, the HT voltage is much higher and could prove fatal.

# Routine maintenance

*For modifications, and information applicable to later models, see Supplement at end of manual*

Maintenance is essential for ensuring safety and desirable for the purpose of getting the best in terms of performance and economy from your car. Over the years the need for periodic lubrication has been greatly reduced if not totally eliminated. This has unfortunately tended to lead some owners to think that because no such action is required, the items either no longer exist, or will last forever. This is certainly not the case; it is essential to carry out regular visual examination as comprehensively as possible in order to spot any possible defects at an early stage before they develop into major expensive repairs.

The following service schedules are a list of the maintenance requirements and the intervals at which they should be carried out, as recommended by the manufacturers. Where applicable these procedures are covered in greater detail throughout this manual, near the beginning of each Chapter.

**Every 250 miles (400 km) or weekly – whichever comes first**

*Engine, cooling system and brakes*
Check the oil level and top up if necessary (photo)
Check the expansion tank and top up if necessary (photos)
Check the brake fluid level in the master cylinder reservoir and top up if necessary (photo)

*Lights and wipers*
Check the operation of all interior and exterior lamps, wipers and washers
Check and if necessary top up the washer reservoir
Check and if necessary top up the washer reservoir, adding a screen wash such as Turtle Wax High Tech Screen Wash

Check and, if necessary, top up the engine oil level

Check the coolant reservoir and, if necessary, raise the level ...

... to between the MINI and MAXI marks

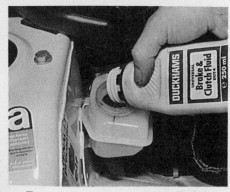
Top up the brake master cylinder reservoir fluid level if necessary

Check the tyre pressures ...

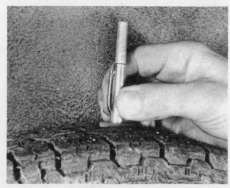
... and the tread depth

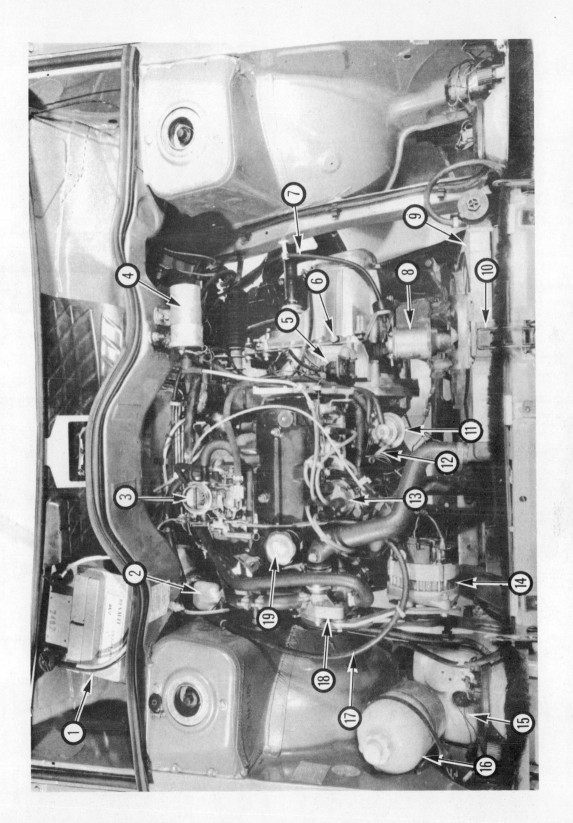

Engine and underbonnet component locations on 1108 cc engine models (air cleaner removed for photographic access)

1 Battery
2 Brake master cylinder reservoir
3 Carburettor
4 Ignition coil
5 Diagnostic socket
6 Gearbox breather
7 Clutch cable
8 Cooling fan motor
9 Radiator
10 Radiator retaining spring clip
11 Fuel pump
12 Engine oil dipstick
13 Distributor
14 Alternator
15 Washer reservoir
16 Cooling system expansion tank
17 Accelerator cable
18 Water pump
19 Oil filler cap

18

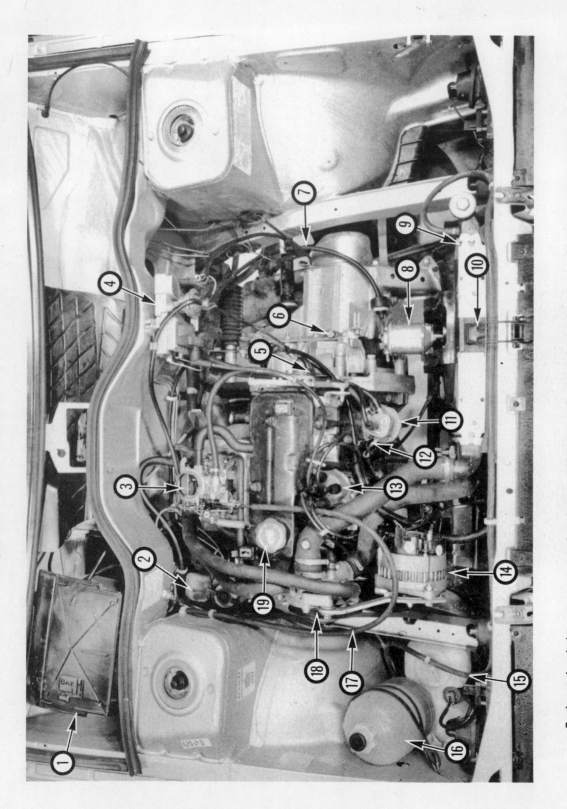

Engine and underbonnet component locations on 1397 cc engine models (air cleaner removed for photographic access)

1 Battery cover
2 Brake master cylinder reservoir
3 Carburettor
4 Electronic igniton computer module
5 TDC sensor
6 Gearbox breather
7 Clutch cable
8 Cooling fan motor
9 Radiator
10 Radiator retaining spring clip
11 Fuel pump
12 Engine oil dipstick
13 Distributor
14 Alternator
15 Washer reservoir
16 Cooling system expansion tank
17 Accelerator cable
18 Water pump
19 Oil filler cap

Engine and underbonnet component locations on 1721 cc engine models (air cleaner removed for photographic access)

| | | | | |
|---|---|---|---|---|
| 1 | Battery cover | 6 | Electronic ignition | 13 Crankcase ventilation system |
| 2 | In-line fuel filter | | computer module | oil separator |
| 3 | Fuel pump | 7 | TDC sensor | 14 Oil filter |
| 4 | Carburettor | 8 | Gearbox breather | 15 Alternator |
| 5 | Distributor | | | |

| | | | |
|---|---|---|---|
| 9 | Clutch cable | 16 | Washer reservoir |
| 10 | Cooling fan motor | 17 | Cooling system |
| 11 | Radiator | | expansion tank |
| 12 | Radiator retaining | 18 | Oil filler cap |
| | spring clip | 19 | Master cylinder reservoir |

**Renault 11 front underbody view**

1 Exhaust intermediate section
2 Anti-roll bar
3 Steering arm
4 Steering arm outer balljoint
5 Lower suspension arm balljoint
6 Lower suspension arm
7 Rack and pinion steering gear
8 Right-hand driveshaft inner joint
9 Engine oil drain plug
10 Selector mechanism fork control shaft
11 Gearbox oil drain plug
12 Gearchange rod

**Renault 11 rear underbody view**

| | | | |
|---|---|---|---|
| 1 Fuel tank filler pipe | 4 Trailing arm | 7 Rear brake flexible hose | 10 Anti-roll bar | 13 Trailing arm |
| 2 Fuel tank | 5 Handbrake cable | 8 Rear brake flexible hose | 11 Exhaust mounting | 14 Handbrake cable |
| 3 Shock absorber lower mounting | 6 Trailing arm mounting bracket | 9 Brake pressure regulating valve | 12 Exhaust intermediate section | 15 Exhaust rear silencer |

Tyres
    Check the tyre pressures (photo)
    Visually examine the tyres for wear or tread damage (photo)

General
    Clean the windscreen and if necessary the windows
    Clean the headlamp and rear lamp lenses

## Every 5000 miles (8000 km) or 6 months – whichever occurs first

Engine (Chapter 1)
    Renew the engine oil

Cooling system (Chapter 2)
    Check the expansion tank and top up if necessary
    Check the hoses for condition, leaks and security
    Check the drivebelt condition and renew it or adjust the tension

Fuel and exhaust system (Chapter 3)
    Alter the air cleaner manual temperature control (where fitted)
    according to season
    Visually inspect the fuel pipes for leaks and security
    Check the exhaust condition and the mountings for security

Automatic transmission (Chapter 6)
    Check the automatic transmission fluid level and top up if
    necessary

Braking system (Chapter 8)
    Check the brake fluid level in the master cylinder reservoir and top
    up if necessary

Electrical system (Chapter 9)
    Check the operation of all interior and exterior lamps and
    instrument panel warning lamps
    Check and if necessary top up the battery (where applicable)
    Check the operation of the wipers and washers
    Check and if necessary top up the washer reservoir

Tyres (Chapter 10)
    Check the tyre pressure
    Visually examine the tyres for wear or tread damage

General
    Clean the windscreen and all the windows and mirrors
    Clean the front and rear exterior lamp lenses

## Every 10 000 miles (16 000 km) or 12 months – whichever occurs first

    In addition to all the items (where applicable) in the 5000 mile
(8000 km) service, carry out the following:

Engine (Chapter 1)
    Renew the engine oil filter
    Check and if necessary adjust the valve clearances (1108 cc and
    1397 cc engines)
    Visually check the engine for oil leaks and for the security and
    condition of all related components and attachments

Cooling system (Chapter 2)
    Check the hoses, hose clips and visible joint gaskets for leaks and
    any signs of corrosion or deterioration

Fuel and exhaust system (Chapter 3)
    Lubricate the accelerator linkage and pedal pivot

Ignition system (Chapter 4)
    Examine the contact breaker points condition (where fitted) and
    renew if necessary
    Check and adjust the contact breaker points gap or dwell angle
    Check and if necessary adjust the ignition timing (where
    applicable)
    Check the condition of the spark plugs, renew if necessary and/or
    adjust the electrode gap
    Lubricate the distributor
    Clean the distributor cap, HT leads and related wiring and check
    the leads and wiring for security

Clutch (Chapter 5)
    Check the operation of the clutch and clutch pedal

Manual gearbox and automatic transmission (Chapter 6)
    Check the gearbox oil level and top up if necessary
    Visually check the gearbox joint faces and oil seals for leaks
    Visually check the automatic transmission joint faces, oil seals and
    fluid cooler hoses and unions for leaks
    Check the security of all wiring harnesses and cables

Driveshafts (Chapter 7)
    Check the condition of the driveshafts, driveshaft joints and rubber
    bellows

Braking system (Chapter 8)
    Check the front brake pads and rear brake shoes for the condition
    and thickness of the friction material
    Visually inspect all brake pipes, hoses and unions for corrosion,
    chafing, leakage and security
    Check the brake servo vacuum hose for condition and security
    Lubricate the handbrake exposed cables and linkage

Electrical system (Chapter 9)
    Check the operation of all electrical equipment and accessories
    Check the condition and security of all accessible wiring
    connectors, harnesses and retaining clips
    Check the headlamp aim
    Check the security of the battery terminals and smear with
    petroleum jelly

Suspension and steering (Chapter 10)
    Check the condition of all balljoint and steering gear rubber
    bellows
    Check all the steering and suspension components for wear or
    excess free play
    Check the operation of the shock absorbers and inspect for fluid
    leaks
    Check the front wheel toe setting
    Check the tyres for damage, tread depth and uneven wear
    Inspect the roadwheels for damage
    Check the tightness of the wheel bolts

Bodywork (Chapter 11)
    Carefully inspect the paintwork for damage and the bodywork for
    condition
    Check the condition of the underseal
    Lubricate all locks and hinges (not the steering lock)

Road test
    Check the function of all instruments and electrical equipment
    Check the operation of the seat belts
    Check for any abnormalities in the steering, suspension, handling
    or road feel
    Check the performance of the engine, clutch and transmission
    Check the operation and performance of the braking system

**Every 20 000 miles (32 000 km) or 24 months – whichever occurs first**

In addition to all the items in the 10 000 mile (16 000 km) service, carry out the following:

*Engine (Chapter 1)*
Check and if necessary adjust the valve clearances on 1721 cc engines

*Cooling system (Chapter 2)*
Drain and flush the system and refill with fresh antifreeze

*Fuel and exhaust system (Chapter 3)*
Adjust the carburettor idle and mixture adjustments
Renew the air cleaner element
Renew the in-line fuel filter (where fitted)
Clean the fuel pump filter

*Bodywork (Chapter 11)*
Check the air conditioner refrigerant level (where fitted)

**Every 40 000 miles (64 000 km) or 48 months – whichever occurs first**

In addition to all the items in the 20 000 mile (32 000 km) service, carry out the following:

*Manual gearbox and automatic transmission (Chapter 6)*
Renew the gearbox oil
Renew the automatic transmission fluid

**Every 80 000 miles (130 000 km) or 96 months – whichever occurs first**

In addition to the items in the 40 000 mile (64 000 km) service, carry out the following:

*Engine (Chapter 1)*
Renew the timing belt on 1721 cc engines

# Fault diagnosis

## Introduction

The vehicle owner who does his or her own maintenance according to the recommended schedules should not have to use this section of the manual very often. Modern component reliability is such that, provided those items subject to wear or deterioration are inspected or renewed at the specified intervals, sudden failure is comparatively rare. Faults do not usually just happen as a result of sudden failure, but develop over a period of time. Major mechanical failures in particular are usually preceded by characteristic symptoms over hundreds or even thousands of miles. Those components which do occasionally fail without warning are often small and easily carried in the vehicle.

With any fault finding, the first step is to decide where to begin investigations. Sometimes this is obvious, but on other occasions a little detective work will be necessary. The owner who makes half a dozen haphazard adjustments or replacements may be successful in curing a fault (or its symptoms), but he will be none the wiser if the fault recurs and he may well have spent more time and money than was necessary. A calm and logical approach will be found to be more satisfactory in the long run. Always take into account any warning signs or abnormalities that may have been noticed in the period preceding the fault – power loss, high or low gauge readings, unusual noises or smells, etc – and remember that failure of components such as fuses or spark plugs may only be pointers to some underlying fault.

The pages which follow here are intended to help in cases of failure to start or breakdown on the road. There is also a Fault Diagnosis Section at the end of each Chapter which should be consulted if the preliminary checks prove unfruitful. Whatever the fault, certain basic principles apply. These are as follows:

**Verify the fault.** This is simply a matter of being sure that you know what the symptoms are before starting work. This is particularly important if you are investigating a fault for someone else who may not have described it very accurately.

**Don't overlook the obvious.** For example, if the vehicle won't start, is there petrol in the tank? (Don't take anyone else's word on this particular point, and don't trust the fuel gauge either!) If an electrical fault is indicated, look for loose or broken wires before digging out the test gear.

**Cure the disease, not the symptom.** Substituting a flat battery with a fully charged one will get you off the hard shoulder, but if the underlying cause is not attended to, the new battery will go the same way. Similarly, changing oil-fouled spark plugs for a new set will get you moving again, but remember that the reason for the fouling (if it wasn't simply an incorrect grade of plug) will have to be established and corrected.

**Don't take anything for granted.** Particularly, don't forget that a 'new' component may itself be defective (especially if it's been rattling round in the boot for months), and don't leave components out of a fault diagnosis sequence just because they are new or recently fitted. When you do finally diagnose a difficult fault, you'll probably realise that all the evidence was there from the start.

## Electrical faults

Electrical faults can be more puzzling than straightforward mechanical failures, but they are no less susceptible to logical analysis if the basic principles of operation are understood. Vehicle electrical wiring exists in extremely unfavourable conditions – heat, vibration and chemical attack – and the first things to look for are loose or corroded connections and broken or chafed wires, especially where the wires pass through holes in the bodywork or are subject to vibration.

All metal-bodied vehicles in current production have one pole of the battery 'earthed', ie connected to the vehicle bodywork, and in nearly all modern vehicles it is the negative (–) terminal. The various electrical components – motors, bulb holders etc – are also connected to earth, either by means of a lead or directly by their mountings. Electric current flows through the component and then back to the battery via the bodywork. If the component mounting is loose or corroded, or if a good path back to the battery is not available, the circuit will be incomplete and malfunction will result. The engine and/or gearbox are also earthed by means of flexible metal straps to the body or subframe; if these straps are loose or missing, starter motor, generator and ignition trouble may result.

Assuming the earth return to be satisfactory, electrical faults will be due either to component malfunction or to defects in the current supply. Individual components are dealt with in Chapter 9. If supply wires are broken or cracked internally this results in an open-circuit, and the easiest way to check for this is to bypass the suspect wire temporarily with a length of wire having a crocodile clip or suitable connector at each end. Alternatively, a 12V test lamp can be used to verify the presence of supply voltage at various points along the wire and the break can be thus isolated.

If a bare portion of a live wire touches the bodywork or other earthed metal part, the electricity will take the low-resistance path thus formed back to the battery: this is known as a short-circuit. Hopefully a short-circuit will blow a fuse, but otherwise it may cause burning of the insulation (and possibly further short-circuits) or even a fire. This is why it is inadvisable to bypass persistently blowing fuses with silver foil or wire.

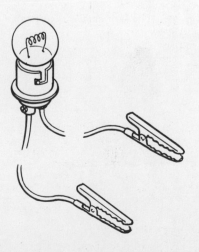

**A simple test lamp is useful for checking electrical circuits**

**Carrying a few spares may save you a long walk!**

## Spares and tool kit

Most vehicles are supplied only with sufficient tools for wheel changing; the *Maintenance and minor repair* tool kit detailed in *Tools and working facilities*, with the addition of a hammer, is probably sufficient for those repairs that most motorists would consider attempting at the roadside. In addition a few items which can be fitted without too much trouble in the event of a breakdown should be carried. Experience and available space will modify the list below, but the following may save having to call on professional assistance:

*Spark plugs, clean and correctly gapped*
*HT lead and plug cap – long enough to reach the plug furthest from the distributor*
*Distributor rotor, condenser and contact breaker points (where applicable)*
*Drivebelt(s) – emergency type may suffice*
*Spare fuses*
*Set of principal light bulbs*
*Tin of radiator sealer and hose bandage*
*Exhaust bandage*
*Roll of insulating tape*
*Length of soft iron wire*
*Length of electrical flex*
*Torch or inspection lamp (can double as test lamp)*
*Battery jump leads*
*Tow-rope*
*Ignition water dispersant aerosol*
*Litre of engine oil*
*Sealed can of hydraulic fluid*
*Emergency windscreen*
*Worm drive clips*

If spare fuel is carried, a can designed for the purpose should be used to minimise risks of leakage and collision damage. A first aid kit and a warning triangle, whilst not at present compulsory in the UK, are obviously sensible items to carry in addition to the above.

When touring abroad it may be advisable to carry additional spares which, even if you cannot fit them yourself, could save having to wait while parts are obtained. The items below may be worth considering:

*Clutch and throttle cables*
*Cylinder head gasket*
*Alternator brushes*
*Tyre valve core*

One of the motoring organisations will be able to advise on availability of fuel etc in foreign countries.

---

### Engine will not start

## Engine fails to turn when starter operated

Flat battery (recharge, use jump leads, or push start)
Battery terminals loose or corroded
Battery earth to body defective
Engine earth strap loose or broken
Starter motor (or solenoid) wiring loose or broken
Automatic transmission selector in wrong position, or inhibitor switch faulty
Ignition/starter switch faulty

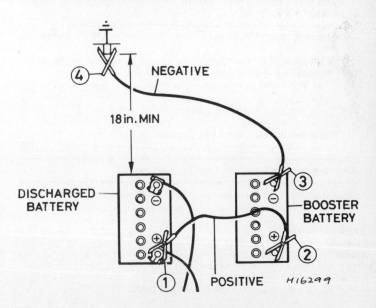

**Jump start lead connections for negative earth vehicles – connect leads in order shown**

Major mechanical failure (seizure)
Starter or solenoid internal fault (see Chapter 9)

## Starter motor turns engine slowly
Partially discharged battery (recharge, use jump leads, or push start)
Battery terminals loose or corroded
Battery earth to body defective
Engine earth strap loose
Starter motor (or solenoid) wiring loose
Starter motor internal fault (see Chapter 9)

## Starter motor spins without turning engine
Flat battery
Starter motor pinion sticking on sleeve
Flywheel gear teeth damaged or worn
Starter motor mounting bolts loose

## Engine turns normally but fails to start
Damp or dirty HT leads and distributor cap (crank engine and check for spark) – try moisture dispersant such as Holts Wet Start
Dirty or incorrectly gapped distributor points (if applicable)
No fuel in tank (check for delivery at carburettor)
Excessive choke (hot engine) or insufficient choke (cold engine)
Fouled or incorrectly gapped spark plugs (remove and regap)
Other ignition system fault (see Chapter 4)
Other fuel system fault (see Chapter 3)
Poor compression (see Chapter 1)
Major mechanical failure (eg camshaft drive)

## Engine fires but will not run
Insufficient choke (cold engine)
Air leaks at carburettor or inlet manifold
Fuel starvation (see Chapter 3)
Ballast resistor defective, or other ignition fault (see Chapter 4)

---

## Engine cuts out and will not restart

## Engine cuts out suddenly – ignition fault
Loose or disconnected LT wires
Wet HT leads or distributor cap (after traversing water splash)
Coil or condenser failure (check for spark) – if applicable
Other ignition fault (see Chapter 4)

## Engine misfires before cutting out – fuel fault
Fuel tank empty
Fuel pump defective or filter blocked (check for delivery)
Fuel tank filler vent blocked (suction will be evident on releasing cap)
Carburettor needle valve sticking
Carburettor jets blocked (fuel contaminated)
Other fuel system fault (see Chapter 3)

## Engine cuts out – other causes
Serious overheating
Major mechanical failure (eg camshaft drive)

---

## Engine overheats

## Ignition (no-charge) warning light illuminated
Slack or broken drivebelt – retension or renew (Chapter 2)

## Ignition warning light not illuminated
Coolant loss due to internal or external leakage (see Chapter 2)
Thermostat defective
Low oil level
Brakes binding
Radiator clogged externally or internally
Electric cooling fan not operating correctly
Engine waterways clogged
Ignition timing incorrect or automatic advance malfunctioning – if applicable
Mixture too weak

**Note:** *Do not add cold water to an overheated engine or damage may result*

---

## Low engine oil pressure

## Gauge reads low or warning light illuminated with engine running
Oil level low or incorrect grade
Defective gauge or sender unit
Wire to sender unit earthed
Engine overheating
Oil filter clogged or bypass valve defective
Oil pressure relief valve defective
Oil pick-up strainer clogged
Oil pump worn or mountings loose
Worn main or big-end bearings

**Note:** *Low oil pressure in a high-mileage engine at tickover is not necessarily a cause for concern. Sudden pressure loss at speed is far more significant. In any event, check the gauge or warning light sender before condemning the engine.*

---

## Engine noises

## Pre-ignition (pinking) on acceleration
Incorrect grade of fuel
Ignition timing incorrect
Distributor faulty or worn
Worn or maladjusted carburettor
Excessive carbon build-up in engine

## Whistling or wheezing noises
Leaking vacuum hose
Leaking carburettor or manifold gasket
Blowing head gasket

## Tapping or rattling
Incorrect valve clearances
Worn valve gear
Worn timing chain or belt
Broken piston ring (ticking noise)

## Knocking or thumping
Unintentional mechanical contact (eg fan blades)
Worn fanbelt
Peripheral component fault (generator, water pump etc)
Worn big-end bearings (regular heavy knocking, perhaps less under load)
Worn main bearings (rumbling and knocking, perhaps worsening under load)
Piston slap (most noticeable when cold)

# Chapter 1 Engine

*For modifications, and information applicable to later models, see Supplement at end of manual*

**Contents**

*To avoid conversion inaccuracies, all specifications are given in metric values only, as specified by the manufacturers*

*Part 1: 1108 cc engine*

# General

| | |
|---|---|
| Type ............................................................................... | Four-cylinder in-line, overhead valve |
| Designation .................................................................. | C1E |
| Bore .............................................................................. | 70 mm |
| Stroke ........................................................................... | 72 mm |
| Capacity ....................................................................... | 1108 cc |
| Compression ratio ....................................................... | 9.25 : 1 |
| Firing order ................................................................. | 1-3-4-2 (No 1 cylinder at flywheel end) |

# Crankshaft

| | |
|---|---|
| Number of main bearings ........................................... | 5 |
| Main journal diameter ................................................. | 54.795 mm |
| Main journal minimum regrind diameter ...................... | 54.545 mm |
| Crankpin journal diameter ........................................... | 43.98 mm |
| Crankpin journal minimum regrind diameter ................ | 43.73 mm |
| Crankshaft endfloat .................................................... | 0.05 to 0.23 mm |

# Connecting rods

| | |
|---|---|
| Small end side-play .................................................... | 0.31 to 0.57 mm |

# Cylinder liners and pistons

| | |
|---|---|
| Liner bore diameter .................................................... | 70 mm |
| Liner protrusion .......................................................... | 0.04 to 0.12 mm |
| Liner base seal type ................................................... | Excelnyl |
| Liner base seal thickness: | |
|     Blue ......................................................................... | 0.08 mm |
|     Red ........................................................................... | 0.10 mm |
|     Green ........................................................................ | 0.12 mm |
| Piston fitted direction ................................................. | Arrow on crown towards flywheel |
| Gudgeon pin fit in piston ........................................... | Hand push-fit |
| Gudgeon pin fit in connecting rod ............................... | Interference |
| Gudgeon pin length ..................................................... | 59 mm |
| Gudgeon pin outside diameter .................................... | 18 mm |

# Piston rings

| | |
|---|---|
| Number ........................................................................ | Three (two compression, one oil control) |
| Compression ring thickness ........................................ | 2.0 mm |
| Oil control ring thickness ............................................ | 3.5 mm |
| Piston ring end gaps .................................................. | Supplied pre-set |

# Camshaft

| | |
|---|---|
| Number of bearings .................................................... | 4 |
| Endfloat ....................................................................... | 0.05 to 0.12 mm |

# Valves

| | |
|---|---|
| Seat angle ................................................................... | 45° |
| Head diameter: | |
|     Inlet .......................................................................... | 33.5 mm |
|     Exhaust ..................................................................... | 30.3 mm |
| Stem diameter ............................................................. | 7.0 mm |
| Valve seat angle in cylinder head ............................... | 45° |
| Valve seat width in cylinder head: | |
|     Inlet .......................................................................... | 1.1 to 1.4 mm |
|     Exhaust ..................................................................... | 1.4 to 1.7 mm |
| Valve guides: | |
|     Bore diameter in cylinder head (nominal) ................. | 11.0 mm |
|     Fitted height above joint face: | |
|         Inlet ...................................................................... | 26.5 mm |
|         Exhaust ................................................................. | 26.2 mm |
| Valve springs: | |
|     Free length ................................................................ | 42 mm |
| Valve timing; at valve clearances of 0.35 mm (inlet), 0.50 mm (exhaust): | |
|     Inlet opens ............................................................... | 14° BTDC |
|     Inlet closes .............................................................. | 38° ABDC |
|     Exhaust opens .......................................................... | 53° BBDC |
|     Exhaust closes ......................................................... | 15° ATDC |
| Valve clearances (cold): | |
|     Inlet .......................................................................... | 0.15 mm |
|     Exhaust ..................................................................... | 0.20 mm |

## Pushrods
Length:
    Early engines ..................................................... 172.3 mm
    Later engines ..................................................... 176.3 mm

## Cam followers
External diameter .................................................... 19.0 mm

## Cylinder head
Maximum permitted warp ......................................... 0.05 mm
Cylinder head height ............................................... 70.15 mm
Maximum permitted refacing cut ............................. 0.5 mm

## Lubrication system
Lubricant type/specification ................................... Multigrade engine oil, viscosity SAE 15W/50 (Duckhams Hypergrade)
Oil pump:
    Gear-to-body clearance ................................... 0.2 mm (maximum)
System pressure:
    Idling ............................................................. 0.7 bar (minimum)
    Running (at 4000 rpm) ................................... 3.5 bar (maximum)
Oil filter ................................................................. Champion C107 (1982 to 6/1984) or F103 (7/1984-on)

## Torque wrench settings

|  | Nm | lbf ft |
| --- | --- | --- |
| Cylinder head bolts | 60 | 44 |
| Rocker shaft pedestal nuts and bolts | 20 | 15 |
| Main bearing cap bolts | 60 | 44 |
| Big-end bearing cap nuts | 35 | 26 |
| Flywheel retaining bolts | 50 | 37 |
| Torque converter driveplate retaining bolts | 65 | 48 |
| Camshaft sprocket retaining bolt | 30 | 22 |
| Engine mounting nuts and bolts | 40 | 30 |

## Part 2: 1397 cc engine
*The engine specification is identical to the 1108 cc unit except for the differences listed below*

## General
Designation ............................................................ C1J or C2J
Bore ...................................................................... 76 mm
Stroke ................................................................... 77 mm
Capacity ................................................................ 1397 cc

## Cylinder liners and pistons
Liner bore diameter ................................................ 76 mm
Liner protrusion (less base seal) ............................. 0.02 to 0.09 mm
Liner base seal type ............................................... O-ring
Gudgeon pin length ................................................ 64 mm
Gudgeon pin outside diameter ................................ 20 mm

## Piston rings
Compression ring thickness:
    Top ring ........................................................ 1.75 mm
    Second ring .................................................. 2.0 mm
Oil control ring thickness ........................................ 4.0 mm

## Valves
Head diameter:
    Inlet ............................................................... 34.2 mm
    Exhaust ......................................................... 29 mm
Valve guides:
    Fitted height above joint face:
        Inlet ......................................................... 30.5 mm
        Exhaust .................................................... 25.2 mm
Valve timing; at valve clearances of 0.30 mm (inlet),
0.35 mm (exhaust):
    Engine suffix 17:
        Inlet opens ............................................... 22° BTDC
        Inlet closes .............................................. 62° ABDC
        Exhaust opens .......................................... 65° BBDC
        Exhaust closes ......................................... 25° ATDC
    Engine suffixes 15 and 18:
        Inlet opens ............................................... 12° BTDC
        Inlet closes .............................................. 56° ABDC
        Exhaust opens .......................................... 56° BBDC
        Exhaust closes ......................................... 12° ATDC

Valve clearances (cold):
    Inlet ................................................................................ 0.15 mm
    Exhaust ........................................................................... 0.20 mm

## Cylinder head
Cylinder head height ....................................................... 72.20 mm

## Torque wrench settings

| | Nm | lbf ft |
|---|---|---|
| Big-end bearing cap nuts | 45 | 33 |
| Crankshaft pulley retaining bolt | 110 | 81 |

## Part 3: 1721 cc engine

### General
Type ................................................................................. Four-cylinder in-line overhead camshaft
Designation ..................................................................... F2N
Bore ................................................................................ 81 mm
Stroke ............................................................................. 83.5 mm
Capacity .......................................................................... 1721 cc
Compression ratio .......................................................... 10 : 1
Firing order ..................................................................... 1-3-4-2 (No 1 cylinder at flywheel end)

### Crankshaft
Number of main bearings ............................................... 5
Main journal diameter ..................................................... 54.794 mm
Main journal minimum regrind diameter .......................... 54.545 mm
Crankpin journal diameter ............................................... 48 mm
Crankpin journal minimum regrind diameter .................... 47.75 mm
Crankshaft endfloat ........................................................ 0.07 to 0.23 mm

### Connecting rods
Connecting rod endfloat ................................................. 0.22 to 0.40 mm

### Pistons
Piston fitted direction ..................................................... V or arrow on crown towards flywheel
Gudgeon pin fit in piston ................................................ Hand push-fit
Gudgeon pin fit in connecting rod .................................. Interference
Gudgeon pin length ........................................................ 64.7 to 65.0 mm
Gudgeon pin outside diameter ........................................ 21 mm

### Piston rings
Number ........................................................................... Three (two compression, one oil control)
Compression ring thickness:
    Top ring ...................................................................... 1.75 mm
    Second ring ................................................................. 2.0 mm
Oil control ring thickness ................................................ 3.0 mm
Piston ring end gaps ...................................................... Supplied pre-set

### Camshaft
Number of bearings ........................................................ 5
Endfloat .......................................................................... 0.048 to 0.133 mm

### Auxiliary shaft
Bush diameter:
    Inner ........................................................................... 39.5 mm
    Outer ........................................................................... 40.5 mm
Endfloat .......................................................................... 0.07 to 0.15 mm

### Valves
Seat angle:
    Inlet ............................................................................ 60°
    Exhaust ....................................................................... 45°
Head diameter:
    Inlet ............................................................................ 38.1 mm
    Exhaust ....................................................................... 32.5 mm
Stem diameter ................................................................ 8.0 mm
Valve seat angle in cylinder head:
    Inlet ............................................................................ 60°
    Exhaust ....................................................................... 45°
Valve seat width in cylinder head ................................... 1.5 to 1.9 mm

Valve guides:
    Bore diameter in cylinder head ............................................... 12.99 mm
    Fitted height above joint face .................................................. 42.8 to 42.2 mm
Valve springs:
    Free length ............................................................................ 44.9 mm
Valve timing; at valve clearances of 0.40 mm (inlet) and
0.50 mm (exhaust):
    Inlet opens ............................................................................ 4° BTDC
    Inlet closes ............................................................................ 40° ABDC
    Exhaust opens ....................................................................... 40° BBDC
    Exhaust closes ....................................................................... 4° ATDC
Valve clearances (cold):
    Inlet ..................................................................................... 0.20 mm
    Exhaust ................................................................................. 0.40 mm

## Tappets
Diameter .................................................................................... 34.99 to 35.04 mm

## Cylinder head
Maximum permitted warp ............................................................ 0.05 mm
Cylinder head height .................................................................. 169.3 to 169.7 mm

## Lubrication system
Oil pump:
    Gear-to-body clearance .......................................................... 0.02 mm (maximum)
    Gear endfloat ........................................................................ 0.085 mm (maximum)
System pressure:
    Idling .................................................................................... 2.0 bar
    Running (at 3000 rpm) ............................................................ 3.5 bar
Oil filter .................................................................................... Champion F105 (1984-on)

## Torque wrench settings

| | Nm | lbf ft |
|---|---|---|
| Cylinder head bolts: | | |
|   1st tightening | 30 | 22 |
|   2nd tightening | 70 | 52 |
|   1st retightening – wait 3 minutes, slacken all bolts | | |
|   then tighten to | 20 | 15 |
|   2nd retightening | Turn through 123° | |
| Main bearing cap bolts | 65 | 48 |
| Big-end bearing cap bolts | 50 | 37 |
| Flywheel retaining bolts | 55 | 41 |
| Camshaft bearing cap bolts: | | |
|   8 mm diameter | 20 | 15 |
|   6 mm diameter | 10 | 7 |
| Camshaft sprocket bolt | 50 | 37 |
| Idler pulley bolt | 20 | 15 |
| Tensioner pulley nut | 40 | 30 |
| Auxiliary shaft sprocket bolt | 50 | 37 |
| Crankshaft pulley bolt | 95 | 70 |
| Oil pump-to-crankcase retaining bolts | 25 | 18 |
| Sump retaining bolts | 15 | 11 |
| Engine mounting nuts and bolts | 40 | 30 |

# Part 1: 1108 cc and 1397 cc engines

## 1 General description

The engines are of four-cylinder, in-line overhead valve type, mounted transversely in the front of the car. Apart from the cylinder liner bore diameter, the crankshaft stroke and minor detail differences, both engine types are virtually identical in design and construction.

The cast iron cylinder block is of the replaceable wet liner type. The crankshaft is supported within the cylinder block on five shell type main bearings. Thrust washers are fitted at the centre main bearing to control crankshaft endfloat.

The connecting rods are attached to the crankshaft by horizontally split shell type big-end bearings, and to the pistons by interference fit gudgeon pins. The aluminium alloy pistons are of the slipper type and are fitted with three piston rings, two compression rings and a scraper type oil control ring.

The camshaft is chain driven from the crankshaft and operates the rocker arms via pushrods. The inlet and exhaust valves are each closed by a single valve spring and operate in guides pressed into the cylinder head. The valves are actuated directly by the rocker arms.

A semi-closed crankcase ventilation system is employed, and crankcase gases are drawn from the rocker cover via a hose to the air cleaner and inlet manifold.

Lubrication is provided by a gear type oil pump driven from the camshaft and located in the crankcase. Engine oil is fed through an externally mounted full-flow filter to the engine oil gallery, and then to the crankshaft, camshaft and rocker shaft bearings. A pressure relief valve is incorporated in the oil pump.

## 2 Maintenance and inspection

1 At the intervals specified in Routine maintenance, carry out the following maintenance operations on the engine.
2 Visually inspect the engine joint faces, gaskets and seals for any

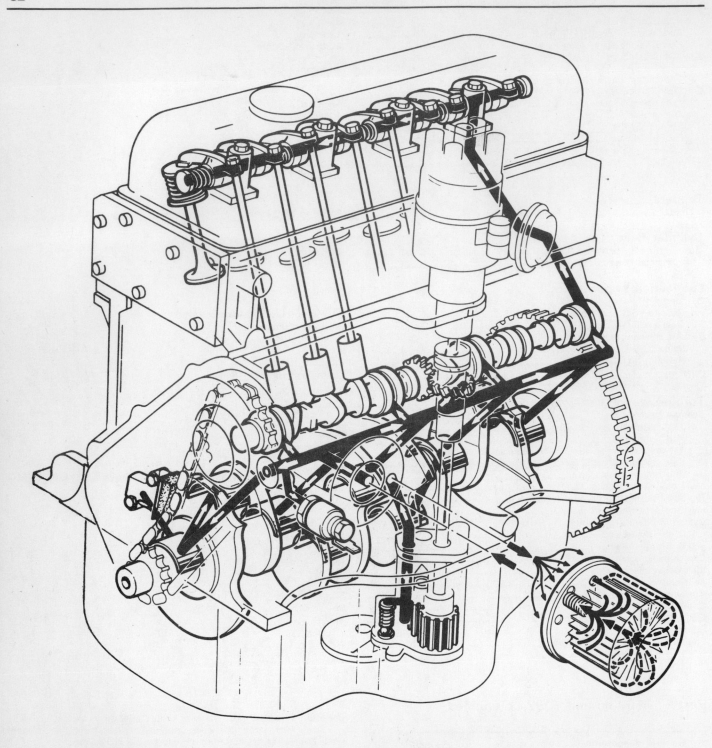

Fig. 1.1 Engine lubrication system (Sec 1)

sign of oil or water leaks. Pay particular attention to the areas around the rocker cover, cylinder head, timing cover and sump joint faces. Rectify any leaks by referring to the appropriate Sections of this Chapter.

3   Place a suitable container beneath the oil drain plug on the sump. Unscrew the plug and allow the oil to drain (photo). Refit and tighten the plug after draining.

4   Refill the engine using the correct grade of oil, through the filler neck on the rocker cover. Fill until the level reaches the upper mark on the dipstick.

5   Move the bowl to the front of the engine, under the oil filter.

6   Using a strap wrench, or filter removal tool, slacken the filter and then unscrew it from the engine and discard.

7   Wipe the mating face on the cylinder block with a rag and then lubricate the seal of a new filter using clean engine oil.

8   Screw the filter into position and tighten it by hand only, do not use any tools.

9   With the engine running, check for leaks around the filter seal.

10  Adjust the valve clearances using the procedure described in Section 47.

# Are your plugs trying to tell you something?

**Normal.**
Grey-brown deposits, lightly coated core nose. Plugs ideally suited to engine, and engine in good condition.

**Heavy Deposits.**
A build up of crusty deposits, light-grey sandy colour in appearance.
Fault: Often caused by worn valve guides, excessive use of upper cylinder lubricant, or idling for long periods.

**Lead Glazing.**
Plug insulator firing tip appears yellow or green/yellow and shiny in appearance.
Fault: Often caused by incorrect carburation, excessive idling followed by sharp acceleration. Also check ignition timing.

**Carbon fouling.**
Dry, black, sooty deposits.
Fault: over-rich fuel mixture.
Check: carburettor mixture settings, float level, choke operation, air filter.

**Oil fouling.**
Wet, oily deposits. Fault: worn bores/piston rings or valve guides; sometimes occurs (temporarily) during running-in period.

**Overheating.**
Electrodes have glazed appearance, core nose very white – few deposits. Fault: plug overheating. Check: plug value, ignition timing, fuel octane rating (too low) and fuel mixture (too weak).

**Electrode damage.**
Electrodes burned away; core nose has burned, glazed appearance. Fault: pre-ignition.
Check: for correct heat range and as for 'overheating'.

**Split core nose.**
(May appear initially as a crack). Fault: detonation or wrong gap-setting technique.
Check: ignition timing, cooling system, fuel mixture (too weak).

# WHY DOUBLE COPPER IS BETTER FOR YOUR ENGINE.

Unique Trapezoidal Copper Cored Earth Electrode — 50% Larger Spark Area — Copper Cored Centre Electrode

Champion Double Copper plugs are the first in the world to have copper core in both centre _and_ earth electrode. This innovative design means that they run cooler by up to 100°C – giving greater efficiency and longer life. These double copper cores transfer heat away from the tip of the plug faster and more efficiently. Therefore, Double Copper runs at cooler temperatures than conventional plugs giving improved acceleration response and high speed performance with no fear of pre-ignition.

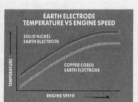

Champion Double Copper plugs also feature a unique trapezoidal earth electrode giving a 50% increase in spark area. This, together with the double copper cores, offers greatly reduced electrode wear, so the spark stays stronger for longer.

 **FASTER COLD STARTING**

 **FOR UNLEADED OR LEADED FUEL**

 **ELECTRODES UP TO 100°C COOLER**

 **BETTER ACCELERATION RESPONSE**

 **LOWER EMISSIONS**

 **50% BIGGER SPARK AREA**

**THE LONGER LIFE PLUG**

**Plug Tips/Hot and Cold.**
Spark plugs must operate within well-defined temperature limits to avoid cold fouling at one extreme and overheating at the other.
Champion and the car manufacturers work out the best plugs for an engine to give optimum performance under all conditions, from freezing cold starts to sustained high speed motorway cruising.
Plugs are often referred to as hot or cold. With Champion, the higher the number on its body, the hotter the plug, and the lower the number the cooler the plug.

**Plug Cleaning**
Modern plug design and materials mean that Champion no longer recommends periodic plug cleaning. Certainly don't clean your plugs with a wire brush as this can cause metal conductive paths across the nose of the insulator so impairing its performance and resulting in loss of acceleration and reduced m.p.g.
However, if plugs are removed, always carefully clean the area where the plug seats in the cylinder head as grit and dirt can sometimes cause gas leakage.
Also wipe any traces of oil or grease from plug leads as this may lead to arcing.

DOUBLE COPPER

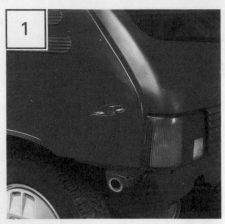

**1** This photographic sequence shows the steps taken to repair the dent and paintwork damage shown above. In general, the procedure for repairing a hole will be similar; where there are substantial differences, the procedure is clearly described and shown in a separate photograph.

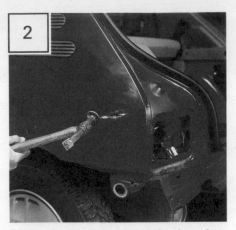

**2** First remove any trim around the dent, then hammer out the dent where access is possible. This will minimise filling. Here, after the large dent has been hammered out, the damaged area is being made slightly concave.

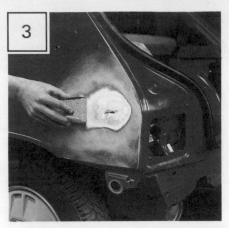

**3** Next, remove all paint from the damaged area by rubbing with coarse abrasive paper or using a power drill fitted with a wire brush or abrasive pad. 'Feather' the edge of the boundary with good paintwork using a finer grade of abrasive paper.

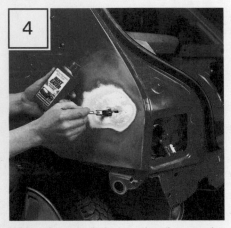

**4** Where there are holes or other damage, the sheet metal should be cut away before proceeding further. The damaged area and any signs of rust should be treated with Turtle Wax Hi-Tech Rust Eater, which will also inhibit further rust formation.

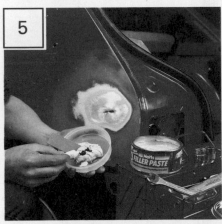

**5** *For a large dent or hole* mix Holts Body Plus Resin and Hardener according to the manufacturer's instructions and apply around the edge of the repair. Press Glass Fibre Matting over the repair area and leave for 20-30 minutes to harden. Then ...

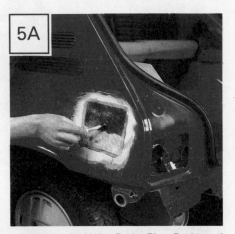

**5A** ... brush more Holts Body Plus Resin and Hardener onto the matting and leave to harden. Repeat the sequence with two or three layers of matting, checking that the final layer is lower than the surrounding area. Apply Holts Body Plus Filler Paste as shown in Step 5B.

**5B** *For a medium dent,* mix Holts Body Plus Filler Paste and Hardener according to the manufacturer's instructions and apply it with a flexible applicator. Apply thin layers of filler at 20-minute intervals, until the filler surface is slightly proud of the surrounding bodywork.

**5C** *For small dents and scratches* use Holts No Mix Filler Paste straight from the tube. Apply it according to the instructions in thin layers, using the spatula provided. It will harden in minutes if applied outdoors and may then be used as its own knifing putty.

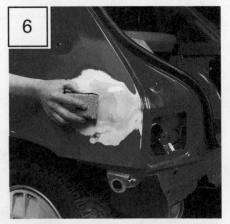

**6** Use a plane or file for initial shaping. Then, using progressively finer grades of wet-and-dry paper, wrapped round a sanding block, and copious amounts of clean water, rub down the filler until glass smooth. 'Feather' the edges of adjoining paintwork.

**7**

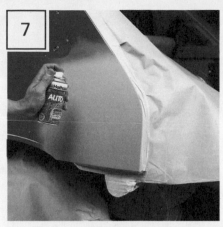

Protect adjoining areas before spraying the whole repair area and at least one inch of the surrounding sound paintwork with Holts Dupli-Color primer.

**8**

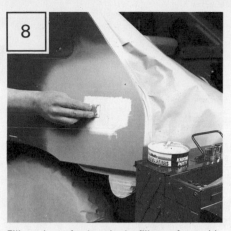

Fill any imperfections in the filler surface with a small amount of Holts Body Plus Knifing Putty. Using plenty of clean water, rub down the surface with a fine grade wet-and-dry paper – 400 grade is recommended – until it is really smooth.

**9**

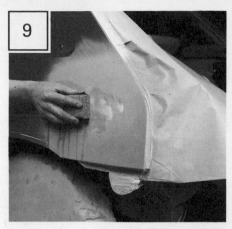

Carefully fill any remaining imperfections with knifing putty before applying the last coat of primer. Then rub down the surface with Holts Body Plus Rubbing Compound to ensure a really smooth surface.

**10**

Protect surrounding areas from overspray before applying the topcoat in several thin layers. Agitate Holts Dupli-Color aerosol thoroughly. Start at the repair centre, spraying outwards with a side-to-side motion.

**10A**

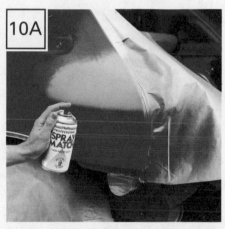

If the exact colour is not available off the shelf, local Holts Professional Spraymatch Centres will custom fill an aerosol to match perfectly.

**10B**

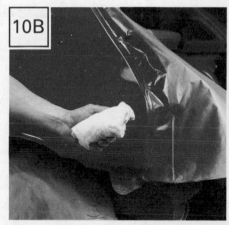

To identify whether a lacquer finish is required, rub a painted unrepaired part of the body with wax and a clean cloth.

**11**

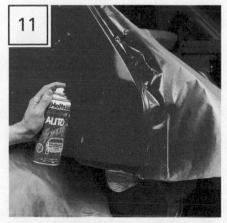

If *no* traces of paint appear on the cloth, spray Holts Dupli-Color clear lacquer over the repaired area to achieve the correct gloss level.

**12**

**13**

The paint will take about two weeks to harden fully. After this time it can be 'cut' with a mild cutting compound such as Turtle Wax Minute Cut prior to polishing with a final coating of Turtle Wax Extra.

**14**

When carrying out bodywork repairs, remember that the quality of the finished job is proportional to the time and effort expended.

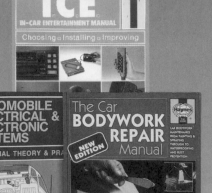

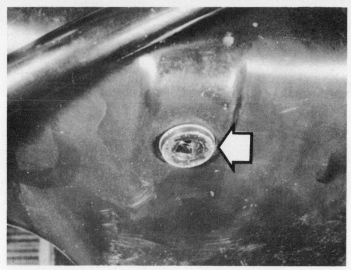

2.3 Engine oil drain plug location (arrowed)

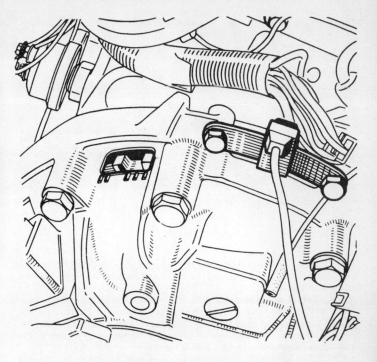

Fig. 1.2 Angular position sensor location on bellhousing (Sec 6)

### 3    Major operations possible with the engine in the car

The following operations can be carried out without having to remove the engine from the car:

(a)  Removal and refitting of the cylinder head
(b)  Removal and refitting of the timing cover, chain and gears
(c)  Removal and refitting of the sump
(d)  Removal and refitting of the connecting rods, pistons and liner assemblies
(e)  Removal and refitting of the oil pump
(f)  Renewal of the engine mountings

### 4    Major operations requiring engine removal

The following operations can only be carried out after removal of the engine from the car.

(a)  Removal and refitting of the camshaft
(b)  Removal and refitting of the crankshaft and main bearings
(c)  Removal and refitting of the flywheel
(d)  Removal and refitting of the crankshaft rear oil seal

### 5    Methods of engine removal

The engine is removed upwards and out of the engine compartment. The engine may be removed on its own, as described in the following Section, or in unit with the gearbox or automatic transmission, as described in Section 7.

### 6    Engine – removal without gearbox or automatic transmission

1    Disconnect the battery negative terminal then remove the bonnet, as described in Chapter 11.
2    Remove the radiator, as described in Chapter 2.
3    Remove the air cleaner, as described in Chapter 3.
4    Remove the starter motor, as described in Chapter 9.
5    Slacken the alternator mountings and adjustment arm bolts, push the alternator in towards the engine and slip the drivebelt off the three pulleys.
6    Undo the bolt and remove the washer securing the crankshaft pulley to the pulley hub. To lock the engine while the bolt is undone, firmly apply the handbrake and engage top gear. On cars wih

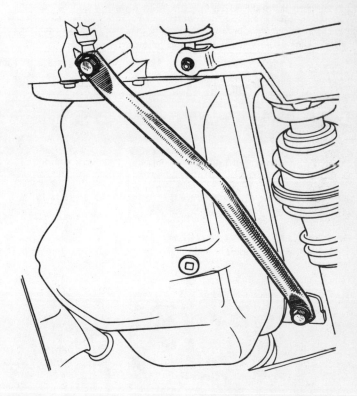

Fig. 1.3 Engine steady rod and retaining bolt locations (Sec 6)

automatic transmission, wedge a screwdriver between the starter ring gear teeth and the bellhousing through the starter motor aperture. With the pulley bolt removed, lift off the pulley and withdraw the pulley hub by carefully levering it off using two screwdrivers.
7    Slacken the hose clips and disconnect the two heater hoses at the water pump (photos).

6.7A Disconnect the heater return hose ...

6.7B ... and feed hose at the water pump

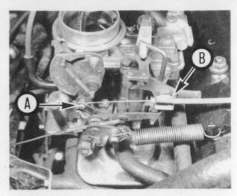

6.8 Disconnect the choke cable loop (A) and retaining clip (B)

8    Release the clip securing the choke cable to its support bracket on the carburettor and disconnect the cable end loop from the stud on the linkage (photo).

9    If a Zenith or Solex carburettor is fitted, detach the throttle linkage return spring, open the throttle and slip the accelerator cable out of the slot on the linkage. Undo the two bolts securing the support bracket to the inlet manifold and move the bracket complete with heater hoses and accelerator cable to one side (photo).

10   On models fitted with a Weber carburettor, detach the throttle linkage return spring, open the throttle and slip the accelerator cable out of the slot on the linkage bellcrank. Slacken the outer cable clamp retaining screw and remove the accelerator cable from its support bracket.

11   Detach the brake servo vacuum hose from the rear of the inlet manifold (photo).

12   Undo the retaining bolt and detach the engine earth lead from the cylinder block below the water pump (photo).

13   Undo the two bolts, remove the tension springs and release the exhaust front section from its attachment at the manifold.

14   Disconnect the fuel feed and return pipes at the fuel pump and plug their ends.

15   Disconnect the ignition coil HT cable from the centre of the distributor cap.

16   Note the locations of the wiring at the rear of the alternator and disconnect the wires (photo).

17   Disconnect the lead at the water temperature gauge sender unit at the water pump.

18   Disconnect the lead at the oil pressure switch located below the alternator.

19   Disconnect the lead to the horn and, where fitted, the two leads at the oil level sensor on the front face of the sump.

20   Undo the bolt securing the cable and hose guide to the left-hand side of the cylinder head (photo).

21   Disconnect the wiring connector at the left-hand end of the engine

6.9 Undo the two support bracket bolts (arrowed)

6.11 Disconnect the brake servo vacuum hose (arrowed)

6.12 Disconnect the engine earth lead (arrowed)

6.16 Disconnect the wiring at the alternator (arrowed)

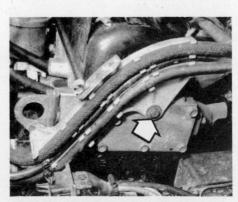

6.20 Undo the bolt (arrowed) and release the cable and hose guide

6.22 Undo the bolt (arrowed) to release the wiring junction box

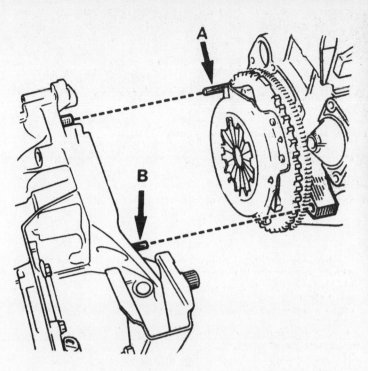

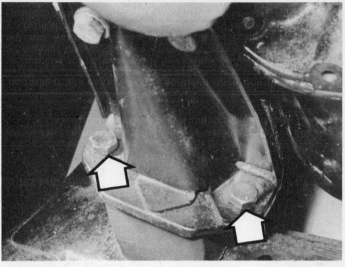

6.33 Undo the engine mounting bolts (arrowed)

Fig. 1.4 Remove studs A and B to provide clearance for engine removal (Sec 6)

withdraw the engine from the gearbox or transmission bellhousing. The engine may be tight due to the locating dowels.

35 Move the engine as far as possible to the right until it is completely clear of the gearbox or transmission and then lift the engine slowly, turning it as necessary to clear any obstructions. As soon as the engine is high enough, swing it over the front body panel and lower the engine to the floor.

and, where fitted, the distributor LT lead at the connector near the distributor.

22 All the wiring to the engine should now have been disconnected and it should be possible to swing the complete harness, including the cable and hose guide, and the wiring junction box (photo), to one side clear of the engine. If there are any additional wires for accessories or optional equipment, disconnect them to permit the loom to be moved clear.

23 Undo the shouldered bolts and remove the TDC sensor or angular position sensor from the gearbox bellhousing. Where fitted place the diagnostic socket to one side.

24 Check that all hoses, cables and attachments likely to impede engine removal have been disconnected, removed from any retaining clips and placed well clear.

25 Jack up the front of the car and support it on axle stands.

26 Undo the retaining bolts and remove the steady rod connecting the gearbox to the engine. Note the position of the distance spacer.

27 Undo the bolts securing the flywheel or torque converter cover plate to the bellhousing lower face.

28 On automatic transmission models rotate the crankshaft as necessary to provide access, and undo the three bolts securing the torque converter to the driveplate. Retain the torque converter in position on the transmission using a flat strip of metal secured to the bellhousing with one of the coverplate bolts.

29 Undo all the bellhousing-to-engine retaining bolts accessible from under the car, then lower the car to the ground.

30 Place a jack with an interposed block of wood under the gearbox or transmission and just take the weight of the unit.

31 Attach a suitable hoist or crane to the engine using chains or rope slings, or by attaching the chains or ropes to the engine lifting brackets. Raise the hoist to just take the weight of the engine.

32 Undo all the bellhousing-to-engine retaining bolts accessible from above and additionally the two nuts or studs, one each side of the engine. To provide sufficient clearance for engine removal, both these studs must be removed. To do this lock two nuts together on the exposed threads and undo the studs using the innermost nut.

33 Undo the bolts securing the front engine mounting bracket to the rubber mounting (photo).

34 Raise the engine and gearbox or transmission very slightly and

## 7 Engine – removal with gearbox or automatic transmission

1  Disconnect the battery negative terminal then remove the bonnet, as described in Chapter 11.

2  Remove the radiator, as described in Chapter 2.

3  Remove the air cleaner, as described in Chapter 3.

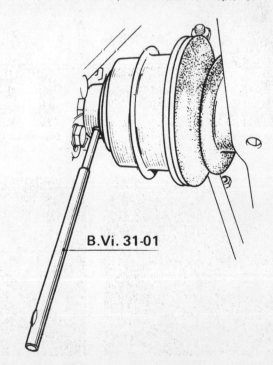

B.Vi. 31-01

Fig. 1.5 Drive out the roll pin securing the right-hand driveshaft inner joint (Sec 7)

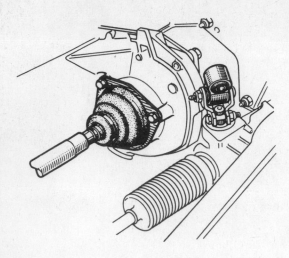

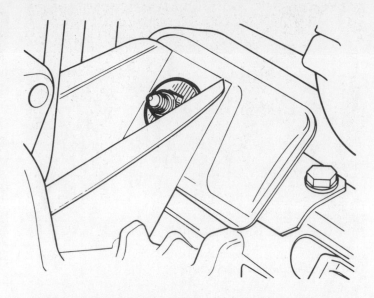

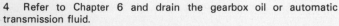

**Fig. 1.6 Undo the three bolts securing the left-hand driveshaft inner joint bellows (Sec 7)**

**Fig. 1.7 Engine rear mounting retaining nut location (Sec 7)**

4  Refer to Chapter 6 and drain the gearbox oil or automatic transmission fluid.

5  Refer to Section 6 of this Chapter and carry out the operations described in paragraphs 7 to 25 inclusive.

6  Make a note of the wiring locations at the rear of the starter motor solenoid and disconnect them.

7  Withdraw the spring wire retaining clip securing the speedometer cable to the gearbox or transmission at the rear and remove the cable. Note the fitted direction of the clip.

8  Remove the earth braid on the right-hand side of the gearbox or transmission.

9  Disconnect the clutch cable from the release fork and the bracket on the bellhousing.

10  If a manual gearbox is fitted, slide back the rubber cover (photo) and undo the nut and bolt securing the gearchange rod to the gearbox fork control shaft. Slide the rod off the shaft and recover the distance sleeve.

11  If automatic transmission is fitted, disconnect the transmission selector control rod from the bracket and bellcrank.

12  On manual gearbox models, disconnect the wiring at the reversing lamp switch and, where fitted, the gear position sensors on the gearbox casing. On automatic transmission models, refer to the layout and description of the switches and sensors shown and described in

Chapter 6, and disconnect as necessary to allow the computer module to be removed with the transmission. Also undo the fluid cooler union nuts and remove the pipes from the transmission. Plug the unions after removal.

13  From under the car on all models, drive out the roll pin, using a parallel pin punch, securing the right-hand driveshaft inner joint to the differential stub shaft (photo). Note that the roll pin is in fact two roll pins, one inside the other.

14  Lower the car to the ground and undo the three bolts securing the left-hand driveshaft inner joint bellows and retaining plate to the side of the gearbox or transmission.

15  Make a final check that all cables, pipes and components likely to impede removal have been detached and are positioned well clear.

16  Attach a crane or hoist to the engine using chain or rope slings or secure the chains or ropes to the engine lifting brackets.

17  Undo the nuts and bolts at the front and the single nut at the rear securing the engine mounting brackets to the rubber mountings. Raise the engine and gearbox or transmission slightly and release the brackets from the mountings.

18  Move the engine assembly to the left as far as possible and tap the right-hand driveshaft inner joint off the stub shaft using a hide or plastic mallet.

19  Now move the engine assembly to the right and lift the left-hand

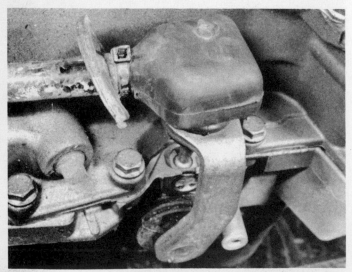

7.10 Slide back the rubber cover to gain access to the gearchange rod retaining bolt

7.13 Remove the driveshaft inner joint roll pin (arrowed)

7.20 Engine and manual gearbox removal

8.1 Remove the flywheel cover plate

driveshaft inner joint spider out of its location in the differential sun wheel.

20 Slowly lift the engine and gearbox or transmission assembly, moving it around as necessary to clear all obstructions. When high enough, lift it over the front body panel and lower the unit to the ground (photo).

## 8 Engine – separation from manual gearbox or automatic transmission

1   With the assembly removed from the car, undo the retaining bolts and lift off the cover plate at the base of the transmission bellhousing (photo).

2   Turn the crankshaft as necessary until the notch on the flywheel or torque converter is in line with the TDC timing mark on the bellhousing timing scale (photo). Now make a reference mark on the cylinder block in line with the flywheel or torque converter notch. This will provide a useful reference because, once the gearbox or transmission is removed, the timing marks go with it, and it then becomes difficult to determine the TDC position of the engine.

3   If automatic transmission is fitted, undo the three bolts securing the torque converter to the driveplate. Using a strip of metal as a suitable bracket, retain the torque converter on the transmission by securing the bracket to one of the cover plate bolt holes.

4   Undo the support bracket bolt and the three bellhousing bolts securing the starter motor in position. Lift off the starter noting the location of the dowel in one of the bolt holes.

5   Undo the two bolts securing the steady rod to the engine and gearbox or transmission. Lift off the rod, noting the location of the distance spacer.

6   Undo the bolts and the two nuts securing the engine to the gearbox or transmission bellhousing. Support the gearbox or transmission and withdraw the engine. The engine may be initially tight due to the locating dowels (photo).

## 9 Engine dismantling – general

1   If possible mount the engine on a stand for the dismantling procedure, but, failing this, support it in an upright position with blocks of wood placed under each side of the sump or crankcase.

2   Drain the oil into a suitable container before cleaning the engine or major dismantling.

3   Cleanliness is most important, and if the engine is dirty it should be cleaned with paraffin or a suitable solvent while keeping it in an upright position.

4   Avoid working with the engine directly on a concrete floor, as grit presents a real source of trouble.

8.2 TDC mark (arrowed) on the bellhousing timing scale

8.6 Separating the engine from the manual gearbox

5   As parts are removed, clean them in a paraffin bath. However, do not immerse parts with internal oilways in paraffin as it is difficult to remove, usually requiring a high pressure hose. Clean oilways with nylon pipe cleaners.

6   It is advisable to have suitable containers to hold small items, as this will help when reassembling the engine and also prevent possible losses.

7   Always obtain complete sets of gaskets when the engine is being dismantled, but retain the old gaskets with a view to using them as a pattern to make a replacement if a new one is not available. Note that in many instances a gasket is not used, but instead the joints are sealed with an RTV sealant. It is recommended that a tube of CAF 4/60 THIXO paste, obtainable from Renault dealers be obtained as it is specially formulated for this purpose.

8   When possible, refit nuts, bolts and washers in their location after being removed, as this helps to protect the threads and will also be helpful when reassembling the engine.

9   Retain unserviceable components in order to compare them with the new parts supplied.

10   The operations described in this Chapter are a step by step sequence, assuming that the engine is to be completely dismantled for major overhaul or repair. Where an operation can be carried out with the engine in the car, the dismantling necessary to gain access to the component concerned is described separately.

---

## 10   Ancillary components – removal

With the engine separated from the gearbox or transmission the externally-mounted ancillary components, as given in the following list, can be removed. In most cases removal is straightforward, but further information will be found in the relevant Chapters.

*Inlet and exhaust manifolds and carburettor (Chapter 3)*
*Fuel pump (Chapter 3)*
*Alternator (Chapter 9)*
*Spark plugs (Chapter 4)*
*Distributor (Chapter 4)*
*Water pump (Chapter 2)*
*Clutch (Chapter 5)*
*Oil filter (Section 2 of this Chapter)*
*Engine front mounting bracket (Section 22 of this Chapter)*

---

## 11   Cylinder head removal – engine in car

1   Disconnect the battery negative terminal.
2   Refer to Chapter 2 and drain the cooling system.
3   Refer to Chapter 3 and remove the air cleaner.
4   Disconnect the HT leads at the spark plugs, release the distributor cap retaining clips or screws and remove the cap and leads.
5   Disconnect the lead at the water temperature gauge sender on the water pump (photo).
6   Slacken the alternator mountings and adjustment arm bolt, push the alternator in towards the engine and slip the drivebelt off the three pulleys (photo).

7   Undo the bolt securing the alternator adjustment arm to the water pump and swing the alternator clear of the engine (photo).
8   Release the hose clips and remove the two heater hoses from the water pump (photo).
9   Release the hose clip and remove the radiator top hose from the water pump (photo).
10   Open the throttle linkage on the carburettor by hand and slip the accelerator cable out of the slot on the linkage or bellcrank connector.
11   Undo the two bolts securing the heater hose and accelerator cable support bracket to the rear of the inlet manifold (photo).
12   On models fitted with a Weber carburettor, slacken the clamp bolt and release the accelerator cable from the support bracket on the manifold.
13   Undo the nut and washer on the inlet manifold and on the cylinder block beneath the water pump, and lift off the heat shield (photo).
14   Disconnect the fuel inlet pipe and the crankcase ventilation hose at the carburettor (photo).
15   Release the choke cable looped end from the stud on the linkage and detach the support clip from the carburettor bracket (photo 6.8). Disconnect the throttle linkage return spring.
16   Disconnect the brake servo vacuum hose from the rear of the inlet manifold and the ignition vacuum advance pipe from the carburettor (photo).
17   Disconnect the distributor LT lead (where applicable) at the wiring connector.
18   Undo the bolt and release the retaining clip securing the cable and hose guide to the side of the cylinder head (photo).
19   Undo the two bolts and withdraw the tension springs securing the exhaust front section to the manifold.
20   Undo the three nuts and remove the rocker cover, complete with gasket, from the cylinder head (photo).
21   Undo the two bolts and two nuts securing the rocker shaft pedestals to the cylinder head (photo). Lift the rocker shaft assembly upwards and off the two studs.
22   Lift out each of the pushrods in turn using a twisting action to release them from their cam followers (photo). Keep them in strict order of removal by inserting them in a strip of cardboard having eight numbered holes punched in it. Note that No 1 should be the pushrod nearest the flywheel.
23   Slacken all the cylinder head retaining bolts half a turn at a time in the reverse order to that shown in Fig. 1.27. When the tension has been relieved remove all the bolts, with the exception of the centre bolt on the distributor side.
24   Using a hide or plastic mallet, tap each end of the cylinder head so as to pivot the head around the remaining locating bolt and unstick the gasket. Do not attempt to lift the head until the gasket has been unstuck, otherwise the cylinder liner seal at the base of each liner will be broken, allowing water and foreign matter to enter the sump.
25   After unsticking the cylinder head from the gasket, remove the remaining bolt and lift the head, complete with water pump, manifolds and carburettor, off the engine (photo). **Note** the crankshaft must not be rotated with the head removed, otherwise the liners will be displaced. If it is necessary to turn the engine (eg to clean the piston crowns), use bolts with suitable washers screwed into the top of the block to retain the liners (photo 35.11).

11.5 Disconnect the lead at the temperature gauge sender

11.6 Slacken the alternator mountings and slip the drivebelt off the pulleys

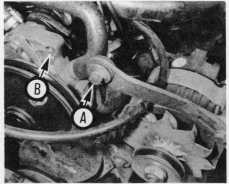

11.7 Undo the bolt (A) and remove the alternator adjustment arm from the pump at (B)

11.8 Disconnect the heater hoses ...

11.9 ... and the radiator top hose at the water pump

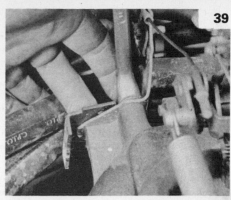

11.11 Undo the bolts and remove the support bracket

11.13 Undo the two nuts (arrowed) and lift off the heat shield

11.14 Disconnect the fuel inlet pipe at the carburettor

11.16 Disconnect the brake servo vacuum hose

11.18 Remove the cable and hose guide

11.20 Undo the three nuts and lift off the rocker cover

11.21 Undo the two nuts and two bolts (arrowed) and withdraw the rocker shaft assembly

11.22 Take out the pushrods and keep them in order

11.25 Free the cylinder head from the gasket then lift the head, complete with manifolds and water pump, off the engine

## 12  Cylinder head removal – engine on bench

The procedure for removing the cylinder head with the engine on the bench is similar to that for removal when the engine is in the car, with the exception of disconnecting the controls and services. Refer to Section 11 and follow the procedure given in paragraphs 7, 13 and 15, then 20 to 25.

## 13  Cylinder head – dismantling

1  Extract the circlip from the end of the rocker shaft, then remove the springs, rocker arms and pedestals, keeping each component in its original fitted sequence.
2  Remove the valves from the cylinder head. Compress each spring in turn with a valve spring compressor until the two halves of the

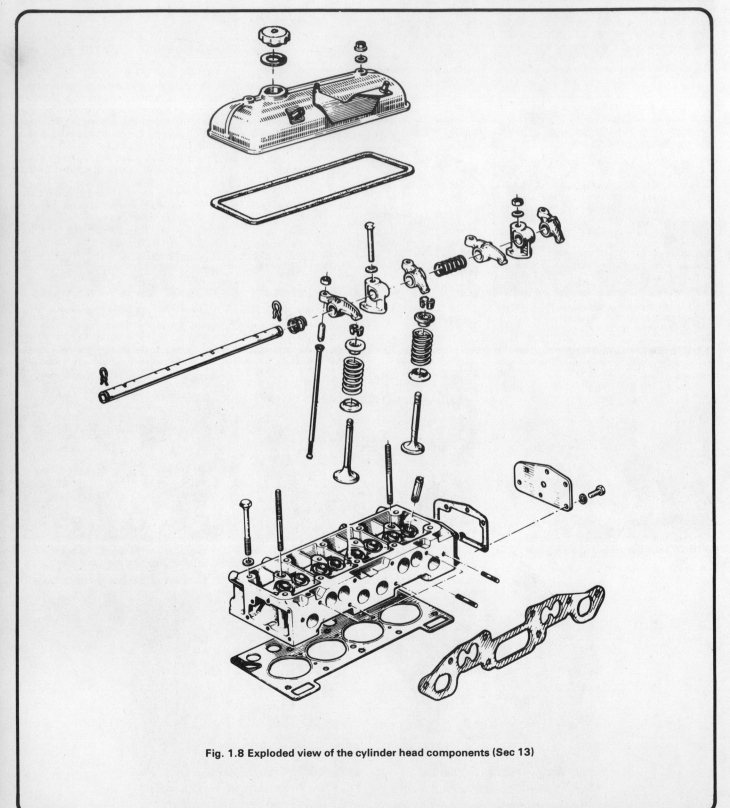

Fig. 1.8 Exploded view of the cylinder head components (Sec 13)

collets can be removed. Release the compressor and remove the spring, spring retainer and thrust washer.

3   If, when the valve spring compressor is screwed down, the valve spring retaining cap refuses to free to expose the split collet, do not continue to screw down on the compressor, but gently tap the top of the tool directly over the cap with a light hammer. At the same time hold the compressor firmly in position with one hand to avoid it jumping off.

4   It is essential that the valves are kept in their correct sequence unless they are so badly worn that they are to be renewed. Numbering from the flywheel end of the cylinder head, exhaust valves are 1-4-5-8 and inlet valves 2-3-6-7.

5   The valve springs and collets should also be kept in their correct sequence as the inlet and exhaust valve components differ.

## 14  Sump – removal

1   If the sump is to be removed with the engine in the car, first carry out the following operations:

   (a)  *Undo the two bolts, noting the position of the spacer, and remove the engine steady rod*
   (b)  *Undo the bolts and remove the flywheel or torque converter cover plate from the bellhousing*
   (c)  *Drain the engine oil*
   (d)  *Where fitted, disconnect the two wires at the oil level sensor on the front face of the sump*

2   Undo and remove the bolts securing the sump to the crankcase (photo). Tap the sump with a hide or plastic mallet to break the seal between sump flange and crankcase, and remove the sump. Note that a gasket is not used, only a sealing compound.

## 15  Oil pump – removal

1   If the oil pump is to be removed with the engine in the car, first remove the sump, as described in the previous Section.

2   Undo the retaining bolts (photo) and withdraw the oil pump from the crankcase and drivegear.

## 16  Timing cover, gears and chain – removal

1   If the engine is In the car, first carry out the following operations:

   (a)  *Remove the alternator drivebelt*
   (b)  *Remove the sump*

2   If the engine is in the car, rotate the crankshaft until the notch in the flywheel or torque converter is aligned with the TDC mark on the bellhousing timing scale (photo), and the distributor rotor is pointing towards the No 1 cylinder HT lead segment in the cap.

3   Using a socket or spanner, undo the crankshaft pulley retaining bolt. If the engine is in the car lock the starter ring gear to prevent the engine turning using a wide-bladed screwdriver between the ring gear teeth and the crankcase or apply the handbrake and engage top gear. If the engine is out of the car the ring gear can be locked using a strip of angle iron engaged with the dowel bolt (photo).

4   With the bolt removed, lift off the pulley and withdraw the pulley hub. If the hub is tight, carefully lever it off using two screwdrivers or use a two- or three-legged puller (photo).

5   Undo the nuts and bolts securing the timing cover to the cylinder block and carefully prise the timing cover off using a screwdriver to release the sealant. Note that a gasket is not used.

6   If the engine is out of the car, rotate the crankshaft by means of the flywheel or torque converter driveplate until No 1 piston is returned to TDC, and the timing marks on the crankshaft and camshaft sprockets are towards each other. If the cylinder head has been removed, make sure that the cylinder liners are retained with bolts and washers, as described in Section 35, otherwise the liners will be displaced when the crankshaft is rotated.

7   Observe the components of the timing chain tensioner, noting that one of three types may be fitted. These are; a mechanical tensioner, identifiable by its coil tensioning spring; a hydraulic tensioner with manual presetting, identifiable by the small bolt on the side of the tensioner body; a hydraulic tensioner with automatic presetting

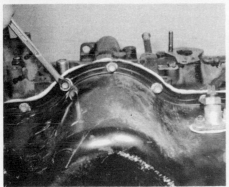

14.2 Undo the retaining bolts and remove the sump

15.2 Undo the retaining bolts and withdraw the oil pump

16.2 Flywheel notch (arrowed) aligned with TDC mark on the bellhousing timing scale

16.3 Lock the starter ring gear using a strip of angle iron

16.4 A puller may be needed to remove the crankshaft pulley hub

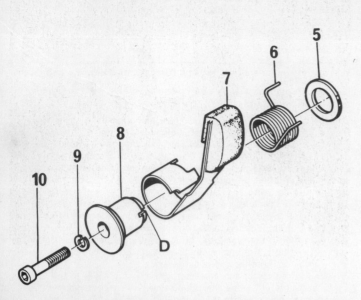

**Fig. 1.9 Mechanical timing chain tensioner components (Sec 16)**

| | | | |
|---|---|---|---|
| 5 | Washer | 8 | Collar |
| 6 | Spring | 9 | Washer |
| 7 | Slipper arm | 10 | Retaining bolt |

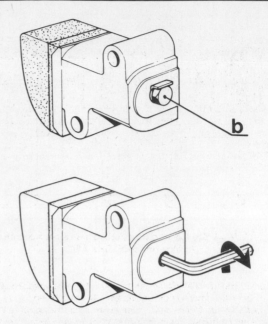

**Fig. 1.10 Hydraulic timing chain tensioner with manual presetting (Sec 16)**

*Remove bolt (b) and turn slipper piston clockwise using an Allen key to retract the tensioner slipper*

identifiable by the absence of a small bolt on the side of the tensioner body.

8    To remove the mechanical tensioner, undo the retaining bolt using an Allen key, hold the tensioner slipper and spring end together and withdraw the assembly from the cylinder block.

9    If an hydraulic tensioner with manual presetting is fitted, bend up the locktab and unscrew the small bolt on the side of the tensioner body. Insert a suitable Allen key into the bolt hole and engage the Allen key with the end of the slipper piston. Turn the key clockwise to retract the tensioner slipper. Now undo the two retaining bolts, lift off the tensioner and recover the spacer plate located behind the tensioner body. Removal of the tensioner with automatic presetting follows the same procedure, except that the piston cannot be retracted manually and must be held in compression by hand as the tensioner is removed.

10 Bend back the locktab then undo and remove the camshaft sprocket retaining bolt.

11 Withdraw the camshaft and crankshaft sprockets, complete with chain, using two screwdrivers to lever the sprockets off if they are tight (photo).

12 With the sprockets and chain removed, check that the Woodruff key in the end of the crankshaft is a tight fit in its groove, but if not, remove it now and store it safely to avoid the risk of it dropping out and getting lost.

## 17 Camshaft and followers – removal

1    Using a suitable bolt screwed into the distributor drivegear, or a length of tapered dowel rod, extract the drivegear from the distributor aperture.

2    Withdraw the camshaft followers from the top of the cylinder block, keeping them in strict order of removal (photo).

3    Undo and remove the two bolts securing the camshaft retaining plate to the cylinder block and carefully withdraw the camshaft from its location (photo).

## 18 Liners, pistons and connecting rods – removal

1    If the engine is in the car, first carry out the following operations:

    (a)  Remove the sump
    (b)  For easier access, remove the oil pump
    (c)  Remove the cylinder head (not necessary if only the big-end bearings are to be removed)

16.11 Removing the timing chain and sprockets

17.2 Withdraw the cam followers and keep them in order

17.3 Undo the bolts (arrowed) and withdraw the camshaft

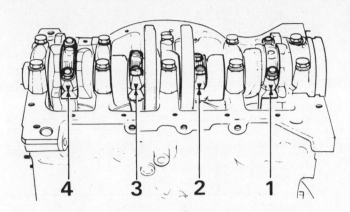

Fig. 1.11 Mark the big-end bearing caps and connecting rods before removal (Sec 18)

20.1 Identification number on main bearing cap

2   Rotate the crankshaft so that No 1 big-end cap (nearest the flywheel) is at the lowest point of its travel. If the big-end cap and rod are not already numbered, mark them with a centre punch on the side opposite the camshaft (rear facing side of engine when in the car). Mark both the cap and rod in relation to the cylinder liner they operate in, noting that No 1 is nearest the flywheel end of the engine.
3   Undo and remove the big-end bearing cap nuts and withdraw the cap, complete with shell bearing from the connecting rod. If only the bearing shells are being attended to, push the connecting rod up and off the crankpin and remove the upper bearing shell. Keep the bearing shells and cap together in their correct sequence if they are to be refitted.
4   Remove the liner clamps and withdraw the liner together with piston and connecting rod, from the top of the cylinder block. Mark the liners using masking tape, so that they may be refitted in their original locations.
5   Push the connecting rod up and remove the piston and rod from the liner.
6   Now repeat these operations on the remaining three liner, piston and connecting rod assemblies.

## 19 Flywheel or torque converter driveplate – removal

1   Lock the crankshaft using a strip of angle iron between the ring gear teeth and the engine dowel bolt, or a block of wood between one of the crankshaft counterweights and the crankcase.
2   Mark the flywheel or driveplate in relation to the crankshaft, undo the retaining bolts and withdraw the unit.

## 20 Crankshaft and main bearings – removal

1   Identification numbers should be cast onto the base of each main bearing cap (photo), but if not, number the cap and crankcase using a centre punch, as was done for the connecting rods and caps.
2   Undo and remove the main bearing cap retaining bolts and withdraw the caps, complete with bearing shells. Withdraw the oil dipstick tube first after undoing the bolts at No 2 bearing cap (photo).
3   Carefully lift the crankshaft from the crankcase (photo).
4   Remove the thrust washers at each side of the centre main bearing, then remove the bearing shell upper halves from the crankcase. Place each shell with its respective bearing cap.

## 21 Crankshaft rear oil seal – renewal

1   With the engine removed from the car and separated from the gearbox or automatic transmission (if these units were removed with it), remove the flywheel or torque converter driveplate.
2   Clean the area around the crankshaft rear oil seal, then use a screwdriver to prise it from the block and bearing cap.
3   Wipe clean the oil seal recess. Dip the new oil seal in clean engine

20.2 The oil dipstick tube is secured to the main bearing cap with the retaining bolt

20.3 Crankshaft removal

oil and carefully install it over the crankshaft rear journal. Take great care not to damage the delicate lip of the seal and make sure that the seal open face is towards the engine.

4    Using a tube of suitable diameter, a block of wood or the old seal, install the new seal squarely into its location until the outer face is flush with the block and bearing cap. If the original seal has worn a groove in the journal, drive the seal in a further 3 mm (0.12 in).

5    Refit the flywheel and the engine, as described in the applicable Sections of this Chapter.

---

### 22  Engine mountings – renewal

#### *Front mountings*

1    Place a jack and an interposed block of wood under the sump if the right-hand mounting is to be removed, or under the gearbox or transmission if the left-hand mounting is to be removed. Raise the jack to just take the weight of the engine and gearbox or automatic transmission.

2    Undo the nut securing the rubber mounting to the subframe from below, and remove the flat washer (photo).

3    Undo the two nuts and bolts securing the rubber mounting to the

engine/gearbox or automatic transmission mounting brackets. Undo the bolts securing the bracket to the engine, gearbox or transmission (photo), lift off the bracket and withdraw the rubber mounting.

4    Refitting is the reverse sequence to removal.

#### *Rear mounting*

5    Disconnect the battery negative terminal and remove the air cleaner, as described in Chapter 3.

6    Place a jack beneath the gearbox or transmission with an interposed block of wood and just take the weight of the unit.

7    Undo the nut and remove the washer securing the rubber mounting to the gearbox or automatic transmission mounting bracket.

8    Undo the two bolts securing the mounting rear support bracket to the subframe, slide out the bracket and withdraw the rubber mounting.

9    Refitting is the reverse sequence to removal.

---

### 23  Crankcase ventilation system – description

The layout of the crankcase ventilation system according to engine type is shown in the accompanying illustrations.

When the engine is idling, or under partial load conditions, the

22.2 Engine rubber mounting-to-subframe retaining nut

22.3 Engine mounting bracket retaining bolts

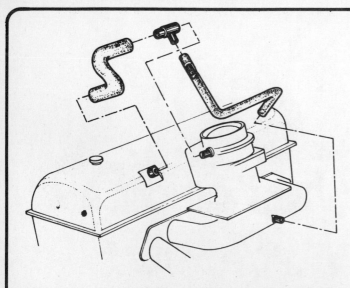

Fig. 1.12 Crankcase ventilation hose layout as fitted to early 1108 cc engines (Sec 23)

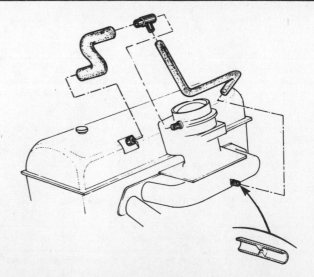

Fig. 1.13 Crankcase ventilation hose layout as fitted to later 1108 cc engines (Sec 23)

high depresssion in the inlet manifold draws the crankcase fumes (diluted by air from the air cleaner) through the calibrated restrictor and into the combustion chambers.

The system ensures that there is always a partial vacuum in the crankcase, and so prevents pressure which could cause oil contamination, fume emission and oil leakage past seals.

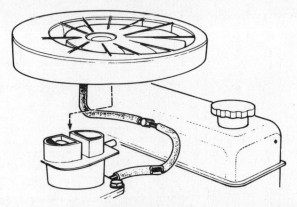

Fig. 1.14 Crankcase ventilation hose layout as fitted to 1397 cc engines (Sec 23)

## 24 Examination and renovation – general

With the engine completely stripped, clean all the components and examine them for wear. Each part should be checked and, where necessary, renewed or renovated as described in the following Sections. Renew main and big-end shell bearings as a matter of course, unless you know that they have had little wear and are in perfect condition.

## 25 Oil pump – examination and renovation

1 Undo the four retaining bolts and lift off the pump cover (photo), taking care not to lose the oil pressure relief valve components which may be ejected under the action of the spring.
2 Remove the pressure relief valve ball seat, ball, spring and spring seat from the pump body (photos).
3 Lift out the idler gear, and the drivegear and shaft.
4 Clean the components and carefully examine the gears, pump body and relief valve ball and seat for any signs of scoring or wear. Renew the pump if these conditions are apparent.
5 If the components appear serviceable, measure the clearance between the pump body and the gears using a feeler blade (photo). If the clearance exceeds the specified amount, the pump must be renewed.

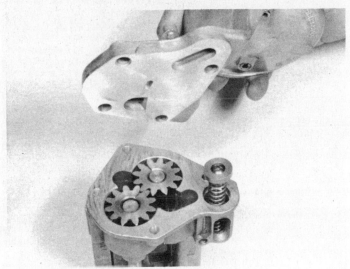

25.1 Lift off the oil pump cover

25.2A Remove the pressure relief valve ball seat and ball ...

25.2B ... followed by the spring and spring seat

25.5 Check the gear-to-body clearance using feeler gauges

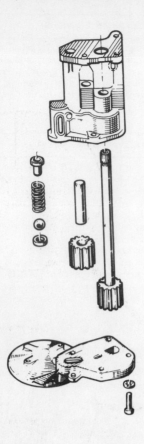

**Fig. 1.15 Exploded view of the oil pump components (Sec 25)**

6    If the pump is satisfactory, reassemble the components in the order of removal, fill the pump with oil and refit the cover.

## 26  Crankshaft and main bearings – examination and renovation

1    Examine the bearing surfaces of the crankshaft for scratches or scoring and, using a micrometer, check each journal and crankpin for ovality. Where this is found to be in excess of 0.0254 mm, the crankshaft will have to be reground and undersize bearings fitted.

2    Crankshaft regrinding should be carried out by a suitable engineering works, who will normally supply the matching undersize main and big-end shell bearings.

3    If the crankshaft endfloat is more than the maximum specified amount, new thrust washers should be fitted to the centre main bearing; these are usually supplied together with the main and big-end bearings on a reground crankshaft.

## 27  Cylinder liners and crankcase – examination and renovation

1    Examine the liners for taper, ovality, scoring and scratches. If a ridge is found at the top of the bore on the thrust side, the bores are worn. The owner will have a good indication of the bore wear prior to dismantling the engine on removing the cylinder head. Excessive oil consumption accompanied by blue smoke from the exhaust is a sure sign of worn bores and pistons rings.

2    Measure the bore diameter just under the ridge with an internal micrometer and compare it with the diameter at the bottom of the bore, which is not subject to wear. If the difference between the two measurements exceeds 0.20 mm then it will be necessary to fit oversize pistons and rings or obtain new piston and liner assemblies. Contrary to popular belief the liners can be rebored if necessary and fitted with oversize pistons.

3    The liners should also be checked for cracking.

4    If the bores are only slightly worn, special oil control rings can be fitted which will restore compression and stop the engine burning oil. Several different types are available and the manufacturer's instructions concerning their fitting must be followed closely.

5    If new pistons only are being fitted and the bores have not been reground, it is essential to slightly roughen the hard glaze on the sides of the bores with fine glasspaper to enable the new piston rings to bed in properly.

6    Examine the crankcase for cracks and leaks, then clean the oil galleries and waterways using a piece of wire.

7    Note that if new piston and liner assemblies have been obtained, each piston is matched to its respective liner and they must not be interchanged.

8    Whether new liners or the original components are being refitted, new liner base seals will be required. On the 1397cc engine the base seals are in the form of a rubber O-ring. On the 1108cc engine the seals are a flat ring type gasket of special material and are available in three sizes colour-coded blue, red or green. The three sizes are necessary so that the liner protrusion can be accurately set.

9    To check the liner protrusion, first ensure that the sealing area at the base of the liner and in the cylinder block is perfectly clean.

10   Place a blue seal on each liner (1108cc engines only, liners on 1397cc engines should have no seal for this check) and place the liner firmly in position in the cylinder block. If previously used liners are being checked, place them in their correct locations. If new liners are being fitted they may initially be placed in any location, but keep their respective matched pistons together with them. With the liners in place, the flats on liners 1 and 2 must be towards each other and the flats on liners 3 and 4 must be towards each other also.

11   Lay a straight-edge across the top of the liner and measure the gap between the straight-edge and the top of the cylinder block ((photo). This is the liner protrusion and must be within the tolerance given in the Specifications. If not, try a red seal or green seal.

12   On both the 1108cc engines and 1397cc engines the liner height variation must be checked, but only if new liners are being fitted. The liner height variation is the difference in cylinder liner protrusion between one liner and the next. The liners must be arranged so that the one with the greatest protrusion becomes No 1 and all the others are stepped down in order so that the one with the least protrusion becomes No 4. This is checked in the same way as for liner protrusion described previously. The base seals must be in position for this check on 1108cc engines, but not on 1397cc engines. Also make sure when moving a liner from one position to another that its matched piston stays with it.

13   Having finally selected the correct location for each liner, identify the liner and its piston with a number 1 to 4 to identify the assembly to be fitted to each location on reassembly.

27.11 Measuring the cylinder liner protrusion

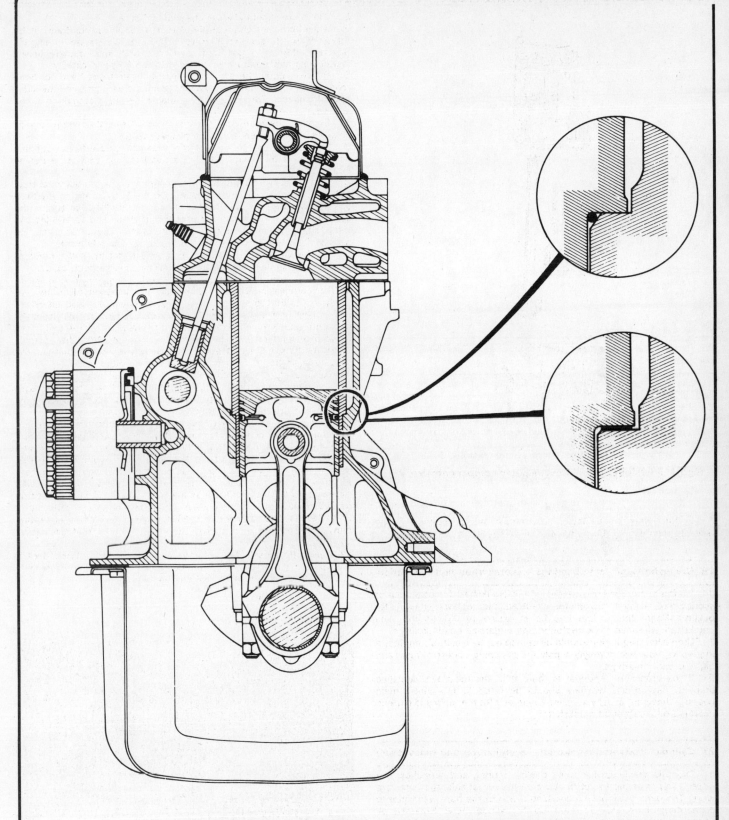

Fig. 1.16 Sectional view of engine showing liner base seal details (Sec 27)

*Upper inset – seal type fitted to 1397 cc engines*        *Lower inset – seal type fitted to 1108 cc engines*

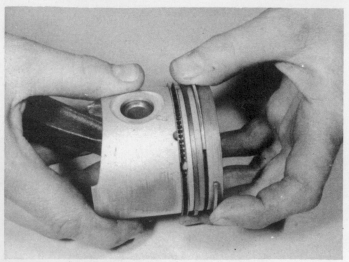

28.3 Remove the piston rings from the top of the pistons

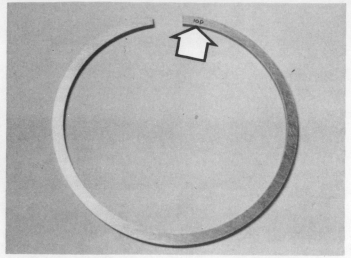

28.5 The word TOP (arrowed) indicates the second compression ring upper face

## 28 Piston and connecting rod assemblies – examination and renovation

1   Examine the pistons for ovality, scoring and scratches, and for wear of the piston ring grooves.
2   If the pistons or connecting rods are to be renewed it is necessary to have this work carried out by a Renault dealer or suitable engineering works who will have the necessary tooling to remove the gudgeon pins.
3   If new rings are to be fitted to the original pistons, expand the old rings over the top of the pistons (photo). The use of two or three old feeler blades will be helpful in preventing the rings dropping into empty grooves.
4   Before fitting the new rings, ensure that the ring grooves in the piston are free of carbon by cleaning them using an old ring. Break the ring in half to do this.
5   Install the new rings by fitting them over the top of the piston, starting with the oil control scraper ring. Note that the second compression ring is tapered and must be fitted with the word TOP uppermost (photo).
6   With all the rings in position, space the ring gaps at 120° to each other.
7   Note that, if new piston and liner assemblies have been obtained, each piston is matched to its respective liner and they must not be interchanged.

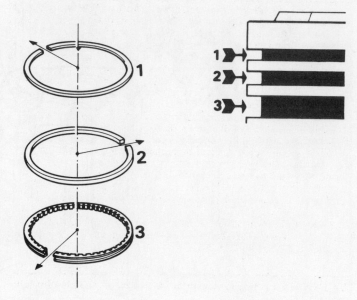

Fig. 1.17 Piston ring fitting and groove spacing details (Sec 28)

## 29 Camshaft and followers – examination and renovation

1   Examine the camshaft bearing surfaces, cam lobes and skew gear for wear ridges, pitting, scoring or chipping of the gear teeth. Renew the camshaft if any of these conditions are apparent.
2   If the camshaft is serviceable, temporarily refit the sprocket and secure with the retaining bolt. Using a feeler gauge measure the clearance between the camshaft retaining plate and the outer face of the bearing journal. If the clearance exceeds the specified dimension, renew the retaining plate. To do this, remove the sprocket and draw off the plate and retaining collar using a suitable puller. Fit the new plate and a new collar using a hammer and tube to drive the collar into position.
3   Examine the condition of the camshaft bearings, and if renewal is necessary have this work carried out by a Renault dealer or engineering works.
4   Inspect the cam followers for wear ridges and pitting of their camshaft lobe contact faces, and for scoring on the sides of the follower body. Light scuff marks and side discolouration are normal, but there should be no signs of scoring or ridges. If the followers show signs of wear, renew them. Note that they must all be renewed if a new camshaft is being fitted.

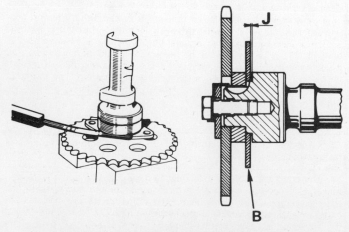

Fig. 1.18 Check the camshaft endfloat using feeler gauges (Sec 29)

B  Camshaft retaining plate                    J  Specified endfloat

30.3 Hydraulic timing chain tensioner with automatic presetting

30.4 Refitting the locked sleeve and slipper piston assembly on the automatic presetting hydraulic tensioner

30.5 Use a socket or tube to renew the timing cover oil seal

## 30 Timing cover, gears and chain – examination and renovation

1   Examine all the teeth on the camshaft and crankshaft sprockets. If these are 'hooked' in appearance, renew the sprockets.
2   If a mechanical chain tensioner is fitted, examine the chain contact pad and renew the tensioner assembly if the pad is heavily scored.
3   If an hydraulic tensioner is fitted, dismantle the components by taking them apart on the automatic presetting type (photo), or by releasing the slipper piston (turn it anti-clockwise with an Allen key) on the manual presetting type. Examine the piston, spring, sleeve and tensioner body bore for signs of scoring and renew if evident. Also renew the tensioner if the chain contact pad is heavily scored.
4   If the hydraulic tensioner is serviceable, lubricate the components and reassemble. On the manual presetting type, retain the slipper piston in the retracted position by turning it clockwise with an Allen key. On the automatic presetting type, lock the sleeve in the slipper piston first, by turning it clockwise with an Allen key, then slide this assembly into the tensioner body (photo). Avoid pressing the slipper now or the sleeve will be released and the whole assembly will fly apart.
5   Renew the oil seal in the timing cover by driving out the old seal using a suitable drift and then install the new seal using a large socket or block of wood (photo).

## 31 Flywheel or torque converter driveplate – examination and renovation

1   Examine the flywheel for scoring of the clutch face and for wear or chipping of the ring gear teeth. If the clutch face is scored, the flywheel may be machined until flat, but renewal is preferable. If the ring gear is worn or damaged it may be renewed separately, but this job is best left to a Renault dealer or engineering works. The temperature to which the new ring gear must be heated for installation is critical and, if not done accurately, the hardness of the teeth will be destroyed.
2   Check the torque converter driveplate carefully for signs of distortion or any hairline cracks around the bolt holes or radiating outwards from the centre.

## 32 Cylinder head and pistons – decarbonizing, valve grinding and renovation

1   The operation will normally only be required at comparatively high mileages. However, if persistent pinking occurs and performance has deteriorated, even though the engine adjustments are correct, de-carbonizing and valve grinding may be required.
2   With the cylinder head removed, use a scraper to remove the carbon from the combustion chambers and ports. Remove all traces of gasket from the cylinder head surface, then wash it thoroughly with paraffin.
3   Use a straight-edge and feeler blade to check that the cylinder

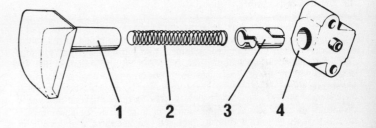

Fig. 1.19 Hydraulic timing chain tensioner components (Sec 30)

1   Piston with tensioner slipper
2   Spring
3   Sleeve
4   Tensioner body

Fig. 1.20 Using an Allen key to lock the sleeve in the hydraulic tensioner with automatic presetting (Sec 30)

head surface is not distorted. If it is, it must be resurfaced by a suitably equipped engineering works.
4   If the engine is still in the car, clean the piston crowns and cylinder bore upper edges, but make sure that no carbon drops between the pistons and bores. To do this, locate two of the pistons at the top of their bores and seal off the remaining bores with paper and masking tape. Press a little grease between the two pistons and their bores to collect any carbon dust; this can be wiped away when the piston is lowered. To prevent carbon build-up, polish the piston crown with metal polish, but remove all traces of polish afterwards.
5   Examine the heads of the valves for pitting and burning, especially the exhaust valve heads. Renew any valve which is badly burnt. Examine the valve seats at the same time. If the pitting is very slight, it can be removed by grinding the valve heads and seats together with coarse, then fine grinding paste.
6   Where excessive pitting has occurred, the valve seats must be recut or renewed by a suitably equipped engineering works.
7   Valve grinding is carried out as follows: Place the cylinder head

upside down on a bench with a block of wood at each end to give
clearance for the valve stems.

8   Smear a trace of coarse carborundum paste on the seat face and
press a suction grinding tool onto the valve head. With a semi-rotary
action, grind the valve head to its seat, lifting the valve occasionally to
redistribute the grinding paste. When a dull matt even surface is
produced on both the valve seat and the valve, wipe off the paste and
repeat the process with fine carborundum paste. A light spring placed
under the valve head will greatly ease this operation. When a smooth
unbroken ring of light grey matt finish is produced on both the valve
and seat, the grinding operation is complete.

9   Scrape away all carbon from the valve head and stem, and clean
away all traces of grinding compound. Clean the valves and seats with
a paraffin-soaked rag, then wipe with a clean rag.

10  If the valve guides are worn, indicated by a side-to-side motion of
the valve, new guides must be fitted. To do this, use a suitable mandrel
to press the worn guides downwards and out through the combustion
chamber. Press the new guides into the cylinder head in the same
direction until they are at the specified fitted height.

11  Examine the pushrods and rocker shaft assembly for wear, and
renew them as necessary.

## 33  Engine reassembly – general

1   To ensure maximum life with minimum trouble from a rebuilt
engine, not only must everything be correctly assembled, but it must
also be spotlessly clean. All oilways must be clear, and locking
washers and spring washers must be fitted where indicated. Oil all
bearings and other working surfaces thoroughly with engine oil during
assembly.

2   Before assembly begins, renew any bolts or studs with damaged
threads and have all new components at hand ready for assembly.

3   Gather together a torque wrench, oil can, clean rags and a set of
engine gaskets, together with a new oil filter. A tube of RTV sealing
compound will also be required for the joint faces that are fitted
without gaskets. It is recommended that CAF 4/60 THIXO paste,
obtainable from Renault dealers is used, as it is specially formulated
for this purpose.

## 34  Crankshaft and main bearings – refitting

1   Clean the backs of the bearing shells and the bearing recesses in
both the cylinder block and main bearing caps.

2   Press the bearing shells without oil holes into the caps, ensuring
that the tag on the shell engages in the notch in the cap.

3   Press the bearing shells with the oil holes into the recesses in the
cylinder block. If all five shells have two oil holes they may be fitted
into any location. If two of the shells only have one oil hole, these must
be fitted to journals No 1 and 3 (No 1 journal being nearest the
flywheel). Fit the remaining shells to any of the three remaining
locations.

4   If the original main bearing shells are being re-used these must be
refitted to their original locations in the block and caps.

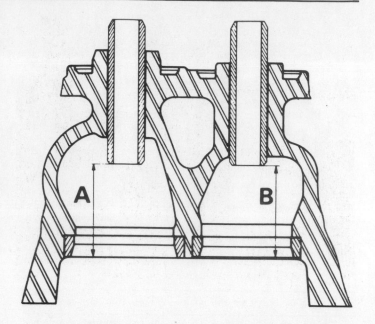

**Fig. 1.21 Valve guide fitted height dimensions (Sec 32)**

*A Inlet*                                    *B Exhaust*

5   Using a little grease, stick the thrust washers to each side of the
centre main bearing journal in the block (photo). Ensure that the oilway
grooves on each thrust washer face outwards.

6   Lubricate the lips of a new crankshaft oil seal and carefully slip it
over the end of the crankshaft. Do this carefully as the seal lips are very
delicate. Ensure that the open side of the seal faces the engine.

7   Liberally lubricate each bearing shell in the cylinder block and
lower the crankshaft into position (photo).

8   Fit the bearing caps in their numbered, or previously noted
locations, so that the bearing shell locating notches in the cap and
block are both on the same side (photo).

9   Fit the main bearing cap retaining bolts and make sure that the
dipstick tube is in position with its bracket located under the No 2
bearing cap retaining bolt.

10  Tighten the bolts until they are moderately tight, but before
tightening No 1 bearing cap position the oil seal so that its face is 3.0
mm (0.12 in) inset from the outer face of the block and bearing cap.
This will ensure that its sealing lip does not bear on the worn section
of the journal.

11  Check that the crankshaft is free to turn and then tighten the main
bearing retaining bolts to the specified torque (photo).

12  Check the crankshaft endfloat using feeler gauges inserted between the thrust washers and the side of the bearing journal (photo).

34.5 Fit the thrust washers with their oilway
grooves (arrowed) facing outwards

34.7 Lubricate the bearing shells, then lower
the crankshaft into place

34.8 Fit the bearing caps and retaining bolts ...

34.11 ... and tighten the bolts to the specified torque

34.12 Measure the crankshaft endfloat using feeler gauges

If new thrust washers have been fitted the endfloat should be in accordance with the dimension given in the Specifications. If the original washers have been refitted and the endfloat is excessive, new thrust washers must be fitted. These are obtainable in a number of oversizes.

13  Finally check that the crankshaft turns reasonably freely without any tight spots.

## 35  Liners, pistons and connecting rods – refitting

1    If the liner protrusion and liner height variation have not already been checked, do this now using the procedure described in Section 27, before proceeding further.

2    Lay the four liners face down in a row on the bench, in their correct order. Turn them as necessary so that the flats on the edges of liners 1 and 2 are towards each other, and the flats on liners 3 and 4 are towards each other also.

3    Lubricate the pistons and piston rings then lay each piston and connecting rod assembly with its respective liner.

4    Starting with assembly No 1, make sure that the piston rings are still spaced out at 120° to each other and clamp the piston rings using a piston ring compressor.

5    Insert the piston and connecting rod assembly into the bottom of the liner ensuring that the arrow on the piston crown faces the flywheel end of the engine (photos). In other words, if the liners are laid out as described, the arrow should face away from the other liners. Using a block of wood or hammer handle against the end of the connecting rod, tap the piston into the liner until the top of the piston is approximately 25 mm (1.0 in) away from the top of the liner.

6    Repeat this procedure for the remaining three piston and liner assemblies.

7    Turn the crankshaft so that No 1 crankpin is at the bottom of its travel.

8    Press the upper half of the big-end shell into the connecting rod and press the lower half into the cap (photo). Ensure that the tags on the shells engage with the notches on the cap and rod.

9    With the liner base seal in position, place No 1 liner, piston and connecting rod assembly into its location in the cylinder block (photo). Ensure that the arrow on the piston crown faces the flywheel end of the engine and the flat on the liner is positioned as described previously.

10  Liberally lubricate the crankpin journal, pull the connecting rod down and engage it with the crankpin. Check that the marks made on the cap and rod during removal are opposite the camshaft side of the engine then refit the cap and retaining nuts. The notches for the bearing shell tags in the cap and rod must be together. Tighten the connecting rod cap retaining nuts to the specified torque (photos).

11  With the liner piston and connecting rod assembly installed, retain

35.5A Check that the arrow on the piston crown will face the flywheel when installed ...

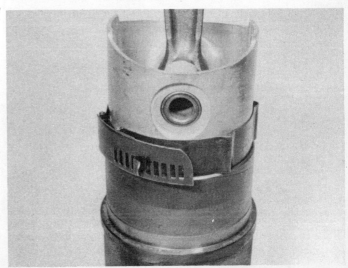

35.5B ... then fit the piston connecting rod assembly to the liner

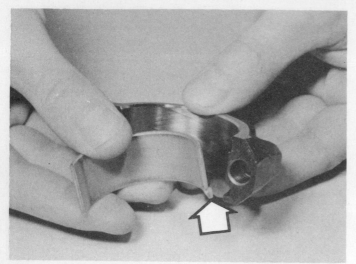

35.8 Fit the bearing shells with their tags (arrowed) engaged with the cap and rod notches

35.9 Fit the liner, piston and connecting rod assemblies

35.10A Fit the bearing caps to their respective connecting rods ...

35.10B ... and tighten the retaining nuts to the specified torque

35.11 Retain the liners using washers, nuts and bolts

the liner using a bolt and washer screwed into the cylinder head bolt holes. This will prevent damage to the base seal due to displacement of the liner as the engine is turned (photo).

12   Repeat the foregoing procedures for the remaining piston and liner assemblies, turning the crankshaft each time to make sure it is free.

13   If the engine is in the car, refit the oil pump, sump and cylinder head.

## 36   Camshaft and followers – refitting

1   Lubricate the camshaft bearings and carefully insert the camshaft from the timing gear end of the engine (photo).

2   Refit the retaining plate bolts and tighten them. Check that the camshaft rotates smoothly.

3   Lubricate the cam followers and insert them into their original bores in the cylinder block.

## 37   Flywheel or torque converter driveplate – refitting

1   Clean the flywheel and crankshaft faces, then fit the flywheel or driveplate making sure that any previously made marks are aligned.

2   Apply a few drops of thread locking compound to the retaining bolt threads, fit the bolts and tighten them in a diagonal sequence to the specified torque (photo).

36.1 Refitting the camshaft

37.2 Use a thread locking compound on the flywheel bolts

## 38 Timing cover, gears and chain – refitting

1    Refit the Woodruff key to the crankshaft groove and then tap the crankshaft sprocket into position. Ensure that the timing mark on the sprocket is on the side facing away from the engine.

2    If the engine is in the car, turn the crankshaft until the timing notch on the flywheel or torque converter is is line with the TDC mark on the bellhousing timing scale (photo 16.2). If the engine is out of the car, turn the crankshaft until Nos 1 and 4 pistons are at the very top of their travel.

3    Temporarily place the camshaft sprocket in position and turn the camshaft so that the timing marks on the sprocket faces are facing each other, and coincide with an imaginary line joining the crankshaft and camshaft centres, then remove the camshaft sprocket.

4    Fit the timing chain to the camshaft sprocket, position the sprocket in its approximate fitted position and locate the chain over the crankshaft sprocket. Position the camshaft sprocket on the camshaft and check that the marks are still aligned when there is an equal amount of slack on both sides of the chain (photo).

5    Refit the camshaft sprocket retaining bolt using a new locktab and tighten the bolt to the specified torque. Bend up the locktab to retain the bolt.

38.4 Correct alignment of crankshaft and camshaft sprocket timing marks (arrowed)

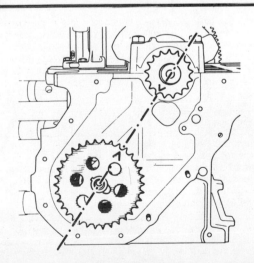

Fig. 1.22 Correct alignment of crankshaft and camshaft sprocket timing marks (Sec 38)

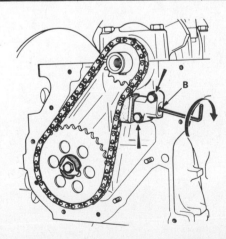

Fig. 1.23 Secure the hydraulic tensioner with the bolts (arrowed), then, if the tensioner has manual presetting, release the piston using an Allen key inserted in hole B (Sec 38)

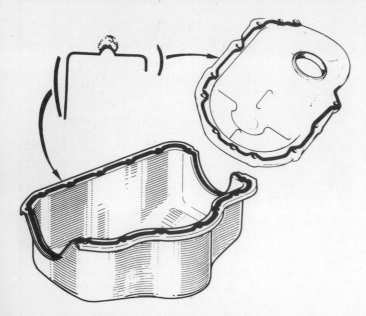

**Fig. 1.24 Apply a bead of sealant paste to the timing cover and sump before fitting (Sec 38)**

Allen key inserted in the end of the tensioner body. With the piston released, refit the small bolt to the tensioner body and secure with a new locktab. If the tensioner is of the automatic presetting type, push the slipper piston in and then release it. The piston should spring out automatically under spring pressure.

9   Ensure that the mating faces of the timing cover are clean and dry with all traces of old sealant removed and a new oil seal in place in the timing cover.

10  Apply a bead of CAF 4/60 THIXO paste to the timing cover joint face then position the cover over the dowels and the two studs. Refit the nuts and retaining bolts then progressively tighten them in a diagonal sequence (photo).

11  Lubricate the crankshaft pulley hub and carefully slide it onto the end of the crankshaft (photo).

12  Place the pulley in position, refit the retaining bolt and washer and tighten the bolt to the specified torque (photos).

13  If the engine is in the car, refit the sump and alternator drivebelt.

## 39 Oil pump – refitting

1   Enter the oil pump shaft into its location in the cylinder block and, if the engine is in the car, engage the shaft with the distributor drivegear (photo).

2   Push the pump up into contact with the block, then refit and tighten the three retaining bolts. Note that a gasket is not used.

3   If the engine is in the car, refit the sump.

## 40 Sump – refitting

1   Make sure that the mating faces of the sump and cylinder block are perfectly clean and dry with all traces of old sealant removed.

2   Apply a uniform bead of CAF 4/60 THIXO paste to the mating face of the sump, ensuring that a liberal quantity of the paste is used at the corners and around the areas that contact the timing cover and No 1 main bearing cap. Also apply paste to the boss and corners of No 1 main bearing cap (flywheel end).

6   If a mechanical tensioner is fitted, place it in position and locate the spring ends in the block and over the slipper arm. Refit the retaining bolt and tighten it securely with an Allen key.

7   If an hydraulic tensioner is fitted, first position the spacer on the cylinder block and retain it in place using a little grease (photo).

8   Locate the tensioner body over the plate then refit and tighten the retaining bolts (photo). If the tensioner is of the manual presetting type, release the slipper piston by turning it anti-clockwise using an

38.7 Fit the hydraulic tensioner spacer ...

38.8 ... followed by the tensioner

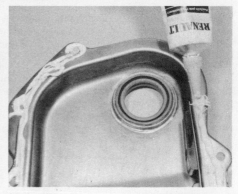

38.10 Apply a bead of sealant to the timing cover face

38.11 Refit the crankshaft pulley hub ...

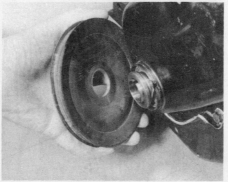

38.12A ... followed by the pulley ...

38.12B ... and retaining bolt

39.1 Refitting the oil pump

40.3 Place the sump in position and secure with the retaining bolts

3   Place the sump in position then refit the retaining bolts (photo). Tighten the bolts progressively and in a diagonal sequence.

4   If the engine is in the car, refit the engine steady rod, the flywheel or torque converter cover plate and, where fitted, the two wires to the engine oil level sensor. Refill the engine with the specified grade of oil.

## 41 Cylinder head – reassembly and refitting

1   Lubricate the stems of the valves and insert them into their original locations. If new valves are being fitted, insert them into the locations to which they have been ground (photo).

2   Working on the first valve, fit the the thrust washer to the cylinder head, followed by the valve spring and retainer. Note that the spring should be fitted with the end where the coils are closest towards the cylinder head (photos).

3   Compress the valve spring and locate the split collets in the recess in the valve stem. Note that the collets are different for the inlet and exhaust valves (photos), the latter type having two curved collars. Release the compressor, then repeat the procedure on the remaining valves.

41.1 Insert the valves into their guides

41.2A Fit the thrust washer ...

41.2B ... followed by the spring and retainer

41.3A Compress the valve spring and locate the split collets ...

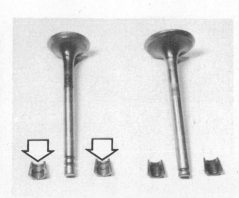

41.3B ... noting that those for the exhaust valves (arrowed) have two curved collars

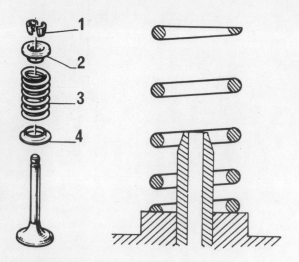

**Fig. 1.25 Valve components and spring fitted position (Sec 41)**

| | | | |
|---|---|---|---|
| 1 | *Split collets* | 3 | *Spring* |
| 2 | *Retainer* | 4 | *Thrust washer* |

4  With all the valves installed, place the cylinder head flat on the bench and, using a hammer and interposed block of wood, tap the end of each valve stem to settle the components.

5  Oil the rocker shaft, then reassemble the springs, rocker arms and pedestals in the reverse order to removal, and finally fit the circlip. Check that the bolt holes in the pedestals are aligned with the recesses in the rocker shaft, and that the pedestal with the oilway (where applicable) is fitted at the flywheel end.

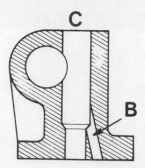

**Fig. 1.26 Sectional view of rocker pedestal (C) with oil hole (B) which must be fitted at the flywheel end of the shaft assembly (Sec 41)**

6  Remove the cylinder liner clamps, if fitted, and make sure that the faces of the cylinder head and the cylinder block are perfectly clean. Lay a new gasket on the cylinder block with the words 'Haut-Top' uppermost (photo). Do not use any kind of jointing compound.

7  Lower the cylinder head into position, insert the cylinder head bolts, and tighten them to the specified torque in the sequence shown in Fig. 1.27 (photos).

8  Install the pushrods in their original locations (photo).

9  Lower the rocker shaft assembly onto the cylinder head, making sure that the adjusting ball-ends locate in the pushrods. Install the spring washer (convex side uppermost), nuts and bolts, and tighten them to the specified torque (photo).

10  Adjust the valve clearances, as described in Section 47 to the cold setting (see Specifications).

11  If the engine is in the car refit the controls, cables and services

41.6 Place the gasket in position

41.7A Lower the cylinder head onto the gasket and ...

41.7B ... fit the retaining bolts and tighten in the correct sequence to the specified torque

41.8 Install the pushrods in their original locations

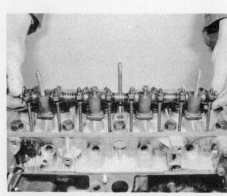

41.9 Refit the rocker shaft assembly

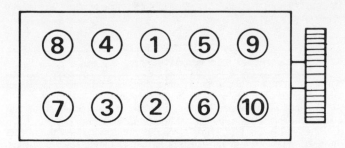

**Fig. 1.27 Cylinder head tightening sequence (Sec 41)**

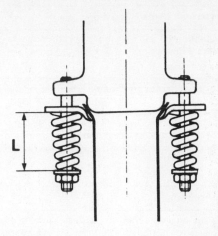

**Fig. 1.28 Exhaust mounting tension spring tightening dimension (Sec 41)**

*L = 43.5 mm (1.71 in)*

using the reverse of the removal procedure described in Section 11, but bearing in mind the following points:

(a) *Tighten the exhaust front section to manifold retaining bolts so that the tension springs are compressed as shown in Fig. 1.28*

(b) *Adjust the choke and accelerator cables, as described in Chapter 3*

(c) *Adjust the drivebelt tension, as described in Chapter 2*

(d) *Refill the cooling system, as described in Chapter 2*

## 42 Distributor drivegear – refitting

1  Using a ring spanner on the crankshaft pulley bolt, turn the crankshaft until No 1 piston (flywheel end) is at the top of its compression stroke. This position can be established by placing a finger over No 1 plug hole and rotating the crankshaft until compression can be felt; continue turning the crankshaft until the piston reaches the top of its stroke. Use a screwdriver through the plug hole to feel the movement of the piston, but be careful not to damage the piston crown or plug threads in the cylinder head.

2  Without moving the crankshaft, position the drivegear so that its slots are at the 2 o'clock and 8 o'clock positions with the larger offset side facing away from the engine (photo).

3  Now lower the drivegear into mesh with the camshaft and oil pump driveshaft. As the gear meshes with the camshaft it will rotate anti-clockwise and should end up with its slot at right angles to the crankshaft centreline and with the larger offset towards the flywheel. It will probably be a tooth out on the first attempt and will take two or three attempts to get it just right (Fig. 1.29 and photo).

42.2 Fit the distributor drivegear ...

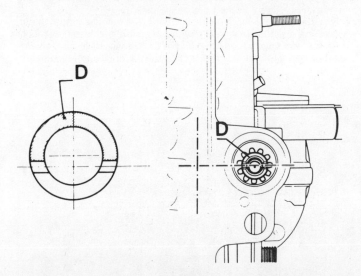

**Fig. 1.29 Fitted position of distributor drivegear (Sec 42)**

*D = Larger offset side*

42.3 ... so that the slot is at right-angles to the crankshaft centreline with its larger offset side facing the flywheel when fitted

## 43 Ancillary components – refitting

Refer to Section 10 and refit the listed components with reference to the Chapters indicated.

## 44 Engine – attachment to manual gearbox or automatic transmission

Refer to Section 8 and attach the engine using the reverse of the removal procedure. Apply a trace of molybdenum disulphide grease to the end of the gearbox input shaft or torque converter locator before fitting.

## 45 Engine – refitting

Refitting the engine, either on its own or complete with manual gearbox or automatic transmission, is a reverse of the removal procedures contained in Sections 6 and 7. In addition bear in mind the following points:

(a) Tighten the exhaust front section-to-manifold retaining bolts so that the tension springs are compressed, as shown in Fig. 1.28
(b) Refill the cooling system with reference to Chapter 2
(c) Adjust the choke and accelerator cables with reference to Chapter 3
(d) If the drivebelt was removed, adjust its tension with reference to Chapter 2
(e) Where applicable, refill the gearbox or automatic transmisssion with oil, as described in Chapter 6, and the engine, as described in Section 2 of this Chapter

## 46 Engine – adjustments after major overhaul

1   With the engine and gearbox refitted to the car, make a final check to ensure that everything has been reconnected and that no rags or tools have been left in the engine compartment.
2   Make sure that the oil and water levels are topped up and then start the engine; this may take a little longer than usual as the fuel pump and carburettor float chamber may be empty.
3   As soon as the engine starts, watch for the oil pressure light to go out and check for any oil, fuel or water leaks. Don't be alarmed if there are some odd smells and smoke from parts getting hot and burning off oil deposits.
4   Allow the engine to run for approximately 20 minutes then switch it off and allow it to cool for at least 2½ hours. Remove the rocker cover and re-torque the cylinder head bolts in the sequence shown in Fig. 1.27. Slacken each bolt in turn half a turn then retighten it to the specified torque before moving on to the next bolt. After retightening, adjust the valve clearances again, as described in Section 47.
5   If new pistons, ring or crankshaft bearings have been fitted the engine must be run-in for the first 500 miles (800 km). Do not exceed 45 mph (72 kph), operate the engine at full throttle or allow it to labour in any gear.

## 47 Valve clearances – adjustment

1   If the engine is in the car, remove the air cleaner and disconnect the choke cable at the carburettor, as described in Chapter 3.
2   Detach the crankcase ventilation hose at the rocker cover and disconnect the throttle linkage return spring (photo).
3   Mark the spark plug HT lead locations and withdraw them from the spark plugs. Remove the distributor cap retaining screws or clips, and move the cap and leads to one side.
4   Undo the three nuts securing the rocker cover in place, tap the cover lightly to free it then manipulate it off the studs.
5   Number the valves 1 to 8 from the flywheel end of the engine then, using a ring spanner on the crankshaft pulley bolt, turn the engine in a clockwise direction until No 8 valve is fully open (ie spring compressed).
6   Insert a feeler blade of the correct thickness for an exhaust valve (see Specifications) between the end of No 1 valve stem and the rocker arm, then adjust the rocker arm ball-end (after loosening the locknut) until the feeler blade is a firm sliding fit (photo). Tighten the locknut and recheck the adjustment, then repeat the procedure on the remaining seven valves in the following sequence:

| Valve open | Valve to adjust |
|------------|------------------|
| No 8 ex | No 1 ex |
| No 6 in | No 3 in |
| No 4 ex | No 5 ex |
| No 7 in | No 2 in |
| No 1 ex | No 8 ex |
| No 3 in | No 6 in |
| No 5 ex | No 4 ex |
| No 2 in | No 7 in |

7   On completion, refit the rocker cover using a new gasket (photo). If the engine is in the car refit the disconnected components using the reverse of the removal sequence. Adjust the choke cable with reference to Chapter 3, if necessary.

# Part 2: 1721 cc engines

## 48 General description

The engine is of four-cylinder, in-line overhead camshaft type, mounted transversely at the front of the car.

The crankshaft is supported in five shell type main bearings. Thrust washers are fitted to No 2 main bearing to control crankshaft endfloat.

The connecting rods are attached to the crankshaft by horizontally split shell type big-end bearings, and to the pistons by interference fit

47.2 Throttle linkage return spring attachment on rocker cover

47.6 Adjusting the valve clearances

47.7 Refit the rocker cover using a new gasket after adjustment

gudgeon pins. The aluminium alloy pistons are of the slipper type and are fitted with three piston rings; two compression rings and a scraper type oil control ring.

The overhead camshaft is mounted directly in the cylinder head and is driven by the crankshaft via a toothed rubber timing belt. The camshaft operates the valves via inverted bucket type tappets which operate in bores machined directly in the cylinder head. Valve clearance adjustment is by selected shims located externally between the tappet bucket and the cam lobe. The inlet and exhaust valves are mounted vertically in the cylinder head and are each closed by a single valve spring.

An auxiliary shaft located alongside the crankshaft is also driven by the toothed timing belt and actuates the oil pump via a skew gear.

A semi-closed crankcase ventilation system is employed, and crankcase fumes are drawn from an oil separator on the cylinder block and passed via a hose to the inlet manifold.

Engine lubrication is by pressure feed from a gear type oil pump located beneath the crankshaft. Engine oil is fed through an externally mounted oil filter to the main oil gallery feeding the crankshaft, auxiliary shaft and camshaft.

The distributor rotor and the fuel pump are driven by the camshaft; the rotor directly and the fuel pump via an eccentric and plunger.

Fig. 1.30 Cutaway view of the 1721 cc engine (Sec 48)

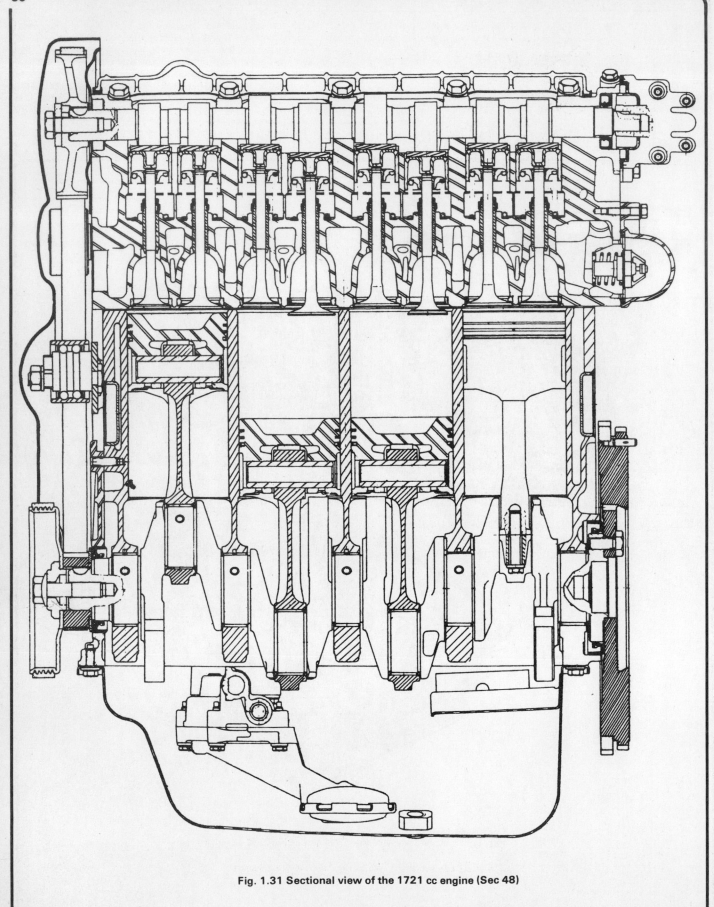

Fig. 1.31 Sectional view of the 1721 cc engine (Sec 48)

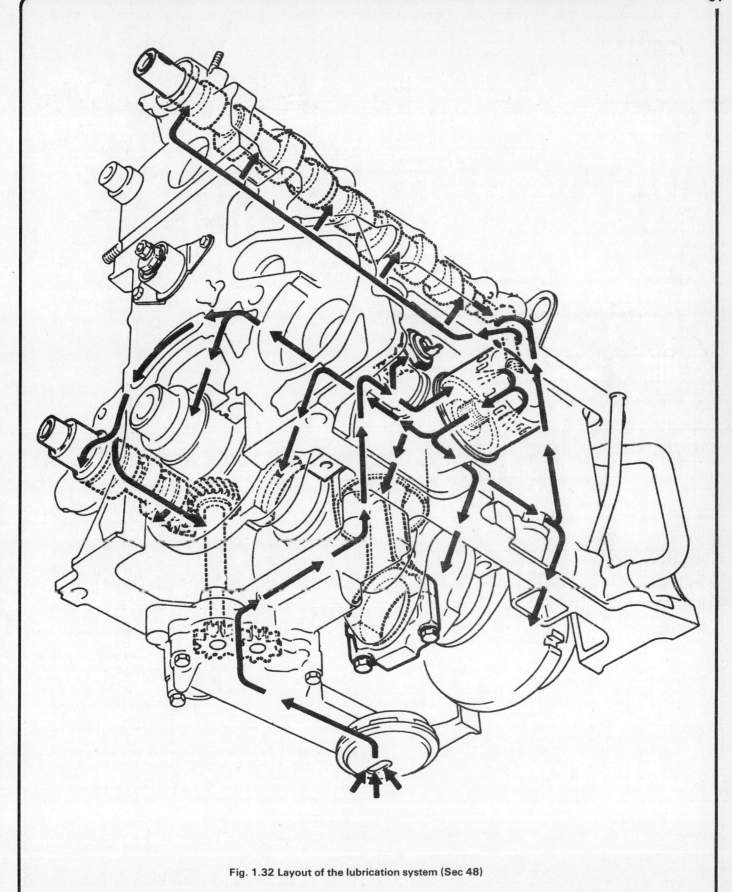

**Fig. 1.32 Layout of the lubrication system (Sec 48)**

## 49 Maintenance and inspection

1   At the intervals specified in Routine maintenance, carry out the following maintenance operations on the engine.

2   Visually inspect the engine joint faces, gaskets, seals and related hoses for any sign of oil or water leaks. Pay particular attention to the areas around the camshaft cover, crankshaft oil seal carrier and sump joint faces. Rectify any leaks by referring to the appropriate Sections of this Chapter.

3   Place a suitable container beneath the oil drain plug in the sump. Working through the access hole in the undertray, undo the drain plug and allow the oil to drain (photo).

4   Refill the engine using the correct grade of oil through the filler neck on the camshaft cover. Fill until the level reaches the upper mark on the dipstick.

5   Place some old rags on the undertray beneath the oil filter. Using a strap wrench or filter removal tool, slacken the filter then unscrew it from the engine and discard.

6   Wipe the mating face on the cylinder block with a rag and then lubricate the seal of a new filter using clean engine oil.

7   Screw the filter into position and tighten it by hand only, do not use any tools.

8   With the engine running, check for leaks around the filter seal.

9   At the specified intervals, check and, if necessary, adjust the valve clearances using the procedure described in Section 95.

49.3 The oil drain plug is accessible through a hole in the undertray

## 50 Major operations possible with the engine in the car

The following operations can be carried out without having to remove the engine from the car:

   (a) *Removal and refitting of the timing belt*
   (b) *Removal and refitting of the camshaft*
   (c) *Removal and refitting of the cylinder head*
   (d) *Removal and refitting of the sump*
   (e) *Removal and refitting of the oil pump*
   (f) *Removal and refitting of the connecting rod and piston assemblies*
   (g) *Removal and refitting of the auxiliary shaft*
   (h) *Removal and refitting of the engine mountings*

## 51 Major operations requiring engine removal

The following operations can only be carried out after removal of the engine from the car:

   (a) *Removal and refitting of the flywheel*
   (b) *Removal and refitting of the crankshaft and main bearings*
   (c) *Removal and refitting of the crankshaft rear oil seal*

## 52 Methods of engine removal

The engine and gearbox assembly can be lifted from the car as a complete unit, as described in the following Section, or the gearbox may first be removed, as described in Chapter 6. It is not possible, due to the limited working clearances, to remove the engine leaving the gearbox in position.

## 53 Engine and gearbox assembly – removal

1   Disconnect the battery negative terminal then remove the bonnet, as described in Chapter 11.

2   Remove the radiator, as described in Chapter 2.

3   Remove the air cleaner, as described in Chapter 3.

4   Refer to Chapter 6 and drain the gearbox oil.

5   Slacken the hose clips and disconnect the two heater hoses at their connections on the engine.

6   Release the clip securing the choke cable to its support bracket on the carburettor and disconnect the cable end loop from the stud on the linkage.

7   Open the throttle and slip the accelerator cable out of the slot on

the linkage bellcrank. Release the outer cable from its support bracket and move the cable to one side.

8   Detach the brake servo vacuum hose from the rear of the inlet manifold.

9   Disconnect the engine earth strap at the timing belt end of the engine and the earth braid at the gearbox.

10  Undo the two bolts, remove the tension springs and release the exhaust front section from its attachment at the manifold.

11  Disconnect the fuel feed and return pipes at the fuel pump and disconnect their ends.

12  Disconnect the ignition HT cable from the centre of the distributor cap.

13  Detach the ignition vacuum pipe at the carburettor.

14  Note the locations of the wiring at the rear of the alternator and disconnect the wires.

15  Note the wiring locations at the starter motor solenoid and disconnect the wires.

16  Disconnect the lead at the water temperature gauge sender unit on the cylinder head and the lead at the oil pressure switch on the front facing side of the cylinder block.

17  Undo the two shouldered bolts and remove the angular position sensor from its location at the top of the bellhousing.

18  Disconnect the wiring at the horn and at the oil level sensor on the sump.

19  All the wiring to the engine should now have been disconnected and, after releasing the clips and ties, it should be possible to move the complete wiring harness to one side.

20  Withdraw the spring wire retaining clip securing the speedometer cable to the gearbox at the rear and remove the cable. Note the fitted direction of the clip.

21  Disconnect the clutch cable from the release fork and the bracket on the bellhousing.

22  Jack up the front of the car and support it on axle stands.

23  Undo the four bolts, one at each corner, and remove the undertray (photo).

24  Slide back the rubber cover and undo the nut and bolt securing the gearchange rod to the gearbox fork control shaft. Slide the rod off the shaft and recover the distance sleeve.

25  Disconnect the wiring at the reversing lamp switch and, where fitted, the gear position sensors on the gearbox casing.

26  Drive out the roll pin, using a parallel pin punch, securing the right-hand driveshaft inner joint to the differential stub shaft. Note that the roll pin is in fact two roll pins, one inside the other.

27  Undo the three bolts securing the left-hand driveshaft inner joint bellows and retaining plate to the side of the gearbox.

28  Lower the car to the ground and make a final check that all cables, pipes and components likely to impede removal have been detached and moved aside.

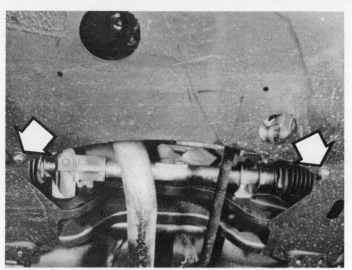

53.23 Undertray rear retaining bolts (arrowed)

29  Attach a crane or hoist to the engine using chain or rope slings, or secure the chains or ropes to the engine lifting brackets.
30  Undo the nuts and bolts at the front, and the single nut at the rear securing the engine mounting brackets to the rubber mountings. Undo the retaining bolts and remove the movement limiter from the engine and subframe.
31  Raise the engine and gearbox slightly and release the brackets from the rubber mountings.
32  Move the engine and gearbox assembly to the left as far as possible and tap the right-hand driveshaft inner joint off the stub shaft using a hide or plastic mallet.
33  Now move the engine assembly to the right and lift the left-hand driveshaft inner joint spider out of its location in the differential sun wheel.
34  Slowly lift the engine and gearbox assembly, moving it around as

necessary to clear all obstructions. When high enough, lift it over the front body panel and lower the unit to the ground.

## 54  Engine – separation from gearbox

1  With the assembly removed from the car, undo the retaining bolts and lift off the cover plate at the base of the gearbox bellhousing.
2  Turn the crankshaft as necessary using a socket on the pulley bolt until the notch on the flywheel is in line with the TDC timing mark on the bellhousing timing scale (see Chapter 4). Now make a reference mark on the cylinder block in line with the flywheel notch. This will provide a useful reference because once the gearbox is removed, the timing marks go with it, and it then becomes difficult to accurately determine the TDC position of the engine.
3  Undo the support bracket bolt and the three bellhousing bolts securing the starter in position. Lift off the starter motor noting the location of the dowel in one of the bolt holes.
4  Undo the bolts and the two nuts securing the engine to the gearbox bellhousing. Support the gearbox and withdraw the engine. The engine may be initially tight due to the locating dowels.

## 55  Engine dismantling – general

Refer to Section 9.

## 56  Ancillary components – removal

Refer to Section 10 and remove all the components listed, with the exception of the distributor. In this case only remove the cap and leads.

## 57  Timing belt – removal

1  If the engine is in the car, first carry out the following operations:

(a)  Disconnect the battery negative terminal
(b)  Remove the air cleaner
(c)  Remove the alternator drivebelt

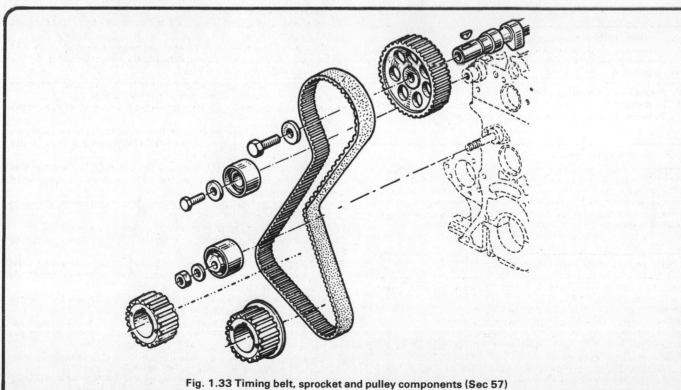

Fig. 1.33 Timing belt, sprocket and pulley components (Sec 57)

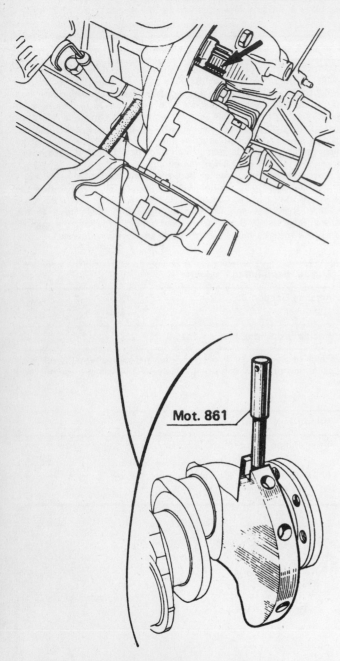

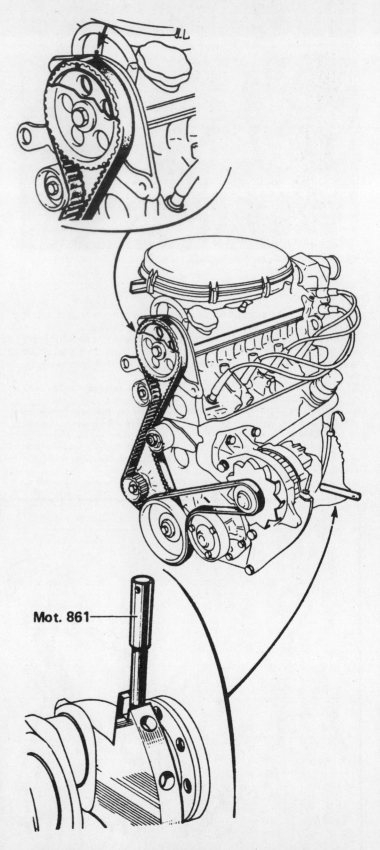

**Fig. 1.34 Using a suitable metal rod to locate in the crankshaft and retain it in the TDC position (Sec 57)**

**Fig. 1.35 The timing marks on the belt and sprocket must align with those on the backing plate when the crankshaft is at TDC with No 1 cylinder on compression (Sec 57)**

2   Undo the four bolts and lift off the timing belt cover (photo).
3   Note the location of the timing mark on the outer edge of the camshaft sprocket. Using a socket or spanner on the crankshaft pulley bolt, turn the crankshaft until the camshaft sprocket timing mark is uppermost and in line with a corresponding mark or notch on the metal plate behind the sprocket. Note that some earlier engines do not have a mark or notch on the plate and if this is the case just turn the crankshaft so that the timing mark on the sprocket is roughly near the top. This will do for the time being.
4   Again using a socket or spanner, undo the crankshaft pulley retaining bolt and withdraw the pulley. If the engine is in the car the crankshaft can be prevented from turning by engaging top gear and firmly applying the handbrake. If the engine is out of the car, lock the flywheel ring gear using a wide-bladed screwdriver or strip of angle iron between the ring gear teeth and the long stud on the side of the cylinder block.

57.2 Timing belt cover retaining bolt locations (arrowed)

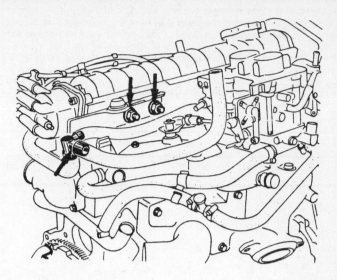

Fig. 1.36 Crankshaft ventilation hoses and bracket location on cylinder head (Sec 58)

5    Remove the plug on the lower front facing side of the engine; at the flywheel end, and obtain a metal rod which is a snug fit in the plug hole. Turn the crankshaft slightly as necessary to the TDC position then push the rod through the hole to locate in the slot in the crankshaft web. Make sure that the crankshaft is exactly at TDC for No 1 piston by aligning the timing notch on the flywheel with the bellhousing mark, or the mark on the camshaft sprocket with the corresponding mark on the metal plate. If the crankshaft is not positioned accurately it is possible to engage the rod with a balance hole in the crankshaft web which is not the TDC slot.

6    Double check that the camshaft sprocket timing mark is aligned with the corresponding mark on the metal plate. If the plate does not have a mark, make one now using paint or by accurately scribing a line aligned with the mark on the sprocket. Also check that there are arrows indicating the running direction of the belt, located between the auxiliary shaft sprocket and the idler pulley. Some belts also have their own timing marks and if so these marks should also be aligned with the marks on the sprocket and plate.

7    Slacken the tensioner pulley retaining nut and rotate the tensioner body until the belt is slack.

8    Slip the timing belt off the sprockets and pulleys and remove it from the engine.

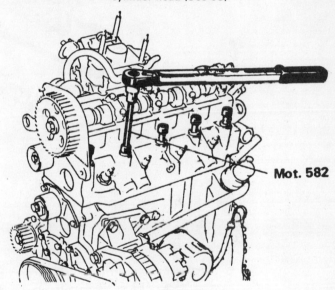

Mot. 582

Fig. 1.37 Using a hexagonal socket bit to remove the cylinder head retaining bolts (Sec 58)

## 58 Cylinder head removal – engine in car

1    Refer to the previous Section and remove the timing belt.
2    Refer to Chapter 2 and drain the cooling system.
3    Disconnect the ignition HT lead at the centre of the distributor cap.
4    Disconnect the lead at the water temperature gauge sender on the cylinder head.
5    Disconnect the fuel feed and return pipes at the fuel pump and plug their ends.
6    Open the throttle linkage by hand and slip the accelerator cable end out of the slot on the linkage bellcrank connector. Release the accelerator cable from its support bracket and move the cable clear.
7    Release the choke cable looped end from the stud on the linkage and detach the support clip from the carburettor bracket.
8    Disconnect the brake servo vacuum hose from the inlet manifold.
9    Disconnect the heater hoses, crankcase ventilation hoses and the two nuts securing the support plate to the rear facing side of the cylinder head.
10   Disconnect the radiator top hose from the thermostat housing.
11   Undo the two bolts and withdraw the tension springs securing the exhaust front section to the manifold.
12   Undo the three domed nuts, lift off the washers and withdraw the camshaft cover from the cylinder head. Recover the gasket.

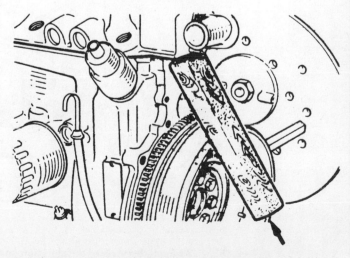

Fig. 1.38 Remove the cylinder head by tapping upwards using a block of wood or a plastic mallet (Sec 58)

13 Using a suitable hexagon-headed socket bit, slacken the cylinder head retaining bolts, half a turn at a time in the reverse order to that shown in Fig. 1.63. When the tension has been relieved, remove all the bolts.

14 Lift the cylinder head, complete with manifolds and carburettor upwards and off the engine. If it is stuck, tap it upwards using a hammer and block of wood. Do not try to turn it as it is located by two dowels and make no attempt whatsoever to prise it free using a screwdriver inserted between the block and head faces.

## 59 Cylinder head removal – engine on bench

The procedure for removing the cylinder head with the engine on the bench is similar to that for removal when the engine is in the car, with the exception of disconnecting the controls and services. Remove the timing belt, as described in Section 57, then refer to Section 58 and follow the procedure given in paragraphs 9, then 12 to 14.

## 60 Camshaft and tappets – removal

1 If the engine is in the car, first carry out the following operations:

(a)  *Remove the timing belt*
(b)  *Remove the distributor cap*
(c)  *Remove the camshaft cover*
(d)  *Remove the fuel pump*

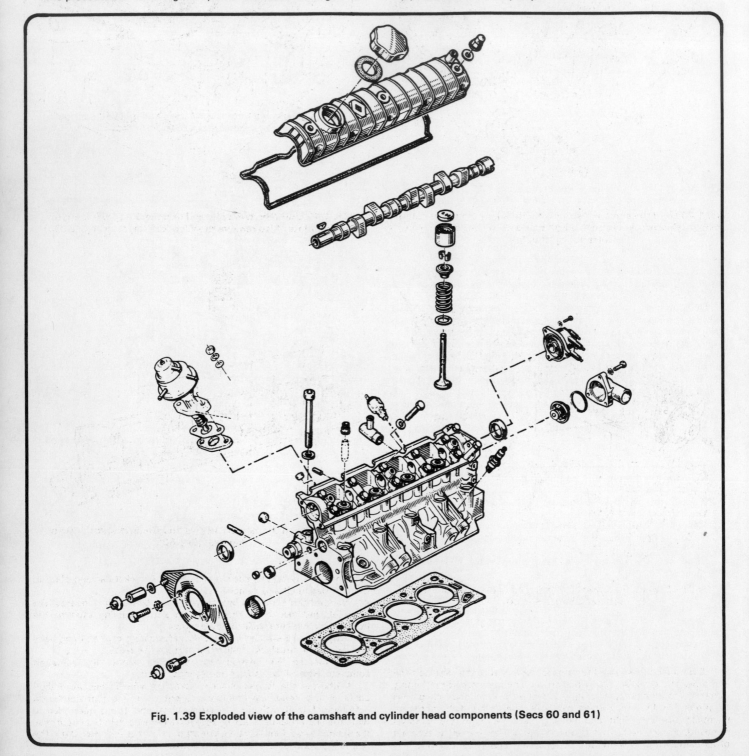

Fig. 1.39 Exploded view of the camshaft and cylinder head components (Secs 60 and 61)

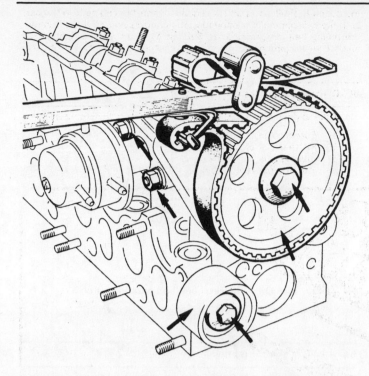

Fig. 1.40 Hold the camshaft sprocket with an old timing belt, then remove the sprocket retaining bolt followed, if necessary, by the idler pulley (Sec 60)

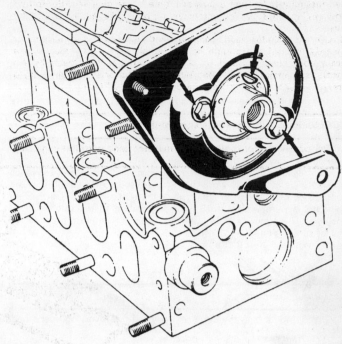

Fig. 1.41 Undo the two bolts and remove the sprocket metal backing plate. Also remove the Woodruff key if loose (Sec 60)

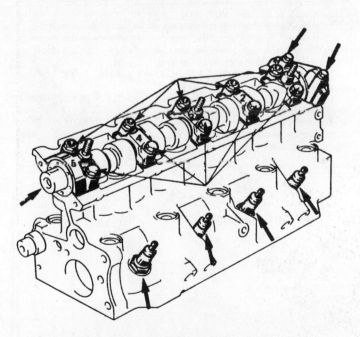

Fig. 1.42 Mark the camshaft bearing caps then remove the retaining bolts (Sec 60)

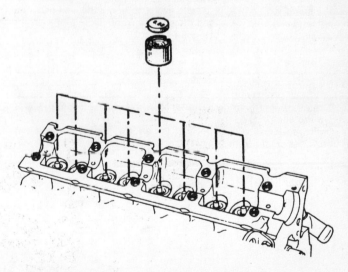

Fig. 1.43 Keep the tappet buckets and shims in strict order of removal (Sec 60)

3   Undo the two bolts securing the metal sprocket backing plate to the cylinder head and remove the plate.

4   Number the camshaft bearing caps 1 to 5 with No 1 nearest the flywheel, and also mark them with an arrow pointing towards the flywheel, to indicate their fitted direction.

5   Progressively slacken all the camshaft bearing cap retaining bolts and, when all are slack, remove them from the caps.

6   Lift off the five bearing caps and then remove the camshaft complete with oil seals from the cylinder head.

7   Withdraw the tappet buckets, complete with shims, from their bores in the head. Lay the buckets out on a sheet of cardboard numbered 1 to 8 with No 1 at the flywheel end. It is a good idea to write the shim thickness size on the card alongside each bucket in case the shims are accidentally knocked off their buckets and mixed up. The size is stamped on the shim bottom face.

2   Undo the bolt securing the camshaft sprocket to the camshaft and withdraw the sprocket. The camshaft may be prevented from turning during this operation by holding it between the cam lobes using grips or, preferably, by wrapping an old timing belt around the sprocket, clamping the belt tight and holding securely. With the sprocket removed, check whether the locating Woodruff key is likely to drop out of its camshaft groove and if it is, remove it and store it safely.

## 61 Cylinder head – dismantling

1   If the cylinder head has been removed with the engine in the car, remove the inlet and exhaust manifolds, fuel pump and fuel filter, as described in Chapter 3, and then the camshaft before proceeding.

2   Using a valve spring compressor, compress each valve spring in turn until the split collets can be removed. Release the compressor and lift off the cap, spring and spring seat.

3   If, when the valve spring compressor is screwed down, the valve spring cap refuses to free and expose the split collets, gently tap the top of the tool, directly over the cap with a light hammer. This will free the cap.

4   Withdraw the oil seal off the top of the valve guide, and then remove the valve through the combustion chamber.

5   It is essential that the valves are kept in their correct sequence unless they are so badly worn that they are to be renewed. If they are going to be kept and used again, place them in a sheet of card having eight holes numbered 1 to 8 – corresponding to the relative fitted positions of the valves. Note that No 1 valve is nearest to the flywheel end of the engine.

6   If required the thermostat can be removed, as described in Chapter 2.

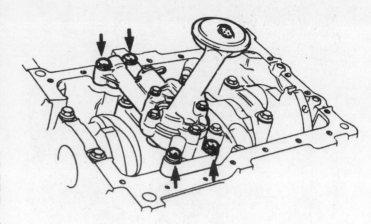

Fig. 1.44 Oil pump retaining bolt locations (Sec 63)

## 62 Sump – removal

1   If the engine is in the car, first carry out the following operations:

   *(a)   Remove the engine undertray*
   *(b)   Drain the engine oil*
   *(c)   Undo the bolts and remove the flywheel cover plate*
   *(d)   Where fitted, disconnect any electrical wiring at the sump sensors*

2   Undo and remove the bolts securing the sump to the crankcase. Tap the sump with a hide or plastic mallet to break the seal between sump flange and crankcase, and remove the sump. Note that a gasket is not used, only a sealing compound.

## 63 Oil pump – removal

1   If the oil pump is to be removed with the engine in the car, first remove the sump.

2   Undo the four retaining bolts at the ends of the pump body and withdraw the pump from the crankcase and drivegear.

## 64 Auxiliary shaft – removal

1   If the engine is in the car, first carry out the following operations:

   *(a)   Remove the timing belt*
   *(b)   Remove the engine undertray*

2   Undo the retaining bolt and remove the washer securing the sprocket to the auxiliary shaft. Hold the sprocket with an old timing belt, tightly clamped and securely held while undoing the bolt.

3   Withdraw the sprocket using two screwdrivers as levers to ease it off. If it is very tight use a two-legged puller. Recover the Woodruff key if it is not securely located in its groove.

4   Undo the four bolts and withdraw the auxiliary shaft housing. Access may be easier from under the car.

5   At the top undo the two bolts and withdraw the oil pump drivegear cover plate. Screw a suitable bolt into the oil pump drivegear or use a tapered wooden shaft and withdraw the drivegear from its location.

6   Undo the two bolts and washers and lift out the auxiliary shaft retaining plate and the auxiliary shaft.

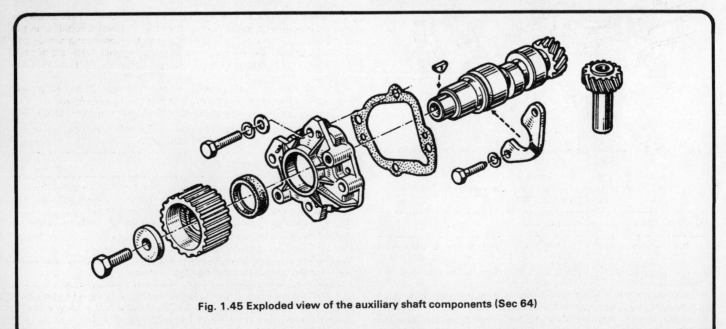

Fig. 1.45 Exploded view of the auxiliary shaft components (Sec 64)

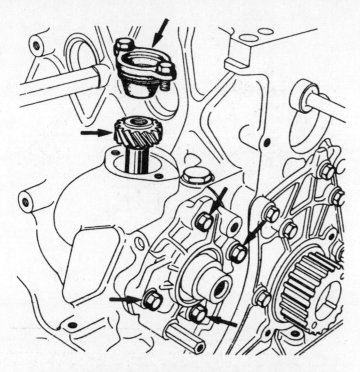

**Fig. 1.46 Auxiliary shaft housing retaining bolt locations, oil pump driveshaft and cover plate (Sec 64)**

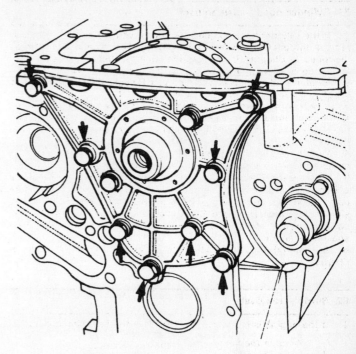

**Fig. 1.47 Crankshaft front plate retaining bolt locations (Sec 65)**

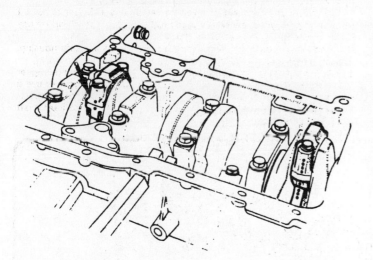

**Fig. 1.48 Number the connecting rods and caps before removal (Sec 66)**

## 65 Crankshaft front plate – removal

1   If the engine is in the car, first carry out the following operations:

   *(a)   Remove the timing belt*
   *(b)   Remove the sump*

2   Withdraw the crankshaft sprocket using two screwdrivers carefully as levers, or by using a suitable puller.
3   Undo the bolts securing the front plate to the cylinder block and withdraw the plate, noting that it is located by dowels in the two lower bolt hole locations.

## 66 Pistons and connecting rods – removal

1   If the engine is in the car, first carry out the following operations:

   *(a)   Remove the sump*
   *(b)   Remove the oil pump*
   *(c)   Remove the cylinder head (not necessary if only the big-end bearings are to be removed)*

2   Rotate the crankshaft so that No 1 big-end cap (nearest the flywheel) is at the lowest point of its travel. Using a centre punch, number the cap and rod on the auxiliary shaft side to indicate the cylinder to which they are fitted.
3   Undo and remove the big-end bearing cap bolts and withdraw the cap, complete with shell bearing from the connecting rod. If only the bearing shells are being attended to, push the connecting rod up and off the crankpin then remove the upper bearing shell. Keep the bearing shells and cap together in their correct sequence if they are to be refitted.
4   Push the connecting rod up and withdraw the piston and connecting rod assembly from the top of the cylinder block.
5   Now repeat these operations on the remaining three piston and connecting rod assemblies.

## 67 Flywheel – removal

1   Lock the crankshaft using a strip of angle iron between the ring gear teeth and the engine dowel bolt, or a block of wood between one of the crankshaft counterweights and the crankcase.
2   Mark the flywheel in relation to the crankshaft, undo the retaining bolts and withdraw the unit.

## 68 Crankshaft and main bearings – removal

1   Identification numbers should be cast onto the base of each main bearing cap, but if not, number the cap and crankcase using a centre punch, as was done for the connecting rods and caps.
2   Undo and remove the main bearing cap retaining bolts noting that a hexagonal socket bit will be needed for No 1 main bearing cap bolts.

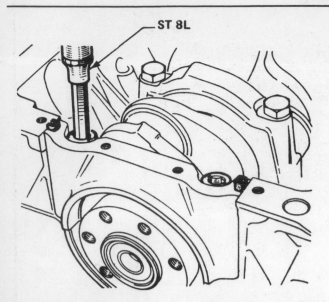

**Fig. 1.49 Removing No 1 main bearing cap bolts (Sec 68)**

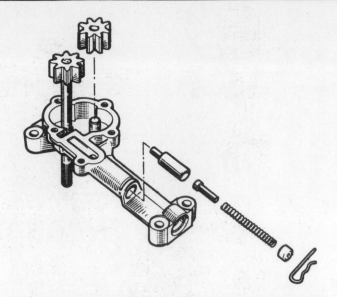

**Fig. 1.50 Exploded view of the oil pump components (Sec 73)**

Withdraw the caps and the bearing shell lower halves.
3   Carefully lift the crankshaft from the crankcase.
4   Remove the thrust washers from each side of No 2 main bearing, then remove the bearing shell upper halves from the crankcase. Place each shell with its respective bearing cap.

**69  Crankshaft rear oil seal – removal**

Refer to Section 21.

**70  Engine mountings – renewal**

Refer to Section 22, but note that additionally a movement limiter is used on these engines and is located at the front between engine and subframe. Removal is simply a matter of undoing the retaining bolts.

**71  Crankcase ventilation system – description**

The layout of the crankcase ventilation systems is similar to the system described in Section 23, with the addition of an oil separator in the cylinder block.

**72  Examination and renovation – general**

With the engine completely stripped, clean all the components and examine them for wear. Each part should be checked and, where necessary, renewed or renovated, as described in the following Sections. Renew main and big-end bearing shells as a matter of course unless you know that they have had little wear and are in perfect condition.

**73  Oil pump – examination and renovation**

1   Undo the retaining bolts and lift off the pump cover.
2   Withdraw the idler gear and the drivegear and shaft.
3   Extract the retaining clip and remove the oil pressure relief valve spring retainer, spring, spring seat and plunger.
4   Clean the components and carefully examine the gears, pump body and relief valve plunger for any signs of scoring or wear. Renew the pump if these conditions are apparent.
5   If the components appear serviceable, measure the clearance between the pump body and the gears and also the gear endfloat

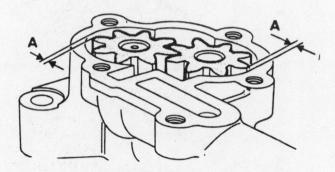

**Fig. 1.51 Check the clearance between the gears and oil pump body (A) (Sec 73)**

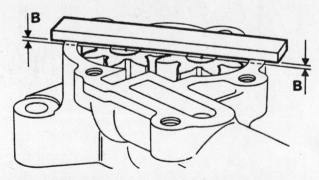

**Fig. 1.52 Check the oil pump gear endfloat (B) (Sec 73)**

using feeler gauges. If the clearances exceed the specified tolerance, the pump must be renewed.
6   If the pump is satisfactory, reassemble the components in the order of removal, fill the pump with oil and refit the cover.

**74  Crankshaft and main bearings – examination and renovation**

Refer to Section 26.

**75  Cylinder block and crankcase – examination and renovation**

1   The cylinder bores must be examined for taper, ovality, scoring and scratches. Start by examining the top of the bores; if these are

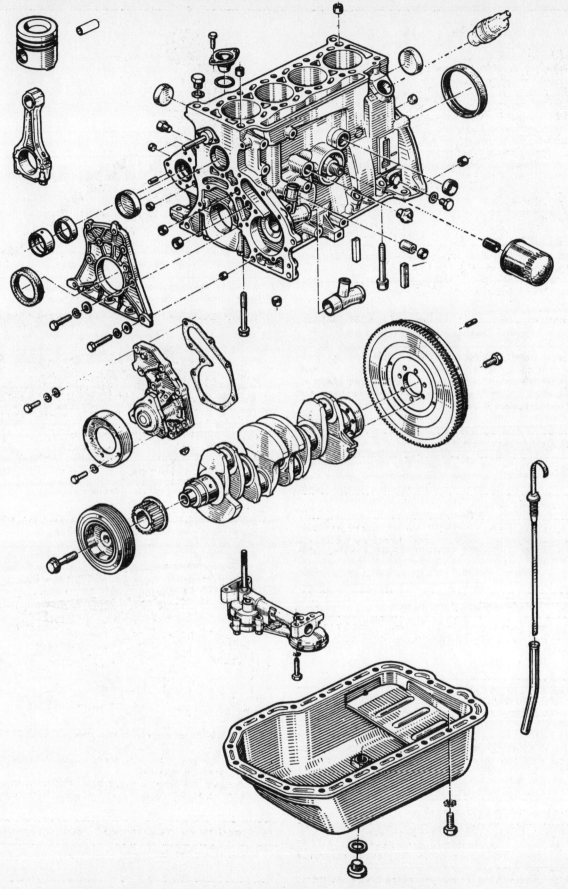

Fig. 1.53 Exploded view of the cylinder block and related components (Sec 75)

worn, a slight ridge will be found which marks the top of the piston ring travel. If the wear is excessive, the engine will have had a high oil consumption rate accompanied by blue smoke from the exhaust.

2   If available, use an inside dial gauge to measure the bore diameter just below the ridge and compare it with the diameter at the bottom of the bore, which is not subject to wear. If the difference is more than 0.152 mm, the cylinders should really be rebored and new oversize pistons fitted.

3   However, provided cylinder bore wear does not exceed 0.203 mm, special oil control rings and pistons can be fitted to restore compression and stop the engine burning oil.

4   If new pistons are being fitted to old bores, it is essential to roughen the bore walls slightly with fine glasspaper to enable the new piston rings to bed in properly.

5   Thoroughly examine the crankcase and cylinder blocks for cracks and damage and use a piece of wire to probe all oilways and waterways to ensure they are unobstructed.

## 76  Piston and connecting rod assemblies – examination and renovation

Refer to Section 28, paragraphs 1 to 6.

## 77  Camshaft and tappets – examination and renovation

1   Examine the camshaft bearing surfaces and cam lobes for wear ridges, pitting or scoring. Renew the camshaft if any of these conditions are apparent.

2   The oil seals at each end of the camshaft should be renewed as a matter of course. To change the oil seal at the flywheel end of the camshaft, the distributor rotor and endplate must first be removed. Unfortunately the rotor is bonded to the end of the camshaft with a special adhesive and can only be removed by breaking it. Having done this the seal and endplate can be slid off. With two new oil seals, new rotor and a quantity of the special adhesive, available from Renault dealers, the new seals can be fitted. Lubricate their seal lips then carefully slip them over the camshaft journals, ensuring that their open sides face the camshaft. Refit the endplate, then bond the new rotor to the camshaft. After fitting the new oil seals, store the camshaft in such a way that the weight of the camshaft is not resting on the oil seals.

3   Examine the camshaft bearings and bearing caps in the cylinder head. The camshaft runs directly in the aluminium housings and separate bearing shells are not used. Check the housings and caps for signs of wear ridges or deep scoring. Any excessive wear in these areas will mean a new cylinder head.

4   Finally inspect the tappet buckets and the little shims for scoring, pitting, especially on the shims, and wear ridges. Renew any components as necessary. Note that some scuffing and discolouration of the tappets is to be expected and is acceptable providing that the tappets are not scored.

## 78  Timing belt and sprockets – examination and renovation

1   Examine the timing belt carefully for any signs of cracking, fraying or general wear, particularly at the roots of the teeth. Renew the belt if there is any sign of deterioration of this nature, or if there is any oil or grease contamination.

2   Also inspect the timing sprockets for cracks or chipping of the teeth. Handle the sprockets with care as they may easily fracture if they are dropped or sharply knocked. Renew the sprockets if they are in any way damaged.

3   Check that the idler and tensioner pulleys rotate freely with no trace of roughness or harshness and without excessive free play. Renew if necessary.

## 79  Auxiliary shaft and bearings – examination and renovation

1   Examine the auxiliary shaft and oil pump driveshaft for pitting, scoring or wear ridges on the bearing journals and for chipping or wear of the gear teeth. Renew as necessary.

2   Check the auxiliary shaft bearings in the cylinder block for wear and, if worn, have these renewed by your Renault dealer or a suitably equipped engineering works.

3   Clean off all traces of old gasket from the auxiliary shaft housing and tap out the oil seal using a tube of suitable diameter. Install the new oil seal using a block of wood and tap it in until it is flush with the outer face of the housing. The open side of the seal must be towards the engine.

## 80  Crankshaft front plate – examination and renovation

1   Check the front plate for signs of distortion or damage to the threads. If serviceable, clean off all traces of sealant and tap out the oil seal using a tube of suitable diameter.

2   Fit a new seal so that it is flush with the outer face of the front plate using a block of wood. Ensure that the open side of the seal is fitted towards the engine.

## 81  Flywheel – examination and renovation

1   Examine the flywheel for scoring of the clutch face and for chipping of the ring gear teeth. If the clutch face is scored, the flywheel may be machined until flat, but renewal is preferable. If the ring gear is worn or damaged it may be renewed separately, but this job is best left to a Renault dealer or engineering works. The temperature to which the new ring gear must be heated for installation is critical, and if not done acccurately the hardness of the teeth will be destroyed.

## 82  Cylinder head and pistons – decarbonizing, valve grinding and renovation

Refer to Section 32, paragraphs 1 to 10.

## 83  Engine reassembly – general

Refer to Section 33.

## 84  Crankshaft and main bearings – refitting

1   Before fitting the crankshaft or main bearings it is necessary to determine the correct thickness of side seals to be fitted to No 1 main bearing cap. To do this, place the bearing cap in position without any seals and secure it with the two retaining bolts. Locate a twist drill, dowel rod or any other suitable implement which will just fit in the side

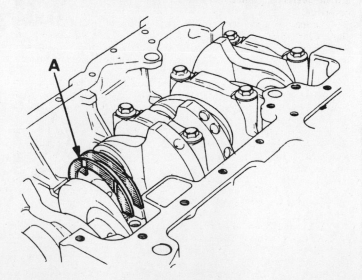

Fig. 1.54 Fit the crankshaft thrust washers with the oilways facing outwards (Sec 84)

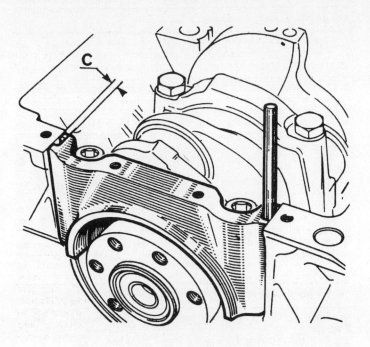

Fig. 1.55 Main bearing cap side seal groove clearance (C) (Sec 84)

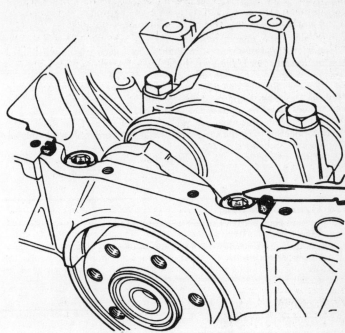

Fig. 1.56 Trim the side seals flush after fitting (Sec 84)

seal groove. Now measure the implement and this dimension is the side seal groove size. If the dimension is less than or equal to 5 mm, a 5.10 mm thick side seal is needed. If the dimension is more than 5 mm, a 5.3 mm thick side seal is required. Having determined the side seal size and obtained the necessary seals, proceed as follows:

2 Clean the backs of the bearing shells and the bearing recesses in both the cylinder block and main bearing caps.

3 Press the bearing shells without oil holes into the caps, ensuring that the tag on the shell engages in the notch in the cap.

4 Press the bearing shells with the oil holes into the recesses in the cylinder block.

5 If the original bearing shells are being refitted, these must be placed in their original locations.

6 Using a little grease, stick the thrust washers to each side of No 2 main bearing, so that the oilway grooves on each thrust washer face outwards.

7 Lubricate the lips of a new crankshaft rear oil seal and carefully slip it over the crankshaft journal. Do this carefully as the seal lips are very delicate. Ensure that the open side of the seal faces the engine.

8 Liberally lubricate each bearing shell in the cylinder block and lower the crankshaft into position.

9 Fit all the bearing caps, with the exception of No 1, in their numbered or previously noted locations so that the bearing shell locating notches in the cap and block are both on the same side. Fit the retaining bolts and tighten them hand tight at this stage.

10 Fit the side seals to No 1 main bearing cap with their seal groove facing outwards. Position the seals so that approximately 0.2 mm (0.008 in) of seal protrudes at the bottom facing side (the side towards the crankcase).

11 Apply some CAF 4/60 THIXO paste to the bottom corners of the cap and then place the retaining bolts through the cap bolt holes.

12 Place the cap in position and just start the bolts two or three turns into their threads. These will now serve as guide studs.

13 Press the cap firmly into place taking care not to displace the side seals. When the cap is nearly home, check that the side seals are still protruding at the bottom, push the cap down fully and tighten the bolts hand tight to hold it.

14 Position the oil seal so that its face is flush with the bearing cap and block, then tighten all the retaining bolts to the specified torque. Check that the crankshaft is free to turn.

15 Check the crankshaft endfloat using feeler gauges inserted between the thrust washers and the side of the bearing journal. If new

thrust washers have been fitted the endfloat should be in accordance with the dimension given in the Specifications. If the original washers have been refitted and the endfloat is excessive, new thrust washers must be obtained. These are available in a number of oversizes.

16 When all the components have been fitted and tightened, trim off the protruding ends of the side seals, flush with the block face.

### 85 Pistons and connecting rods – refitting

1 Clean the backs of the bearing shells and the recesses in the connecting rods and big-end caps. If new shells are being fitted, ensure that all traces of the protective grease are cleaned off using paraffin.

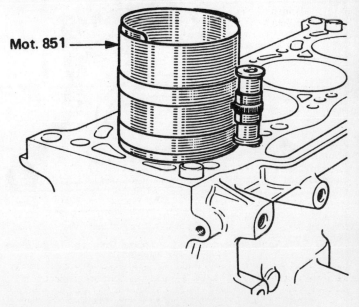

Mot. 851

Fig. 1.57 Using a piston ring compressor to compress the rings for piston installation (Sec 85)

2    Press the big-end bearing shells into the connecting rods and caps in their correct positions and oil them liberally.

3    Fit a ring compressor to No 1 piston then insert the piston and connecting rod into No 1 cylinder. With No 1 crankpin at its lowest point, drive the piston carefully into the cylinder with the wooden handle of a hammer and at the same time guide the connecting rod onto the crankpin. Make sure that the V mark on the piston crown, or arrow, is facing the flywheel end of the engine.

4    Fit the big-end bearing cap in its previously noted position then tighten the nuts to the specified torque.

5    Check that the crankshaft turns freely.

6    Repeat the procedure given in paragraphs 3 to 5 for No 4 piston and connecting rod, then turn the crankshaft through half a turn and repeat the procedure on No 2 and No 3 pistons.

7    If the engine is in the car, refit the oil pump, sump and cylinder head.

## 86  Flywheel – refitting

1    Clean the flywheel and crankshaft faces then fit the flywheel, making sure that any previously made marks are aligned.

2    Apply a few drops of thread locking compound to the retaining bolt threads, fit the bolts and tighten them in a diagonal sequence to the specified torque.

## 87  Crankshaft front plate – refitting

1    Apply a bead of CAF 4/60 THIXO paste to the mating face of the front plate and liberally lubricate the oil seal lips.

2    Refit the front plate and the retaining bolts. The two bolts around the oil seal opening at the 2 o'clock and 8 o'clock positions should also have a small quantity of the sealant paste applied to their threads, as they protrude into the crankcase. Progressively tighten the retaining bolts in a diagonal sequence.

3    Make sure that the Woodruff key is located in its crankshaft groove then refit the crankshaft sprocket.

4    If the engine is in the car, refit the sump and timing belt.

## 88  Auxiliary shaft – refitting

1    Liberally lubricate the auxiliary shaft and slide it into its bearings.

2    Place the retaining plate in position with its curved edge away from the crankshaft and refit the two retaining bolts. Tighten the bolts fully.

3    Place a new gasket in position over the dowels of the cylinder block. If a gasket was not used previously, apply a bead of CAF 4/60 THIXO paste to the housing mating face.

4    Liberally lubricate the oil seal lips and then locate the housing in place. Refit and tighten the housing retaining bolts progressively in a diagonal sequence.

5    Lubricate the oil pump drivegear and lower the gear into its location.

6    Position a new O-ring seal on the drivegear cover plate, fit the plate and secure with the two retaining bolts.

7    With the Woodruff key in place, refit the auxiliary shaft sprocket, washer and retaining bolt. Hold the sprocket using the method employed for removal, and tighten the bolt to the specified torque.

8    If the engine is in the car, refit the timing belt and, if removed, the engine undertray.

## 89  Oil pump – refitting

1    Place the oil pump in position with its shaft engaged with the drivegear.

2    Refit the retaining bolts and tighten them securely.

3    If the engine is in the car, refit the sump.

## 90  Sump – refitting

1    Ensure that the mating faces of the sump and crankcase are clean and dry.

2    Apply a bead of CAF 4/60 THIXO paste to the sump face and place the sump in position. Refit the retaining bolts and tighten them progressively in a diagonal sequence.

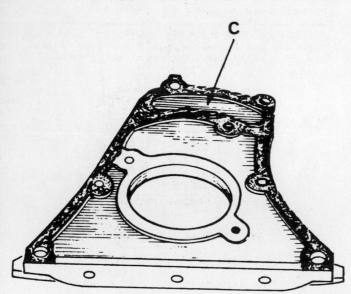

Fig. 1.58 Apply sealant to the front plate. Do not block the oilway in zone C (Sec 87)

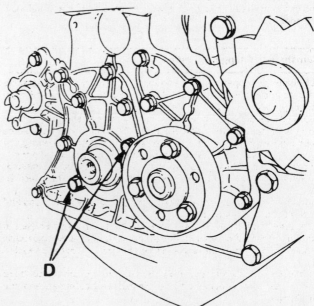

Fig. 1.59 Apply sealant to the threads of the two bolts (D) (Sec 87)

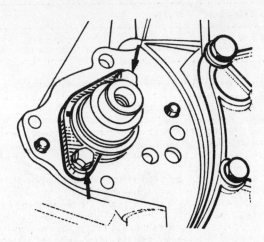

Fig. 1.60 Fit the auxiliary shaft retaining plate with its curved side away from the crankshaft and secure with the two bolts (Sec 88)

3   If the engine is in the car, reconnect the wiring to the sump sensors, refit the flywheel cover plate and the undertray, then fill the engine with oil.

## 91  Cylinder head – reassembly

1   Using a suitable tube fit new oil seals to each of the valve guides.
2   Lubricate the stems of the valves and insert them into their original locations. If new valves are being fitted, insert them into the locations to which they have been ground.
3   Working on the first valve, fit the spring seat to the cylinder head followed by the valve spring and cap.
4   Compress the valve spring and locate the split collets in the recess in the valve stem. Release the compressor then repeat the procedure on the remaining valves.
5   With all the valves installed, lay the cylinder head on one side and tap each valve stem with a plastic mallet to settle the components.
6   If the cylinder head has been removed with the engine in the car, refit the camshaft and tappets, the fuel pump, fuel filter and manifolds, and the thermostat.

## 92  Camshaft and tappets – refitting

1   Lubricate the tappet buckets and insert them into their respective locations as noted during removal. Make sure that each bucket has its correct tappet shim in place on its upper face.
2   Lubricate the camshaft bearings, then lay the camshaft in position. Position the oil seals so that they are flush with the cylinder head faces and refit the bearing caps. Ensure that the caps are fitted facing the same way as noted during removal and in their original locations.
3   Apply a thread locking compound to the bearing cap retaining bolts, refit the bolts and progressively tighten them to the specified torque.
4   Refit the camshaft sprocket backing plate to the cylinder head and secure with the retaining bolts.
5   With the Woodruff key in its groove, fit the camshaft sprocket and retaining bolt. Prevent the camshaft turning using the same method as for removal and tighten the sprocket retaining bolt to the specified torque.
6   If the engine is in the car, refit the fuel pump, timing belt and distributor cap, then check the valve clearances before refitting the camshaft cover.

## 93  Cylinder head – refitting

1   Ensure that the mating faces of the cylinder block and head are spotlessly clean, that the retaining bolt threads are also clean and dry and that they screw easily in and out of their locations.

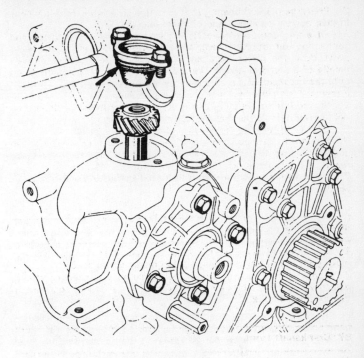

Fig. 1.61 Fit a new O-ring to the cover plate (Sec 88)

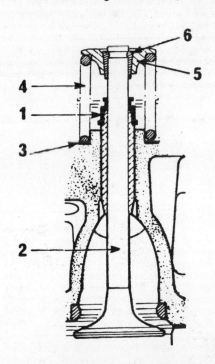

Fig. 1.62 Valve components (Sec 91)

| | |
|---|---|
| 1   Oil seal | 4   Spring |
| 2   Valve | 5   Cap |
| 3   Spring seat | 6   Split collets |

2   Turn the crankshaft as necessary to bring No 1 piston to the TDC position. Retain the crankshaft in this position using a metal rod in the TDC locating hole in the cylinder block.
3   Place a new gasket on the block face and located over the studs. Do not use any jointing compound on the gasket.
4   Turn the camshaft sprocket until the mark on its outer face is aligned with the mark on the sprocket backing plate.
5   Lower the cylinder head into position on the block and engage the dowels.

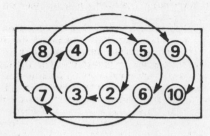

**Fig. 1.63 Cylinder head bolt tightening sequence (Sec 93)**

6    Lightly lubricate the cylinder head retaining bolt threads and under the bolt heads with clean engine oil and screw in the bolts finger tight.
7    Tighten the retaining bolts in the sequence shown in Fig. 1.63, to the 1st tightening setting given in the Specifications. Now repeat the sequence, but this time to the 2nd tightening setting.
8    Wait 3 minutes then loosen all the bolts completely. Tighten them again this time to the 1st retightening setting, still in the correct sequence.
9    The final, or 2nd retightening is done using an angular measurement. To do this, draw two lines at 123° to each other on a sheet of card and punch a hole for the socket bit at the point where the lines intersect. Starting with bolt No 1, engage the socket through the card and into the bolt head. Position the first line on the card under, and directly in line with the socket extension bar. Hold the card, and in one movement tighten the bolt until the extension bar is aligned with the second line on the card. Repeat this procedure for the remaining bolts in the correct sequence.
10   Refit the timing belt and check the valve clearances. If the engine is in the car, refit the controls cables and services using the reverse of the removal procedure described in Section 58, but bearing in mind the following points:

   (a) Tighten the exhaust front section-to-manifold retaining bolts so that the tension springs are compressed as shown in Fig. 1.28
   (b) Adjust the choke and accelerator cables, as described in Chapter 3
   (c) Adjust the drivebelt tension, as described in Chapter 2
   (d) Refill the cooling system, as described in Chapter 2

## 94 Timing belt – refitting

1    Check that the crankshaft is at the TDC position for No 1 cylinder and that the crankshaft is locked in this position using the metal rod through the hole in the crankcase.
2    Check that the timing mark on the camshaft sprocket is in line with the corresponding mark on the metal backing plate.
3    Align the timing marks on the belt with those on the sprockets, noting that the running direction arrows on the belt should be positioned between the auxiliary shaft sprocket and the idler pulley.
4    Hold the belt in this position and slip it over the crankshaft, auxiliary shaft and camshaft sprockets in that order, then around the idler tensioner pulleys.
5    Check that all the timing marks are still aligned then temporarily tension the belt by turning the tensioner pulley anti-clockwise and tightening the retaining nut.
6    Remove the TDC locating rod.
7    Refit the crankshaft pulley and retaining bolt. Prevent the crankshaft turning by whichever method was used during removal and tighten the pulley bolt to the specified torque.
8    Using a socket or spanner on the pulley bolt, turn the crankshaft at least two complete turns in the normal direction of rotation then return it to the TDC position with No 1 cylinder on compression.
9    Check that the timing marks are still aligned. If not, slacken the tensioner, move the belt one tooth as necessary on the camshaft sprocket and check again.
10   With the timing correct, tension the belt by turning the tensioner as necessary so that under moderate pressure applied at a point

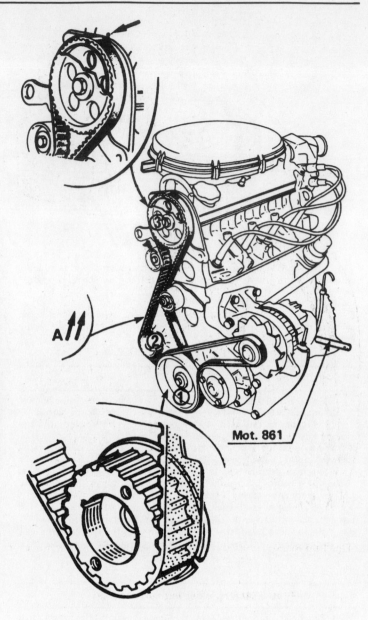

**Fig. 1.64 Arrangement of the timing belt, sprockets, timing marks and belt direction arrows (Sec 94)**

midway between the auxiliary sprocket and idler pulley, the belt deflects by 7.5 mm (0.3 in). When the tension is correct, tighten the tensioner pulley retaining nut.
11   Refit the timing belt cover and secure with the four retaining bolts.
12   If the engine is in the car, refit the alternator drivebelt and air cleaner, then reconnect the battery.

## 95 Valve clearances – adjustment

1    If the engine is in the car, remove the air cleaner and disconnect the choke cable, as described in Chapter 3. Undo the three domed retaining nuts and lift off the camshaft cover and gasket.
2    Using a socket or spanner on the crankshaft pulley bolt, turn the engine until the peak of the cam lobe for valve No 1 (nearest the flywheel) is uppermost. Using feeler gauges measure and record the clearance between the heel of the cam lobe and the shim on the top of the tappet bucket. Repeat this procedure for the remaining valves in turn.

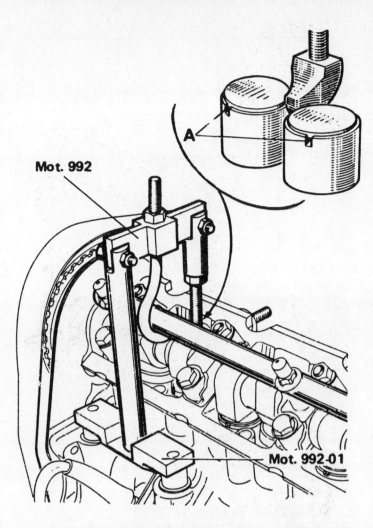

**Mot. 992**

**Mot. 992-01**

**Fig. 1.65 Renault tool for compressing tappet buckets to change tappet shims (Sec 95)**

*Fit slots (A) at right-angles to the camshaft*

from the measured clearance. A shim thicker by this amount from the one now in place, is needed. The shim size is stamped on the bottom face of the shim.

5   The shims can be removed from their locations on top of the tappet buckets without removing the camshaft if the Renault tool shown in the accompanying illustrations can be borrowed, or a suitable alternative fabricated. To remove the shim the tappet bucket has to be pressed down against valve spring pressure just far enough to allow the shim to be slid out. Theoretically this could be done by levering against the camshaft between the cam lobes with a suitable pad to push the bucket down, but this is not recommended by the manufacturers. Alternatively an arrangement similar to the Renault tool can be made by bolting a bar to the camshaft bearing studs and levering down against this with a stout screwdriver. The contact pad should be a triangular-shaped metal block with a lip filed along each side to contact the edge of the bucket. Levering down against this will open the valve and allow the shim to be withdrawn. Make sure that the cam lobe peaks are uppermost when doing this and rotate the buckets so that the notches are at right angles to the camshaft centreline.

6   If the Renault tool cannot be borrowed or a suitable alternative made up then it will be necessary to remove the camshaft, as described in Section 60, to gain access to the shims.

7   When refitting the shims ensure that the size markings face the tappet buckets (ie downwards).

8   On completion refit the camshaft cover using a new gasket. If the engine is in the car refit the air cleaner and choke cable with reference to Chapter 3.

## 96 Ancillary components – refitting

Refer to Section 10 and refit all the components listed with reference to the Chapters indicated.

## 97 Engine – attachment to gearbox

Refer to Section 54 and attach the engine using the reverse of the removal procedure. Apply a trace of molybdenum disulphide grease to the end of the gearbox input shaft before fitting.

## 98 Engine – refitting

Refitting the engine is a reverse of the removal procedure contained in Section 53, but bear in mind the following additional points:

(a) *Tighten the exhaust front section-to-manifold retaining bolts so that the tension springs are compressed as shown in Fig. 1.28*

(b) *Refill the cooling system with reference to Chapter 2*

(c) *Adjust the choke and accelerator cables with reference to Chapter 3*

(d) *Refill the gearbox with oil, as described in Chapter 6, and the engine, as described in Section 49 of this Chapter*

## 99 Engine – adjustments after major overhaul

Refer to Section 46, but note that it is not necessary to re-torque the cylinder head.

3   Once all the clearances have been recorded, compare the figures with the specified valve clearances given in the Specifications, noting that valve Nos 2, 4, 5 and 7 are inlet and valve Nos 1, 3, 6 and 8 are exhaust.

4   If the clearance of any of the valves differs from the specified value then the shim for that valve must be replaced with a thinner or thicker shim accordingly. The size of shim required can be calculated as follows: If the measured clearance is less than specified, subtract the measured clearance from the specified clearance. A shim thinner by this amount from the one now in place, is needed. If the measured clearance is greater than specified, subtract the specified clearance

**Fault diagnosis overleaf**

## Part 3: All Engines

### 100 Fault diagnosis – engine

| Symptom | Reason(s) |
| --- | --- |
| Engine fails to start | Discharged battery |
| | Loose battery connection |
| | Loose or broken ignition leads |
| | Moisture on spark plugs, distributor cap, or HT leads |
| | Incorrect spark plug gaps |
| | Cracked distributor cap or rotor |
| | Other ignition system fault |
| | Dirt or water in carburettor |
| | Empty fuel tank |
| | Faulty fuel pump |
| | Other fuel system fault |
| | Faulty starter motor |
| | Low cylinder compressions |
| Engine idles erratically | Inlet manifold air leak |
| | Leaking cylinder head gasket |
| | Worn rocker arms, timing chain or belt, gears or sprockets |
| | Worn camshaft lobes |
| | Faulty fuel pump |
| | Incorrect valve clearances |
| | Loose crankcase ventilation hoses |
| | Carburettor adjustment incorrect |
| | Uneven cylinder compressions |
| Engine misfires | Spark plugs worn or incorrectly gapped |
| | Dirt or water in carburettor |
| | Carburettor adjustment incorrect |
| | Burnt out valve |
| | Leaking cylinder head gasket |
| | Distributor cap cracked |
| | Incorrect valve clearances |
| | Uneven cylinder compressions |
| | Worn carburettor |
| Engine stalls | Carburettor adjustment incorrect |
| | Inlet manifold air leak |
| | Ignition timing incorrect |
| Excessive oil consumption | Worn pistons, cylinder bores or piston rings |
| | Valve guides and valve stem seals worn |
| | Oil leaking from rocker cover, camshaft cover, engine gaskets or oil seals |
| Engine backfires | Carburettor adjustment incorrect |
| | Ignition timing incorrect |
| | Incorrect valve clearances |
| | Inlet manifold air leak |
| | Sticking valve |

# Chapter 2  Cooling system

*For modifications, and information applicable to later models, see Supplement at end of manual*

## Contents

## Specifications

**System type** ..................................................................... Pressurized, pump-assisted thermo-syphon with front-mounted radiator and electric cooling fan

**Antifreeze type** ............................................................... Ethylene glycol antifreeze (Duckhams Universal Antifreeze and Summer Coolant)

**Thermostat opening temperature** ............................... 86°C or 89°C (187°F or 192°F), depending on model and options

**System capacity (including heater)**
1108 cc and 1397 cc engines ......................................... 6.0 litres (10.6 Imp pints)
1721 cc engines ............................................................. 6.7 litres (11.8 Imp pints)

## 1  General description

The cooling system is of the pressurized, pump-assisted thermo-syphon type. The system consists of the radiator, water pump, thermostat, electric cooling fan, expansion tank and associated hoses.

The system functions as follows: Cold coolant in the bottom of the radiator right-hand tank passes through the bottom hose to the water pump where it is pumped around the cylinder block and head passages. After cooling the cylinder bores, combustion surfaces and valve seats, the coolant reaches the underside of the thermostat, which is initially closed, and is diverted through passages in the water pump to the heater and carburettor hose outlets. After passing through the heater matrix and through passages in the carburettor body, the coolant is returned to the water pump. When the engine is cold the thermostat remains closed and the coolant circulates only through the engine, heater and carburettor. When the coolant reaches a predetermined temperature, the thermostat opens and the coolant passes through the top hose and back to the radiator. As the coolant circulates through the radiator it is cooled by the inrush of air when the car is in forward motion. Airflow is supplemented by the action of the electric cooling fan when necessary. Upon reaching the bottom right-hand side of the radiator, the coolant is now cooled and the cycle is repeated.

When the engine is at normal operating temperature the coolant expands and some of it is displaced into the expansion tank. This coolant collects in the tank and is returned to the radiator when the system cools.

The electric cooling fan mounted behind the radiator is controlled by a thermostatic switch located in the radiator side tank. At a predetermined coolant temperature the switch contacts close, thus actuating the fan.

## 2  Maintenance and inspection

1  Check the coolant level in the system weekly and, if necessary, top up with a water and antifreeze mixture until the level is between the MINI and MAXI marks on the expansion tank. With a sealed type cooling system, topping-up should only be necessary at very infrequent intervals. If this is not the case, and frequent topping-up is required, it is likely there is a leak in the system. Check all hoses and joint faces for any straining or actual wetness, and rectify if necessary. If no leaks can be found it is advisable to have the system pressure tested as the leak could possibly be internal. It is a good idea to keep a check on the engine oil level as a serious internal leak can often cause the level in the sump to rise, thus confirming suspicions.

2  At the intervals given in Routine maintenance at the beginning of this manual the following checks should also be carried out on the cooling system components.

3  Carefully inspect all the hoses, hose clips and visible joint gaskets of the system for cracks, corrosion, deterioration or leakage. Renew any hoses and clips that are suspect and also renew any gaskets, if necessary.

4  Carefully inspect the condition of the drivebelt and renew it if there is any sign of cracking or fraying, using the procedure described in Section 12. Check and adjust the tension of the belt, as described in the same Section.

5  Drain, flush and refill the cooling system at the specified intervals, as described in Sections 3, 4 and 5.

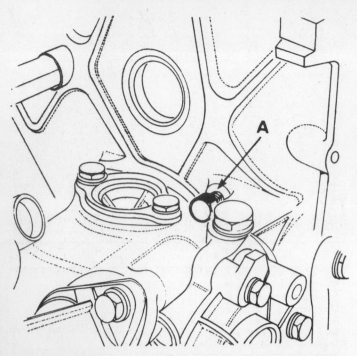

**Fig. 2.1 Cylinder block drain plug location (A) – 1721 cc engine (Sec 3)**

4    If the system needs to be flushed after draining, refer to the next Section, otherwise refit the drain plug and secure the bottom hose to the radiator.

### 4    Cooling system – flushing

1    With time the cooling system may gradually lose its efficiency as the radiator core becomes choked with rust, scale deposits from the water and other sediment.
2    To flush the system, first drain the coolant, as described in the previous Section.
3    Remove the radiator filler cap, insert a hose through the filler neck and allow water to circulate through the radiator until it runs clear from the bottom outlet.
4    To flush the engine and the remainder of the system, disconnect the top hose at the water pump or thermostat housing, place a hose in the outlet and allow water to circulate until it runs clear from the bottom hose. Set the heater controls to maximum heat during this operation to allow water to circulate through the heater matrix.
5    In severe cases of contamination the radiator should be reverse-flushed. To do this, first remove it from the car, as described in Section 7, invert it and insert a hose in the bottom outlet. Continue flushing until clear water runs from the top hose outlet.
6    If, after a reasonable period, the water still does not run clear, the radiator can be flushed with a good proprietary cleaning agent such as Holts Radflush or Holts Speedflush. The regular use of corrosion inhibiting antifreeze should prevent severe contamination of the system.

### 3    Cooling system – draining

1    It is preferable to drain the cooling system when the engine is cold. If the engine is hot the pressure in the system must be released before attempting to drain the system. Place a cloth over the pressure cap of the expansion tank and slowly unscrew the cap. Wait until the pressure has escaped and then remove the cap.
2    Place a suitable container beneath the right-hand side of the radiator. Slacken the hose clip and carefully ease the hose clip off the radiator outlet. Allow the coolant to drain into the container.
3    Now position the container beneath the cylinder block drain plug. On 1108 cc and 1397 cc engines the drain plug is located on the crankshaft pulley end of the engine, below the water pump (photo). On 1721 cc engines the drain plug is located on the rear facing side of the engine, towards the crankshaft pulley end (Fig. 2.1). Unscrew the plug and drain the coolant into the container.

### 5    Cooling system – filling

1    Refit the cylinder block drain plug, radiator bottom hose and any other hoses removed if the system has just been flushed.
2    Unclip the expansion tank from its location and tie it up, as high as the hose will allow, on the open bonnet (photo).
3    Set the heater temperature control to the maximum heat position.
4    On 1108 cc and 1397 cc engines open the bleed screws on the radiator top hose, heater hose and, if fitted, on the coolant supply hose to the carburettor. On 1721 cc engines open the bleed screw on the coolant hose at the rear of the engine (photo).
5    Pour the appropriate mixture of water and antifreeze (see Section 6) into the radiator through the filler neck (photo). When the radiator is full, refit the filler cap.
6    Continue filling the system by adding coolant to the expansion tank until the level is approximately 70 mm (2.76 in) above the MAXI mark.

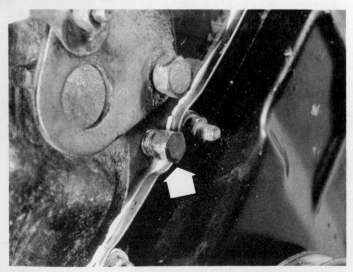

3.3 Cylinder block drain plug location (arrowed) – 1108 cc and 1397 cc engines

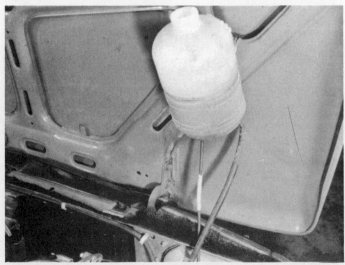

5.2 Support the expansion tank on the bonnet as high as possible prior to filling the system

5.4 Coolant hose bleed screw location (arrowed) on 1721 cc engine

5.5 Fill the radiator first using the appropriate mixture of antifreeze and water

5.7A When coolant flows through the top hose bleed screw ...

7  Close each bleed screw in turn as soon as a continuous flow of coolant can be seen flowing from it (photos).

8  Refit the expansion tank cap, start the engine and allow it to reach normal operating temperature.

9  With the engine idling, *on 1108 cc and 1397 cc engines only,* open each bleed screw in turn until a continuous flow of coolant with no trace of air appears, then close the bleed screw.

10  Switch off the engine and refit the expansion tank to its normal location.

11  When the engine has cooled down completely, check the coolant level in the expansion tank and top up, if necessary, so that the level is between the MINI and MAXI marks.

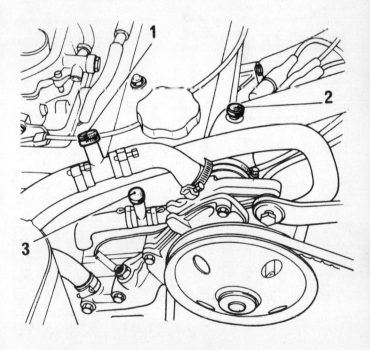

Fig. 2.2 Cooling system bleed screw locations – 1108 cc and 1397 cc engines (Sec 5)

1   Heater hose
2   Radiator top hose
3   Coolant hose to carburettor

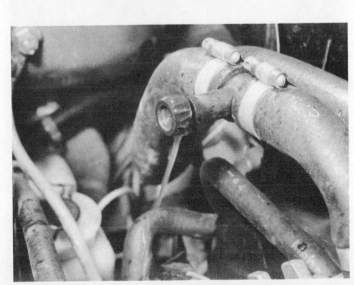

5.7B ... and heater hose bleed screw, close each screw in turn

## 6  Antifreeze mixture

1  The antifreeze should be renewed at regular intervals (see Routine maintenance). This is necessary not only to maintain the antifreeze properties, but also to prevent corrosion which would otherwise occur as the corrosion inhibitors become progressively less effective.

2  Always use a good quality ethylene glycol based antifreeze which is suitable for use in mixed metal cooling systems.

3  Before adding fresh antifreeze the cooling system should be completely drained, preferably flushed, and all hoses checked for security and condition.

4  Follow the antifreeze manufacturer's recommendations as to concentration, but generally a 50% solution of antifreeze will give protection down to −40°C (−40°F) and a 33% solution will give protection down to −20°C (−4°F). Do not allow the concentration of antifreeze in the system to fall below 25% regardless of the temperature or time of year.

5  After filling with antifreeze, a label should be attached to the radiator stating the type and concentration of antifreeze used and the date installed. Any subsequent topping-up should be made with the same type and concentration of antifreeze.

6  **Do not** use engine antifreeze in the screen washer system as it will cause damage to the vehicle paintwork. Screen washer antifreeze is available from most accessory shops.

## 7  Radiator – removal, inspection, cleaning and refitting

1  Disconnect the battery negative terminal and then drain the cooling system, as described in Section 3.

2  Slacken the hose clip and detach the radiator top hose and also the bottom hose if this has not already been done to drain the system.

3  Release the retaining clip and detach the expansion tank hose from the outlet beneath the filler cap (photo).

4  Disconnect the two wires from the thermostatic switch on the right-hand side of the radiator (photo).

5  Disconnect the cooling fan wires at the two-pin connector (photo). Where fitted, unscrew the transmission oil cooler unions.

6  Lift up the large wire retaining clip at the top, move the radiator towards the engine and lift it upwards to disengage the two lower retaining pegs (photos). Withdraw the radiator, complete with cooling fan assembly, from the engine compartment.

7  Minor leaks from the radiator can be cured using Holts Radweld, with the radiator still *in situ*. Extensive damage should be repaired by a specialist, or the unit exchanged for a new or reconditioned radiator. Clear the radiator matrix of flies and small leaves with a soft brush, or by hosing.

8  If the radiator is to be left out of the car for more than 48 hours, special precautions must be taken to prevent the brazing flux used during manufacture from reacting with the chloride elements remaining from the coolant. This reaction could cause the aluminium core to oxidize causing leakage. To prevent this, either flush the radiator thoroughly with clean water, dry with compressed air and seal all outlets, or refill the radiator with coolant and temporarily plug all outlets.

9  Refitting the radiator is the reverse sequence to removal. Fill the cooling system, as described in Section 5, and on automatic transmission models top up the fluid, as described in Chapter 6.

## 8  Cooling fan assembly – removal and refitting

1  Remove the radiator, as described in Section 7.

2  Drill the heads off the rivets securing the shroud or fan motor bracket to the radiator. Tap out the rivets using a small punch and lift off the shroud or bracket, complete with motor and fan.

3  Undo the nut or extract the retaining clip and slide the fan off the motor shaft. Note which way the fan is fitted.

4  The motor can now be removed by drilling out the retaining rivets, as previously described.

5  Drilling is the reverse sequence to removal using new rivets obtainable from Renault parts stockists.

7.3 Disconnect the expansion tank hose at the radiator

7.4 Disconnect the thermostatic switch wires ...

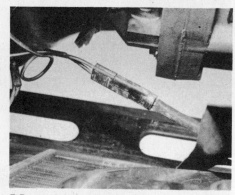

7.5 ... and the cooling fan wires at the two-pin connector

7.6A Lift up the radiator retaining clip, move the radiator towards the engine at the top ...

7.6B ... and lift it upwards to remove

## 9 Cooling fan thermostatic switch – testing, removal and refitting

1 If the thermostatic switch, located on the right-hand side of the radiator, develops a fault it is most likely to fail open circuit. This will result in the fan motor remaining stationary even though the coolant may reach boiling point.

2 To test for a faulty thermostatic switch, disconnect the two switch wires and join them together with a suitable length of wire. If the fan now operates with the ignition switched on, the thermostatic switch is proved faulty and must be renewed.

3 To remove the switch, disconnect the battery negative terminal and drain the cooling system, as described in Section 3.

4 Disconnect the two wires and then unscrew the switch from the radiator.

5 Refitting is the reverse sequence to removal. Refill the cooling system, as described in Section 5, after refitting the switch.

## 10 Thermostat – removal, testing and refitting

### 1108 cc and 1397 cc engines

1 The thermostat is located in the end of the radiator top hose at the water pump and is retained by a hose clip.

2 To remove the thermostat, first unscrew the expansion tank filler cap. If the engine is hot, place a cloth over the cap and unscrew it slowly allowing all the pressure to escape before removing the cap completely.

3 Place a suitable container beneath the radiator bottom hose outlet. Disconnect the bottom hose and drain approximately 1 litre (1.76 pints) of the coolant. Reconnect the bottom hose and tighten the clip.

4 Slacken the two clips on the radiator top hose adjacent to the water pump. Detach the hose from the pump outlet and withdraw the thermostat from the hose (photo).

5 To test whether the unit is serviceable, suspend it on a string in a saucepan of cold water together with a thermometer. Heat the water and note the temperature at which the thermostat begins to open. Continue heating the water until the thermostat is fully open and then remove it from the water.

6 The temperature at which the thermostat should start to open is stamped on the unit. If the thermostat does not start to open at the specified temperature, does not fully open in boiling water or does not fully close when removed from the water, then it must be discarded and a new one fitted.

7 Refitting the thermostat is the reverse sequence to removal, but make sure that the thermostat bleed hole is in the slot on the end of

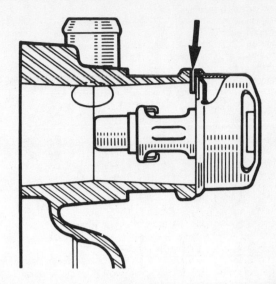

Fig. 2.3 On 1108 cc and 1397 cc engines the thermostat bleed hole must be in line with the pump outlet slot (arrowed) when refitting (Sec 10)

the water pump outlet. After fitting, fill the cooling system, with reference to Section 5.

### 1721 cc engines

8 The thermostat is located in a housing bolted to the left-hand side of the cylinder head beneath the distributor.

9 To remove the thermostat, first partially drain the cooling system, as described in paragraphs 2 and 3.

10 Slacken the clip securing the radiator top hose to the thermostat housing and remove the hose.

11 Undo the three bolts (photo), lift off the housing and take out the thermostat. Remove the thermostat rubber sealing ring.

12 The thermostat may be tested, as described in paragraphs 5 and 6.

13 Refitting is the reverse sequence to removal, but renew the thermostat rubber sealing ring if it shows any signs of deterioration. After fitting, fill the cooling system, with reference to Section 5.

10.4 Removing the thermostat from the radiator top hose – 1108 cc and 1397 cc engines

10.11 Thermostat housing retaining bolts (arrowed) on 1721 cc engine

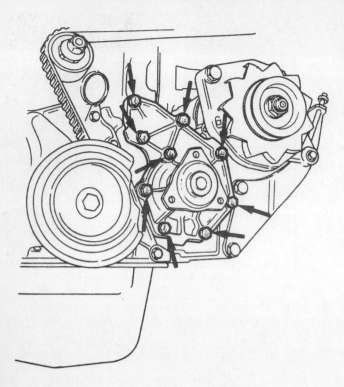

Fig. 2.4 Water pump retaining bolt locations (arrowed) – 1721 cc engines (Sec 11)

11.6 Using a socket and bar to remove the water pump retaining bolt located behind the pulley

11.7 Removing the water pump from the cylinder head

## 11  Water pump – removal and refitting

**Note:** *Water pump failure is indicated by water leaking from the gland at the front of the pump, or by rough and noisy operation. This is usually accompanied by excessive play of the pump spindle which can be checked by moving the pulley from side to side. Repair or overhaul of a faulty pump is not possible, as internal parts are not available separately. In the event of failure a replacement pump must be obtained.*

### 1108 cc and 1397 cc engines

1  Disconnect the battery negative terminal and then refer to Section 3 and drain the cooling system.
2  Refer to Section 12 and remove the drivebelt.
3  Undo the bolt securing the alternator adjusting arm to the pump body, remove the bolt and swing the arm clear.
4  Slacken the hose clips and disconnect the hoses from the pump.
5  Disconnect the lead from the coolant temperature switch on top of the pump body.
6  Undo and remove the bolts securing the water pump to the cylinder head. Access to the bolt behind the pulley can be gained by inserting a socket and extension bar through the holes in the pulley (photo).
7  With all the bolts removed, withdraw the pump from the cylinder head (photo). If it is stuck, strike it sharply with a plastic or hide mallet.
8  Refitting is the reverse sequence to removal, bearing in mind the following points:

　　(a)  *Remove all traces of old gasket from the cylinder head and pump faces, and ensure that both mating surfaces are clean and dry*
　　(b)  *Use a new gasket, lightly smeared with jointing compound*
　　(c)  *Adjust the drivebelt tension, as described in Section 12, and refill the cooling system, as described in Section 5*

### 1721 cc engines

9  Disconnect the battery negative terminal and then refer to Section 3 and drain the cooling system.

10  Refer to Section 12 and remove the drivebelt.
11  Undo the three bolts and remove the pump pulley.
12  Undo the bolts securing the pump to the cylinder block and withdraw the pump from its location. If it is stuck, strike it sharply with a plastic or hide mallet.
13  Refitting is the reverse sequence to removal, bearing in mind the points detailed in paragraph 8. Note also that the gasket should be fitted *without* jointing compound.

## 12  Drivebelt – renewal and adjustment

1  The drivebelt should be checked and if necessary re-tensioned at regular intervals (see Routine maintenance). It should be renewed if it shows any signs of fraying or deterioration and, in particular on 1721 cc engines, any sign of rubber accumulation in the belt grooves, torn, cut or worn grooves or signs of oil contamination.

### 1108 cc and 1397 cc engines

2  To remove the drivebelt, slacken the nuts at the alternator pivot mounting and at the adjustment arm (photo).

12.2 Alternator adjustment arm retaining nut and bolt (arrowed)

12.7 Alternator pivot mounting (arrowed) on 1721 cc engine

3    Move the alternator towards the engine and slip the drivebelt off the three pulleys.

4    Fit the new drivebelt over the pulleys then lever the alternator away from the engine until it is just possible to deflect the belt using moderate finger pressure by 4 mm (0.16 in) at a point midway between the alternator and water pump pulleys. The alternator must only be levered at the drive end bracket.

5    Hold the alternator in this position and tighten the adjusting arm bolt and nut followed by the pivot mounting nut.

6    Run the engine for approximately ten minutes and then recheck the tension.

*1721 cc engines*

7    To remove the drivebelt, slacken the nuts and bolts at the alternator pivot mounting (photo) and at the adjustment rod.

8    Slacken the two nuts on the adjustment rod (photo) until the drivebelt can be easily slipped off the pulleys. Do not use a screwdriver or any other tool to lever off the belt.

9    Fit the new drivebelt over the pulleys, then turn the alternator adjustment arm rod nut until it is possible to deflect the belt by 4 mm (0.16 in) using moderate finger pressure at a point midway between the crankshaft and alternator pulleys.

10   With the belt correctly tensioned, lock the two nuts together on the adjustment rod, and tighten the mountings.

11   Run the engine for approximately ten minutes and then recheck the tension.

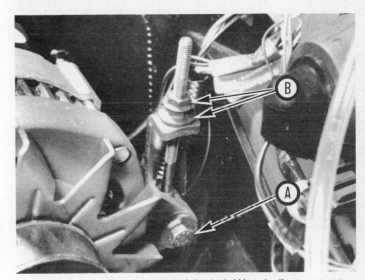

12.8 Alternator adjustment rod retaining bolt (A) and adjustment nuts (B) on 1721 cc engine

## 13  Temperature gauge sensor – removal and refitting

1    Unscrew the expansion tank filler cap. If the engine is hot, place a cloth over the cap and unscrew it slowly allowing all the pressure to escape before removing the cap completely.

2    Place a suitable container beneath the radiator bottom hose outlet. Disconnect the bottom hose and drain approximately 1 litre (1.76 pints) of the coolant. Reconnect the hose and tighten the clip.

3    Disconnect the lead at the sensor, located on top of the water pump on 1108 cc and 1397 cc engines, and on the rear facing side of the cylinder head at the thermostat housing end on 1721 cc engines. Unscrew the sensor from its location.

4    Refitting is the reverse sequence to removal. Fill the cooling system, as described in Section 5, on completion.

**Fault finding tables appear overleaf**

## 14 Fault diagnosis – cooling system

| Symptom | Reason(s) |
|---|---|
| Overheating | Low coolant level (this may be the result of overheating for other reasons)<br>Drivebelt slipping or broken<br>Radiator blockage (internal or external), or grille restricted<br>Thermostat defective<br>Ignition timing incorrect or distributor defective (automatic advance inoperative)<br>Carburettor maladjustment<br>Faulty cooling fan thermostatic switch<br>Faulty cooling fan<br>Blown cylinder head gasket (combustion gases in coolant)<br>Water pump defective<br>Expansion tank pressure cap faulty<br>Brakes binding |
| Overcooling | Thermostat missing, defective or wrong heat range |
| Water loss – external | Loose hose clips<br>Perished or cracked hoses<br>Radiator core leaking<br>Heater matrix leaking<br>Expansion tank pressure cap leaking<br>Boiling due to overheating<br>Water pump leaking<br>Core plug leaking |
| Water loss – internal | Cylinder head gasket blown<br>Cylinder head cracked or warped<br>Cylinder block cracked |
| Corrosion | Infrequent draining and flushing<br>Incorrect antifreeze mixture or inappropriate type<br>Combustion gases contaminating coolant |

# Chapter 3  Fuel and exhaust systems

*For modifications, and information applicable to later models, see Supplement at end of manual*

## Contents

## Specifications

**Air cleaner** ................................................... Automatic or manual air temperature control type with renewable paper element. Champion W145 (1108 cc and 1397 cc) or W190 (1721 cc)

**Fuel pump** ................................................... Mechanical, driven by camshaft

**Fuel filter** ................................................... Champion L101

### Carburettor
Type ................................................... Single or dual throat downdraught
Application:
C1F, 1108 cc engines ................................................... Zenith 32IF2
C1J, 1397 cc engines ................................................... Solex 32BIS
C2J, 1397 cc and F2N, 1721 cc engines ................................................... Weber 32DRTM

### Carburettor data
Zenith 32IF2:

| | V10501 | V10501B |
|---|---|---|
| Type identification number | **V10501** | **V10501B** |
| Venturi | 23 | 23 |
| Main jet | 123 | 123 |
| Idling jet | 61 | 61 |
| Air compensating jet | 90 x 200 | 90 x 200 |
| Pneumatic enrichment jet | 66 | 66 |
| Accelerator pump jet | 45 | 45 |
| Auxiliary jet | 100 | 100 |
| Fuel needle valve | 1.25 | 1.25 |
| Initial throttle opening (fast idle) adjustment | 0.75 mm (0.030 in) | 0.75 mm (0.030 in) |
| Float height dimension | 13.55 to 13.75 mm (0.53 to 0.54 in) | 13.55 to 13.75 mm (0.53 to 0.54 in) |
| Auxiliary jet tube setting | 6.0 mm (0.24 in) | 6.0 mm (0.24 in) |
| Accelerator pump delivery tube setting | 60 mm (2.36 in) | 60 mm (2.36 in) |
| Accelerator pump stroke | 28.3 mm (1.11 in) | 28.3 mm (1.11 in) |
| Defuming valve setting | 2.0 mm (0.079 in) minimum | 2.0 mm (0.079 in) minimum |
| Pneumatic cold start device choke flap opening | – | 1.6 mm (0.06 in) |
| Pneumatic part open setting | | 2.1 mm (0.083 in) |
| Idling speed | 625 to 675 rpm | 625 to 675 rpm |
| CO mixture | 0.5 to 1.5% | 0.5 to 1.5% |

Solex 32BIS:
    Venturi ................................................................................ 24
    Main jet ............................................................................... 117.5
    Idling jet ............................................................................. 45
    Air compensating jet .......................................................... 155
    Accelerator pump jet .......................................................... 40
    Auxiliary jet ........................................................................ 30
    Fuel needle valve ............................................................... 1.8
    Initial throttle opening (fast idle) adjustment ...................... 0.70 mm (0.028 in)
    Accelerator pump stroke .................................................... 3.0 mm (0.12 in)
    Defuming valve setting ....................................................... 2.5 to 3.5 mm (0.098 to 0.138 in)
    Idling speed ....................................................................... 600 to 650 rpm
    CO mixture ......................................................................... 0.5 to 1.5%

Weber 32DRTM:

| | O/OC | 1/1C |
|---|---|---|
| Type identification number | **O/OC** | **1/1C** |
| Venturi: | | |
|   Primary | 23 | 23 |
|   Secondary | 24 | 24 |
| Main jet: | | |
|   Primary | 100 | 105 |
|   Secondary | 140 | 130 |
| Idling jet | 57 | 57 |
| Air compensating jet: | | |
|   Primary | 200 | 200 |
|   Secondary | 230 | 230 |
| Emulsifier: | | |
|   Primary | F44 | F44 |
|   Secondary | F25 | F25 |
| Mixture centralizer: | | |
|   Primary | 4R | 4R |
|   Secondary | 4R | 4R |
| Accelerator pump jet | 50 | 50 |
| Fuel needle valve | 1.75 | 1.75 |
| Float height dimension | 11 mm (0.43 in) | 11 mm (0.43 in) |
| Float travel dimension | 18 mm (0.71 in) | 18 mm (0.71 in) |
| Initial throttle opening (fast idle) adjustment | 0.70 mm (0.028 in) | 0.90 mm (0.035 in) |
| Defuming valve throttle opening | 0.50 mm (0.02 in) | 0.50 mm (0.02 in) |
| Choke flap pneumatic part open setting | 4.5 mm (0.177 in) | 3.5 mm (0.138 in) |
| Idling speed, C2J, 1397 cc engine: | | |
|   Manual transmission | 675 to 725 rpm | 675 to 725 rpm |
|   Automatic transmission (selector lever in D) | 575 to 625 rpm | 575 to 625 rpm |
| Idling speed, F2N, 1721 cc engine | 600 to 700 rpm | 600 to 700 rpm |
| CO mixture | 1.5% | 1.5% |

## Fuel tank capacity ...........................................  47 litres (10.34 gallons)

## Fuel octane rating
Except C1J engine .............................................. 97 RON (four star)
C1J engine .......................................................... 90 RON (two star)

## Torque wrench settings

| | Nm | lbf ft |
|---|---|---|
| Manifold retaining nuts and bolts | 30 | 22 |

## 1   General description

The fuel system consists of a rear-mounted fuel tank, mechanical fuel pump and a single or dual throat downdraught carburettor.

The mechanical fuel pump is operated by an eccentric on the camshaft and is mounted on the forward facing side of the cylinder block on 1108 cc and 1397 cc engines, and on the rear facing side of the cylinder head on 1721 cc engines. Located in the pump is a small filter to which access is gained after removing the pump top cover. On certain models a disposable in-line filter is also fitted in the outlet pipe from the pump.

The air cleaner contains a disposable paper filter element and incorporates a flap valve air temperature control system. This system allows cold air from the air cleaner main intake spout, or warm air from the exhaust manifold stove, to enter the air cleaner via a secondary intake according to the position of the flap valve. Depending on model, the flap valve may be either manually-controlled by a two position selector on the side of the air cleaner body, or automatically-controlled by a temperature sensitive wax capsule located in the intake spout.

Carburettors may be of Zenith, Solex or Weber manufacture according to model. All types incorporate a water-heated lower body to improve fuel atomization, particularly when the engine is cold.

Mixture enrichment for cold starting is by a manually-operated choke control on all models.

The exhaust system consists of three push-fit sections secured with circular clamps, and a cast iron exhaust manifold. A spring-loaded semi ball and socket joint is used to connect the exhaust front pipe section to the manifold and to provide a certain degree of flexibility, thus catering for engine and exhaust system movement. A silencer is fitted to the tailpipe section on all models, with an additional silencer incorporated in the intermediate section on certain versions. The system is suspended throughout its length on rubber block type mountings.

**Warning**: *Many of the procedures in this Chapter entail the removal of fuel pipes and connections which may result in some fuel spillage. Before carrying out any operation on the fuel system, refer to the precautions given in Safety First! at the beginning of this manual and follow them implicity. Petrol is a highly dangerous and volatile liquid, and the precautions necessary when handling it cannot be overstressed.*

## 2   Maintenance and inspection

1   At the service intervals shown in Routine maintenance the

following checks and adjustments should be carried out on fuel and exhaust system components.

2    With the car over a pit, raised on a vehicle lift or securely supported on axle stands, carefully inspect the underbody fuel pipes, hoses and unions for chafing, leaks and corrosion. Renew any pipes that are severely pitted with corrosion or in any way damaged. Renew any hoses that show signs of cracking or other deterioration.

3    Check the fuel tank for leaks, for any signs of corrosion or damage, and the security of the mountings.

4    Check the exhaust system condition, as described in Section 19.

5    From within the engine compartment, check the security of all fuel hose attachments and inspect them for chafing, kinks, leaks or deterioration.

6    Clean the fuel filter in the fuel pump, as described in Section 4, and, where fitted, renew the additional filter in the pump outlet pipe (photo). Ensure that this filter is fitted with the arrows stamped on the filter body pointing in the direction of fuel flow.

7    Renew the air cleaner paper filter element, as described in Section 3. On models with a manually-operated air temperature control, set the control to the summer or winter position according to season. On models with automatically-operated air cleaner air temperature control, check the operation of the flap valve, as described in Section 3.

8    Check the operation of the accelerator and choke control linkage and lubricate the linkage, cables and accelerator pedal pivot with a few drops of engine oil.

9    Check the carburettor idle speed and mixture settings and adjust, if necessary, as described in Section 14.

---

### 3    Air cleaner and filter element – removal and refitting

1    To remove the air cleaner filter element, unscrew the wing nut or the screw and three locknuts, then release the clips securing the top cover to the air cleaner body (photos). Lift off the cover and remove the filter element (photo).

2    Clean the inside of the air cleaner body and fit a new filter if the old one is dirty or has exceeded its service life (see Routine maintenance). Refit the top cover and secure with the wing nut or screw and locknuts, and the clips.

3    To remove the air cleaner assembly from the engine, proceed according to engine and carburettor type as follows:

#### 1108 cc and 1397 cc engines with Zenith or Solex carburettor

4    Undo the two nuts securing the air cleaner to the rocker cover (photo) and the bolt securing the air cleaner to the left-hand rear support bracket. Note the arrangement of rubber spacer, washers and sleeve under each front mounting nut.

2.6 On certain models an in-line fuel filter is fitted between pump and carburettor

3.1A To gain access to the air cleaner filter element, undo the wing nut and release the retaining clips (arrowed) ...

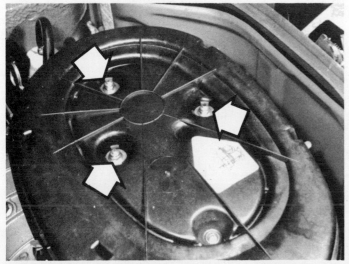

3.1B ... or undo the three locknuts and retaining screw (arrowed), followed by the clips

3.1C Lift off the cover and take out the paper element

3.4 On 1108 cc and 1397 cc engines fitted with Zenith or Solex carburettors undo the nuts securing the air cleaner in position

3.5A Detach the hot air duct at the exhaust manifold stove (arrowed) ...

3.5B ... and lift off the air cleaner

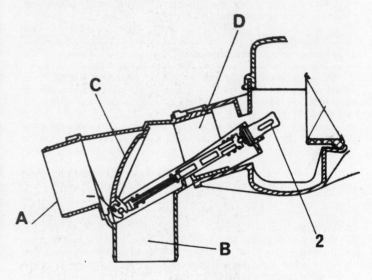

Fig. 3.1 Air cleaner automatic air temperature control layout (Sec 3)

A   Cold air intake
B   Hot air intake
C   Flap valve

D   Air cleaner body intake
    spout
2   Wax capsule

5   Detach the hot air duct from the stove on the exhaust manifold and lift the air cleaner assembly off the engine (photos).

### 1397 cc engines with Weber carburettor
6   Remove the air cleaner top cover and filter element, as previously described.
7   Undo the nut securing the air cleaner body to the rocker cover, noting the arrangement of rubber spacer, washers and sleeve under the nut.
8   Undo the three nuts securing the air cleaner body to the top of the carburettor. Detach the hot air duct from the stove on the exhaust manifold, detach the peg on the side of the body from the support bracket and lift up the air cleaner. Disconnect the crankcase ventilation hose and remove the air cleaner from the car. Recover the gasket.

### 1721 cc engines
9   Undo the three nuts securing the air cleaner to the carburettor and detach the hot air duct from the stove on the exhaust manifold. Release the wiring harness clips (photos).
10   Lift the air cleaner off the carburettor, disconnect the crankcase ventilation hose and remove the unit from the engine. Recover the gasket on the carburettor (photos).

### All models
11   If the air cleaner is equipped with an automatic air temperature control device, this may be tested as follows:
12   First remove the air filter element, if still in place, and the hot air duct.
13   Immerse the air cleaner body in water at 26°C (79°F) or less, ensuring that the wax capsule in the intake spout is completely submerged. After 5 minutes observe the position of the flap valve which should be blanking off the cold air intake.
14   Now repeat the test in water at 36°C (97°F) and after 5 minutes check that the flap is blanking off the hot air intake. If the flap valve does not operate as described at the specified temperatures, the wax capsule control assembly is faulty and must be renewed.
15   After completing the tests, dry off the air cleaner body and refit the hot air duct.
16   Refitting the air cleaner and element is the reverse sequence to removal. On models with a manually-operated air temperature control, set the flap valve to the summer or winter setting (photo), as applicable, after refitting.

3.9A On 1721 cc engines undo the air cleaner retaining locknuts then detach the hot air duct at the exhaust manifold stove (arrowed)

3.9B Release the wiring harness clips at the hot ...

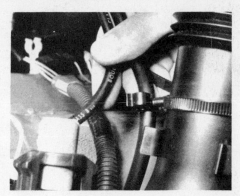

3.9C ... and cold air intakes

3.10A Lift up the air cleaner and detach the breather hose from the outlet ...

3.10B ... and at the support clip then lift off the air cleaner

3.10C Recover the gasket from the carburettor after removal

3.16 Air cleaner manually-operated air temperature control winter position (A) and summer position (B)

## 4  Fuel pump – testing and cleaning

**Note:** *Refer to the warning note in Section 1 before proceeding*
1   One of two different types of fuel pump may be fitted to Renault models covered in this manual. Both are similar in construction and identical in operation.
2   To test the operation of the pump, first remove it from the engine, as described in Section 5.
3   Refit the fuel inlet pipe to the pump and hold a wad of rag near the outlet. Operate the pump lever by hand and if the pump is in a satisfactory condition a strong jet of fuel should be ejected from the pump outlet as the lever is released. If this is not the case, check that fuel will flow from the inlet pipe when it is held below tank level, if so the pump is faulty.
4   To clean the pump filter, first disconnect the fuel inlet pipe at the

pump and plug it to prevent loss of fuel. Disconnect the outlet pipe, unscrew the retaining screw(s) and lift off the cover and gasket.
5   The filter, which will be either a flat or circular fine gauze screen, can now be withdrawn. Blow through the filter and brush or wipe out any dirt and sediment from the pump interior.
6   Reassemble the components in the reverse order to dismantling, but make sure that the retaining screws are not overtightened. If crimp type retaining clips were used to secure the fuel pipes, these should be replaced by screw type clips when reassembling.

## 5  Fuel pump – removal and refitting

**Note:** *Refer to the warning note in Section 1 before proceeding*
1   Disconnect the battery negative terminal.

2    Note the location of the fuel inlet, outlet and return pipes and disconnect them from the pump (photos).

3    Undo the two nuts and washers or nut, bolt and washers securing the pump to the engine and withdraw it from its location (photo).

4    On 1108 cc and 1397 cc engines, note the arrangement of insulating blocks and gaskets and remove them from the cylinder block after undoing the lower retaining bolt. On 1721 cc engines, remove the insulating block and gaskets from the cylinder head studs.

5    Before refitting the pump, thoroughly clean the pump and cylinder block or head mating faces.

6    On 1108 cc and 1397 cc engines place the insulating block in position with a large gasket each side (photos). If a second insulating block is used (depending on pump type), place this in position followed by the small gasket then secure the insulating block assembly with the lower retaining bolt (photos). On 1721 cc engines, place the insulating block and gaskets over the cylinder head studs.

7    Refit the pump and secure with the two nuts and washers or nut, bolt and washers.

8    Reconnect the fuel pipes to their original positions, as noted during removal. If crimp type retaining clips were used to secure the fuel pipes, these should be replaced by screw type clips.

9    Reconnect the battery negative terminal.

5.2A Fuel pump and fuel pipe locations on 1108 cc and 1397 cc engines ...

5.2B ... and on 1721 cc engines

5.3 Removing the fuel pump from an 1108 cc engine

5.6A On 1108 cc and 1397 cc engines place the fuel pump insulating block inner gasket in position ...

5.6B ... followed by the insulating block ...

5.6C ... outer gasket ...

5.6D ... second insulating block (if fitted) ...

5.6E ... then the final gasket

5.6F Secure this assembly with the retaining bolt then refit the fuel pump

## 6  Fuel tank – removal, servicing and refitting

**Note:** *Refer to the warning note in Section 1 before proceeding*

1    A drain plug is not provided on the fuel tank and it is therefore preferable to carry out the removal operation when the tank is nearly empty. Before proceeding, disconnect the battery negative terminal and then syphon or hand pump the remaining fuel from the tank.

2    Jack up the rear of the car and securely support it on axle stands. Remove the spare wheel.

3    Lift up the luggage compartment floor covering and withdraw the plastic cover to gain access to the fuel pipes at the sender unit (photo).

4    Disconnect the electrical multi-plug, the vent pipes and the fuel feed and return pipes at the sender unit (photo).

5    From under the car, release the retaining clips and detach the fuel filler pipe connecting hose from the tank outlet (photo).

6    Take the weight of the tank on a suitable jack with a block of wood interposed.

7    Undo the bolts securing the tank to the underbody (photo) and carefully lower the tank. When sufficient clearance exists, release the clips securing the vent pipes to the top of the tank.

8    Lower the tank completely and withdraw it from under the car.

9    If the tank is contaminated with sediment or water, remove the sender unit, as described in Section 7, and swill the tank out with clean

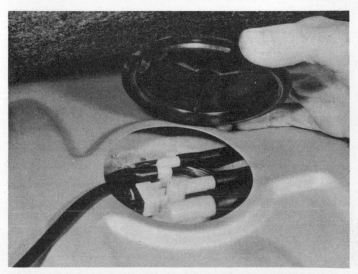

6.3 The fuel pipes and connections at the sender are accessible after removing the plastic cover in the luggage compartment floor

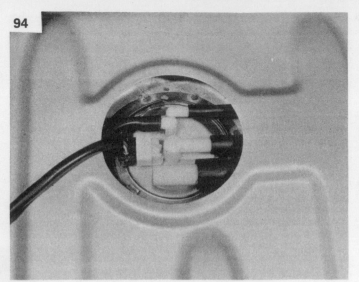

6.4 Wiring and fuel pipe connections at the sender unit

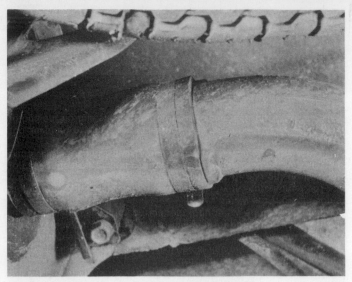

6.5 Fuel filler pipe connecting hose at the tank outlet

6.7 Fuel tank retaining bolt (arrowed)

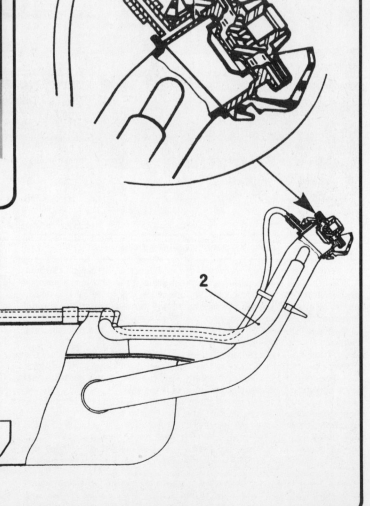

Fig. 3.2 Fuel tank and filler neck details (Sec 6)

1    Filler neck vent        2    Vent tube

fuel. If the tank is damaged, or leaks, it should be repaired by a specialist or, alternatively, renewed. **Do not** under any circumstances solder or weld the tank.
10  Refitting the tank is the reverse sequence to removal.

### 7  Fuel gauge sender unit – removal and refitting

**Note:** *Refer to the warning note in Section 1 before proceeding*
1  Disconnect the battery negative terminal.
2  Lift up the luggage compartment floor covering and withdraw the plastic cover to gain access to the sender unit (photo 6.3).
3  Disconnect the electrical multi-plug, the vent pipes and the fuel feed and return pipes at the sender unit (photos 6.4).
4  Turn the unit with a screwdriver or a flat blade to release it from the tangs of the tank.
5  Withdraw the unit carefully to avoid damaging the float arm and recover the gasket.
6  Refitting is a reversal of the removal sequence, but use a new gasket if the old one is damaged or shows any sign of deterioration.

### 8  Accelerator cable – removal and refitting

1  Remove the air cleaner assembly, as described in Section 3.
2  From inside the car, release the cable end fitting, which is a push fit in the accelerator pedal rod.
3  At the carburettor, slacken the clamp bolt and remove the outer cable from the support bracket on the manifold.
4  Detach the throttle return spring, open the throttle by hand and slip the cable end out of the slot on the linkage or bellcrank connector (photos).
5  According to model, the cable may be secured to a bracket attached to the brake master cylinder or engine compartment bulkhead, or it may be retained by a circlip adjacent to its bulkhead

grommet. Disconnect the cable, depending on its method of retention and withdraw it from the car.
6  Refitting the cable is the reverse sequence to removal. Before finally securing the outer cable to the support bracket on the manifold, adjust its position so that there is a small amount of slack in the cable when the throttle is closed.

### 9  Accelerator pedal – removal and refitting

1  Working inside the car, release the accelerator cable end fitting, which is a push fit in the pedal rod.
2  Undo the bolt securing the pedal assembly to the bulkhead and withdraw it from inside the car.
3  Refitting is the reverse sequence to removal.

### 10  Choke cable – removal and refitting

1  Disconnect the battery negative terminal.
2  Remove the air cleaner assembly, as described in Section 3.
3  Release the choke outer cable from its support bracket on the carburettor by carefully prising the retaining clip tangs out of the bracket slots (photos).
4  Disconnect the cable end from the carburettor by prising the spring loop off the stud on the linkage.
5  The procedure for removing the cable from the facia now varies according to model, as follows:

*Renault 9 models*
6  Reach up under the facia and disconnect the electrical lead for the choke warning lamp from the choke control body. If necessary greater access can be gained by removing the air duct between the heater and facia vent unit.
7  Compress the sides of the choke body and push it out of its location (photo).

8.4A Detach the accelerator cable from the linkage ...

8.4B ... or bellcrank connector (arrowed)

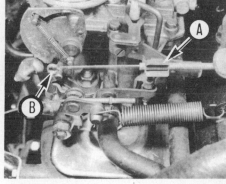

10.3A Choke cable support bracket clip (A) and cable end loop (B) on Zenith and Solex carburettors

10.3B Choke cable support bracket clip (A) and cable end loop (B) on Weber carburettors

10.7 Remove the choke cable from the facia on Renault 9 models by reaching behind and pushing it out of its location

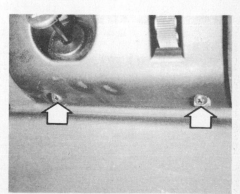

10.9 On Renault 11 models undo the screws (arrowed) and release the side panel to gain access to the choke cable

8   Release the grommet in the engine compartment bulkhead and pull the choke cable through and into the car.

### Renault 11 models

9   Undo the two screws securing the side panel to the facia (photo). Lift the panel up at the bottom and disengage the upper retaining lugs.
10   Disconnect the electrical lead for the choke warning lamp from the choke control body.
11   Compress the sides of the choke body and push it out of its location in the facia side panel.
12   Release the grommet in the engine compartment bulkhead and pull the choke cable through and into the car.

### All models

13   Refitting is the reverse sequence to removal. Adjust the position of the outer cable in its carburettor support bracket clip as necessary so that the choke linkage opens fully when the knob is pushed in, and closes fully when the knob is pulled out.

## 11  Zenith carburettor – description and identification

1   The Zenith 32IF2 carburettor is a single throat downdraught type and is fitted to the C1E, 1108 cc engine. Two versions of this carburettor are available. Both are virtually identical except for a pneumatically-controlled cold start device which is only fitted to one version. The type identification number is stamped on the float chamber cover and reference should be made to this number before consulting the Specifications for repair or adjustment data.
2   The carburettor functions as follows: Fuel, maintained at a constant level in the float chamber by the float and needle valve, passes through the main jet where it reaches the emulsion tube.
3   Air is drawn through the air calibration jet to mix with the fuel in the emulsion tube. The vacuum created in the main and secondary venturis, according to engine speed and load, causes this emulsified mixture to be discharged into the airstream through the carburettor. The calibration of the main and air jets and the shape of the venturi ensures that this emulsified mixture is in the right proportions at all engine speeds.
4   Under conditions of high engine speed, high engine load or acceleration, additional enrichment is provided by a pneumatic enrichment device and by an accelerator pump. The pneumatic enrichment device senses high manifold vacuum below the throttle valve and opens an additional fuel circuit calibrated by a jet. A tube immersed in the float chamber and also fitted with a jet supplies fuel through the auxiliary jet tube when the vacuum rises above the throttle valve. Movement of the throttle linkage actuates the accelerator pump assembly through a series of levers. The pump, consisting of two pistons, springs and two valves, pumps fuel to the delivery tube where it is injected into the airstream.
5   When the engine is idling, the high manifold vacuum below the throttle valve draws fuel from the float chamber to the idling jet. The fuel is emulsified with air drawn through a calibrated jet and atomized as it is discharged into the airstream below the throttle valve. As the throttle is opened during the progression stage, the mixture is discharged through additional holes. The strength of the mixture is controlled by the mixture adjusting screw.
6   A manually-operated cold start (choke) control is used to provide the necessary rich mixture for starting. When the choke knob is pulled out the choke flap is closed by the action of the linkage. When the engine is cranking, high vacuum is created below the choke flap and a very rich mixture is discharged. The linkage also opens the throttle valve by a predetermined amount so that the engine will run at a fast idle speed. On versions having a pneumatically-controlled cold start device, manifold vacuum passes through drillings and a valve to act on a diaphragm connected to the choke flap. According to engine load, this 'override' device alters the position of the choke flap on demand, thus altering the strength of the cold start mixture.

## 12  Solex carburettor – description and identification

1   The Solex 32BIS carburettor is a single throat downdraught type and is fitted to the C1J, 1397 cc engine. The carburettor type identification number is stamped to a plate attached to one of the float chamber retaining screws.
2   The function of the unit is as follows: Fuel, maintained at a

constant level in the float chamber by the float and needle valve, passes through the main jet to the emulsion tube. The fuel is emulsified with air drawn in through the air compensating jet. The vacuum created in the carburettor venturi causes the emulsified mixture to be discharged and atomized by the air passing through the venturi. The calibration of the main and air jets and the shape of the venturi ensures that this emulsified mixture is in the right proportions at all engine speeds.
3   Under condition of high engine speed, high engine load or acceleration, additional enrichment is provided by a full throttle enrichment device and an accelerator pump. The diaphragm of the full throttle enrichment device moves under the influence of manifold vacuum and spring pressure to open an additional fuel circuit calibrated by a jet. This provides an additional fuel mixture at high engine speed. The accelerator pump is operated by a cam and rod connected to the throttle valve spindle. The necessary rich mixture needed for acceleration is provided by the accelerator pump diaphragm which ejects a stream of neat fuel through the discharge nozzle whenever the throttle is operated.
4   When the engine is idling, the high manifold vacuum below the throttle valve draws fuel from the float chamber to the idling jet. The fuel is emulsified with air drawn through a calibrated orifice and atomized as it is discharged into the airstream below the throttle valve. The strength of the mixture is controlled by the mixture adjusting screw. An additional idling circuit is also used, whereby an emulsified mixture of fuel from the auxiliary jet and air from a calibrated orifice are mixed with air from a drilling in the venturi wall. This mixture is regulated by the volume control screw before being discharged below the throttle plate. This circuit allows a fine degree of engine idling speed adjustment via the volume control screw without upsetting the mixture strength to any degree.
5   A slotted bypass machined in line with the higher edge of the throttle valve is supplied with an emulsified mixture in the same way as the main idling circuit. This provides the correct mixture strength during progression from the idling phase to the main jet phase.
6   A manually-operated cold start (choke) control is used to provide the necessary rich mixture from starting. When the choke knob is pulled out the choke flap is closed by the action of the linkage. When the engine is cranking, high vacuum is created below the choke flap and a very rich mixture is discharged. The linkage also opens the throttle valve by a predetermined amount so that the engine will run at a fast idle speed.

## 13  Weber carburettor – description and identification

1   The Weber 32DRTM carburettor is a dual throat downdraught type and is fitted to the C2J, 1397 cc engine and F2N, 1721 cc engine. Two versions of this carburettor are available. Both are identical in operation, but are externally different with respect to their mounting arrangement (one type is secured to the inlet manifold by through-bolts, the other locates over studs), and position of the mixture adjusting screw. The type identification number is stamped on the carburettor lower flange and reference should be made to this number before consulting the Specifications for repair or adjustment data.
2   The carburettor functions as follows: During normal running, fuel maintained at a constant level in the float chamber by the float and needle valve passes through the main jet to the emulsion tubes.
3   Air is drawn through the air calibration jets to mix with the fuel in the emulsion tubes. The vacuum created in the main and secondary venturis, according to engine speed and load causes this emulsified mixture to be discharged into the airstream through the carburettor. The calibration of the main and air jets and the shape of the venturi ensures that this emulsified mixture is in the right proportions at all engine speeds.
4   Under conditions of high engine speed, high engine load or acceleration, additional enrichment is provided by a pneumatic enrichment device and by an accelerator pump. Under the action of manifold vacuum and spring pressure a diaphragm in the pneumatic enrichment device opens a valve to allow fuel, calibrated by a jet, to enter the main jet circuit to the primary throat. Under full load and at high engine speed, the vacuum created in the venturi of the secondary throat draws an emulsified mixture of fuel and air from the secondary enrichment jets and discharges it into the airstream above the secondary venturi. The accelerator pump is actuated by movement of

the throttle valve to inject fuel into the primary throat via a discharge nozzle.

5   When the engine is idling the high manifold vacuum below the throttle valve draws fuel from the float chamber to the idling jet. The fuel is emulsified with air drawn through a calibrated jet and atomized as it is discharged into the airstream below the throttle valve. As the throttle is opened during the progression stage, the mixture is discharged through additional holes. The strength of the mixture is controlled by the mixture adjusting screw.

6   A manually-operated cold start (choke) control is used, operating on the primary throat only, to provide the necessary rich mixture for starting. When the choke knob is pulled out, the choke flap is closed by the action of the linkage. With the engine cranking, high vacuum is created below the choke flap and a very rich mixture is discharged. The linkage also opens the primary throat throttle valve by a predetermined amount so that the engine will run at a fast idle, but holds the secondary throat throttle valve closed while the choke is in operation. A pneumatically-controlled cold start device allows manifold vacuum to act on a diaphragm connected to the choke flap. Under certain conditions this 'override' device alters the position of the choke flap on demand, thus altering the strength of the cold start mixture.

## 14  Carburettor – idle speed and mixture adjustment

1   The procedure for idle speed and mixture adjustment is the same on each of the three carburettor types that may be fitted. Refer to the accompanying photos and illustrations and identify the carburettor type fitted and the adjustment screw locations. Note that on later Weber carburettors, the mixture adjustment screw is contained in an extension housing attached to the side of the carburettor body (photos).

2   Before carrying out the following adjustments, ensure that the spark plugs are in good condition and correctly gapped and that, where applicable, the contact breaker points and ignition timing settings are correct.

3   Connect a tachometer to the engine in accordance with the manufacturer's instructions if one is not already fitted to the car. The use of an exhaust gas analyser (CO meter) is also preferable, although not essential. If a CO meter is available this should also be connected in accordance with the maker's recommendations.

4   Before proceeding with the adjustments, remove the tamperproof cap (if fitted) over the mixture adjustment screw by hooking it out with a scriber or small screwdriver.

5   Run the engine until it reaches normal operating temperature. Increase the engine speed to 2500 rpm for 30 seconds and repeat this at three minute intervals during the adjustment procedure. This will ensure that any excess fuel is cleared from the inlet manifold.

6   With the engine idling, turn the idle speed screw on Zenith and Weber carburettors, or the volume control screw on Solex carburettors until the engine is idling at the specified speed.

7   Turn the mixture adjustment screw clockwise to weaken the mixture until the engine speed just starts to drop or the tickover becomes lumpy. Now turn the screw slowly anti-clockwise to richen the mixture until the maximum engine speed is obtained consistent with even running. If a CO meter is being used, turn the mixture adjustment screw as necessary to obtain the specified CO content.

8   Return the engine idling speed to the specified setting by means of the idle speed screw or volume control screw.

9   Repeat the above procedure a second time and then switch off the engine and disconnect the instruments.

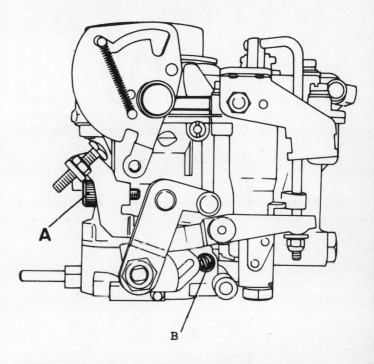

**Fig. 3.3 Zenith carburettor idle speed screw (A) and mixture adjustment screw (B) (Sec 14)**

14.1A Idle speed screw (A) and mixture adjustment screw in extension housing (B) on later Weber carburettors

14.1B On the 1721 cc engine the idle speed screw is accessible through a hole in the air cleaner

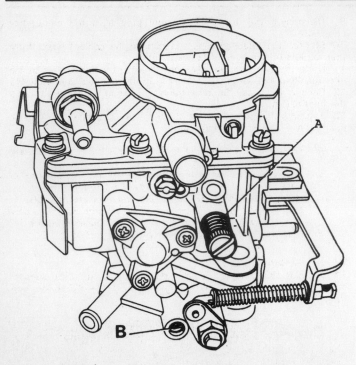

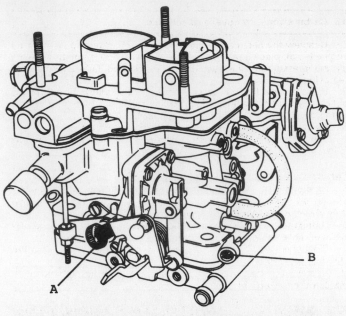

Fig. 3.5 Weber carburettor idle speed screw (A) and mixture
adjustment screw (B) (Sec 14)

Fig. 3.4 Solex carburettor volume control screw (A) and mixture
adjustment screw (B) (Sec 14)

## 15 Carburettor – anti-stall device adjustment

1   On models equipped with air conditioning, an anti-stall device
consisting of a vacuum-operated throttle opener diaphragm is used to
raise the engine idling speed slightly when the air conditioner is in
operation. The throttle opener diaphragm is attached to the carburettor
and acts directly on the throttle linkage via an adjustable plunger.
2   To adjust the anti-stall device, first ensure that the engine idling
speed is correctly adjusted, as described in the previous Section.
3   With the engine idling, switch on the air conditioning and check
that the engine speed increases to between 900 and 1000 rpm. If
necessary turn the adjusting screw located on top of the unit to obtain
the specified setting.

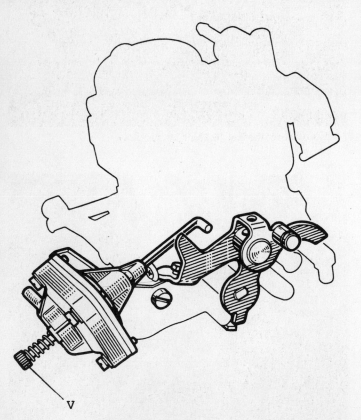

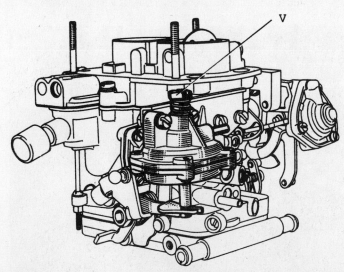

Fig. 3.6 Solex carburettor anti-stall device adjustment screw (V)
(Sec 15)

Fig. 3.7 Weber carburettor anti-stall device adjustment screw (V)
(Sec 15)

## 16 Carburettor – removal and refitting

1    Unscrew the filler cap on the cooling system expansion tank. If the engine is hot, place a rag over the cap and unscrew it slowly, allowing all the pressure in the system to be released before completely removing the cap.

2    Place a suitable container beneath the radiator bottom hose outlet. Disconnect the hose and drain approximately 1 litre (1.76 pints) of the coolant. Refit the hose and tighten the clip.

3    Refer to Section 3, and remove the air cleaner assembly.

4    The procedure now varies according to carburettor type as follows:

### Zenith and Solex carburettors

5    Carefully prise the choke cable retaining clip out of its support bracket on the carburettor and disconnect the cable end spring loop from the stud on the linkage (photo).

6    Detach the throttle return spring, open the throttle by hand and slip the cable end out of the slot on the linkage connector.

7    Disconnect the fuel inlet pipe from the carburettor and plug the pipe end after removal (photo).

8    Remove the crankcase ventilation hoses from the connector on the carburettor (photo).

9    Disconnect the distributor vacuum pipe from the carburettor connector.

10   Slacken the retaining clips and remove the coolant hoses from their outlets on the base of the carburettor.

11   Undo the two nuts and washers securing the carburettor to the inlet manifold and withdraw the unit from the manifold studs (photo).

12   Recover the gasket fitted between the base of the carburettor and the heat shield.

13   Refitting the carburettor is the reverse sequence to removal, bearing in mind the following points:

(a)   Ensure that the mating faces of the carburettor and heat shield are clean and use a new gasket

(b)   If crimp type clips were used to secure the coolant or fuel hoses these should be replaced by the screw type clips

(c)   Adjust the position of the choke and accelerator cables in their support bracket slips to give a small amount of free play at rest, consistent with full travel of the relevant linkage

(d)   Refill the cooling system, with reference to Chapter 2

### Weber carburettors

14   Carefully prise the choke cable retaining clip out of its support bracket on the carburettor and disconnect the cable end spring loop from the stud on the linkage.

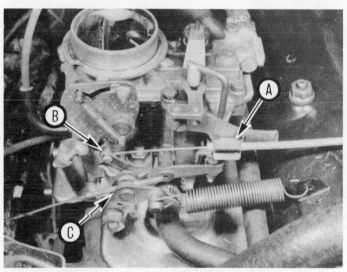

16.5 Disconnect the choke cable at the retaining clip (A) and at the linkage stud (B) then release the accelerator cable end (C) from the linkage

16.7 Disconnect the fuel inlet pipe (arrowed) ...

16.8 ... and the crankcase ventilation hoses

16.11 Undo the retaining nuts and lift off the carburettor

15  Carefully prise the accelerator bellcrank rod ball socket off the stud on the carburettor linkage.

16  Disconnect the fuel inlet pipe from the carburettor and plug the pipe end after removal.

17  Remove the crankcase ventilation hose and vacuum pipes from their connectors on the carburettor.

18  Slacken the retaining clips and remove the coolant hoses from their outlets on the base of the carburettor.

19  Undo the four nuts and washers, or the four socket-headed bolts and washers securing the carburettor to the inlet manifold. Withdraw the carburettor from the manifold and recover the gasket.

20  Refitting the carburettor is the reverse sequence to removal, but refer to the additional points listed in paragraph 13.

## 17  Carburettors – overhaul

1   Under normal circumstances, overhaul means removing the fixing screws and separating the main bodies of the carburettor so that the float chamber can be cleaned out and the jets and other passages cleaned with compressed air.

2   If the carburettor has been in service for a high mileage or the throttle spindles and their bushes have become worn, it is recommended that a new carburettor is obtained. It is unlikely that the individual parts will be available to recondition the carburettor yourself, and the cost involved in purchasing a new unit will soon be offset by the increase in fuel economy.

3   When reassembling the carburettor, carry out the following adjustments as work proceeds and use all the new gaskets, seals and other items supplied in the special repair kit for each carburettor.

4   It is necessary to remove the carburettor from the engine to carry out the following adjustments.

### Zenith carburettors

**Initial throttle opening (fast idle) adjustment**

5   Turn the choke operating cam on the side of the carburettor by hand as far as it will go, so that the choke flap is fully closed.

6   A twist drill or suitable rod having a diameter equal to the initial throttle opening setting given in the Specifications, should just slide between the throttle valve and the venturi wall (Fig. 3.9).

7   If adjustment is necessary, slacken the locknut and turn the fast idle adjusting screw to obtain the special setting. Tighten the locknut when adjustment is complete.

**Float height adjustment**

8   Turn the carburettor top cover upside down and hold the float arm clear so that it is not touching the needle valve.

9   Measure the distance between the upper face of the needle valve body washer and the end of the needle valve (Fig. 3.10). If the measured dimension is greater than specified, tighten the needle valve body to compress the washer until the dimension is correct. If the measured dimension is less than specified, renew the washer and tighten the needle valve body until the correct dimension is obtained.

**Auxiliary jet tube (Econostat) setting**

10  Measure the distance between the top of the carburettor venturi and the top of the tube (Fig. 3.11).

11  If necessary bend the tube up or down slightly to obtain the specified dimension.

**Accelerator pump delivery tube setting**

12  Measure the distance between the end of the tube and the bottom of the carburettor mounting flange. If necessary bend the tube slightly to achieve the specified setting.

13  Also make sure that the jet of fuel that flows from the tube strikes the diffuser in the position shown in Fig. 3.12. Again bend the tube slightly as required.

**Accelerator pump stroke**

14  With the carburettor top cover removed, withdraw the fuel delivery valve.

15  With the choke flap open and the throttle valve fully closed, measure the depth between the delivery valve locating face and the bottom of the piston (Fig. 3.13).

16  Turn the nut on the pump operating rod as necessary to obtain the specified dimension.

**Defuming valve adjustment**

17  With the throttle valve open in the idling position the defuming valve on the float chamber should also be open by the amount shown

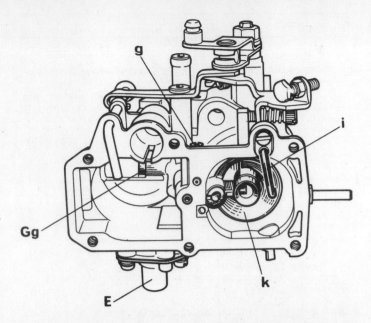

**Fig. 3.8 Zenith carburettor overhaul (Sec 17)**

E  Pneumatic enrichment device      i  Accelerator pump jet
Gg Main jet                         k  Venturi
g  Idling jet

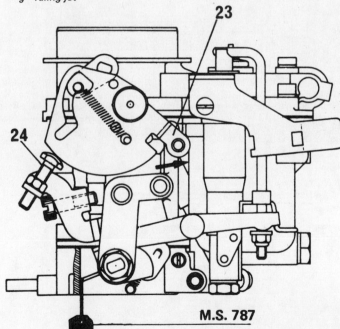

**Fig. 3.9 Initial throttle opening adjustment – Zenith carburettor (Sec 17)**

*M.S. 787 Gauge rod equal to specified initial throttle opening setting*

23  Choke operating cam         24  Fast idle adjusting
    fully open                      screw

in Fig. 3.14. With the choke flap closed, the valve should also be closed and a small amount of free play should exist between the spring blade and the lifting peg. Bend the spring blade as necessary to achieve these conditions.

**Pneumatically-controlled cold start device adjustment**

18  On certain Zenith carburettors a vacuum diaphragm is used to

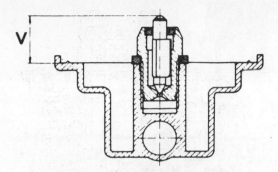

**Fig. 3.10 Float height adjustment – Zenith carburettor (Sec 17)**

*V Specified float height dimension*

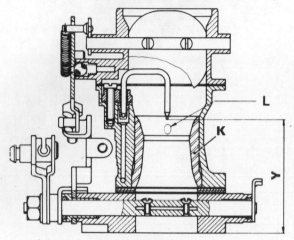

**Fig. 3.12 Accelerator pump delivery tube setting – Zenith carburettor (Sec 17)**

*Y Specified delivery tube height setting*
*Fuel should strike diffuser (K) in the zone indicated (L)*

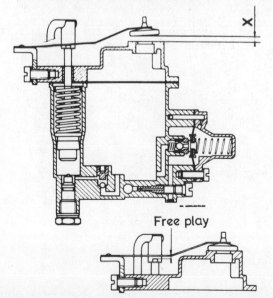

**Fig. 3.14 Defuming valve adjustment – Zenith carburettor (Sec 17)**

*X Specified defuming valve setting*
*Lower illustration indicates desired free play between blade and lifting peg with choke flap closed*

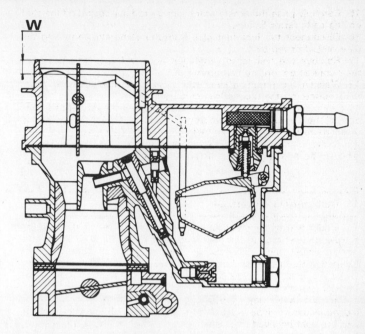

**Fig. 3.11 Auxiliary jet tube setting – Zenith carburettor (Sec 17)**

*W Specified auxiliary jet tube setting dimension*

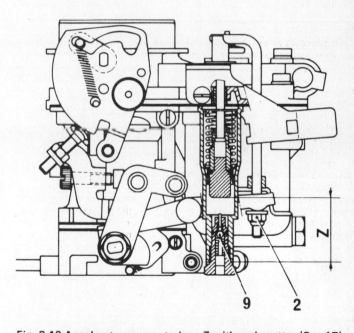

**Fig. 3.13 Accelerator pump stroke – Zenith carburettor (Sec 17)**

*2 Pump operating rod adjusting nut*
*9 Fuel delivery valve*
*Z Specified accelerator pump stroke dimension*

control the opening of the choke flap when the choke is in operation. Adjustment of the unit is as follows:

19 Move the choke linkage by hand to the fully closed position. A twist drill or suitable rod having a diameter equal to the specified choke flap opening dimension should just fit between the edge of the flap and the venturi wall (Fig. 3.15). Bend the vacuum diaphragm mounting bracket as necessary to achieve the specified dimension.

**Pneumatic part open setting**

20 Move the choke linkage by hand to the fully closed position. Push the spindle into contact with the adjusting screw on the vacuum

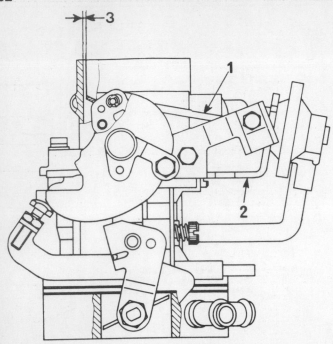

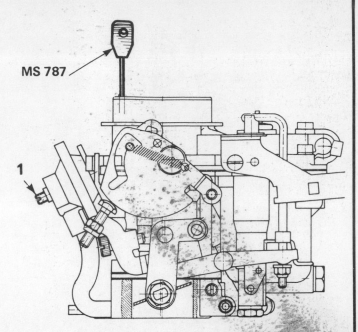

Fig. 3.15 Pneumatic cold start device choke flap opening – Zenith carburettor (Sec 17)

1   Operating rod        3   Specified choke
2   Mounting bracket         flap opening

Fig. 3.16 Pneumatic part open setting – Zenith carburettor (Sec 17)

*M.S. 787 Gauge rod equal to specified pneumatic part opening setting*
1   Vacuum unit adjusting screw

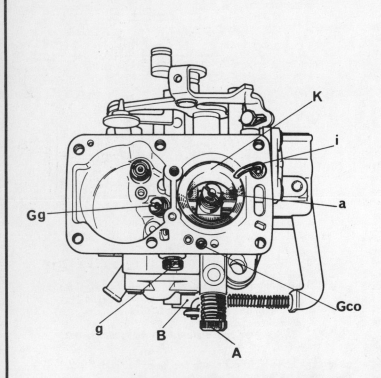

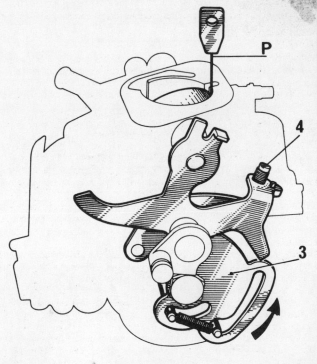

ACCELERATOR PUMP STROKE

Fig. 3.17 Solex carburettor overhaul (Sec 17)

| A | Volume control screw | Gg | Main jet |
| a | Air compensating jet | g | Idling jet |
| B | Mixture adjustment screw | i | Accelerator pump jet |
| GCo | Auxiliary jet | k | Venturi |

Fig. 3.18 Initial throttle opening adjustment – Solex carburettor (Sec 17)

3   Choke flap fully closed
4   Fast idle adjusting screw
P   Gauge rod equal to specified initial throttle opening setting

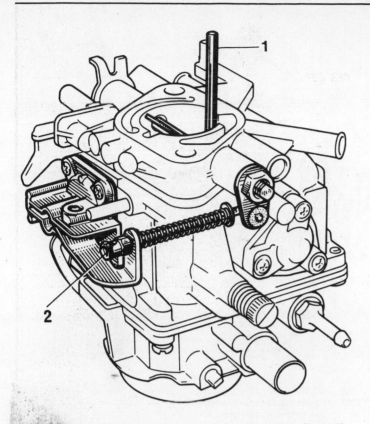

Fig. 3.19 Accelerator pump stroke – Solex carburettor (Sec 17)

1  Twist drill equal to specified accelerator pump stroke dimension
2  Connecting rod nut

diaphragm unit (Fig. 3.16). A twist drill or suitable rod having a diameter equal to the specified pneumatic part open setting should just fit between the edge of the choke flap and the venturi wall. Turn the adjusting screw on the vacuum unit if adjustment is necessary.

## Solex carburettors
**Initial throttle opening (fast idle) adjustment**
21  Turn the carburettor upside down and turn the choke linkage by hand as far as it will go, so that the choke flap is fully closed.
22  A twist drill or suitable rod having a diameter equal to the specified initial throttle opening should just slide between the throttle valve and the venturi wall (Fig. 3.18).
23  If adjustment is necessary, remove the tamperproof cap (where fitted) and turn the fast idle adjusting screw as necessary to obtain the specified setting.
**Accelerator pump stroke**
24  With the carburettor upside down, insert a twist drill or suitable rod having a diameter equal to the specified accelerator pump stroke, between the throttle valve and venturi wall (Fig. 3.19).
25  In this position the accelerator pump operating arm should be at the end of its stroke. Alter the position of the connecting rod nut as necessary if adjustment is required.
**Defuming valve adjustment**
26  With the choke flap fully open and the throttle valve against the idling stop, the defuming valve should be open by an amount equal to the specified defuming valve stroke. If adjustment is required, bend the defuming valve lever as necessary (Fig. 3.20).

## Weber carburettors
**Float level adjustment**
27  With the float chamber cover held vertically so that the float just closes the fuel needle valve without causing the valve ball to enter the housing, the dimension A in Fig. 3.22 should be as specified. Note that the cover gasket should be in position. Bend the tag of the float arm that contacts the needle valve if adjustment is necessary.
28  Allow the float to hang under its own weight and measure

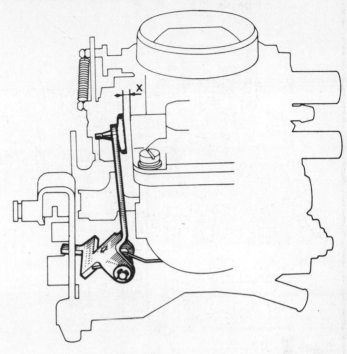

Fig. 3.20 Defuming valve adjustment – Solex carburettor (Sec 17)

*X  Specified defuming valve setting*

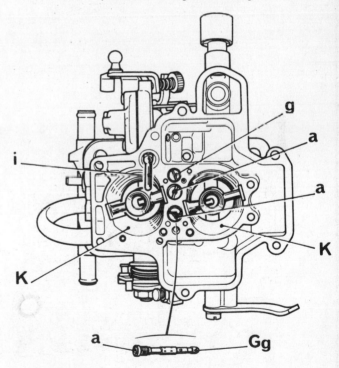

Fig. 3.21 Weber carburettor overhaul (Sec 17)

| | |
|---|---|
| a  Air compensating jets | i  Accelerator pump jet |
| Gg Main jet | k  Venturis |
| g  Idling jet | |

dimension B in Fig. 3.22. Bend the float stop tag as necessary to achieve the specified dimension.
**Initial throttle opening (fast idle) adjustment**
29  Turn the carburettor upside down and turn the choke linkage by hand as far as it will go, so that the choke flap is fully closed.
30  A twist drill or suitable rod having a diameter equal to the

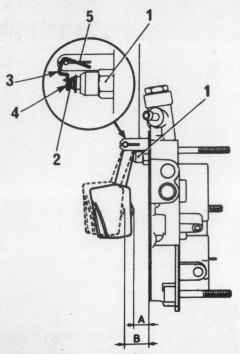

**Fig. 3.22 Float level adjustment – Weber carburettor (Sec 17)**

1 Needle valve
2 Needle valve ball
3 Float arm tag
4 Float arm tag end must remain at right-angles to the valve ball

5 Float stop tag
A Specified float height dimension
B Specified float travel dimension

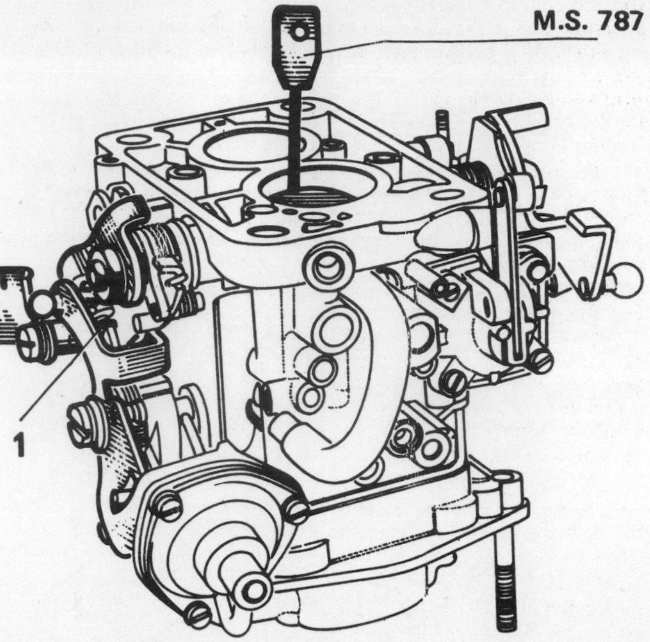

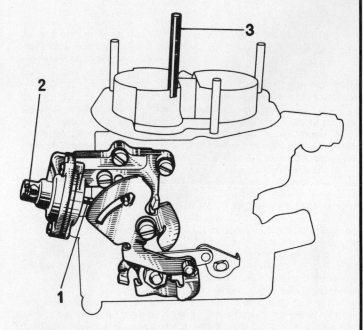

**Fig. 3.23 Initial throttle opening adjustment – Weber carburettor (Sec 17)**

*M.S. 787 Gauge rod equal to specified initial throttle opening*
1 Fast idle adjusting screw

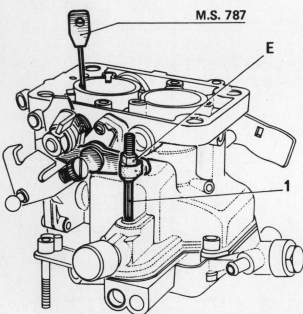

**Fig. 3.24 Defuming valve adjustment – Weber carburettor (Sec 17)**

*M.S.787 Gauge rod equal to the specified defuming valve throttle opening dimension*
1 Defuming valve rod
E Defuming valve rod nut

**Fig. 3.25 Choke flap pneumatic part opening setting – Weber carburettor (Sec 17)**

1 Operating rod
2 Adjusting screw
3 Twist drill equal to the specified choke flap pneumatic part opening setting dimension

specified initial throttle opening should just slide between the throttle valve and the venturi wall (Fig. 3.23).

31  If adjustment is required, slacken the locknut and turn the fast idle adjusting screw on the linkage as necessary. Tighten the locknut after adjustment.

**Defuming valve adjustment**

32  With the carburettor upside down and the choke flap open, press the defuming valve rod down as far as it will go (Fig. 3.24).

33  In this position a twist drill or suitable rod having a diameter equal to the specified defuming valve throttle opening should just fit between the throttle valve and venturi wall.

34  Alter the position of the nuts on the defuming valve rod as necessary to achieve the correct setting.

**Choke flap pneumatic part open setting**

35  Move the choke linkage by hand to the fully closed position and push the operating rod as far as it will go into the vacuum diaphragm unit (Fig. 3.25). In this position a twist drill or suitable rod having a diameter equal to the choke flap pneumatic part open setting should just fit between the choke flap and venturi wall.

36  If adjustment is necessary, turn the small screw in the vacuum unit cover as required.

---

**18  Inlet and exhaust manifolds – removal and refitting**

*1108 cc and 1397 cc engines*

1  Remove the carburettor, as described in Section 16.

2  Slacken the retaining clips and disconnect the brake servo vacuum hose and the crankcase ventilation hose from the inlet manifold.

3  Lift the carburettor heat shield off the manifold studs followed by the spacer block and gaskets (photos).

4  Undo the two bolts and washers securing the air cleaner support bracket and hot air outlet to the manifolds. Withdraw the bracket and outlet (photo).

5  Undo the two nuts securing the heat shield to the manifold and cylinder block at the crankshaft pulley end of the engine (photo). Undo the nuts and remove the heater hose bracket.

6  Undo the two nuts, washers and tension springs securing the exhaust front pipe to the manifold. Slide the flange plate off the manifold studs to separate the joint.

7  Undo the two nuts and washers securing the hot air stove to the manifold and withdraw the stove (photo).

8  Undo the nuts and washers securing the manifolds to the cylinder head and withdraw the assembly from the engine (photos). Recover the manifold gasket.

9  Refitting the manifold assembly is the reverse sequence to removal. Ensure that the cylinder head and manifold mating faces are clean and use a new gasket. Tighten the manifold nuts to the specified torque and tighten the front pipe flange nuts so that the springs are compressed as shown in Fig. 3.29. Refit the carburettor, as described in Section 16.

18.3A On 1108 cc and 1397 cc engines, lift off the carburettor heat shield ...

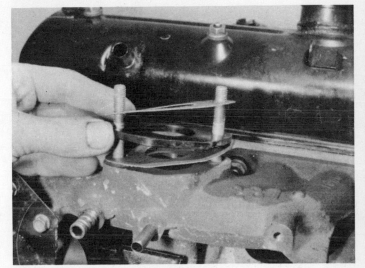

18.3B ... then remove the spacer block and gaskets

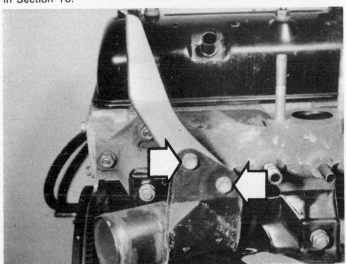

18.4 Undo the two retaining bolts (arrowed) and remove the hot air outlet and air cleaner support bracket

18.5 Undo the two nuts (arrowed) and remove the heat shield

18.7 Undo the two nuts (arrowed) and remove the stove

18.8A Undo the manifold retaining nuts and bolts (arrowed) ...

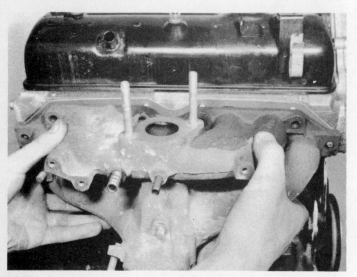

18.8B ... and withdraw the manifold from the cylinder head

*1721 cc engine*

10  Remove the carburettor, as described in Section 16.

11  Undo the retaining bolts and lift off the air cleaner support plate above the throttle linkage bellcrank.

12  Undo the nuts securing the heat shield and bellcrank mounting to the manifold and remove the shield.

13  Slacken the retaining clip and detach the brake servo vacuum hose from the manifold.

14  Undo the two nuts, washers and tension springs securing the exhaust front pipe to the manifold. Slide the flange plate off the manifold studs to separate the joint.

15  Undo the three nuts securing the hot air stove to the manifold and remove the stove.

16  Undo the nuts and bolts securing the inlet and exhaust manifolds to the cylinder head and withdraw the assembly from the engine. Recover the manifold gasket.

17  Refitting is the reverse sequence to removal. Ensure that the cylinder head and manifold mating faces are clean and use a new gasket. Tighten the manifold nuts and bolts to the specified torque and tighten the front pipe flange nuts so that the springs are compressed as shown in Fig. 3.29. Refit the carburettor, as described in Section 16.

**Fig. 3.26 Heat shield and bellcrank mounting attachments (arrowed) at the inlet manifold – 1721 cc engines (Sec 18)**

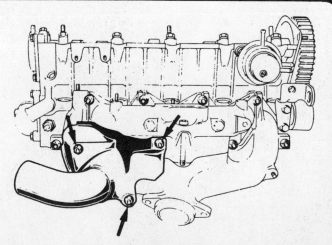

**Fig. 3.27 Hot air stove to inlet manifold attachments (arrowed) – 1721 cc engines (Sec 18)**

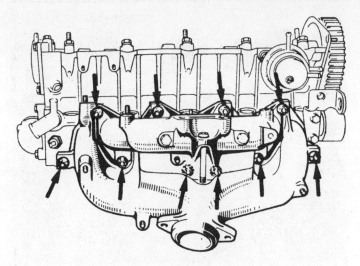

Fig. 3.28 Inlet and exhaust manifold retaining nut locations (arrowed) – 1721 cc engines (Sec 18)

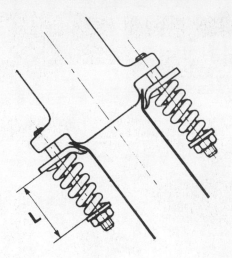

Fig. 3.29 Exhaust front pipe flange tension spring dimension (Sec 19)

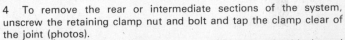

L = 43.5 mm (1.7 in)

## 19 Exhaust system – checking, removal and refitting

1   The exhaust system should be examined for leaks, damage and security at regular intervals (see Routine maintenance). To do this, apply the handbrake and allow the engine to idle. Lie down on each side of the car in turn and check the full length of the exhaust system for leaks while an assistant temporarily places a wad of cloth over the end of the tailpipe. If a leak is evident, stop the engine and use a proprietary repair kit to seal it. Holts Flexiwrap and Holts Gun Gum exhaust repair systems can be used for effective repairs to exhaust pipes and silencer boxes, including ends and bends. Holts Flexiwrap is an MOT approved permanent exhaust repair. Check the rubber mountings for deterioration and renew them if necessary.
2   To remove the system, jack up the front and/or the rear of the car and support it securely on axle stands. Alternatively drive the front or rear wheels up on ramps.
3   The system consists of three sections which can be individually removed. If the intermediate section is to be removed, it will, however, be necessary to remove the front or rear section first.

4   To remove the rear or intermediate sections of the system, unscrew the retaining clamp nut and bolt and tap the clamp clear of the joint (photos).
5   Release the mounting hooks from the rubber mounting blocks and twist the section clear (photos). If the joint is stubborn, liberally apply penetrating oil and leave it to soak. Tap the joint with a hammer and it should now be possible to twist it free. If necessary, carefully heat the joint with a blowlamp to assist removal, but shield the fuel tank, fuel pipes and underbody adequately from heat.
6   To remove the front section, undo the nuts and tension springs securing the front pipe flange to the exhaust manifold. Slide the flange off the manifold studs and separate the joint (photo). Undo the retaining clamp nut and bolt and withdraw the front section forwards, as previously described.
7   Refitting is the reverse sequence to removal. Position the joints so that there is adequate clearance between all parts of the system and the underbody, and ensure that there is equal load on all mounting blocks. When refitting the front section tighten the front pipe flange retaining nuts so that the tension springs are compressed as shown in Fig. 3.29. The springs must not become coil bound.

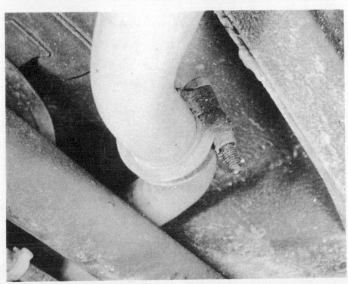

19.4A Exhaust rear section ...

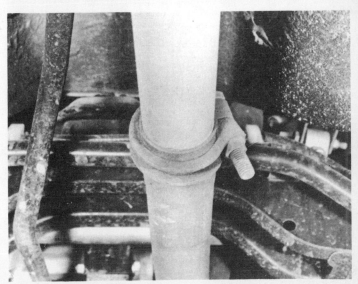

19.4B ... and intermediate section retaining clamps

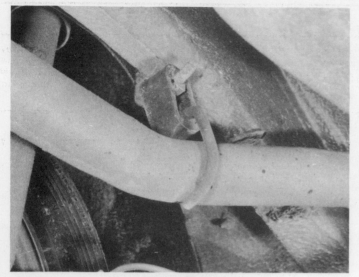

19.5A The exhaust sections are suspended from single ...

19.5B ... or double rubber mounting blocks

19.5C On certain models the spire type retaining clips (arrowed) must be released to allow the section to be removed from the mounting block

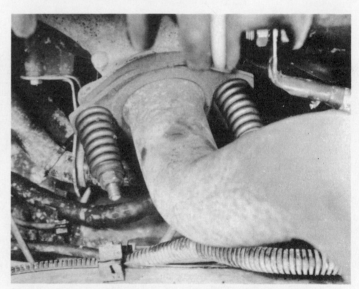

19.6 Exhaust front section-to-manifold joint with retaining nuts, washers and tension springs

## 20 Fault diagnosis – fuel and exhaust systems

*Unsatisfactory engine performance and excessive fuel consumption are not necessarily the fault of the fuel system or carburettor. In fact they more commonly occur as a result of ignition and timing faults, particularly on models equipped with conventional contact breaker point ignition systems. Before acting on the following it is necessary to check the ignition system first. Even though a fault may lie in the fuel system it will be difficult to trace unless the ignition system is correct. The faults below, therefore, assume that this has been attended to first (where appropriate).*

| Symptom | Reason(s) |
| --- | --- |
| Engine difficult to start when cold | Choke cable incorrectly adjusted<br>Choke flap not closing<br>Insufficient fuel in float chamber |
| Engine difficult to start when hot | Choke cable incorrectly adjusted<br>Air cleaner element dirty or choked<br>Insufficient fuel in float chamber<br>Float chamber flooding |
| Engine will not idle or idles erratically | Air cleaner dirty or choked<br>Choke cable incorrectly adjusted<br>Carburettor idling adjustments incorrectly set<br>Blocked carburettor jets or internal passages<br>Disconnected, perished or leaking crankcase ventilation hoses<br>Air leaks at carburettor or manifold joint faces<br>Generally worn carburettor<br>Engine internal defect |
| Engine performance poor accompanied by hesitation, missing or cutting out | Blocked carburettor jets or internal passages<br>Accelerator pump faulty or diaphragm punctured<br>Float level low<br>Fuel filter choked<br>Fuel pump faulty or delivery pressure low<br>Fuel tank vent blocked<br>Fuel pipes restricted<br>Air leaks at carburettor or manifold joint faces<br>Engine internal components worn or out of adjustment |
| Fuel consumption excessive | Choke cable incorrectly adjusted or linkage sticking<br>Air cleaner dirty or choked<br>Fuel leaking from carburettor, fuel pump, fuel tank or fuel pipes<br>Float chamber flooding |
| Excessive noise or fumes from exhaust system | Leaking pipe or manifold joints<br>Leaking, corroded or damaged silencers or pipe<br>System in contact with body or suspension due to broken mounting |

# Chapter 4 Ignition system

*For modifications, and information applicable to later models, see Supplement at end of manual*

## Contents

## Specifications

*Part 1: Conventional ignition system*
### System type
Application ........................................................................ Battery, coil, contact breaker distributor
1108 cc engines

### Distributor
Type ................................................................................ Ducellier
Rotor arm rotation ............................................................ Clockwise
Firing order ...................................................................... 1-3-4-2 (No 1 cylinder nearest flywheel)
Contact breaker points gap ............................................... 0.4 mm (0.016 in)
Dwell angle ...................................................................... 54 to 60°

### Ignition timing
Static or dynamic at idling speed with vacuum pipe disconnected ...... 9 to 11° BTDC

### Spark plugs
Type ................................................................................ Champion N9YCC or N281YC
Electrode gap ................................................................... 0.75 to 0.85 mm (0.030 to 0.034 in)

### HT leads ............................................................................ Champion CLS 1, boxed set

### Torque wrench settings
|  | Nm | lbf ft |
|---|---|---|
| Spark plugs | 25 | 18 |

*Part 2: Electronic ignition system*
### System type
Application ........................................................................ Breakerless with electronic computer module and allied components
1397 cc and 1721 cc engines

### Distributor
Rotor arm rotation:
    1397 cc engine ......................................................... Clockwise
    1721 cc engine ......................................................... Anti-clockwise
Firing order ...................................................................... 1-3-4-2 (No 1 cylinder nearest flywheel)

## Ignition timing*

*At engine idling speed with vacuum pipe disconnected*
Computer module serial number:

| | |
|---|---|
| RE007 ............................................................................ | 3 to 5° BTDC |
| RE008 ............................................................................ | 1° BTDC to 1° ATDC |
| RE025 ............................................................................ | 7 to 9° BTDC |
| RE026 ............................................................................ | 5 to 7° BTDC |
| RE042 ............................................................................ | 7 to 9° BTDC |
| RE227 ............................................................................ | 3 to 5° BTDC |

*Non-adjustable, for checking purposes only — see text*

## Spark plugs
Type ................................................................................     Champion N9YCC or N281YC (1397 cc), Champion N7YCC or N279YC (1721 cc)

Electrode gap ..................................................................     0.75 mm to 0.85 mm (0.030 to 0.034 in)

## Torque wrench settings

| | Nm | lbf ft |
|---|---|---|
| Spark plugs ...................................................... | 25 | 18 |

## PART 1: CONVENTIONAL IGNITION SYSTEM

### 1 General description

In order that the engine may run correctly it is necessary for an electrical spark to ignite the fuel/air mixture in the combustion chamber at exactly the right moment in relation to engine speed and load.

Basically the ignition system functions as follows: Low tension voltage from the battery is fed to the ignition coil where it is converted into high tension voltage. The high tension voltage is powerful enough to jump the spark plug gap in the cylinder many times a second under high compression pressure, providing that the ignition system is in good working order and that all adjustments are correct.

The ignition system consists of two individual circuits known as the low tension (LT) circuit and high tension (HT) circuit.

The low tension circuit (sometimes known as the primary circuit) consists of the battery, lead to ignition switch, lead to the low tension or primary coil windings and the lead from the low tension coil windings to the contact breaker points and condenser in the distributor.

The high tension circuit (sometimes known as the secondary circuit) consists of the high tension or secondary coil winding, the heavily insulated ignition lead from the centre of the coil to the centre of the distributor cap, the rotor arm, the spark plug leads and the spark plugs.

The complete ignition system operation is as follows: Low tension voltage from the battery is changed within the ignition coil to high tension voltage by the opening and closing of the contact breaker points in the low tension circuit. High tension voltage is then fed, via a contact in the centre of the distributor cap, to the rotor arm of the distributor. The rotor arm revolves inside the distributor cap, and each time it comes in line with one of the four metal segments in the cap, the opening and closing of the contact breaker points causes the high tension voltage to build up, jump the gap from the rotor arm to the appropriate metal segment and so, via the spark plug lead, to the spark plug where it finally jumps the gap between the two spark plug electrodes, one being earthed.

The ignition timing is advanced and retarded automatically to ensure the spark occurs at just the right instant for the particular load at the prevailing engine speed.

The ignition advance is controlled both mechanically and by a vacuum-operated system. The mechanical governor mechanism consists of two weights which move out under centrifugal force from the central distributor shaft as the engine speed rises. As they move outwards they rotate the cam relative to the distributor shaft, and so advance the spark. The weights are held in position by two light springs, and it is the tension of these springs which is largely responsible for correct spark advancement.

The vacuum control consists of a diaphragm, one side of which is connected, via a small bore tube, to the carburettor and the other side to the contact breaker plate. Depression in the induction manifold and

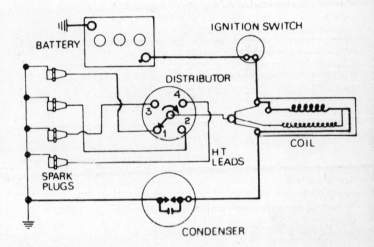

**Fig. 4.1 Diagrammatic representation of the ignition circuit (Sec 1)**

carburettor, which varies with engine speed and throttle opening, causes the diaphragm to move so rotating the contact breaker plate and advancing or retarding the spark.

### 2 Maintenance and inspection

1 At the intervals given in Routine maintenance at the beginning of this manual, the following operations should be carried out to the ignition system components.

2 Check the condition of the distributor cap and contact breaker points, as described in Section 3. Renew the points if necessary using the procedure contained in Section 4.

3 With the distributor cap removed, lift off the rotor arm and the plastic shield. Carefully apply two drops of engine oil to the felt pad in the centre of the cam spindle. Also lubricate the centrifugal advance mechanism by applying two or three drops of oil through one of the holes in the distributor baseplate. Wipe away any excess oil and refit the plastic shield, rotor arm and distributor cap.

4 Remove, clean and reset the spark plugs using the procedure described in Section 10. Preferably using a stroboscopic timing light, check and, if necessary, reset the ignition timing, as described in Section 8. Finally wipe off all traces of dirt, oil and grease from the HT and LT leads and all wiring and also check the security of all cables and connectors.

3.1 With the distributor cap removed, lift off the rotor arm and plastic shield to gain access to the contact breaker points

3.6 Measure the points gap with a feeler gauge and adjust if necessary by turning nut (A)

## 3  Contact breaker points – adjustment

1   Release the two spring clips and lift off the distributor cap. Pull the rotor arm off the shaft and remove the plastic shield (photo).
2   Clean the distributor cap on the inside and outside with a clean dry cloth and examine the four HT lead segments inside the cap. Scrape away any deposits that may have built up on the segments, using a knife or small screwdriver. If the segments appear badly burned or pitted, renew the cap.
3   Push in the carbon brush located in the centre of the cap, and ensure that it moves freely and stands proud by at least 3 mm (0.1 in). Renew the cap if the brush is worn or if there are signs of burning on the brush holder.
4   Gently prise the contact breaker points open to examine the condition of their faces. If they are rough and pitted, or dirty, they should be renewed, as described in Section 4.
5   Assuming that the points are in a satisfactory condition, or that they have been renewed, the gap between the two faces should be measured using feeler gauges. To do this turn the engine over using a socket or spanner on the crankshaft pulley bolt, until the heel of the contact breaker arm is on the peak of one of the four cam lobes.
6   With the points fully open, a feeler gauge equal to the contact breaker points gap, as given in the Specifications, should now just fit between the contact faces (photo).
7   If the gap is too large or too small turn the adjusting nut on the side of the distributor body using a small spanner until the specified gap is obtained.
8   With the points correctly adjusted, refit the plastic shield, rotor arm and distributor cap.
9   If a dwell meter is available, a far more accurate method of setting the contact breaker points is by measuring and setting the distributor dwell angle.
10  The dwell angle is the number of degrees of distributor shaft rotation during which the contact breaker points are closed, ie the period from when the points close after being opened by one cam lobe until they are opened again by the next cam lobe. The advantages of setting the points by this method are that any wear of the distributor shaft or cam lobes is taken into account, and also the inaccuracies of using a feeler gauge are eliminated.
11  To check and adjust the dwell angle connect one lead of the meter to the ignition coil + terminal and the other lead to the coil - terminal, or in accordance with the maker's instructions.
12  Start the engine, allow it to idle and observe the reading on the dwell meter scale. If the dwell angle is not as specified, turn the adjusting nut on the side of the distributor body as necessary to obtain the correct setting. **Note:** Due to machining tolerances, or wear in the distributor shaft or bushes, it is not uncommon for a contact breaker points gap correctly set with feeler gauges, to give a dwell angle

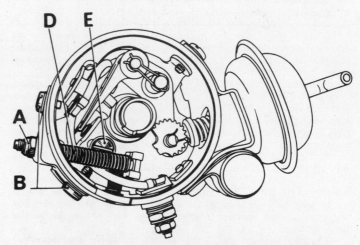

Fig. 4.2 Conventional ignition distributor components
(Secs 3 and 4)

A   Contact breaker points
    adjusting nut
B   Baseplate retaining
    screws
D   Adjustment rod and spring
E   Fixed contact retaining
    screw

outside the specified tolerance. If this is the case the dwell angle shoud be regarded as the preferred setting.
13  After completing the adjustment, switch off the engine and disconnect the dwell meter.

## 4  Contact breaker points – removal and refitting

1   Release the two spring clips and lift off the distributor cap. Pull the rotor arm off the shaft and remove the plastic shield.
2   Undo the contact breaker adjusting nut on the side of the distributor body and then unscrew the two baseplate retaining screws (photo). Lift off the support bracket.
3   Disengage the end of the adjustment rod from the fixed contact and slide the rod and spring out of the distributor body (photo).
4   Prise out the small plug and then remove the retaining clip, noting that the hole in the clip is uppermost (photos).
5   Slacken the LT terminal nut and detach the lead (photo).
6   Remove the spring retaining clip from the top of the moving contact pivot post and take off the fibre insulating washer (photo).
7   Ease the spring blade away from its nylon support and lift the moving contact upwards and off the pivot post (photo).

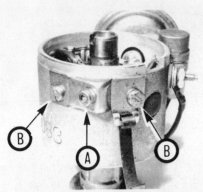

4.2 To remove the contact breaker points, undo the adjusting nut (A), the two screws (B) and lift off the support bracket

4.3 Disengage the adjustment rod from the fixed contact and withdraw the rod and spring

4.4A Prise out the small plastic plug ...

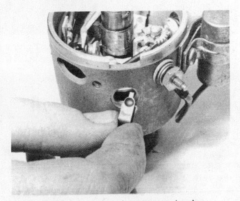

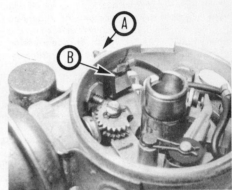

4.4B ... to gain access to the retaining clip (arrowed) ...

4.4C ... which can then be removed using pliers. Note the fitted position of the clip

4.5 Slacken the LT terminal nut (A) and detach the lead (B) from the connector

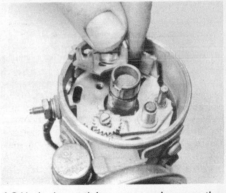

4.6 Remove the spring retaining clip and fibre washer from the pivot post

4.7 Ease the spring blade off its support and withdraw the moving contact from the pivot post

4.8 Undo the retaining screw and remove the fixed contact

8   Undo the retaining screw and remove the fixed contact from the baseplate (photo).
9   Examine the faces of the breaker points and if they are rough, pitted or dirty they should be renewed.
10  Refitting the contact breaker points is the reverse sequence to removal, but clean the point faces with methylated spirit, to ensure complete freedom from greasy deposits.
11  After refitting adjust the contact breaker points gap, as described in Section 3.

## 5   Condenser – testing, removal and refitting

1   The purpose of the condenser, which is located externally on the side of the distributor body, is to ensure that, when the contact breaker points open, there is no sparking across them, which would cause

wear of their faces and prevent the rapid collapse of the magnetic field in the coil. This would cause a reduction in coil HT voltage and ultimately lead to engine misfire.
2   If the engine becomes very difficult to start, or begins to miss after several miles of running, and the contact breaker points show signs of excessive burning, the condition of the condenser must be suspect. A further test can be made by separating the points by hand with the ignition switched on. If this is accompanied by a strong bright flash, it is indicative that the condenser has failed.
3   Without special test equipment, the only sure way to diagnose condenser trouble is to substitute a suspect unit with a new one and note if there is any improvement.
4   To remove the condenser, unscrew the nut at the LT terminal post and slip off the lead. Undo the condenser retaining screw and remove the component from the side of the distributor body.
5   Refitting is the reverse sequence to removal.

## 6    Distributor – removal and refitting

1    Mark the spark plug HT leads to aid refitting and pull them off the ends of the plugs. Release the distributor cap retaining clips and place the cap and leads to one side.
2    Remove No 1 spark plug (nearest the flywheel end of the engine).
3    Place a finger over the plug hole and turn the engine in the normal direction of rotation (clockwise from the crankshaft pulley end) until pressure is felt in No 1 cylinder. This indicates that the piston is commencing its compression stroke. The engine can be turned with a socket or spanner on the crankshaft pulley bolt.
4    Continue turning the engine until the mark on the flywheel is aligned with the TDC notch on the clutch bellhousing (photo).
5    Using a dab of paint or a small file, make a reference mark between the distributor base and the cylinder block.
6    Detach the vacuum advance pipe and disconnect the LT lead at the wiring connector. Release the wiring loom from the support clip on the distributor body.
7    Unscrew the distributor clamp retaining nut and lift off the clamp. Withdraw the distributor from the engine and recover the seal.
8    To refit the distributor, first check that the engine is still at the TDC position with No 1 cylinder on compression. If the engine has been turned while the distributor was removed return it to the correct position, as previously described.
9    With the rotor arm pointing directly away from the engine and the vacuum unit at approximately the 5 o'clock position, slide the distributor into the cylinder block and turn the rotor arm slightly until the offset peg on the distributor drive dog positively engages with the drivegear.
10    Align the previously made reference marks or, if a new distributor is being fitted, position the distributor body so that the rotor arm points toward the No 1 spark plug HT lead segment in the cap. Hold the distributor in this position, refit the clamp and secure with the retaining nut.
11    Reconnect the LT lead at the connector, refit the vacuum advance pipe and secure the wiring loom in the support clip.
12    Before refitting the distributor cap, leads and spark plug, refer to Section 8 and adjust the ignition timing as necessary.

## 7    Distributor – overhaul

1    Renewal of the contact breaker assembly, condenser, rotor and distributor cap should be regarded as the limit of overhaul on these units, as few other spares are available separately. It is possible to renew the vacuum unit, but this must then be set up to suit the advance curve of the engine, by adjustment of the serrated cam on the baseplate (photo), and is best left to a dealer or automotive electrician.
2    When the distributor has seen extended service and the shaft, bushes and centrifugal mechanism become worn it is advisable to purchase a new distributor.

## 8    Ignition timing – adjustment

1    In order that the engine can run efficiently, it is necessary for a spark to occur at the spark plug and ignite the fuel/air mixture at the instant just before the piston on the compression stroke reaches the top of its travel. The precise instant at which the spark occurs is determined by the ignition timing, and this is quoted in degrees before top-dead-centre (BTDC).
2    The timing may be checked and adjusted in one of two ways: either by using a test bulb to obtain a static setting with the engine stationary or by using a stroboscopic timing light to obtain a dynamic setting with the engine running.
3    Before checking or adjusting the ignition timing, make sure that the contact breaker points are in good condition and correctly adjusted, as described in Section 3.

### Static setting

4    Refer to the Specifications at the beginning of this Chapter and note the specified setting for static ignition timing. This value will also be found stamped on a clip fastened to one of the HT leads (photo).
5    Pull off the HT lead and remove No 1 spark plug (nearest the flywheel end of the engine).

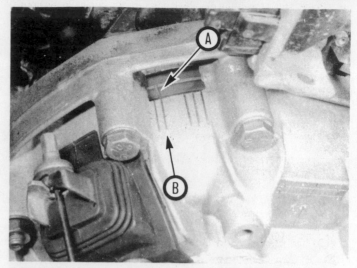

6.4 With Nos 1 and 4 cylinders at TDC the mark on the flywheel (A) will be aligned with the notch (B) in the bellhousing

7.1 Distributor vacuum unit serrated cam adjuster (arrowed)

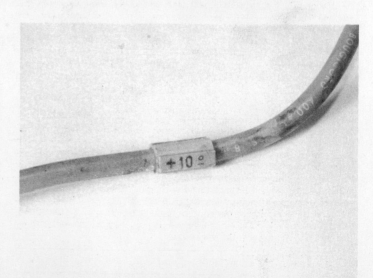

8.4 Ignition timing static setting is stamped on a clip fastened to one of the HT leads

6   Place a finger over the plug hole and turn the engine in the normal direction of rotation (clockwise from the crankshaft pulley end) until pressure is felt in No 1 cylinder. This indicates that the piston is commencing its compression stroke. The engine can be turned using a socket or spanner on the crankshaft pulley bolt.

7   Continue turning the engine until the mark on the flywheel is aligned with the appropriate notch on the clutch bellhousing (Fig. 4.3).

8   Remove the distributor cap and check that the rotor arm is pointing toward the No 1 spark plug HT lead segment in the cap.

9   Connect a 12 volt test lamp and leads between a good earth and the LT terminal nut on the side of the distributor body.

10  Slacken the distributor clamp retaining nut and then switch on the ignition.

11  If the test lamp is on, turn the distributor slightly clockwise until the lamp goes out.

12  Now turn the distributor anti-clockwise until the test lamp just lights up, hold the distributor in this position and tighten the clamp retaining nut.

13  Test the setting by turning the engine two complete revolutions and observing when the lamp lights up in relation to the timing marks.

14  Switch off the ignition and remove the test lamp. Refit No 1 spark plug, the distributor cap and HT lead.

## Dynamic setting

15  Refer to the Specifications at the beginning of this Chapter and note the specified setting for dynamic ignition timing. This initial value will also be found stamped on a clip fastened to one of the HT leads. To make subsequent operations easier it is advisable to highlight the mark on the flywheel and the appropriate notch on the clutch bellhousing with white paint or chalk (Fig. 4.3).

16  Connect the timing light in accordance with the manufacturer's instructions (usually interposed between the end of No 1 spark plug HT lead and No 1 spark plug terminal).

17  Disconnect the vacuum advance pipe from the distributor vacuum unit and plug its end.

18  Start the engine and leave it idling at the specified idling speed (refer to Specifications, Chapter 3).

19  Point the timing light at the timing marks and they should appear to be stationary with the mark on the flywheel aligned with the appropriate notch on the clutch bellhousing.

20  If adjustment is necessary (ie the flywheel mark does not line up with the appropriate notch) slacken the distributor clamp retaining nut and turn the distributor body anti-clockwise to advance the timing, and clockwise to retard it. Tighten the clamp nut when the setting is correct.

21  Gradually increase the engine speed while still pointing the timing light at the marks. The mark on the flywheel should appear to advance further, indicating that the distributor centrifugal advance mechanism is functioning. If the mark remains stationary or moves in a jerky, erratic fashion, the advance mechanism must be suspect.

22  Reconnect the vacuum pipe to the distributor and check that the advance alters when the pipe is connected. If not, the vacuum unit on the distributor may be faulty.

23  After completing the checks and adjustments, switch off the engine and disconnect the timing light.

## 9   Diagnostic socket and TDC sensor – general

1   A diagnostic socket, used in conjunction with special test equipment to check the function of the complete ignition system, is mounted on the left-hand side of the engine, adjacent to the TDC sensor. Although the related test equipment is not normally available to the home mechanic it is useful to know of the existence and purpose of these components.

2   When connected to the appropriate equipment the socket enables the following checks to be carried out:

*LT circuit voltage*
*Ignition timing*
*Centrifugal and vacuum advance curves*
*Dwell angle*
*Engine rpm*

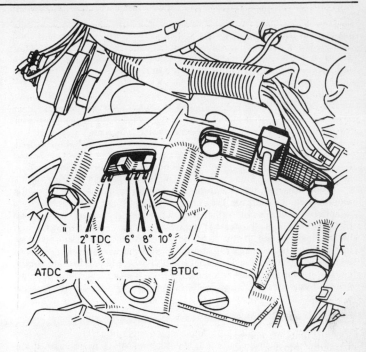

Fig. 4.3 Timing mark positions on clutch bellhousing (Sec 8)

3   The six pins in the socket are connected to various engine earthing points, to the supply voltage terminal of the ignition coil and to the TDC sensor. The sensor itself is mounted on a bracket attached to the clutch bellhousing. The probe of the sensor is positioned directly in line with the periphery of the flywheel and is used to check the ignition timing and advance curves.

## 10  Spark plugs and HT leads – general

1   The correct functioning of the spark plugs is vital for the correct running and efficiency of the engine. It is essential that the plugs fitted are appropriate for the engine, and the suitable type is specified at the beginning of this chapter. If this type is used and the engine is in good condition, the spark plugs should not need attention between scheduled replacement intervals. Spark plug cleaning is rarely necessary and should not be attempted unless specialised equipment is available as damage can easily be caused to the firing ends.

2   To remove the plugs, first mark the HT leads to ensure correct refitment, and then pull them off the plugs. Using a spark plug spanner, or suitable deep socket and extension bar, unscrew the plugs and remove them from the engine.

3   The condition of the spark plugs will also tell much about the overall condition of the engine.

4   If the insulator nose of the spark plug is clean and white, with no deposits, this is indicative of a weak mixture, or too hot a plug. (A hot plug transfers heat away from the electrode slowly – a cold plug transfers it away quickly).

5   If the tip and insulator nose are covered with hard black-looking deposits, then this is indicative that the mixture is too rich. Should the plug be black and oily, then it is likely that the engine is fairly worn, as well as the mixture being too rich.

6   If the insulator nose is covered with light tan to greyish brown deposits, then the mixture is correct and it is likely that the engine is in good condition.

7   The spark plug gap is of considerable importance as, if it is too large or too small, the size of spark and its efficiency will be seriously impaired. The spark plug gap should be set to the figure given in the Specifications at the beginning of this Chapter.

8   To set it, measure the gap with a feeler gauge, and then bend open, or close, the *outer* plug electrode until the correct gap is achieved. The centre electrode should **never** be bent as this may crack the insulation and cause plug failure, if nothing worse.

9   To fit the plugs, screw them in by hand initially and then fully tighten to the specified torque. If a torque wrench is not available, tighten the plugs until initial resistance is felt as the sealing washer contacts its seat and then tighten by a further eighth of a turn. Refit the HT leads in the correct order, ensuring that they are a tight fit over the plug ends. Periodically wipe the leads clean to reduce the risk of HT leakage by arcing.

## 11  Fault diagnosis – conventional ignition system

By far the majority of breakdown and running troubles are caused by faults in the ignition system, either in the low tension or high tension circuits.

There are two main symptoms indicating ignition faults. Either the engine will not start or fire, or the engine is difficult to start and misfires. If it is a regular misfire, ie the engine is running on only two or three cylinders, the fault is almost sure to be in the secondary or high tension circuit. If the misfiring is intermittent, the fault could be in either the high or low tension circuits. If the car stops suddenly, or will not start at all, it is likely that the fault is in the low tension circuit. Loss of power and overheating, apart from faulty carburation settings, are normally due to faults in the distributor or to incorrect ignition timing.

### Engine fails to start

1   If the engine fails to start and the car was running normally when it was last used, first check that there is fuel in the petrol tank. If the engine turns over normally on the starter motor and the battery is evidently well charged, then the fault may be in either the high or low tension circuits. First check the HT circuit. If the battery is known to be fully charged, the ignition light comes on, and the starter motor fails to turn the engine, check the tightness of the leads on the battery terminals and also the secureness of the earth lead to its connection to the body. It is quite common for the leads to have worked loose, even if they look and feel secure. If one of the battery terminal posts gets very hot when trying to work the starter motor this is a sure indication of a faulty connection to that terminal.

2   One of the commonest reasons for bad starting is wet or damp spark plug leads and distributor. Remove the distributor cap. If condensation is visible internally, dry the cap with a rag and also wipe over the leads. To disperse moisture, Holts Wet Start can be very effective, Holts Damp Start should be used for providing a sealing coat to exclude moisture from the ignition system. In extreme difficulty, Holts Cold Start will help to start a car when only a very poor spark occurs. Refit the cap.

3   If the engine still fails to start, check that the current is reaching the plugs, by disconnecting each plug lead in turn at the spark plug end, and holding the end of the cable about 5 mm (0.2 in) away from the cylinder block. Spin the engine on the starter motor.

4   Sparking between the end of the cable and the block should be fairly strong with a good, regular blue spark. (Hold the lead with rubber to avoid electric shocks). If current is reaching the plugs then remove them and regap or renew them. The engine should now start.

5   If there is no spark at the plug leads, take off the HT lead from the centre of the distributor cap and hold it to the block as before. Spin the engine on the starter once more. A rapid succession of blue sparks between the end of the lead and the block indicates that the coil is in order and that the distributor cap is cracked, the rotor arm faulty, or the carbon brush in the top of the distributor cap is not making good contact with the rotor arm.

6   If there are no sparks from the end of the lead from the coil check the connections at the coil end of the lead. If it is in order start checking the low tension circuit.

7   Use a 12V voltmeter or a 12V bulb and two lengths of wire. With the ignition switched on and the points open, test between the low tension wire to the coil positive (+) terminal and earth. No reading indicates a break in the supply from the ignition switch. Check the connections at the switch to see if any are loose. Refit them and the engine should run. A reading shows a faulty coil or condenser, or broken lead between the coil and the distributor.

8   Take the condenser wire off the points assembly, and with the points open test between the moving point and earth. If there is now a reading then the fault is in the condenser. Fit a new one, as described in this Chapter, Section 5, and the fault should clear.

9   With no reading from the moving point to earth, take a reading between earth and the coil negative (-) terminal. A reading here shows a broken wire which will need to be renewed between the coil and distributor. No reading confirms that the coil has failed and must be renewed, after which the engine will run once more. Remember to refit the condenser wire to the points assembly. For these tests it is sufficient to separate the points with a piece of dry paper while testing with the points open.

### Engine misfires

10  If the engine misfires regularly, run it at a fast idling speed. Pull off each of the plug caps in turn and listen to the note of the engine. Hold the plug cap in a dry cloth or with a rubber glove as additional protection against a shock from the HT supply.

11  No difference in engine running will be noticed when the lead from the defective circuit is removed. Removing the lead from one of the good cylinders will accentuate the misfire.

12  Remove the plug lead from the end of the defective plug and hold it about 5 mm (0.2 in) away from the block. Restart the engine. If the sparking is fairly strong and regular the fault must lie in the spark plug.

13  The plug may be loose, the insulation may be cracked, or the electrodes may have burnt away, giving too wide a gap for the spark to jump. Worse still, one of the electrodes may have broken off.

14  If there is no spark at the end of the plug lead, or if it is weak and intermittent, check the ignition lead from the distributor to the plug. If the insulation is cracked or perished, renew the lead. Check the connections at the distributor cap.

15  If there is still no spark, examine the distributor cap carefully for tracking. This can be recognised by a very thin black line running between two or more electrodes, or between an electrode and some other part of the distributor. These lines are paths which now conduct electricity across the cap, thus letting it run to earth. The only answer is a new distributor cap.

16  Apart from the ignition timing being incorrect, other causes of misfiring have already been dealt with under the section dealing with the failure of the engine to start. To recap – these are that:

(a)   The coil may be faulty giving an intermittent misfire
(b)   There may be a damaged wire or loose connection in the low tension circuit
(c)   The condenser may be short circuiting
(d)   There may be a mechanical fault in the distributor (broken driving spindle or contact breaker spring)

17  If the ignition timing is too far retarded, it should be noted that the engine will tend to overheat, and there will be quite a noticeable drop in power. If the engine is overheating and the power is down, and the ignition timing is correct, then the carburettor should be checked, as it is likely that this is where the fault lies.

# PART 2: ELECTRONIC IGNITION SYSTEM

## 12  General description

The electronic ignition system operates on an advanced principle whereby the main functions of the distributor are replaced by a computer module.

The system consists of three main components, namely the computer module which incorporates an ignition coil and a vacuum advance unit, the distributor which directs the HT voltage received from the coil to the appropriate spark plug, and an angular position sensor which determines the position and speed of the crankshaft by sensing special magnetic segments in the flywheel.

The computer module receives information on crankshaft position relative to TDC and BDC and also engine speed from the angular position sensor, and receives information on engine load from the vacuum advance unit. From these constantly changing variables, the computer calculates the precise instant at which HT voltage should be supplied and triggers the coil accordingly. The voltage then passes from the coil to the appropriate spark plug, via the distributor in the conventional way. The function of the centrifugal and vacuum advance mechanisms as well as the contact breaker points normally associated with a distributor, are all catered for by the computer module, so that the sole purpose of the distributor is to direct the HT voltage from the coil to the appropriate spark plug.

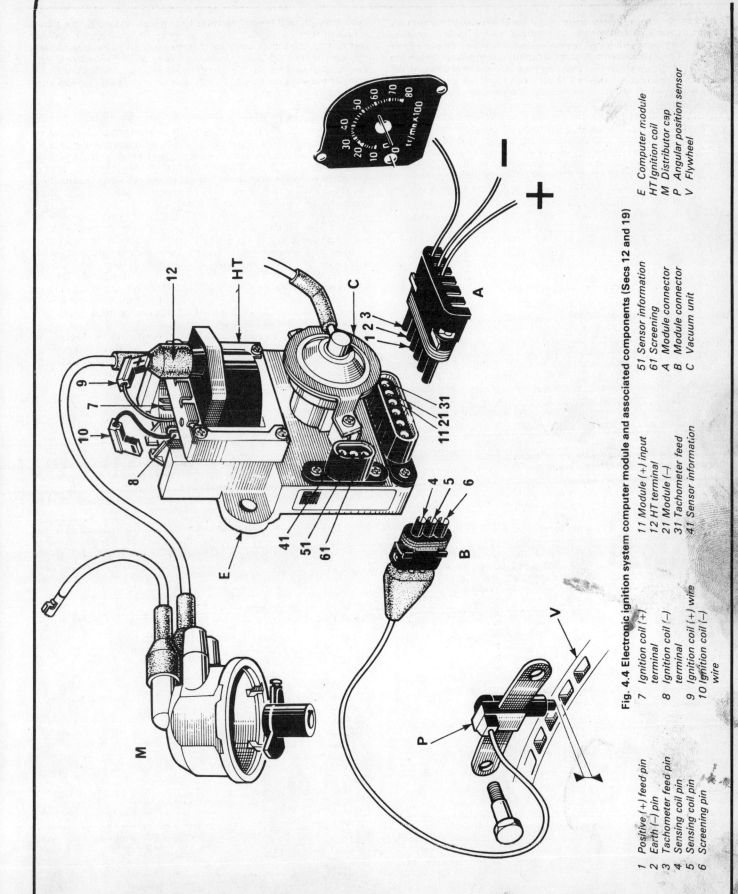

Fig. 4.4 Electronic ignition system computer module and associated components (Secs 12 and 19)

1  Positive (+) feed pin
2  Earth (−) pin
3  Tachometer feed pin
4  Sensing coil pin
5  Sensing coil pin
6  Screening pin

7  Ignition coil (+)
   terminal
8  Ignition coil (−)
   terminal
9  Ignition coil (+) wire
10 Ignition coil (−)
   wire

11 Module (+) input
12 HT terminal
21 Module (−)
31 Tachometer feed
41 Sensor information

51 Sensor information
61 Screening
A  Module connector
B  Module connector
C  Vacuum unit

E  Computer module
HT Ignition coil
M  Distributor cap
P  Angular position sensor
V  Flywheel

## 13 Electronic ignition system – precautions

*Due to the sophisticated nature of the electronic ignition system the following precautions must be observed to prevent damage to the components and reduce the risk of personal injury.*

1   Ensure that the ignition is switched off before disconnecting any of the ignition wiring.
2   Ensure that the ignition is switched off before connecting or disconnecting any ignition test equipment such as a timing light.
3   Do not connect a suppression condenser or test lamp to the ignition coil negative terminal.
4   Do not connect any test appliance or stroboscopic timing light requiring a 12 volt supply to the ignition coil positive terminal.
5   Do not allow an HT lead to short out or spark against the computer module body.

## 14 Maintenance and inspection

1   The only components of the electronic ignition system which require periodic maintenance are the distributor cap, HT leads and spark plugs. These should be treated in the same way as on a conventional system and reference should be made to Section 2 and other applicable Sections of Part 1.
2   On this system dwell angle and ignition timing are a function of the computer module and there is no provision for adjustment. It is possible to check the ignition timing using a stroboscopic timing light, but this should only be necessary as part of a fault finding procedure, as any deviation from the specified setting would indicate a possible fault in the computer module. If it is necessary to check the timing, it will be noted that the initial advance figures given in the Specifications relate to the serial number of the computer module. This number will be found stamped on a label attached to the side of the module body.

## 15 Distributor – removal and refitting

### 1397 cc engines

1   Undo the two screws securing the distributor cap to the distributor body, lift off the cap and move it to one side (photo).
2   Release the engine wiring harness from the clip at the base of the distributor.
3   Undo the bolt securing the distributor to the cylinder block, withdraw the distributor from its location and recover the seal (photo).
4   To refit the distributor, place it in position in the cylinder block and turn the rotor arm until the drive dog at the base of the distributor shaft positively engages with the driveshaft.
5   Align the hole at the base of the distributor with that in the block and refit the retaining bolt.
6   Refit the distributor cap and locate the wiring harness in the clip.

### 1721 cc engines

7   The 1721 cc engine does not have a distributor, as such, but instead the rotor arm is bonded to the end of the camshaft and the distributor cap fitted over it and secured directly to the cylinder head with three screws.
8   To remove the cap, undo the three screws (photo) and place it to one side.
9   It will be necessary to break the rotor arm using pliers if removal is necessary.
10  When refitting a new rotor arm it must be retained in position using Loctite FRENBLOC compound or equivalent.

## 16 Computer module – removal and refitting

1   Disconnect the battery negative terminal.
2   Disconnect the HT lead from the ignition coil on the front of the module.
3   Detach the vacuum pipe from the vacuum advance unit and release the pipe from its support clip.
4   Disconnect the two multi-plug wiring connectors from the front of the module.

15.1 Undo the two screws and lift off the distributor cap

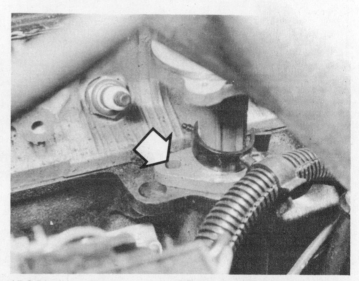

15.3 Distributor flange-to-cylinder block retaining bolt location (arrowed) on 1397 cc engine

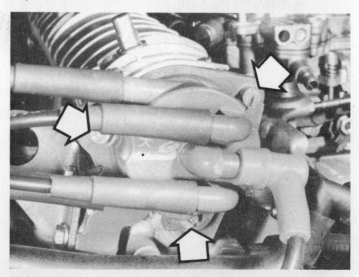

15.8 Distributor cap retaining screws (arrowed) on 1721 cc engine

16.5A Computer module attachments
A  HT lead at ignition coil    C  Wiring multi-plug connectors
B  Vacuum pipe                 D  Retaining nuts

16.5B On models equipped with the 1721 cc engine the computer module is located on the left-hand inner wing panel

5  Undo the two nuts securing the unit to the engine compartment bulkhead or inner wing panel and remove it from the car (photos).
6  If required, the ignition coil may be removed after disconnecting the two wires and undoing the four retaining screws. Do not, however, attempt to remove the vacuum unit, as it is attached internally by a very fine wire which will break if the unit is removed.
7  Refitting the ignition coil to the module, and the module to the car is the reverse sequence to removal.

2  Disconnect the smaller of the two wiring multi-plugs from the front of the computer module.
3  Undo and remove the two bolts securing the sensor to the top of the clutch bellhousing and lift off the unit. Note that the two retaining bolts are of the shouldered type and must not be replaced with ordinary bolts.
4  Refitting is the reverse sequence to removal.

## 17  Angular position sensor – removal and refitting

1  Disconnect the battery negative terminal.

## 18  Spark plugs and HT leads

Refer to Section 10.

## 19  Fault diagnosis – electronic ignition system

Problems associated with the electronic ignition system can usually be grouped into one of two areas, those caused by the more conventional HT side of the system, such as the spark plugs, HT leads, rotor arm and distributor cap, and those caused by the LT circuitry including the computer module and its related components.

It is recommended that the checks described in Section 11 paragraphs 1 to 6 under the heading 'Engine fails to start' or paragraphs 10 to 15 under the heading 'Engine misfires' should be carried out first, according to the symptoms, paying careful attention to Section 13. If the fault still exists, the following step by step test procedure should be used. For these tests a good quality 0 to 12 volt voltmeter and an ohmmeter will be required.

*Engine fails to start*
**Note**: *The figures and numbers shown in brackets refer to the multi-plug connectors and terminal locations shown in Fig. 4.4*

| Test conditions | Test | Remedy |
|---|---|---|
| 1  Connector (A) disconnected, ignition switched on, starter cranking | Is the voltage between pin (1) in connector (A) and earth at least 9.5 volts? | Yes: Proceed to next test<br>No: Check battery condition, check feed wire to connector (A) |
| 2  Connector (A) disconnected, ignition switched off | Is the resistance between pin (2) in connector (A) and earth 0 ohms? | Yes: Proceed to next test<br>No: Check module earth wire to connector (A) |
| 3  Connector (A) disconnected, ignition ignition switched off | Is the resistance between module pin (11) and coil feed wire (9) 0 ohms? | Yes: Proceed to next test<br>No: Renew the computer module |
| 4  Connector (A) plugged in, ignition switched on | Is the voltage between coil terminal (7) and earth at least 9.5 volts? | Yes: Proceed to next test<br>No: Move connector (A) in and out, if still incorrect, renew connector |

| Test conditions | Test | Remedy |
|---|---|---|
| 5  Connector (B) disconnected, ignition switched off | Is the resistance between pins (4) and (5) in connector (B) 100 to 200 ohms | Yes: Proceed to next test<br>No: Renew the angular position sensor |
| 6  Connector (B) disconnected, ignition switched off | Does the ohmmeter read infinity when connected between pins (4) and (6) and also between pins (5) and (6) of connector (B) | Yes: Proceed to next test<br>No: Renew the angular position sensor |
| 7  Connector (B) disconnected, ignition switched off | Is the distance between the angular position sensor and the flywheel 0.5 to 1.5 mm (0.02 to 0.06 in) | Yes: Proceed to next test<br>No: Renew the angular position sensor |
| 8  Connectors (A) and (B) plugged in, wires (9) and (10) disconnected, starter cranking | Does a test bulb connected between wires (9) and (10) flash at starter motor speed? | Yes: Proceed to next test<br>No: Renew the computer module |
| 9  Ignition coil HT lead disconnected, ignition switched off | Is the resistance between coil terminals (7) and (12) 2500 to 5500 ohms? | Yes: Proceed to next test<br>No: Renew the ignition coil |
| 10 Wires (9) and (10) disconnected, ignition switched off | Is the resistance between coil terminals (7) and (8) 0.4 to 0.8 ohms? | Yes: Proceed to next text<br>No: Renew the ignition coil |
| 11 Connector (A) disconnected, ignition switched off | Is the resistance between pins (2) and (3) of connector (A) greater than 20 000 ohms? | Yes: Renew computer module<br>No: Repair wiring or renew tachometer |

*Engine is difficult to start, but performs satisfactorily once running*

| Test conditions | Test | Remedy |
|---|---|---|
| 1  Disconnect HT lead from centre of distributor cap, hold lead 5 mm away from the cylinder block | Is there a rapid succession of blue sparks between the end of the lead and the cylinder block with the engine cranking? | Yes: Proceed to next test<br>No: Carry out the test procedure under 'Engine fails to start' earlier in this Section |
| 2  Stroboscopic timing light connected to No 1 cylinder, engine idling, vacuum pipe disconnected | Is the ignition timing in accordance with the specified setting? | Yes: Check carburetion and engine mechanical condition<br>No: Renew the computer module |

*Engine performance unsatisfactory*

| Test conditions | Test | Remedy |
|---|---|---|
| 1  Run engine at a steady 3000 rpm, disconnect vacuum pipe at computer module | Does the engine speed drop as the vacuum pipe is disconnected? | Yes: Carry out the previous tests under 'Engine difficult to start'<br>No: Renew the computer module |

# Chapter 5  Clutch

*For modifications, and information applicable to later models, see Supplement at end of manual*

Contents

Specifications

**Type** .......................................................................... Single dry plate, self-adjusting cable operation

**Clutch disc diameter**
1108 cc and 1397 cc engines ..................................................... 181.5 mm (7.15 in)
1721 cc engines ............................................................................. 200 mm (7.87 in)

**Torque wrench settings**

| | Nm | lbf ft |
|---|---|---|
| Clutch cover bolts | 25 | 18 |

## 1  General description

All manual transmission models are equipped with a cable-operated, single dry plate diaphragm spring clutch assembly. The unit consists of a steel cover which is dowelled and bolted to the rear face of the flywheel, and contains the pressure plate and diaphragm spring.

The clutch disc is free to slide along the splined gearbox input shaft and is held in position between the flywheel and the pressure plate by the pressure of the diaphragm spring. Friction lining material is riveted to the clutch disc which has a spring cushioned hub to absorb transmission shocks and help ensure a smooth take-up of the drive.

The clutch is actuated by a cable controlled by the clutch pedal. The clutch release mechanism consists of a release arm and bearing which are in permanent contact with the fingers of the diaphragm spring.

Depressing the clutch pedal actuates the release arm by means of the cable. The arm pushes the release bearing against the diaphragm fingers, so moving the centre of the diaphragm spring inwards. As the centre of the spring is pushed in, the outside of the spring pivots out, so moving the pressure plate backwards and disengaging its grip on the clutch disc.

When the pedal is released, the diaphragm spring forces the pressure plate into contact with the friction linings on the clutch disc. The disc is now firmly sandwiched between the pressure plate and the flywheel, thus transmitting engine power to the gearbox.

Wear of the friction material on the clutch disc is automatically compensated by a self-adjusting mechanism attached to the clutch pedal. The mechanism consists of a serrated quadrant, a notched cam and a tension spring. One end of the clutch cable is attached to the quadrant which is free to pivot on the pedal, but is kept in tension by the spring. As the pedal is depressed the notched cam contacts the quadrant thus locking it and allowing the pedal to pull the cable and operate the clutch. As the pedal is released the tension spring causes the quadrant to move free of the notched cam and rotate slightly, thus taking up any free play that may exist in the cable.

## 2  Clutch assembly – removal and refitting

1  Access to the clutch may be gained in one of two ways. Either the engine, or engine transmission unit, can be removed, as described in Chapter 1, and the transmission separated from the engine, or the engine may be left in the car and the transmission unit removed independently, as described in Chapter 6.

2  Having separated the transmission from the engine, undo and remove the clutch cover retaining bolts, working in a diagonal sequence and slackening the bolts only a few turns at a time.

3  Ease the clutch cover off its locating dowels and be prepared to catch the clutch disc which will drop out as the cover is removed. Note which way round the disc is fitted.

4  It is important that no oil or grease is allowed to come into contact with the friction material of the clutch disc or the pressure plate and flywheel faces. It is advisable to refit the clutch assembly with clean hands and to wipe down the pressure plate and flywheel faces with a clean dry rag before assembly begins.

5  Begin reassembly by placing the clutch disc against the flywheel with the side having the larger offset facing away from the flywheel.

6  Place the clutch cover over the dowels, refit the retaining bolts and tighten them finger tight so that the clutch disc is gripped, but can still be moved.

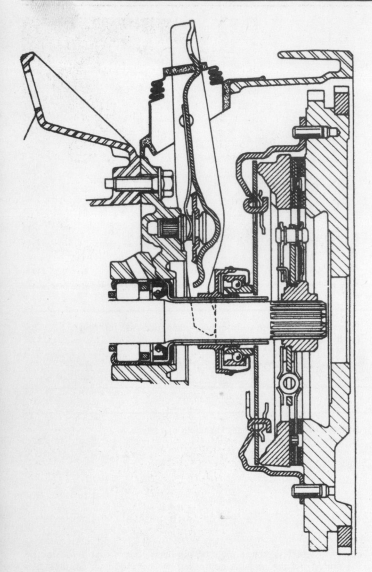

Fig. 5.1 Sectional view of the clutch mechanism (Sec 1)

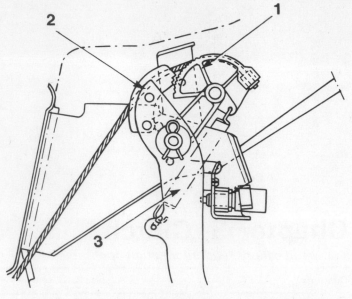

Fig. 5.2 Layout of the cable self-adjusting mechanism on the clutch pedal (Sec 1)

1   Serrated quadrant          3   Tension spring
2   Notched cam

7   The clutch disc must now be centralised so that, when the engine and transmission are mated, the splines of the gearbox input shaft will pass through the splines in the centre of the clutch disc hub.

8   Centralisation can be carried out quite easily by inserting a round bar or long screwdriver through the hole in the centre of the clutch disc so that the end of the bar rests in the hole in the end of the crankshaft containing the input shaft support bearing.

9   Using the support bearing as a fulcrum, moving the bar sideways or up and down will move the clutch disc in whichever direction is necessary to achieve centralisation.

10  Centralisation is easily judged by removing the bar and viewing the clutch disc hub in relation to the support bearing. When the support bearing appears exactly in the centre of the clutch disc hub, all is correct.

11  An alternative and more accurate method of centralisation is to use a commercially available clutch aligning tool obtainable from most accessory shops (photos).

2.11A Fitting the clutch disc with an aligning tool for centralisation

2.11B Using the tool to align the disc prior to tightening the cover retaining bolts

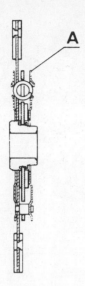

Fig. 5.3 The clutch disc must be fitted with the larger offset side (A) away from the flywheel (Sec 2)

12  Once the clutch is centralised, progressively tighten the cover bolts in a diagonal sequence to the torque setting given in the Specifications.

13  The transmission can now be mated to the engine by referring to the relevant Sections and Chapters of this manual.

## 3  Clutch assembly – inspection

1  With the clutch assembly removed, clean off all traces of asbestos dust using a dry cloth. This is best done outside or in a well ventilated area; *asbestos dust is harmful, and must not be inhaled.*

2  Examine the linings of the clutch disc for wear and loose rivets, and the disc rim for distortion, cracks, broken torsion springs and worn splines. The surface of the friction linings may be highly glazed, but, as long as the friction material pattern can be clearly seen, this is satisfactory. If there is any sign of oil contamination, indicated by a continuous, or patchy, shiny black discolouration, the disc must be renewed and the source of the contamination traced and rectified. This will be either a leaking crankshaft oil seal or gearbox input shaft oil seal – or both. Renewal procedures are given in Chapter 1 and Chapter 6 respectively. The disc must also be renewed if the lining thickness has worn down to, or just above, the level of the rivet heads.

3  Check the machined faces of the flywheel and pressure plate. If either is grooved, or heavily scored, renewal is necessary. The pressure plate must also be renewed if any cracks are apparent, or if the diaphragm spring is damaged or its pressure suspect.

4  With the gearbox removed it is advisable to check the condition of the release bearing, as described in the following Section.

## 4  Clutch release bearing – removal, inspection and refitting

1  To gain access to the release bearing it is necessary to separate the engine and transmission either by removing the engine or transmission individually, or by removing both units as an assembly and separating them after removal. Depending on the method chosen, the appropriate procedures will be found in Chapter 1 or Chapter 6.

2  With the transmission removed from the engine, tilt the release fork and slide the bearing assembly off the gearbox input shaft guide tube (photo).

3  To remove the bearing from its holder, release the four tags of the spring retainer, lift off the retainer and remove the bearing (photos).

4  Check the bearing for smoothness of operation and renew it if there is any roughness or harshness as the bearing is spun.

5  To remove the release fork, disengage the rubber cover and then pull the fork upwards to release it from its ball pivot stud.

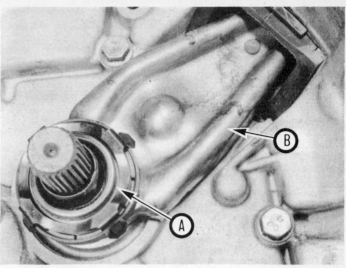

4.2 Clutch release bearing (A) and release fork (B) locations within the bellhousing

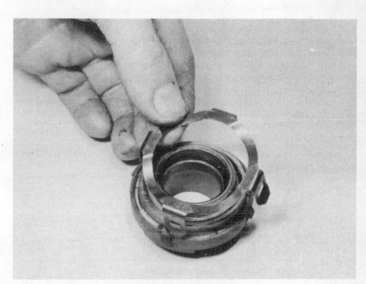

4.3A Remove the release bearing spring retainer ...

4.3B ... and lift out the bearing

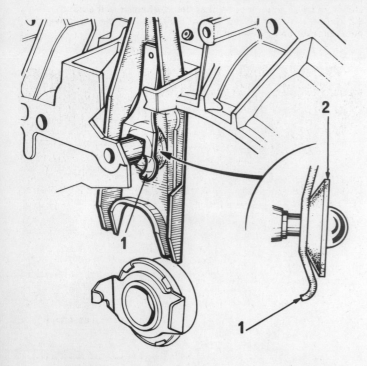

**Fig. 5.4 Correct fitting of the clutch release fork (Sec 4)**

1   *Spring retainer located behind the flat shoulder of the ball pivot stud*
2   *Rubber cover (where fitted)*

6   Refitting the release fork and release bearing is the reverse sequence to removal, but note the following points:

   (a)  *Lubricate the release fork pivot ball stud and the release bearing-to-diaphragm spring contact areas sparingly with molybdenum disulphide grease*
   (b)  *Ensure that the release fork spring retainer locates behind the flat shoulder of the ball pivot stud*

---

### 5   Clutch cable – removal and refitting

1   Disconnect the battery negative terminal.
2   Slip the cable end out of the release fork and disengage the outer cable from the bracket on the bellhousing (photo).
3   Working inside the car detach the moulded plastic cover from the pedal bracket assembly (photo).
4   Press the clutch pedal to the floor and then release it to free the cable end from the serrated quadrant on the self-adjusting mechanism (photo).

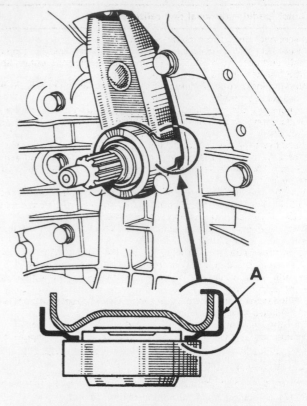

**Fig. 5.5 Correct fitting of the clutch release bearing (Sec 4)**

*A   Shoulder of bearing holder locates behind release fork*

5   Remove the cable from the quadrant and then push the outer cable out of its location in the bulkhead using a screwdriver.
6   Pull the cable through into the engine compartment, detach it from the support clips and remove it from the car.
7   To refit the cable thread it through from the engine compartment, lay it over the self-adjusting cam and connect the cable end to the quadrant.
8   Slip the other end of the cable through the bellhousing bracket and into the release fork.
9   Depress the clutch pedal to draw the outer cable into its locating hole in the bulkhead, ensuring that it locates properly.
10  Turn the quadrant on the self-adjusting mechanism towards the front of the car to introduce some slack in the cable then depress the clutch pedal several times so that the mechanism self adjusts.
11  Refit the cover over the pedal bracket assembly, reconnect the battery and attach the cable to the support clips.

5.2 Clutch cable attachments at release fork (A) and bellhousing bracket (B)

5.3 Detach the moulded plastic cover to gain access to the pedal assembly

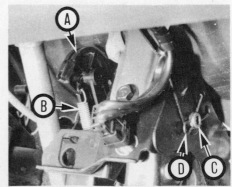

5.4 Clutch cable self-adjusting quadrant (A), tension spring (B), pedal cross-shaft (C) and retaining clip (D)

## 6  Clutch pedal – removal and refitting

1   Disconnect the battery negative terminal.
2   Disconnect the clutch cable at the transmission end by slipping the cable end out of the release fork and disengaging the outer cable from the bracket on the bellhousing.
3   Working inside the car detach the moulded plastic cover from the pedal bracket assembly.
4   If necessary the air duct at the base of the facia can be removed to provide greater access by detaching it from the heater unit and vent tube (photo).
5   Press the clutch pedal to the floor and then release it to free the cable end from the serrated quadrant on the pedal self-adjusting mechanism. Lift the cable out of the quadrant and self-adjusting cam on the pedal.
6   Prise off the retaining clips on both ends of the pedal cross-shaft (photo 5.4). Slide the shaft out of the pedal bracket, towards the right-hand side of the car, and withdraw the clutch pedal.
7   With the pedal removed, inspect the two bushes and renew them if worn.
8   To refit the pedal, place it in position in the pedal bracket and slide the cross-shaft through. Refit the retaining clips at both ends.
9   Lay the clutch cable over the self-adjusting cam and connect the cable end to the quadrant.
10  Slip the other end of the cable through the bellhousing bracket and into the release fork.
11  Turn the quadrant on the self-adjusting mechanism towards the front of the car to introduce some slack in the cable, then depress the clutch pedal several times so that the mechanism self adjusts.
12  Refit the air duct at the base of the facia, refit the cover over the pedal bracket and reconnect the battery.

6.4 Removing the air duct for greater access to the pedal assembly

## 7  Fault diagnosis – clutch

| Symptom | Reason(s) |
| --- | --- |
| Judder when taking up drive | Loose or worn engine mountings<br>Clutch disc contaminated with oil, or linings worn<br>Clutch cable sticking or frayed<br>Faulty pressure plate assembly |
| Clutch fails to disengage | Clutch self-adjusting mechanism faulty or inoperative<br>Clutch disc sticking on input shaft splines<br>Faulty pressure plate assembly<br>Cable broken |
| Clutch slips | Clutch self-adjusting mechanism faulty or inoperative<br>Clutch disc contaminated with oil or linings worn<br>Faulty pressure plate assembly<br>Diaphragm spring broken |
| Noise when depressing clutch pedal | Worn release bearing<br>Faulty pressure plate assembly<br>Diaphragm spring broken<br>Worn or dry cable or pedal bushes |
| Noise when releasing clutch pedal | Faulty pressure plate assembly<br>Broken clutch disc cushioning springs<br>Gearbox internal wear (see Chapter 6) |

# Chapter 6
# Manual gearbox and automatic transmission

*For modifications, and information applicable to later models, see Supplement at end of manual*

## Contents

## Specifications

### Part 1: Manual gearbox
#### Type ........................................................................................................

Four or five forward speeds (all synchromesh) and reverse. Final drive differential integral with main gearbox

Designation:
    Four-speed units ........................................................................... JB0
    Five-speed units ............................................................................ JB1 or JB3

#### Gearbox ratios

JB0:

| | |
|---|---|
| 1st .................................................................................................... | 3.54 : 1 |
| 2nd ................................................................................................... | 2.06 : 1 |
| 3rd .................................................................................................... | 1.32 : 1 |
| 4th .................................................................................................... | 0.90 : 1 |
| Reverse ............................................................................................ | 3.54 : 1 |

JB1 and JB3 (1397 cc engine):

| | |
|---|---|
| 1st .................................................................................................... | 3.54 : 1 |
| 2nd ................................................................................................... | 2.06 : 1 |
| 3rd .................................................................................................... | 1.32 : 1 |
| 4th .................................................................................................... | 0.90 : 1 |
| 5th .................................................................................................... | 0.75 : 1 |
| Reverse ............................................................................................ | 3.54 : 1 |

JB3 (1721 cc engine):

| | |
|---|---|
| 1st .................................................................................................... | 3.73 : 1 |
| 2nd ................................................................................................... | 2.05 : 1 |
| 3rd .................................................................................................... | 1.32 : 1 |
| 4th .................................................................................................... | 0.97 : 1 |
| 5th .................................................................................................... | 0.79 : 1 |
| Reverse ............................................................................................ | 3.54 : 1 |

#### Final drive ratios

| | |
|---|---|
| JB0 ..................................................................................................... | 3.86 : 1 |
| JB1 and JB3 (1397 cc engine) ....................................................... | 4.21 : 1 |
| JB3 (1721 cc engine) ...................................................................... | 3.56 : 1 |

#### Lubrication
Capacity:
    JB0 ................................................................................................. 3.25 litres (5.72 Imp pints)
    JB1 and JB3 ................................................................................. 3.40 litres (5.98 Imp pints)
Lubricant type/specification ......................................................... Hypoid gear oil, viscosity SAE 80 EP (Duckhams Hypoid 80S)

#### Torque wrench settings

| | Nm | lbf ft |
|---|---|---|
| Gearbox rubber mounting nuts and bolts ............................................ | 45 | 33 |
| Bellhousing-to-engine nuts and bolts .................................................. | 50 | 37 |
| Gearbox casing to clutch and differential housing ........................... | 25 | 18 |
| 5th speed driving gear to input shaft nut ............................................ | 135 | 100 |
| 5th speed driven gear to mainshaft: | | |
|     8mm dia bolt ............................................................................... | 20 | 15 |
|     10mm dia bolt ............................................................................. | 80 | 59 |

*Part 2: Automatic transmission*

**Type** ............................................................................... Three forward speeds and reverse, final drive differential integral with transmission

Designation ...................................................................... MB1

## Lubrication

Capacity:
    Total – dry unit .......................................................... 4.5 litres (7.92 Imp pints)
    Refill after fluid change (approximate) ...................... 2.0 litres (3.52 Imp pints)
Fluid type/specification ................................................. Dextron type ATF (Duckhams Uni-Matic or D-Matic)

| Torque wrench settings | Nm | lbf ft |
|---|---|---|
| Transmission mountings | 40 | 30 |
| Bellhousing-to-engine nuts and bolts | 50 | 37 |
| Torque converter to driveplate | 30 | 22 |
| Fluid cooler union nuts | 20 | 15 |

## PART 1: MANUAL GEARBOX

### 1   General description

The gearbox is equipped with either four forward and one reverse gear or five forward and one reverse gear, according to model. Baulk ring synchromesh gear engagement is used on all forward gears.

The final drive (differential) unit is integral with the main gearbox and is located between the mechanism casing and clutch and differential housing. The gearbox and differential both share the same lubricating oil.

Gearshift is by means of a floor-mounted lever connected by a remote control housing and gearchange rod to the gearbox fork contact shaft.

If gearbox overhaul is necessary, due consideration should be

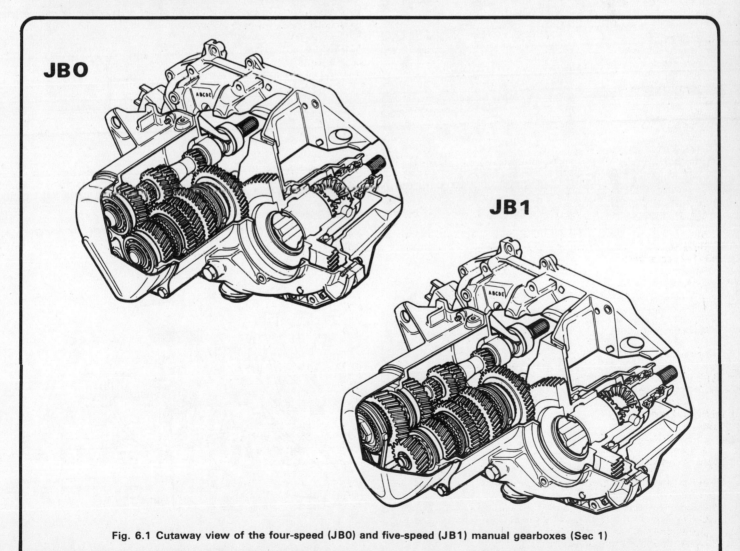

**Fig. 6.1 Cutaway view of the four-speed (JB0) and five-speed (JB1) manual gearboxes (Sec 1)**

given to the costs involved, since it is often more economical to obtain a service exchange or good secondhand gearbox rather than fit new parts to the existing unit.

## 2   Maintenance and inspection

1    At the intervals specified in Routine maintenance, inspect the gearbox joint faces and oil seals for any signs of damage, deterioration or oil leakage.
2    At the same service internal check and, if necessary, top up the gearbox oil using the procedure described in Section 3.
3    At less frequent intervals (see Routine maintenance) the gearbox should be drained and refilled with fresh oil, and this procedure is also described in Section 3.
4    It is also advisable to check for excess free play or wear in the gear linkage joints and rods and check the gear lever adjustment, as described in Section 15.

## 3   Gearbox – draining and refilling

1    Position the car on level ground and place a suitable container beneath the gearbox drain plug (photo). On models fitted with the 1721 cc engine it will be necessary to remove the four bolts, one at each corner, and lift off the undertray to gain access to the drain plug.
2    Unscrew the drain plug and allow the oil to drain into the container. If the gearbox is fitted with a filler plug located in the position shown in Fig. 6.2, remove this also to assist draining.
3    When all the oil has drained, refit the drain plug and, where applicable, the undertray.
4    Before refilling the gearbox, locate the breather assembly on the upper face of the casing (photo), and identify the type fitted by referring to Fig. 6.3. If a type 1 breather is fitted, withdraw the breather body, but take care not to pull its rubber breather hose out of the casing as well. If a type 2 breather is fitted there is no need to disturb it.
5    Remove the filler plug located on top of the casing on early models (Fig. 6.2) or on the front facing side of the casing on later models (photo).
6    Slowly refill the gearbox using the specified grade of oil until the oil overflows from the filler plug orifice. Wait a few minutes to allow any trapped air to escape and then, if possible, add more oil. Repeat this process two or three times until no more oil can be added and then, with the level right to the top of the plug orifice, refit the filler plug. Take care over this operation as this type of gearbox may take quite some time to fill.
7    After filling refit the breather body, where applicable.

3.1 Gearbox drain plug location (arrowed)

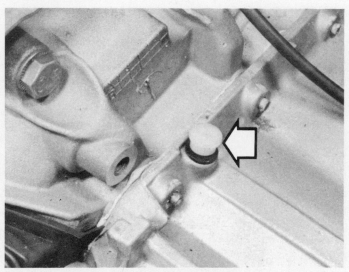

3.4 Type 1 breather location on the upper face of the gearbox casing (arrowed)

3.5 Gearbox filler plug location on later models (arrowed) viewed from below

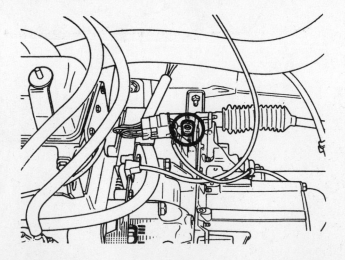

Fig. 6.2 Gearbox filler plug location – early models (Sec 3)

## 4  Gearbox – removal and refitting

1   After disconnecting all the relevant attachments, controls and services, the gearbox is removed upwards and out of the engine compartment. Due to the weight of the unit, it will be necessary to have some form of lifting equipment available, such as an engine crane or suitable hoist to enable the unit to be removed in this way.

2   Begin by disconnecting the battery negative terminal and then refer to Section 3 and drain the gearbox oil.

3   Jack up the front of the car and support it on axle stands. Remove both front roadwheels.

4   Refer to Chapter 7, Section 3 and remove the left-hand driveshaft inner joint spider, as described in paragraphs 3 to 9, and the right-hand driveshaft inner joint yoke, as described in paragraphs 3 to 6 and 11 to 13.

5   Working in the engine compartment, remove the air cleaner, as described in Chapter 3.

6   Slip the clutch cable end out of the release fork and disengage the outer cable from the bracket on the bellhousing. Move the cable to one side.

7   Undo the two shouldered bolts and remove the TDC sensor and diagnostic socket (photo), or the angular position sensor from their locations on the bellhousing.

8   Extract the speedometer cable wire retaining clip from its locating holes in the rear engine mounting bracket and gearbox casing. Note the fitted direction of the clip. Withdraw the speedometer cable from the gearbox (photo).

9   Undo the two bolts and remove the tension springs securing the exhaust front section flange to the exhaust manifold.

10  Note the locations of the wires at the starter solenoid and disconnect them.

11  Undo the starter motor support bracket bolt and the three bolts

Fig. 6.3 Gearbox breather type identification (Sec 3)

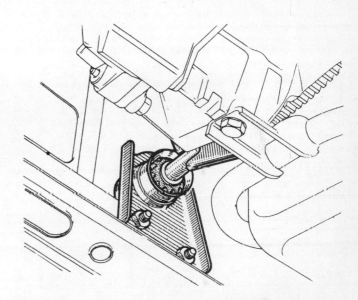

Fig. 6.4 Engine movement limiter location on 1721 cc engines (Sec 4)

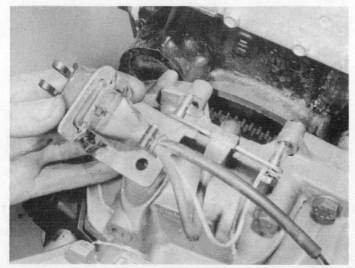

4.7 TDC sensor and diagnostic socket removal

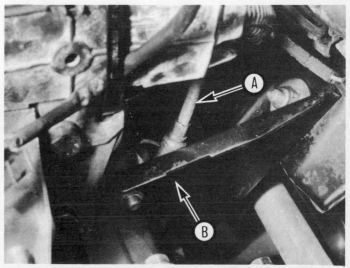

4.8 Speedometer cable (A) and retaining clip location (B)

securing the starter to the bellhousing, then remove the starter. Note the locating dowel in the upper rear bolt location and note also that the wiring terminal box is retained by one of the starter bolts.

12 Disconnect the wiring to the radiator fan motor and thermostatic switch on the right-hand side of the radiator. Release the radiator upper spring retaining clamp, lift the radiator up and lay it over the engine with the hoses still attached. Protect the matrix with a sheet of card.

13 Undo the retaining nut and disconnect the gearbox earthing braid.

14 Detach any clips, as necessary, and position all the disconnected wiring, harness and cables to one side so that there is clear access to the gearbox from above.

15 On models fitted with the 1721 cc engine undo the retaining bolts and remove the movement limiter from the front of the engine and the subframe.

16 From under the car, slide back the rubber cover and undo the nut and bolt securing the gearchange rod to the gearbox fork control shaft (photos). Slide the rod off the shaft and recover the distance sleeve (photo).

17 Undo the bolts securing the flywheel cover plate to the lower face of the gearbox bellhousing and remove the plate.

18 Undo the bolts securing the steady rod to the engine and gearbox, noting the angled fitting of the rod and the spacer position at the engine end (photos).

19 Disconnect the wiring at the reversing lamp switch (photo), and, where fitted, the gear position sensors on the gearbox casing.

20 Position a jack under the engine sump with an interposed block of wood, and attach a crane or hoist to the gearbox using chain or rope slings. Depending on the type of lifting equipment being used, it may be beneficial to remove the bonnet, as described in Chapter 11.

21 Raise the jack and crane and just take the weight of the engine and gearbox.

22 Undo all the bolts around the periphery of the bellhousing securing the gearbox to the engine. In addition to the bolts there are two nuts on studs, one each side of the bellhousing. After undoing the nuts, the

studs must be removed and this can be done by locking two nuts tightly together on the stud then unscrewing it using the innermost nut.

23 Undo the two bolts at the front securing the gearbox mounting

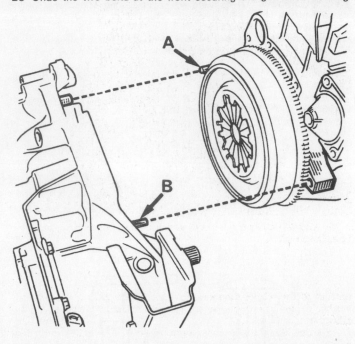

**Fig. 6.5 The two studs (A and B) must be removed to allow the transmission to clear the engine (Sec 4)**

4.16A Slide back the gearchange rod rubber cover ...

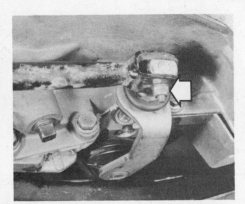

4.16B ... undo the retaining nut and bolt (arrowed)

4.16C ... then slide off the rod and recover the distance sleeve (arrowed)

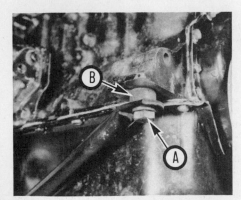

4.18A Steady rod retaining bolt (A) and spacer (B) at the engine ...

4.18B ... and retaining bolt (C) at the gearbox

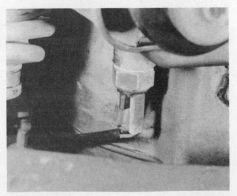

4.19 Wiring connections at the reversing lamp switch

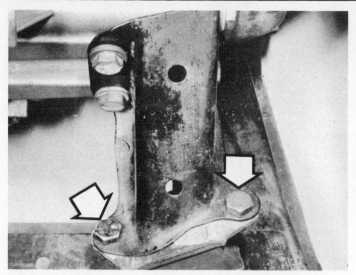

4.23A Gearbox mounting bracket-to-front rubber mounting retaining bolts (arrowed)

4.23B Gearbox rear rubber mounting stud for retaining nut (arrowed)

bracket to the rubber mounting (photo). Similarly undo the nut and washer at the rear securing the gearbox mounting bracket to the rubber mounting (photo).

24 Slacken the front engine mounting bracket-to-rubber mounting bolts.

25 Raise the engine and gearbox until the mountings are released, then undo the four bolts and remove the front mounting bracket completely.

26 Lower the engine and gearbox as necessary then withdraw the gearbox from the engine by moving it sideways and under the left-hand chassis member. When the gearbox is clear of the clutch and flywheel, turn it clockwise slightly so that the differential will clear the rear of the engine then raise the crane. Move the gearbox around to keep it clear as it is raised then, when it is high enough, lift it over the wing or front panel and lower it to the ground.

27 Refitting the gearbox is the reverse sequence to removal, but bear in mind the following points:

(a) Fit the two studs on either side of the bellhousing before fitting the gearbox-to-engine retaining bolts

(b) Tighten the exhaust front section-to-manifold retaining bolts so that the tension springs are compressed as shown in Fig. 6.6

(c) Refit the driveshaft inner joints, as described in Chapter 7, Section 3.

(d) Refill the gearbox with oil, as described in Section 3 of this Chapter

## 5  Gearbox overhaul – general

Complete dismantling and overhaul of the gearbox, particularly with respect to the differential and the bearings in the clutch and differential housing, entails the use of a hydraulic press and a number of special tools. For this reason it is not recommended that a complete overhaul be attempted by the home mechanic unless he has access to the tools required and feels reasonably confident after studying the procedure. However, the gearbox can at least be dismantled into its major assemblies without too much difficulty, and the following Sections describe this and the overhaul procedure.

Before starting any repair work on the gearbox, thoroughly clean the exterior of the casings using paraffin or a suitable solvent. Dry the unit with a lint-free rag. Make sure that an uncluttered working area is available with some small containers and trays handy to store the various parts. Label everything as it is removed.

Before starting reassembly all the components must be spotlessly clean and should be liberally lubricated with the recommended grade of gear oil during assembly.

Apart from the additional 5th gear and slight differences in the

Fig. 6.6 Exhaust mounting tension spring tightening dimension (Sec 4)

$L = 43.5 \, mm \, (1.7 \, in)$

selector mechanism, the four- and five-speed gearboxes are virtually identical and the following Sections are applicable to both types. Where any significant differences occur, these will be described in the text.

After dismantling, all roll pins, circlips and snap-rings must be renewed, regardless of their condition, before reassembling.

## 6  Gearbox – separating the housings

1  With the gearbox on the bench, begin by removing the clutch release bearing and release fork, referring to Chapter 5 if necessary.

2  Undo the bolts securing the rear gearbox mounting bracket to the clutch and differential housing and remove the bracket.

3  Remove the rubber O-ring from the splines of the differential stub shaft (photo).

4  Undo the retaining bolts and lift off the mechanism casing rear cover (photo). Recover the rubber O-ring seal.

6.3 Remove the differential stub shaft O-ring

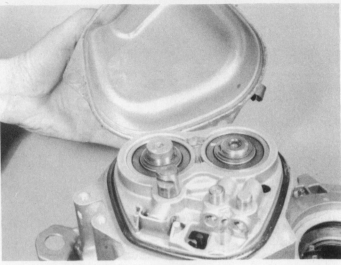

6.4 Undo the retaining bolts and lift off the rear cover

5  If working on the four-speed gearbox, proceed to paragraph 13, if working on the five-speed gearbox, proceed as follows:

6  Support the 5th speed selector shaft using a block of wood between the shaft and gears, then drive out the selector fork roll pin using a parallel pin punch.

7  Engage 1st gear by moving the gear linkage fork control shaft and engage 5th gear by moving the 5th speed selector fork. With the geartrain now locked, undo the 5th gear retaining nut on the end of the input shaft.

8  Return the geartrain to neutral.

9  Withdraw the 5th speed driving gear, synchroniser unit, and selector fork as an assembly using a suitable puller. Engage the puller legs over flat strips of metal slid under the teeth of the driven gear.

10  Recover the needle roller bearing, bearing bush and the washer from the input shaft.

11  Where fitted, undo the bolt then remove the washer and collar over the 5th speed driven gear on the mainshaft.

12  Extract the 5th speed circlip and dished washer then remove the gear, as described previously for the driven gear.

13  Extract the circlip and dished washer over the end of the input shaft and mainshaft (photos).

14  Lift out the reverse shaft detent retaining plate then remove the spring and ball (photos). If the ball won't come out, leave it in place, but don't forget to retrieve it once the casing has been separated.

6.13A Extract the circlip ...

6.13B ... and dished washer from the input shaft and mainshaft

6.14A Lift out the reverse shaft detent retaining plate ...

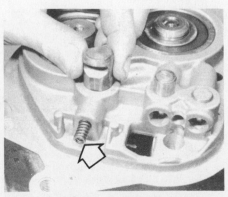

6.14B ... followed by the spring (arrowed) ...

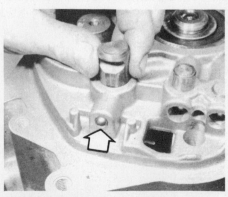

6.14C ... and detent ball (arrowed)

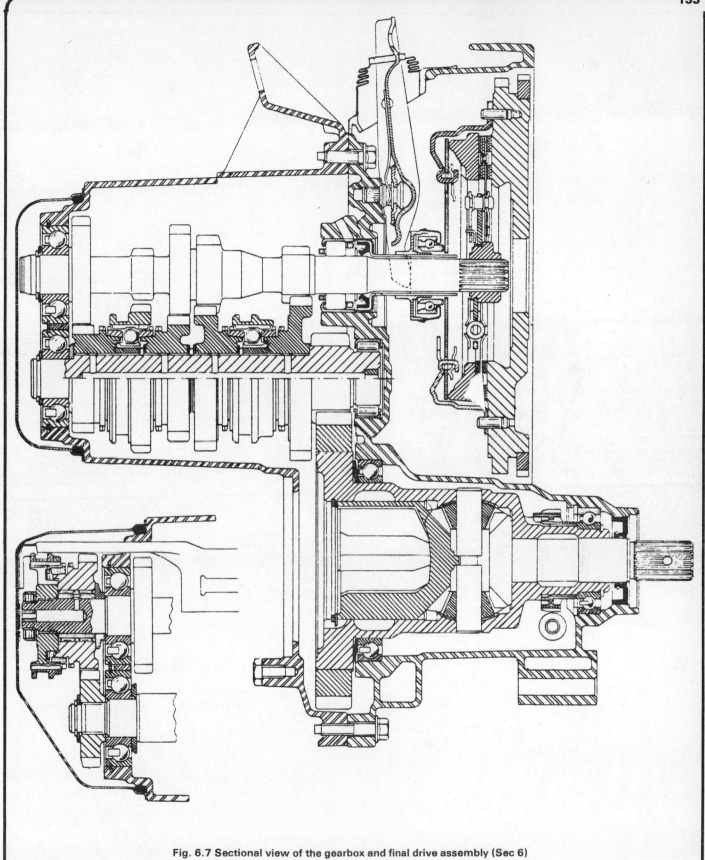

Fig. 6.7 Sectional view of the gearbox and final drive assembly (Sec 6)

6.15 Unscrew the limit stop threaded plug ...

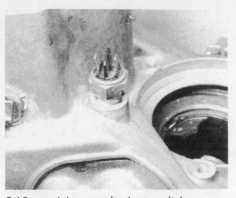

6.16 ... and the reversing lamp switch

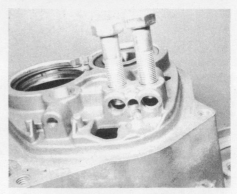

6.18 Two bolts in position to retain the selector shaft detent balls and springs

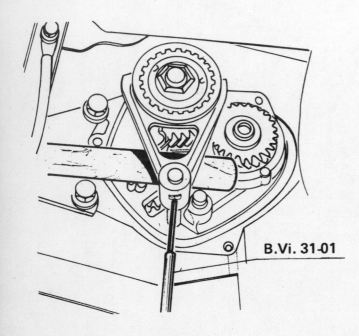

Fig. 6.8 Remove the 5th speed selector fork roll pin with a drift while supporting the shaft with a block of wood (Sec 6)

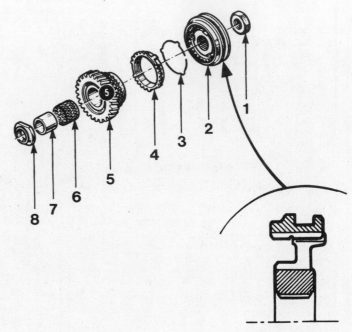

Fig. 6.9 5th speed driving gear components (Sec 6)

| 1 | 5th gear retaining nut | 5 | 5th speed driven gear |
| 2 | 5th speed synchroniser unit | 6 | Needle roller bearing |
| 3 | Spring clip | 7 | Bearing bush |
| 4 | Baulk ring | 8 | Washer |

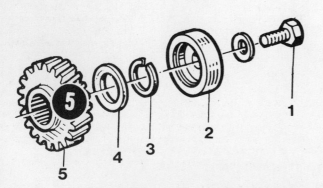

Fig. 6.10 5th speed driven gear components (Sec 6)

| 1 | Bolt (later models only) | 4 | Dished washer |
| 2 | Collar (later models only) | 5 | 5th speed driving gear |
| 3 | Circlip | | |

15  Unscrew the limit stop threaded plug (photo) on four-speed units, or the 5th speed detent assembly on five-speed units.

16  Unscrew the reversing lamp switch (photo).

17  Undo and remove the bolts securing the mechanism casing to the clutch and differential housing, noting their different lengths.

18  Pull the fork control shaft on the side of the gearbox out as far as it will go and then lift the mechanism casing, complete with 5th speed selector shaft on five-speed units, up and off the geartrain and housing. It may be necessary to tap the input shaft down using a plastic mallet to free the casing and bearings from the shaft. As soon as the casing comes free, insert two bolts or suitable rods into the selector shaft holes and push them down firmly. These will retain the detent balls and springs and prevent them being ejected as the casing is lifted off (photo).

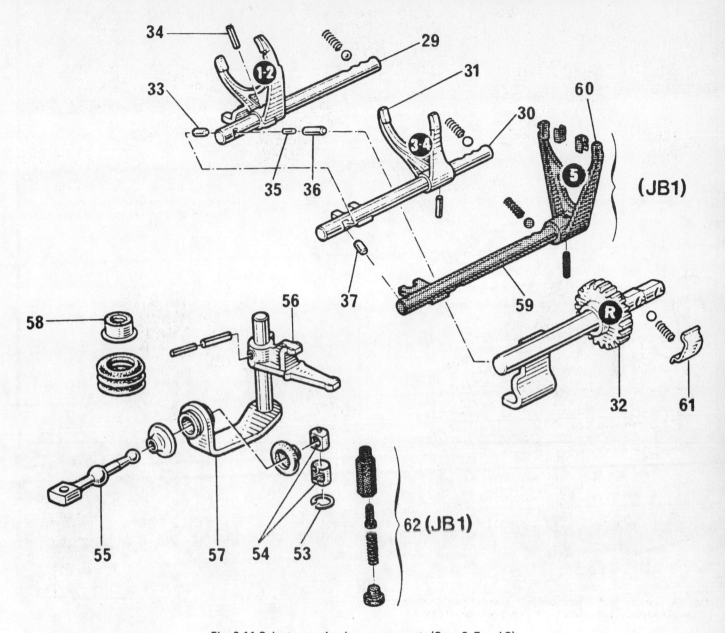

**Fig. 6.11 Selector mechanism components (Secs 6, 7 and 8)**

| | | | |
|---|---|---|---|
| 29 | 1st/2nd selector shaft | 34 | Selector fork roll pin |
| 30 | 3rd/4th selector shaft | 35 | Detent plunger |
| 31 | 3rd/4th selector fork | 36 | Detent plunger |
| 32 | Reverse shaft | 37 | Detent plunger (five-speed only) |
| 33 | Detent plunger | 53 | Circlip |

| | | | |
|---|---|---|---|
| 54 | Pivot arm bushes | 59 | 5th speed selector shaft |
| 55 | Pivot arm | 60 | 5th speed selector fork |
| 56 | Fork finger | 61 | Reverse shaft detent retaining plate |
| 57 | Fork control shaft | 62 | 5th speed detent assembly |
| 58 | Bush | | |

## 7  Gearbox mainshaft, input shaft and differential – removal

1   Having separated the casings, the geartrain components can now be dismantled as follows:

2   On the five-speed gearbox, recover the detent plunger from the location in the clutch and differential housing vacated by the 5th speed selector shaft.

3   Using a parallel pin punch, drive out the roll pin securing the 3rd/4th selector fork to the shaft (photo). Slip a tube of suitable diameter down over the shaft and support it while the roll pin is being driven out.

4   Ensure that all the gears are in neutral, and then withdraw the 3rd/4th selector shaft, leaving the fork behind. It will be necessary to move the reverse shaft around slightly until the exact neutral position is found, otherwise the detent plungers will not locate properly in their grooves and it will be impossible to remove the 3rd/4th shaft (photo). With the shaft removed, lift off the selector fork.

5   Recover the detent plunger from the shaft location in the housing (photo).

6   Using the same procedure as for the 3rd/4th shaft, remove the 1st/2nd selector shaft and fork. As the shaft is withdrawn, recover the small detent plunger from the hole in the centre of the shaft (photos).

7   Withdraw the long detent plunger from its location at the base of the housing (photo).

8   Take hold of the mainshaft, input shaft and reverse shaft

Fig. 6.12 Exploded view of the differential assembly (Sec 7)

38 O-ring
39 Oil seal
40 Circlip
41 Speedometer drivegear
42 Differential inner bearing
43 Plain thrust washer
44 Dished thrust washer
45 Differential crownwheel
   assembly

46 Snap-ring
47 Shim
48 Spider sun wheel
49 Planet wheel shaft
50 Planet wheels
51 Planet wheel thrust
   washers
52 Sun wheel and stub shaft

7.3 3rd/4th selector fork roll pin location (arrowed)

7.4 Withdraw the 3rd/4th selector shaft, followed by the fork

7.5 Recover the detent plunger (arrowed) after removing the 3rd/4th shaft

7.6A As the 1st/2nd selector shaft is withdrawn, recover the small detent plunger from the hole (arrowed) ...

7.6B ... then remove the fork

7.7 Remove the long detent plunger (arrowed) after removing the 1st/2nd shaft

7.8 Remove the mainshaft, input shaft and reverse shaft together from the housing ...

7.9 ... then recover the magnet from its location

geartrains and lift them as an assembly out of their locations in the clutch and differential housing (photo).

9    Recover the magnet from the bottom of the housing (photo).

10  The differential can now be removed, if necessary, but a hydraulic press will be needed. It is recommended that the differential be left alone unless it is absolutely essential to remove it. The removal procedure is as follows:

11  Using a small punch and pliers, tip the oil seal in its location by tapping it down on one side. As the seal tips, prise it out using a screwdriver and pliers.

12  Place the differential crownwheel face down on the press bed, with a block of wood beneath it to spread the load.

13  Press the clutch and differential housing down and extract the circlip securing the differential to the outer bearing.

14  Support the housing on blocks of wood and remove the differential assembly by pressing on the splined stub shaft. Recover the dished and, where fitted, the plain thrust washer.

## 8    Gearbox mechanism casing – overhaul

1    To renew the bearings in the mechanism casing, spread the retaining circlips with a pair of outward opening circlips pliers, and drive the bearings out towards the inside of the casing. Use a hammer and tube of suitable diameter to do this.

2    To fit the new bearings, first locate the circlips in their grooves in the casing so that their ends are together (photo).

3    Fit the bearings to the casing, ensuring that force is applied to the bearing outer race only. As the bearings are being fitted spread the circlips to allow the bearings to enter.

4    With the bearings in place, locate the circlips into the bearing grooves and ensure that the circlip ends are together (photo).

5    If it is necessary to renew the selector shaft detent balls and springs, remove the bolts or rods used to hold them in place during removal of the casing and withdraw the balls and springs as required.

6    Examine the condition of the fork control shaft and its mechanism for wear, particularly at the fork fingers, and renew these components if necessary as follows:

7    Extract the circlip (photo) then slide out the pivot arm bush and the arm.

8    Using a parallel pin punch, tap out the double roll pin, securing the fork finger assembly to the fork control shaft (photo). Withdraw the shaft and recover the fork and oil seal.

9    With the new components at hand, reassemble the fork control assembly using the reverse of the removal procedure.

10  If the oil flow guide on the five-speed gearbox is to be renewed, bend flat the retaining lip edge on the guide and push it into the casing.

11  Push the new guide up into position and bend over the lip edge to lock it in place.

8.2 Mainshaft and input shaft bearing circlips (arrowed)

8.4 With the bearings fitted the circlip ends (arrowed) must be together and on the same side

8.7 Fork control shaft pivot arm retaining circlip (arrowed) ...

8.8 ... and fork finger retaining roll pin (arrowed)

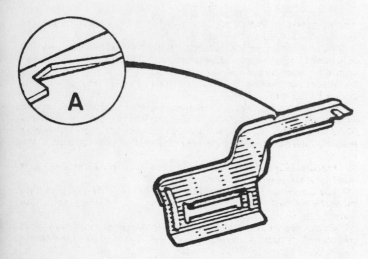

Fig. 6.13 Oil flow guide retaining lip edge (A) – five-speed gearbox
(Sec 8)

## 9 Clutch and differential housing – overhaul

1    If a press is available the differential bearings can be removed quite easily. After removing the differential, as described previously, support the housing, bellhousing face downwards, and press the relevant bearing out. If the smaller bearing is to be removed, extract the circlip first. Fit the new bearings in the same way and use a new circlip to secure the smaller bearing.

2    If it is necessary to renew the mainshaft support bearing, take the housing to a Renault dealer and have him renew the bearing for you using the Renault removal and refitting tools.

3    The gearbox input shaft oil seal is part of a complete assembly containing the input shaft roller bearing, and is located within a tubular housing. The complete assembly must be renewed if either the oil seal or the bearing require attention (photo).

4    To remove the assembly, extract it using tubes of suitable diameter with washers, a long bolt or threaded rod and nuts (photos). Tighten the nuts and draw the assembly out of its location and into the tube. Alternatively a press can be used, if available.

5    Refit the new oil seal and bearing assembly in the same way, but position it so that the bearing lubrication holes in the bearing assembly and clutch and differential housing will be directly in line after fitting (photo).

9.3 Input shaft oil seal and roller bearing assembly (arrowed)

9.4A Home made tool consisting of a tube, threaded rod, nut and washers on one side of the housing ...

9.4B ... and a socket, nut and washer on the other side for removing and refitting the input shaft oil seal and bearing

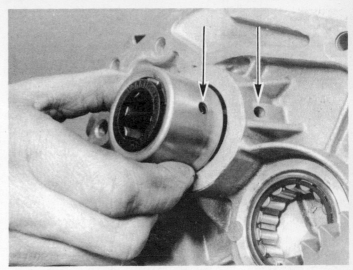

9.5 The input shaft bearing lubrication hole and the hole in the housing (arrowed) must be aligned after fitting

## 10  Differential — overhaul

1    It is not advisable to dismantle the differential unless it is known that its components are suspect or require attention.
2    If dismantling is to be undertaken, remove the sun and planet wheels from the differential by referring to Fig. 6.12. Keep the planet wheels together with their respective thrust washers, and lay them out in strict order of removal.
3    If any of the sun wheels, planet wheels or thrust washers require renewal, it will be necessary to renew all the components as a matching set.
4    Reassemble the differential using the reverse of the dismantling sequence.

## 11  Gearbox mainshaft — dismantling and reassembly

1    Support the mainshaft in a vice with protected jaws and commence dismantling at the 4th gear end as follows:
2    Lift off the 3rd/4th and reverse synchroniser unit, complete with the 4th gear baulk ring, 4th gear and the upper thrust washer as a complete assembly.
3    Extract the snap-ring and thrust washer then lift off 3rd gear and its baulk ring.
4    Remove the thrust washer, snap-ring and second thrust washer, then lift off 2nd gear.
5    Remove the thrust washer and snap-ring above the 1st/2nd

synchroniser unit and lift off 1st gear, the 1st/2nd synchroniser unit and the baulk rings as an assembly.
6    With the mainshaft now completely dismantled, examine the gears and synchroniser units, as described in Section 12, then proceed with the reassembly as follows:
7    Place 1st gear on the mainshaft with the flat face of the gear towards the pinion (photo).
8    Place the baulk ring over 1st gear and then position the 1st/2nd synchroniser unit over it (photos). Fit the synchroniser unit with the offset side of the hub and sliding sleeve towards 1st gear, and ensure that the lugs on the baulk ring engage with the roller grooves in the hub.
9    Place the 2nd gear baulk ring on the 1st/2nd synchroniser unit then refit the snap-ring (photos).
10  Lay the thrust washer over the snap-ring, then slide 2nd gear onto the mainshaft with its flat side facing away from the pinion end of the shaft (photos).
11  Fit the assembly of thrust washer, snap-ring and thrust washer to the mainshaft, then slide on 3rd gear with its flat face towards the pinion end of the mainshaft (photos).
12  Place a thrust washer over 3rd gear and secure it with the remaining snap-ring (photos).
13  Fit the 3rd gear baulk ring to 3rd gear followed by the 3rd/4th and reverse synchroniser unit. The offset side of the hub and the selector fork groove in the sliding sleeve should face away from 3rd gear. Ensure that the lugs on the baulk ring engage with the roller grooves in the hub (photos).
14  Fit the 4th gear baulk ring to the 3rd/4th synchroniser unit, then slide on 4th gear followed by the final thrust washer (photos).

11.7 Slide 1st gear on the mainshaft flat face towards the pinion

11.8A Place the baulk ring on the gear ...

11.8B ... followed by the 1st/2nd synchroniser unit

11.9A Place the baulk ring on the synchroniser unit ...

11.9B ... then refit the snap-ring

11.10A Lay the thrust washer over the snap-ring ...

11.10B ... then slide 2nd gear onto the mainshaft

11.11A Fit the assembly of thrust washer ...

11.11B ... snap-ring ...

11.11C ... and thrust washer to the mainshaft ...

11.11D ... followed by 3rd gear

11.12A Place a thrust washer over 3rd gear ...

11.12B ... and secure with the remaining snap-ring

11.13A Fit the baulk ring to 3rd gear ...

11.13B ... followed by the 3rd/4th synchroniser unit

11.14A Fit the 4th gear baulk ring ...

11.14B ... followed by 4th gear ...

11.14C ... and the final thrust washer

## 12  Shafts, gears and synchroniser units – inspection

1   With the gearbox completely dismantled, inspect the mainshaft, input shaft and reverse shaft for signs of damage, wear or chipping of the teeth, or wear or scoring of the shafts where they engage with their bearings (photos). If any of these conditions are apparent, the relevant shaft must be renewed.

2   If necessary, the synchroniser units can be dismantled for inspection by covering the assembly with a rag and then pushing the hub out of the sliding sleeve. Collect the spring keys and rollers which will have been ejected into the rag. Note that each synchroniser unit hub and sliding sleeve is a matched set and they must not be interchanged.

3   Check that the hub and sleeve slide over each other easily and that there is a minimum of backlash or axial rock. Examine the dog teeth of the sliding sleeve for excessive wear and renew the assembly if wear is obvious. Note that if the car had a tendency to jump out of a particular gear, then a worn synchroniser unit is the most likely cause and the relevant assembly should be renewed.

4   To reassemble the synchroniser units slide the hub into the sliding sleeve, noting that for the 1st/2nd unit the selector fork groove in the sleeve and the offset boss of the hub are on opposite sides. On the 3rd/4th unit, the selector fork groove and the hub offset boss are on the same side. On the 5th speed unit the chamfered outer edge of the sleeve is on the same side as the hub offset boss.

5   Place the synchroniser on the bench with the offset side of the hub facing downwards. Locate the end of the spring key, having the two tangs, against the hub and position the roller between the loop of the spring key and the side of the sleeve (photo).

6   Push down on the roller and key until they locate correctly with the roller located in the internal groove of the sliding sleeve (photo). Repeat this for the remaining rollers and spring keys.

7   Check the condition of the baulk rings by sliding them onto the land of the relevant gears and note whether they lock on the tapered land before reaching the gear shoulder. Also inspect the baulk rings for cracks or wear of the dog teeth and renew as necessary. It is recommended, having dismantled the gearbox this far, that all the baulk rings are renewed as a matter of course. The improvement in the gear changing action, particularly if the car has covered a considerable mileage, will be well worth the expense.

8   Finally check the selector fork clearance in the synchro-hub sliding sleeve groove, this should be minimal. If in doubt about the clearance, compare the forks with new ones and renew as necessary. On five-speed units two contact pads fitted to the fork ends actually engage with the sleeve grooves and only these, not the complete fork, need to be renewed if wear has taken place.

## 13  Gearbox mainshaft, input shaft and differential – refitting

1   If the differential has been removed this should be refitted first, as follows:

2   Position the dished thrust washer against the crownwheel face with the base of the dished face towards the crownwheel. Where fitted, place the flat thrust washer over the dished thrust washer.

3   Place a block of wood under the flat face of the crownwheel and locate this assembly on the press bed. Position the clutch and differential housing over the differential and press the housing on. Keep the housing pressed down to compress the dished thrust washer and fit a new outer retaining circlip.

4   Remove the clutch and differential housing complete with differential, from the press, lubricate the lips of a new oil seal and carefully slide it over the splined shaft (photo). Tap the seal into the housing using a block of wood or tube until it is flush with the edge of the internal land.

5   Place the magnet in its location in the bottom of the housing.

6   Hold the assembled mainshaft, input shaft and reverse shaft together and locate all three shafts as an assembly into the housing.

7   Insert the long detent plunger into its location and push it through

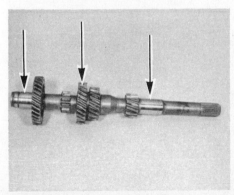
12.1A Inspect the shafts for wear or scoring of the teeth and bearing contact areas (arrowed) ...

12.1B ... checking closely for chipped teeth (arrowed)

12.5 Locate the roller and spring key in the synchroniser unit ...

12.6 ... then push down to locate the roller in its groove

13.4 Fit a new oil seal to the clutch and differential housing

13.7 Push the detent plunger into its location with a screwdriver

13.8 Insert the small detent plunger (arrowed) into the 1st/2nd selector shaft

13.11A Refit the 1st/2nd selector fork roll pin ...

13.11B ... and the 3rd/4th selector fork roll pin ...

13.11C ... then tap in the pins until they are flush with the forks

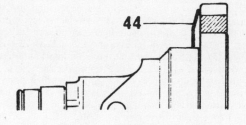

Fig. 6.14 Dished thrust washer fitting position against differential crownwheel (Sec 13)

*44 Dished thrust washer*

into contact with the reverse shaft detent grooves using a screwdriver (photo).

8    Locate the 1st/2nd selector fork in its groove in the synchro sleeve and engage the 1st/2nd selector shaft into it. Turn the shaft so that the detent grooves at the top are towards the mainshaft, insert the small detent plunger into the hole in the shaft and push the shaft down through the fork (photo). Manipulate the reverse shaft as necessary in the neutral position so that the 1st/2nd shaft can be pushed fully home.

9    Place the 3rd/4th selector fork into the groove in the synchro sleeve with its thicker side towards the differential.

10   Locate the detent plunger in its groove in the housing then slide the 3rd/4th selector shaft through the fork. Ensure that all the shafts are in neutral and push the 3rd/4th shaft fully home. It may take a few attempts to get all the shafts, particularly reverse, in just the right position so that the detent plungers all locate fully into their grooves enabling the 3rd/4th shaft to be fitted.

11   Support the selector shafts using a tube of suitable diameter and refit the 1st/2nd and 3rd/4th selector fork roll pins. Tap in the pins until they are flush with the side of the forks (photos).

12   On five-speed models, refit the remaining detent plunger to its location in the housing.

## 14   Gearbox – reassembling the housings

1    Make sure that the thrust washer is in position on top of the mainshaft on four-speed units, and that the 5th speed selector shaft, detent ball and spring are in place in the mechanism casing on five-speed units.

2    Wipe clean the mating faces of the two housings then apply a bead of CAF 4/60 THIXO jointing compound, available from Renault dealers, to both mating faces. *Note that no gasket is used.*

3   Make sure that all the shafts are in neutral and that the engagement slots on the 1st/2nd and 3rd/4th shafts are exactly in line.

4   Pull the fork control shaft on the mechanism casing outwards as far as it will go then lower the mechanism casing over the geartrains. Align the selector shafts with the holes in the casing and, as the shafts protrude, remove the two bolts or rods used to retain the detent balls and springs (photo).

5   As the input shaft and mainshaft enter their bearings, tap the casing with a plastic mallet to assist entry.

6   Pass a hooked piece of wire through the aperture in the top of the casing (photo). Lift up the reverse shaft and gear then retain the shaft with the detent ball, spring and retaining plate.

7   Fit two of the retaining bolts to secure the housings, then check that it is possible to engage all the gears.

8   If satisfactory so far, refit the limit stop threaded plug on four-speed units, or the 5th speed detent assembly on five-speed units.

9   On the four-speed gearbox refit the dished washer and circlip to the end of the input shaft, then compress the washer by striking the circlip with a hammer and suitable socket or tube. As the washer compresses, the circlip will locate into its groove (photos). Repeat this procedure for the mainshaft dished washer and circlip, but on this shaft compress the washer using a socket and bolt screwed into the end of the mainshaft (photos).

10  Refit all the remaining housing retaining bolts tightened to the specified torque.

14.4 Refit the mechanism casing over the geartrains

14.6 Use a hooked piece of wire to lift the reverse shaft

14.9A Refit the dished washer and circlip to the input shaft ...

14.9B ... then tap the circlip using a hammer and tube to compress the washer

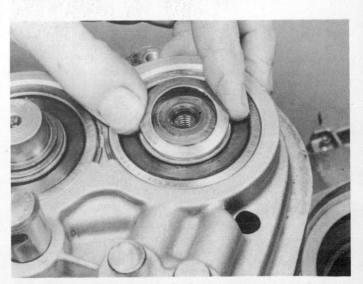

14.9C Refit the dished washer ...

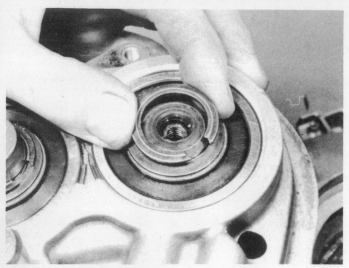

14.9D ... and circlip to the mainshaft

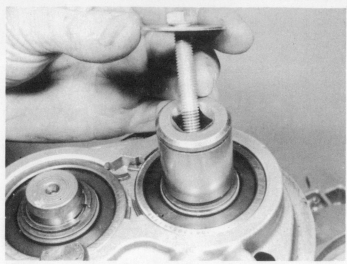

14.9E Compress the dished washer using a socket, bolt and washer ...

14.9F ... in contact with the circlip

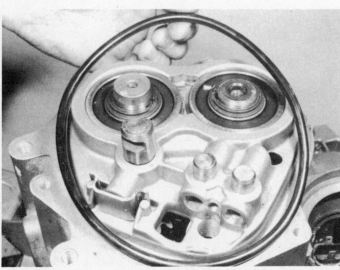

14.17A Place a new rubber O-ring seal on the casing ...

11 On the five-speed gearbox, apply a few drops of Loctite FRENBLOC to the 5th speed driven gear, fit the gear to the mainshaft and push it fully onto the shaft using a socket with a bolt through its centre and screwed into the threaded end of the mainshaft. Tighten the bolt and the socket will force the gear fully home.

12 Remove the socket and bolt, fit the dished washer and circlip then compress the washer using the same bolt and socket method. As the washer is compressed the circlip will enter its groove.

13 Where fitted, refit the collar, bolt and washer to the end of the mainshaft after applying a few drops of locking compound to the bolt threads.

14 Fit the washer, bearing bush and needle roller bearing to the input shaft, apply a few drops of thread locking compound to the 5th speed synchro-hub splines then refit the driving gear, synchro-hub and selector fork as an assembly. Ensure that the offset boss of the synchro-hub is towards the driven gear.

15 Engage 1st gear by moving the gear linkage fork control shaft, and engage 5th gear by moving the 5th speed selector fork. With the gear-train now locked, refit and tighten the 5th gear retaining nut to the specified torque.

16 Return the gears to neutral and refit the 5th gear selector fork roll pin.

17 On all types, place a new rubber O-ring seal on the mechanism casing and refit the rear cover. Secure the cover with the retaining bolts (photos).

14.17B ... and refit the rear cover

18  Refit the O-ring to the splines of the differential stub shaft.
19  Refit the gearbox mounting bracket then refer to Chapter 5 and refit the cluch release bearing and fork assembly.
20  The gearbox can now be refitted to the car, as described in Section 4.

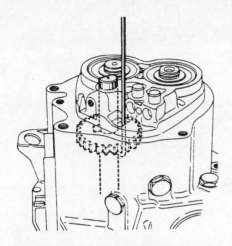

**Fig. 6.15 Using a hooked piece of wire to lift the reverse shaft and gear (Sec 14)**

## 15  Gear lever and remote control housing – removal, refitting and adjustment

1  To remove the gear lever and remote control housing first jack up the front of the car and support it on axle stands.
2  From underneath, unhook the tension spring fitted between the gearchange rod and the stud on the vehicle floor (photo).
3  Slacken the clamp bolt securing the gearchange rod to the gear lever yoke and withdraw the yoke from the rod.
4  Refer to Chapter 11 and remove the centre console.
5  With the console removed, undo the four bolts securing the remote control housing to the floor and withdraw the assembly from the car. Recover the sealing gasket.
6  If necessary the gear lever assembly may be dismantled by referring to the component locations shown in Fig. 6.16. Note that the gear lever knob is bonded with adhesive to the lever.
7  Reassembly and refitting are the reverse of the above procedures. Adjust the gear lever as follows before tightening the yoke clamp bolt.
8  Select 2nd gear at the gearbox by moving the fork control shaft.
9  Move the gear lever so that the O-ring on the gear lever rests against the side of the remote control housing, as shown in Fig. 6.18. With the gear lever in this position leave a space of 5 mm (0.2 in) between the end of the gearchange rod and the fork of the gear lever yoke. Hold the components in this position and tighten the clamp bolt.
10  Check that all the gears can be selected and then refit the centre console, as described in Chapter 11, and lower the car to the ground.

**Fig. 6.16 Exploded view of the gear lever and remote control housing components (Sec 15)**

 1  Gearchange rod
 2  Tension spring
 3  Remote control housing
 4  Gear lever knob
 5  Rubber gaiter
 6  Roll pin
 7  Reverse stop release
 8  Circlip
 9  Gear lever
10  O-ring
11  Roll pin
12  Reverse stop release holder
13  Spring
14  Top cup
15  Damper
16  Half cup
17  Bottom cup
18  Half cup holder
19  Bellows
20  Limit stop
21  Roll pin
22  Stop

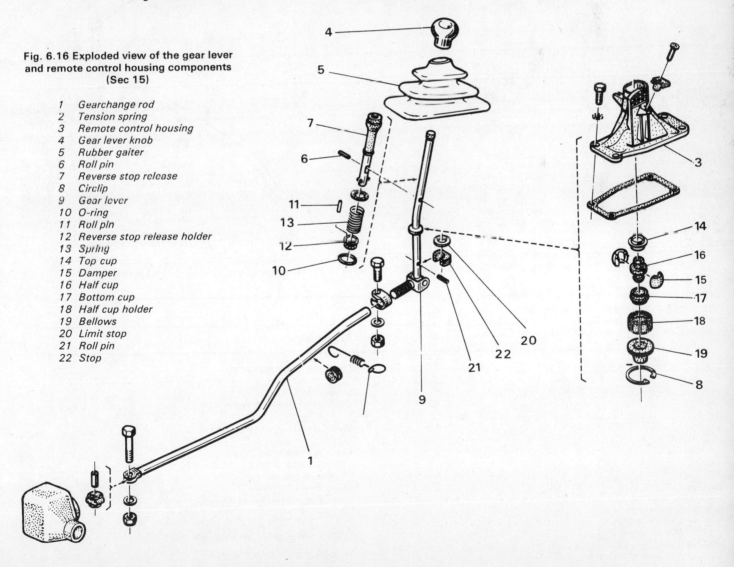

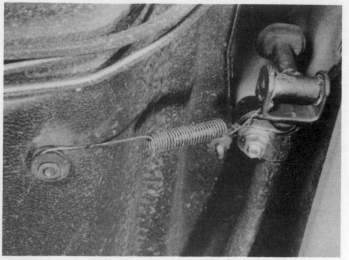

15.2 Gearchange rod tension spring location

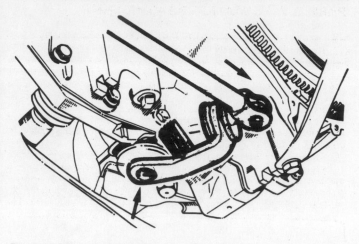

Fig. 6.17 Move the fork control shaft as shown to engage 2nd gear in the gearbox (Sec 15)

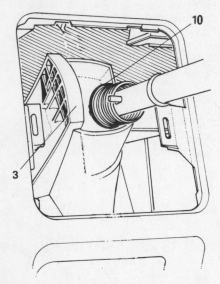

Fig. 6.18 Position the gear lever so that the O-ring (10) rests against the side of the remote control housing (3) (Sec 15)

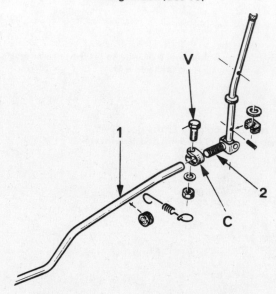

Fig. 6.19 Gear linkage adjustment (Sec 15)

| | | | |
|---|---|---|---|
| 1 | Gearchange rod | C | Gear lever yoke clamp |
| 2 | Gear lever yoke | V | Clamp bolt |

## 16 Fault diagnosis – manual gearbox

| Symptom | Reason(s) |
|---|---|
| Gearbox noisy in neutral | Input shaft bearings worn |
| Gearbox noisy only when moving (in all gears) | Mainshaft bearings worn<br>Differential bearings worn |
| Gearbox noisy in only one gear | Worn, damaged or chipped gear teeth |
| Jumping out of gear | Worn synchroniser units<br>Worn selector shaft detent grooves or broken plunger or ball spring<br>Worn selector forks<br>Gear or synchroniser unit loose on shaft<br>(5th gear only) |
| Ineffective synchromesh | Worn baulk rings or synchroniser units |
| Difficulty in engaging gears | Clutch fault<br>Gear lever out of adjustment |

## PART 2: AUTOMATIC TRANSMISSION

### 17 General description

Renault 9 and 11 Automatic models are equipped with a three-speed fully automatic transmission. The transmission consists of a torque converter, an epicyclic geartrain, hydraulically-operated clutches and brakes, and an electronic control unit.

The torque converter provides a fluid coupling between engine and transmission which acts as an automatic clutch, and also provides a degree of torque multiplication when accelerating.

The epicyclic geartrain provides either of the three forward or one reverse gear ratios according to which of its component parts are held stationary or allowed to turn. The components of the geartrain are held or released by brakes and clutches which are activated by a hydraulic control unit. An oil pump within the transmission provides the necessary hydraulic pressure to operate the brakes and clutches.

Impulses from switches and sensors connected to the transmission, throttle and selector linkage are directed to a computer module which determines the ratio to be selected from the information received. The computer activates solenoid valves which in turn open or close ducts within the hydraulic control unit. This causes the clutches and brakes to hold or release the various components of the geartrain and provide the correct ratio for the particular engine speed or load. The information from the computer module can be overriden by use of the selector lever and a particular gear can be held if required, regardless of engine speed.

Due to the complexity of the automatic transmission any repair or overhaul work must be left to a Renault dealer with the necessary special equipment for fault diagnosis and repair. The contents of the following Sections are therefore confined to supplying general information and any service information and instruction that can be used by the owner.

**Fig. 6.20 Sectional view of the automatic transmission (Sec 17)**

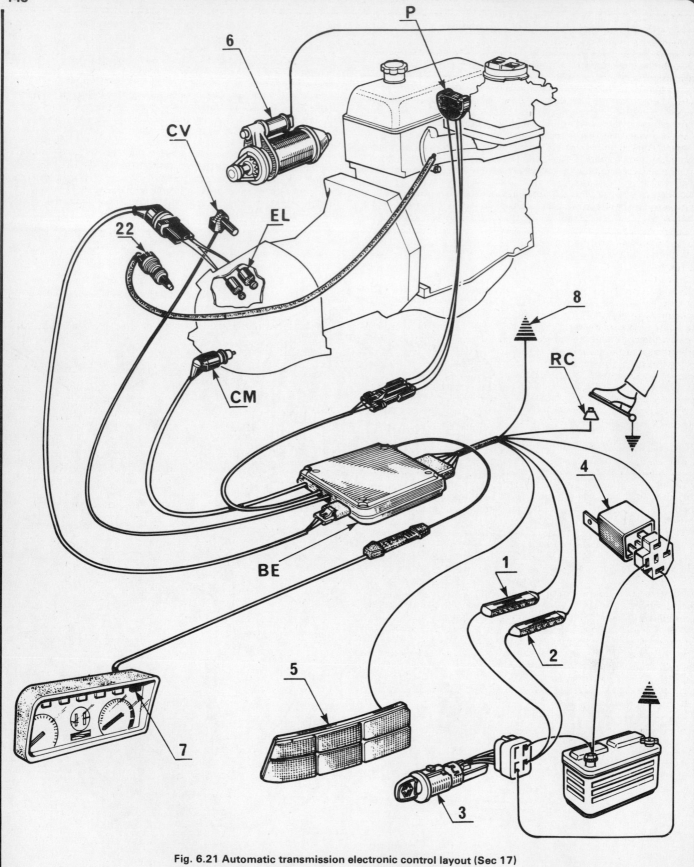

**Fig. 6.21 Automatic transmission electronic control layout (Sec 17)**

| | | | |
|---|---|---|---|
| 1 | Fuse | 5 | Reversing lamps | 8 | Transmission earth | CV | Speed sensor |
| 2 | Fuse | 6 | Starter | 22 | Vacuum capsule | EL | Solenoid valves |
| 3 | Ignition switch | 7 | Automatic transmission | BE | Computer module | RC | Kick-down switch |
| 4 | Starter relay | | warning lamp | CM | Multi-function switch | P | Load potentiometer |

## 18 Maintenance and inspection

1 At the intervals specified in Routine maintenance, inspect the transmission joint faces and oil seals for any sign of damage, deterioration or oil leakage. Check that the fluid cooler pipes and electrical wiring are secure and that there are no leaks at the pipe unions.

2 At the same service intervals check and, if necessary, top up the transmission fluid using the procedure described in Section 19.

3 At less frequent intervals (see Routine maintenance) the automatic transmission fluid should be drained and refilled with fresh fluid, and this procedure is described in Section 20.

## 19 Automatic transmission fluid – level checking

1 Check the fluid level when the car has been standing for some time and the fluid is cold.

2 With the car standing on level ground, start the engine and allow it to run for a few minutes.

3 Move the selector lever to P if not already in this position.

4 With the engine still idling withdraw the dipstick from the front of the transmission, wipe it on a clean cloth, insert it again then withdraw it once more and read off the level. Ideally the level should be in the centre of the mark on the dipstick. The fluid must never be allowed to fall below the bottom of the mark and the transmission must never be overfilled so that the level is above the top of the mark.

5 If topping-up is necessary, switch off the engine and add a quantity of the specified fluid to the transmission through the dipstick tube. Use a funnel with a fine mesh screen to avoid spillage and to ensure that any foreign matter is trapped.

6 After topping-up recheck the level again, as described above, refit the dipstick and switch off the engine.

## 20 Automatic transmission fluid – draining and refilling

1 The fluid must only be drained when cold.

2 Position the car on level ground and place a suitable container beneath the drain plug on the transmission fluid pan and at the base of the transmission housing (Fig. 6.24).

3 Remove the dipstick to speed up the draining operation, undo the two drain plugs and allow the fluid to drain.

4 When all the fluid has drained (this may take quite some time) refit the drain plugs.

5 Place a funnel with fine mesh screen in the dipstick tube and fill the transmission with the specified type of fluid. Depending on the extent to which the fluid was allowed to drain, refilling will only require approximately 2 litres (3.5 Imp pints). Add about half this amount and then check the level on the dipstick. When the level approaches the mark, place the selector lever in P, start the engine and allow it to run for approximately 2 minutes. Now check the level and complete the final topping up, as described in Section 19.

## 21 Automatic transmission – removal and refitting

1 After disconnecting all the relevant attachments, controls and services, the automatic transmission is removed upwards and out of the engine compartment. Due to the weight of the unit, it will be necessary to have some form of lifting equipment available, such as an engine crane or suitable hoist to enable the unit to be removed in this way.

2 Begin by disconnecting the battery negative terminal and then refer to Section 20 and drain the transmission fluid.

3 Jack up the front of the car and support it on axle stands. Remove both front roadwheels.

4 Refer to Chapter 7, Section 3 and remove the left-hand driveshaft completely. Remove the right-hand driveshaft inner joint yoke as described in Chapter 7, Section 3, paragraphs 3 to 6 and 11 to 13.

5 Working in the engine compartment, remove the air cleaner, as described in Chapter 3.

6 Undo the two shouldered bolts and remove the angular position sensor from the bellhousing.

7 Extract the speedometer cable, wire retaining clip from its locating

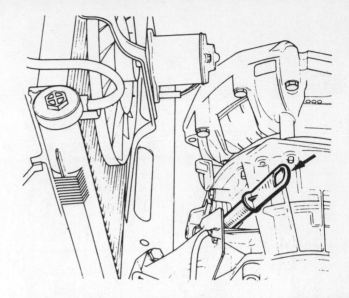

Fig. 6.22 Transmission fluid dipstick location (arrowed) (Sec 19)

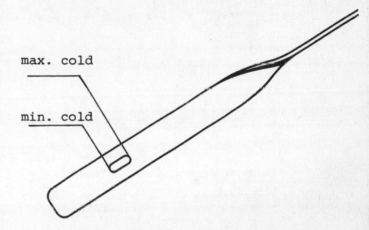

max. cold

min. cold

Fig. 6.23 Dipstick fluid level markings (Sec 19)

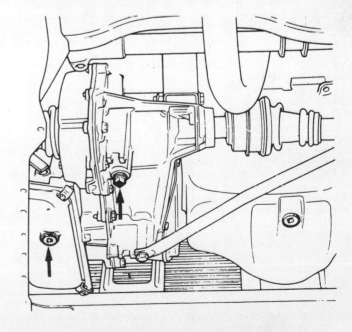

Fig. 6.24 Transmission drain plug locations (arrowed) (Sec 20)

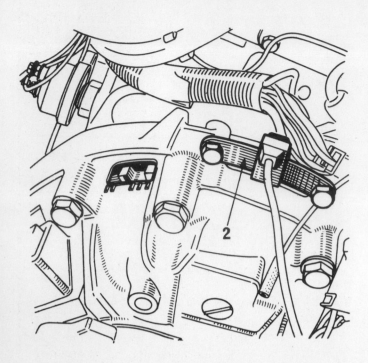

**Fig. 6.25 Angular position sensor location (2) on bellhousing (Sec 21)**

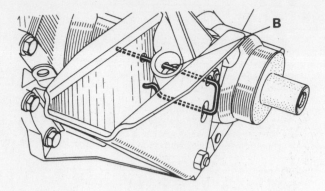

**Fig. 6.26 Speedometer cable retaining clip position (B) (Sec 21)**

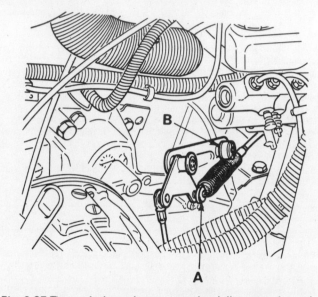

**Fig. 6.27 Transmission selector control rod disconnection points (A and B) (Sec 21)**

holes in the rear engine mounting bracket and transmission housing. Note the fitted direction of the clip. Withdraw the speedometer cable from the transmission.

8 Undo the two bolts and remove the tension springs securing the exhaust front section flange to the exhaust manifold.

9 Note the locations of the wires at the starter solenoid and disconnect them.

10 Undo the starter motor support bracket bolt and the three bolts securing the starter to the bellhousing, then remove the starter. Note the locating dowel in the upper rear bolt location.

11 Disconnect the wiring to the radiator fan motor and thermostatic switch on the right-hand side of the radiator. Release the radiator upper spring retaining clamp, lift the radiator up and lay it over the engine with the hoses still attached. Protect the matrix with a sheet of card.

12 Disconnect the transmission selector control rod from the bracket and bellcrank, as shown in Fig. 6.27.

13 Disconnect the vacuum hose from the vacuum capsule on the front of the transmission.

14 Remove the multi-function switch from the left-hand side of the transmission.

15 Detach any clips and remaining cables as necessary and position all the disconnected wiring, harness and cables to one side so that there is clear access to the transmission from above.

16 From under the car, undo the bolts securing the lower cover plate to the bellhousing and remove the plate.

17 Turn the flywheel as necessary for access, then undo the three bolts securing the torque converter to the driveplate.

18 Undo the bolts securing the steady rod to the engine and transmission, then remove the rod.

19 Undo the fluid cooler union nuts and remove the pipes from the transmission. Plug the unions to prevent dirt entry.

20 Bolt a suitable strip of metal, using one of the coverplate bolt holes, so that the torque converter will remain in place on the transmission as it is removed.

21 Position a jack under the engine sump with an interposed block of wood, and attach a crane or hoist to the transmission using chain slings. Depending on the type of lifting equipment being used, it may be beneficial to remove the bonnet, as described in Chapter 11.

22 Raise the jack and crane and just take the weight of the engine and transmission.

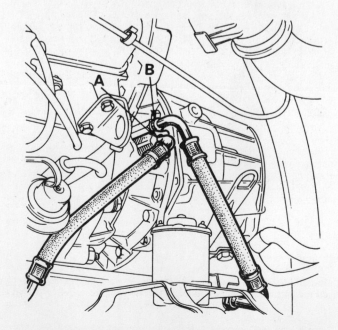

**Fig. 6.28 Fluid cooler union nuts (A and B) at the transmission (Sec 21)**

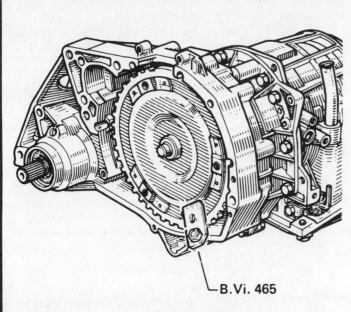

B.Vi. 465

Fig. 6.29 The Renault tool shown or a suitable strip of metal can be used to retain the torque converter on the transmission (Sec 21)

Fig. 6.30 The two studs (C and D) must be removed to enable the transmission to be withdrawn (Sec 21)

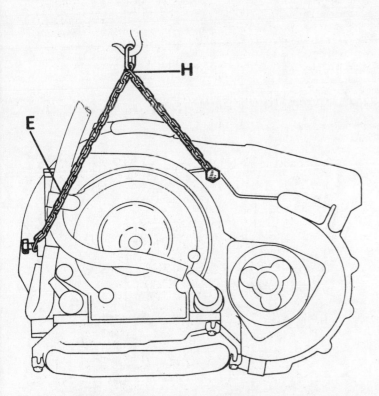

Fig. 6.31 After separating the transmission from the engine, attach the lifting chains as shown and position the crane (H) at point (E) on the chain (Sec 21)

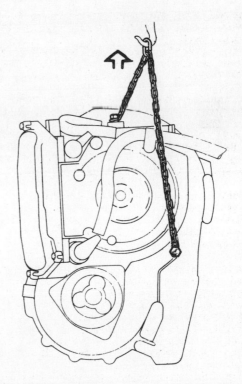

Fig. 6.32 The transmission must be tipped up vertically to allow removal from the engine compartment (Sec 21)

23 Undo all the bolts around the periphery of the bellhousing securing the transmission to the engine. In addition to the bolts there are two nuts or studs, one each side of the bellhousing. After undoing the nuts, the studs must be removed and this can be done by locking two nuts tightly together on the stud then unscrewing it using the innermost nut.

24 Undo the bolts and nuts securing the transmission mounting brackets to the rubber mountings. Raise the engine and transmission slightly to free the mountings then remove the transmission mounting brackets. Also slacken the engine mountings.

25 Move the engine and transmission as necessary and withdraw the transmission sideways off the engine.

26 Temporarily lower the transmission onto blocks and reposition the chain, as shown in Fig. 6.31. The transmission must be tipped up vertically to provide clearance for removal.

27 Lift the transmission using the crane, move the engine within its limits and allow the transmission to adopt the position shown in Fig. 6.32. Continue carefully lifting the transmission until it can swing over the wing or front panel, then lower the unit to the ground.

28 Refitting the automatic transmission is the reverse sequence to removal, but bear in mind the following points:

(a) *Lubricate the torque converter location in the crankshaft with molybdenum grease*

(b) *Fit the two studs to either side of the bellhousing before refitting the remainder of the transmission-to-engine retaining bolts*

(c) *Tighten the exhaust front section-to-manifold bolts so that the tension springs are compressed as shown in Fig. 6.6*

(d) *Refit the driveshafts, as described in Chapter 7, Section 3*

(e) *Refill the transmission with fluid, as described in Section 20 of this Chapter*

## 22 Selector mechanism – adjustment

1 Jack up the front of the car and support it on axle stands.

2 Move the selector lever inside the car to the P position.

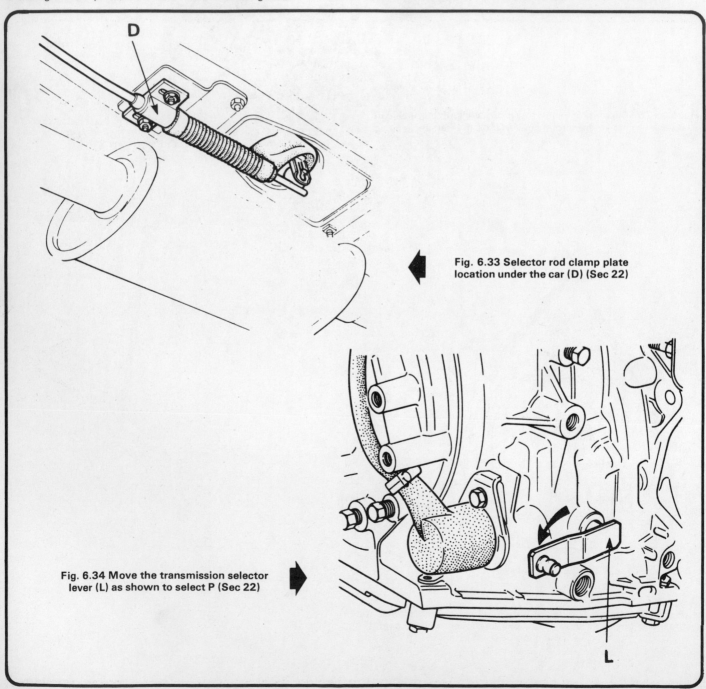

Fig. 6.33 Selector rod clamp plate location under the car (D) (Sec 22)

Fig. 6.34 Move the transmission selector lever (L) as shown to select P (Sec 22)

3   Slacken the selector rod clamp plate nuts under the car so that the rod is free to move within the clamp plate.
4   Check that the selector lever on the transmission is also in the P position by turning it anti-clockwise as far as it will go if not already in this position.
5   Now tighten the selector rod clamp plate nuts.
6   Lower the car to the ground and check that all the selector positions can be engaged and that the starter only operates in the P and neutral positions.

## 23  Selector mechanism – removal and refitting

1   Jack up the front of the car and support it on axle stands.
2   Remove the centre console, as described in Chapter 11.
3   From under the car, extract the retaining clip, washer and clevis pin securing the gear selector lever to the selector rod.
4   Undo the nuts and bolts securing the gear selector housing to the floor, disconnect the illumination bulb wiring and remove the housing from the car.
5   If necessary the housing can be dismantled by referring to the component locations shown in Fig. 6.35.
6   Reassembling and refitting are the reverse of the above procedures. Adjust the mechanism, as described in Section 22, after refitting.

## 24  Fault diagnosis – automatic transmission

In the event of a fault occurring on the transmission, it is first necessary to determine whether it is of an electrical, mechanical or hydraulic nature and to do this special test equipment is required. It is therefore essential to have this work carried out by a Renault dealer if a transmission fault is suspected or if the transmission warning lamp on the instrument panel illuminates.

Do not remove the transmission from the car for possible repair before professional fault diagnosis has been carried out, since most tests require the transmission to be in the vehicle.

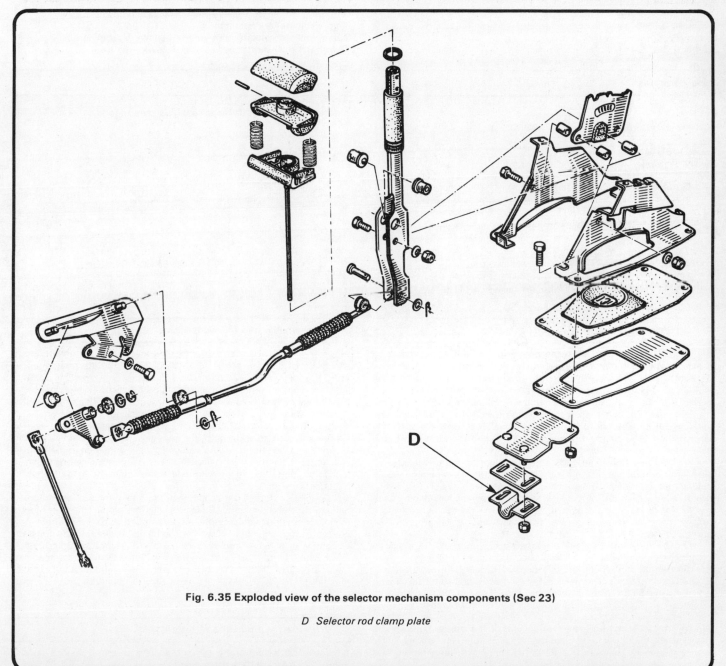

**Fig. 6.35 Exploded view of the selector mechanism components (Sec 23)**

*D  Selector rod clamp plate*

# Chapter 7  Driveshafts

*For modifications, and information applicable to later models, see Supplement at end of manual*

## Contents

## Specifications

**Type** ..................................................................................................  Unequal length solid driveshafts with sliding tripode constant velocity joints

### Lubrication
*Assembly only – see text*
Type:
   Outer constant velocity joints and right-hand inner spider
   and yoke................................................................................... Elf S747 or equivalent (Duckhams LBM 10)
Quantity:
   Outer constant velocity joint ................................................. 195g (6.88 oz)
   Inner spider and yoke ............................................................ 140g (4.94 oz)

### Torque wrench settings

| | Nm | lbf ft |
|---|---|---|
| Driveshaft retaining nut | 250 | 185 |
| Left-hand inner bellows retaining plate | 25 | 18 |

## 1  General description

Drive is transmitted from the differential to the front wheels by means of two, unequal length, solid steel driveshafts.

Both driveshafts are fitted with a constant velocity joint of the sliding tripode type at their outer ends. The constant velocity joint consists of the stub axle member which is splined to engage with the front wheel hub, and a spider containing needle roller bearings and cups which engage with the driveshaft yoke. The complete assembly is protected by a rubber bellows secured to the driveshaft and stub axle member.

At the driveshaft inner ends a different arrangement is used each side. On the right-hand side the driveshaft is splined to engage with a spider also containing needle roller bearings and cups. The spider is free to slide within the joint yoke which is splined and retained by a roll pin to the differential sun wheel stub shaft. As on the outer joints a rubber bellows secured to the driveshaft and yoke protects the complete assembly.

On the left-hand side the driveshaft also engages with a spider, but the yoke in which the spider is free to slide is an integral part of the differential sun wheel. On this side the rubber bellows is secured to the transmission casing with a retaining plate and to a ball-bearing on the driveshaft with a retaining clip. The bearing allows the driveshaft to turn within the bellows which do not revolve.

The design and construction of the driveshaft components is such that the only repairs possible are renewal of the rubber bellows and renewal of the inner joint spiders. Wear or damage to the outer constant velocity joints or the driveshaft splines can only be rectified by fitting a complete new driveshaft assembly.

## 2  Maintenance and inspection

1   A thorough inspection of the driveshafts and driveshaft joints should be carried out at the intervals given in Routine maintenance, using the following procedure:
2   Jack up the front of the car and support it securely on axle stands.
3   Slowly rotate the roadwheel and inspect the condition of the outer constant velocity joint rubber bellows. Check for signs of cracking, splits or deterioration of the rubber which may allow the grease to escape and lead to water and grit entry into the joint. Also check the security and condition of the retaining clips and then repeat these checks on the inner joint bellows. If any damage or deterioration is found the joints should be attended to immediately, as described in Sections 4, 5 or 6.
4   Continue rotating the roadwheel and check for any distortion or damage to the driveshafts. Check for any free play in the outer joints by holding the driveshaft firmly and attempting to turn the wheel. Any noticeable movement indicates wear in the joints, wear in the constant velocity joint or wheel hub splines, a loose driveshaft retaining nut or loose wheel bolts. Carry out any necessary repairs with reference to the appropriate Sections of this, and other applicable Chapters of this manual.

## 3  Driveshaft – removal and refitting

1   Jack up the front of the car and securely support it on axle stands. Remove the appropriate roadwheel.

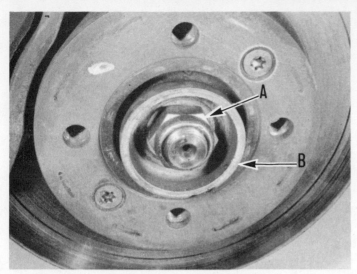

3.2 Driveshaft retaining nut (A) and dished thrust plate (B)

axle carrier (photo). Using a suitable extractor tool, release the balljoint and move the steering arm to one side.

5   Undo and remove the two nuts and withdraw the bolts securing the stub axle carrier to the suspension strut (photo).

6   The procedure now varies according to whether the left-hand or right-hand driveshaft is being removed.

*Left-hand driveshaft*

7   Refer to Chapter 6 and drain the gearbox oil or automatic transmission fluid.

8   Undo the three bolts securing the rubber bellows retaining plate to the side of the transmission casing (photo).

9   Disengage the stub axle carrier from the suspension strut and tip the carrier outwards at the top (photo). At the same time, carefully withdraw the driveshaft inner joint spider from the yoke in the transmission (photo).

10  Withdraw the outer constant velocity joint stub axle from the wheel hub and remove the driveshaft from the car. If the stub axle is a tight fit in the wheel hub, tap it out using a plastic mallet or use a suitable puller.

*Right-hand driveshaft*

11  Using a parallel pin punch of suitable diameter, drive out the roll pin securing the driveshaft inner joint yoke to the differential stub shaft (photo). Note that the roll pin is in fact two roll pins, one inside the other.

12  Disengage the stub axle carrier from the suspension strut and tip the carrier out at the top.

13  Using a soft metal drift, tap the inner joint off the differential stub shaft.

14  Withdraw the outer control velocity joint stub axle from the wheel hub and remove the driveshaft from the car. If the stub axle is a tight fit in the wheel hub, tap it out using a plastic mallet or use a suitable puller.

2   Have an assistant firmly depress the footbrake and then, using a socket and long knuckle bar, undo the driveshaft retaining nut. Recover the dished thrustplate fitted behind the nut (photo).

3   Undo the two bolts securing the brake caliper to the stub axle carrier. Slide the caliper, complete with pads, off the disc and tie it up using string or wire from a suitable place under the wheel arch.

4   Undo the locknut securing the steering arm balljoint to the stub

3.4 Undo the steering arm balljoint locknut (arrowed) and release the balljoint using a suitable extractor

3.5 Undo the two nuts (arrowed) securing the stub axle carrier to the suspension strut and remove the bolts

3.8 On the left-hand driveshaft undo the bolts and lift off the rubber bellows retaining plate

3.9A Disengage the stub axle carrier from the suspension strut and tip the carrier outwards ...

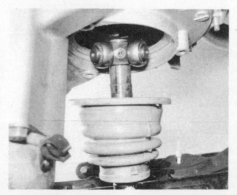

3.9B ... then withdraw the inner joint spider from the transmission

3.11 On the right-hand driveshaft tap out the roll pin securing the inner joint yoke to the transmission stub shaft using a punch

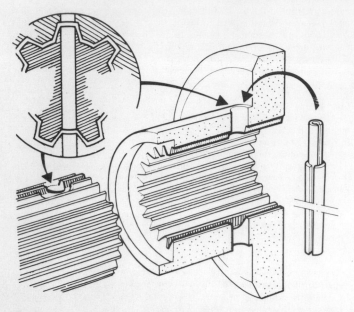

Fig. 7.1 Arrangement of right-hand driveshaft inner joint yoke and roll pin (Sec 3)

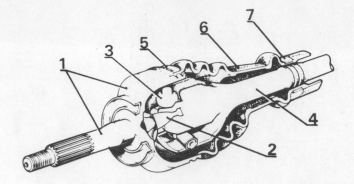

Fig. 7.2 Cutaway view of outer constant velocity joint (Sec 4)

| 1 | Stub axle member | 5 | Retaining clip |
|---|---|---|---|
| 2 | Starplate | 6 | Rubber bellows |
| 3 | Spider and roller cup | 7 | Retaining clip |
| 4 | Driveshaft yoke | | |

*Refitting*

15  Refitting the left-hand or right-hand driveshaft is basically a reverse of the removal procedure with reference to the following additional points:

(a)  *Lubricate the driveshaft joint splines with molybdenum disulphide grease*

(b)  *On the right-hand side, position the inner joint splines so that the roll pin holes will align when the joint is pushed fully home. Position the two roll pins so that their slots are 90° apart (Fig. 7.1)*

(c)  *Ensure that all retaining nuts and bolts are tightened to the specified torque and that the stub axle carrier-to-suspension strut bolts are fitted with their bolt heads toward the rear of the car*

(d)  *If the left-hand driveshaft has been removed, refer to Chapter 6 and refill the transmission with oil or automatic transmission fluid*

---

**4    Outer constant velocity joint rubber bellows – renewal**

1    Remove the appropriate driveshaft from the car, as described in Section 3.

2    If the bellows is secured by metal band type retaining clips, remove them either by releasing the locking tags or by cutting through them using a small hacksaw or chisel. If wire coil type clips are fitted, ease them off using a screwdriver.

3    Slide the bellows down the driveshaft to give access to the constant velocity joint. Remove as much grease as possible from within the joint.

4    Carefully prise up the arms of the starplate, using a screwdriver, so that they are clear of the grooves in the driveshaft yoke.

5    Slide the stub axle member off the driveshaft and then remove the rubber bellows. Recover the thrust ball and spring.

6    Clean the driveshaft yoke and remove as much of the remaining grease as possible from the spider and stub axle member. Do this using a wooden spatula or old rags; *do not use any cleaning solvent, petrol or paraffin.*

7    Obtain a new rubber bellows, retaining clips and a small quantity of the special lubricating grease. All these parts are available in the form of a repair kit obtainable through Renault parts stockists.

8    In order to fit the new bellows a special tool is required to expand the small end of the bellows and allow it to slide over the driveshaft yoke. The manufacturer's tool is shown in the accompanying illustrations, but a suitable alternative can be made by bending a sheet of tin

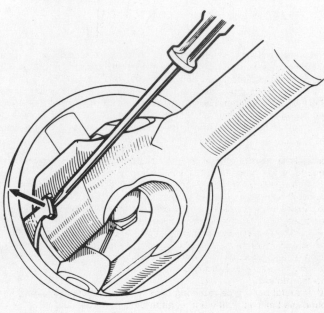

Fig. 7.3 Using a screwdriver to prise up the starplate arms (Sec 4)

in conical fashion and then bonding the seams using superglue or pop rivets. An old 5 litre oil container is quite useful for this purpose. Make sure that the seam is well protected with tape to prevent it cutting the new bellows.

9    Before fitting the new bellows generously lubricate the expander tool and the inside of the bellows with clean engine oil.

10  Position the small end of the bellows over the small end of the tool and move it up and down the expander two or three times to make the rubber more pliable.

11  Position the large end of the expander against the driveshaft yoke and pull the bellows up the expander and onto the yoke. Make sure that the end of the bellows does not tuck under as it is being fitted, and use plenty of lubricant.

12  When the small end of the bellows is in place over the yoke, remove the tool and slide the bellows up the driveshaft.

13  Fit the spring and thrust ball to the spider, move the spider roller cups toward the centre and position the starplate arms centrally between each roller cup.

14  Insert the driveshaft yoke into the stub axle member and then

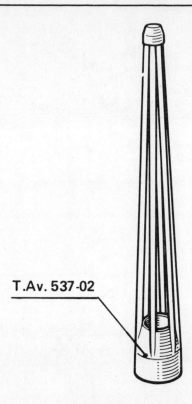

T.Av. 537-02

**Fig. 7.4 Manufacturer's expander tool for fitting rubber bellows (Sec 4)**

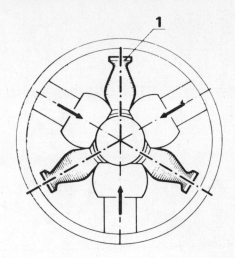

**Fig. 7.5 Correct positioning of starplate arm (1) and roller cups prior to fitting driveshaft yoke (Sec 4)**

carefully bend the starplate arms using a screwdriver so that they engage in the grooves in the yoke.

15 Turn the stub axle member through all angles and ensure that it moves freely.

16 Distribute the grease supplied in the repair kit evenly around the spider and the grooves in the driveshaft yoke.

17 Slide the bellows into position so that it locates in the grooves in the stub axle member and driveshaft. Lift up the lip of the bellows using a blunt instrument, such as a knitting needle, to allow any trapped air to escape. Squeeze the bellows very slightly and remove the instrument.

18 If metal band type retaining clips have been supplied, wrap them round the bellows tightly and engage the slot on one end with the tag on the other. Squeeze the raised portion with pliers to fully tighten the clip.

19 If wire coil type clips have been supplied these can be easily fitted using two short lengths of small diameter tube or two drilled rods. Slip the tube or rods over the ends of the wire coils and then squeeze them together. This will expand the wire coils allowing the clip to be easily placed in position.

20 The driveshaft can now be refitted, as described in Section 3.

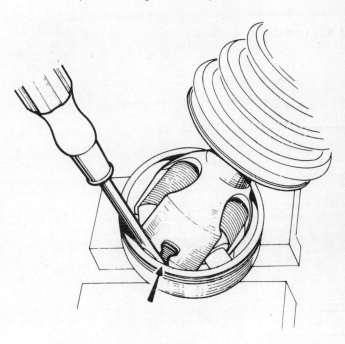

**Fig. 7.6 Engaging the starplate arms with their grooves in the driveshaft yoke (Sec 4)**

## 5 Right-hand driveshaft inner rubber bellows – renewal

1 Remove the driveshaft from the car, as described in Section 3.

2 Using a screwdriver, slip off the retaining spring securing the bellows to the yoke.

3 Release the rubber retaining collar securing the bellows to the driveshaft and slide the bellows down the shaft.

4 Using pliers, carefully bend back the anti-separation plate tags and then slide the yoke off the spider. Be prepared to catch the roller cups which will fall off the spider trunnions as the yoke is withdrawn. Secure the roller cups in place using tape after removal of the yoke. The roller cups are matched to their trunnions and it is most important that they are not interchanged.

5 Extract the circlip securing the spider to the driveshaft using circlip pliers. Using a dab of paint or a small file mark, identify the position of

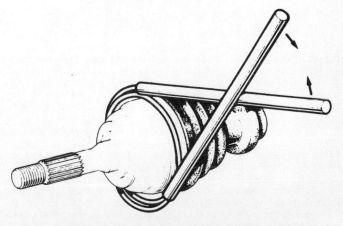

**Fig. 7.7 Fitting bellows coil type wire clips using two small diameter tubes (Sec 4)**

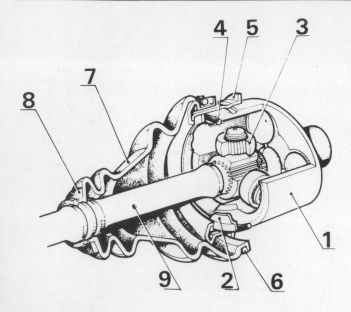

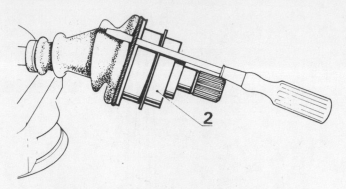

Fig. 7.9 Removing the bellows retaining spring (Sec 5)

2    Yoke

**Fig. 7.8 Cutaway view of the right-hand driveshaft inner joint (Sec 5)**

| | | | |
|---|---|---|---|
| 1 | Yoke | 6 | Bellows retaining spring |
| 2 | Anti-separation plate | 7 | Rubber bellows |
| 3 | Spider roller cup | 8 | Bellows retaining collar |
| 4 | Seal | 9 | Driveshaft |
| 5 | Cover | | |

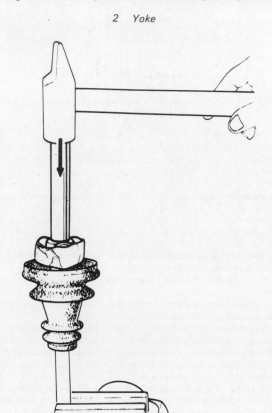

Fig. 7.11 Refitting the spider to the driveshaft splines (Sec 5)

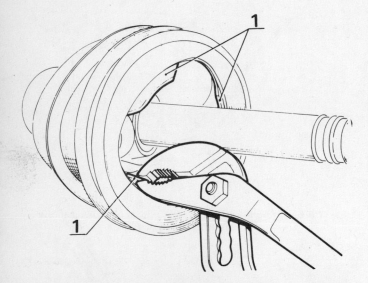

**Fig. 7.10 Using pliers to bend back the anti-separation plate tags (1) in the yoke (Sec 5)**

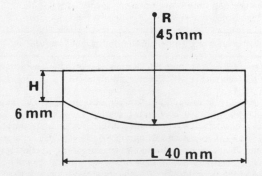

**Fig. 7.12 Form plate fabrication diagram (Sec 5)**

*Material = 2.5 mm (0.1 in) thick*

the spider in relation to the driveshaft, as a guide to refitting.

6    The spider can now be removed in one of the following ways. Preferably using a press or by improvisation with a hydraulic puller, support the spider under the roller cups and press out the driveshaft. If a press is not available support the spider under its central boss, using suitable half-round packing pieces, and drive the shaft out using a hammer and brass drift. It is important, if this method is used, that only the central boss of the spider is supported and not the roller cups. The shock loads imposed could easily damage the inner faces of the cups and spider and the small needle roller bearings.

7    With the spider removed the rubber bellows can now be slid off the driveshaft.

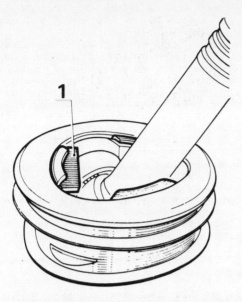

**Fig. 7.13 Using the form plate (1) to reshape the anti-separation plate tags (Sec 5)**

8  Clean the driveshaft and remove as much of the grease as possible from the spider and yoke using a wooden spatula or old rags. *Do not use any cleaning solvent, petrol or paraffin.*

9  Examine the spider, roller cups and yoke for any signs of scoring or wear and for smoothness of movement of the roller cups on the spider trunnions. If wear is evident, renew the spider assembly or the yoke. Also obtain a new rubber bellows, retaining clips and a quantity of the special lubricating grease. These parts are available in the form of a repair kit available from Renault parts stockists.

10  Begin reassembly by lubricating the driveshaft and the inside of the bellows generously with engine oil.

11  Place the rubber retaining collar over the driveshaft and then fit the bellows.

12  Place the spider on the driveshaft splines in the same position as noted prior to removal.

13  Drive the spider fully onto the driveshaft using a hammer and tubular drift, then refit the retaining circlip.

14  Evenly distribute the special grease contained in the repair kit around the spider and inside the yoke.

15  Slide the yoke into position over the spider.

16  Using a piece of 2.5 mm (0.1 in) thick steel or similar material, make up a form plate to the dimensions shown in Fig. 7.12.

17  Position the form plate under each anti-separation plate tag in the yoke in turn, and tap the tag down onto the form plate. Remove the plate when all the tags have been returned to their original shape.

18  Slide the bellows up the driveshaft and locate the bellows in its respective grooves in the driveshaft and in the yoke.

19  Slip the rubber retaining collar into place over the bellows.

20  Insert a thin blunt instrument, such as a knitting needle, under the lip of the bellows to allow all trapped air to escape. With the instrument in position, compress the joint until the dimension from the small end of the bellows to the flat end face of the yoke is as shown in Fig. 7.14. Hold the yoke in this position and withdraw the instrument.

21  Slip a new retaining spring into place to secure the bellows and then refit the driveshaft, as described in Section 3.

---

**6  Left-hand driveshaft inner rubber bellows – renewal**

1  Remove the driveshaft, as described in Section 3.

2  Using circlip pliers, extract the circlip securing the spider to the driveshaft. Using a dab of paint or a small file mark, identify the position of the spider in relation to the driveshaft, as a guide to refitting.

3  The spider can now be removed in one of the following ways. Preferably using a press or by improvisation with a hydraulic puller,

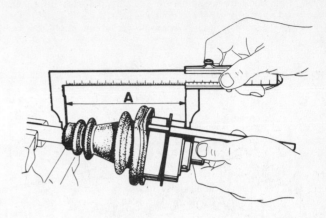

**Fig. 7.14 Bellows setting diagram (Sec 5)**

*A = 153.5 mm (6.04 in)*

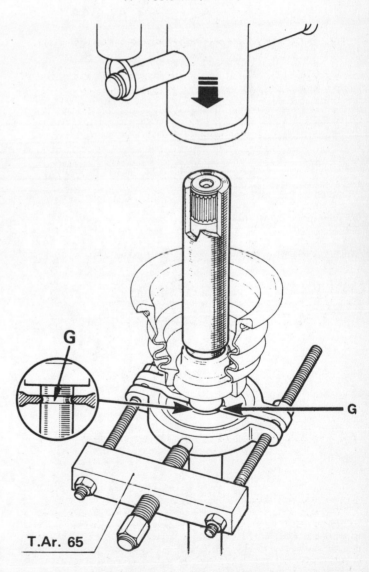

**Fig. 7.15 Arrangement of hydraulic press and manufacturer's tool for refitting bellows bearing (Sec 6)**

*G    Machined groove in driveshaft*

T.Ar. 65

support the spider under the roller cups and press out the driveshaft. Alternatively support the spider under its central boss, using suitable half-round packing pieces, and drive the shaft out using a hammer and brass drift. It is important, if this method is used, that only the central

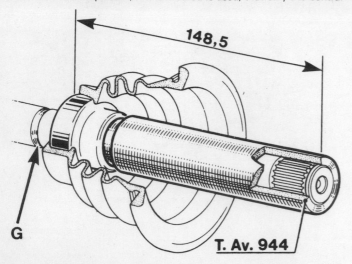

**Fig. 7.16 Bellows bearing setting dimension (Sec 6)**

*G     Machined groove in driveshaft*
*Manufacturer's tool for fitting bearing shown in position over end of driveshaft*

boss of the spider is supported and not the roller cups. The shock loads imposed could easily damage the inner faces of the cups and spider and the small needle roller bearings.

4    Now support the bearing at the small end of the bellows and press or drive the shaft out of the bellows and bearing assembly.

5    Carefully inspect the spider and roller cups for signs of wear or deterioration. The roller cups should be free from any signs of scoring and the cups should turn smoothly on the spider trunnions. The bellows should be renewed, not only because of splitting or deterioration of the rubber, but also if there is any sign of excessive free play of the integral bearing or harshness when it is spun.

6    Due to the lip type oil seal used in the bearing, the bearing and bellows must be refitted using a press or by improvising using a hydraulic puller. There is a very great risk of damaging the seal by distortion if a hammer and tubular drift are used to drive the assembly onto the driveshaft.

7    Fig. 7.15 shows the arrangement for fitting the bellows and bearing if a press is being used. The bellows and bearing must be positioned so that the distance from the end of the driveshaft to the flat face at the small diameter end of the bellows is 148.5 mm (5.85 in) — see Fig. 7.16.

8    Now place the spider on the driveshaft in the same position as noted during removal. Drive or press the spider onto the shaft and refit the circlip.

9    Refit the driveshaft to the car, as described in Section 3.

## 7    Driveshaft inner joint spiders – removal and refitting

1    Removal and refitting of the spiders is an integral part of the rubber bellows renewal procedure and reference should be made to Section 5 or Section 6, as appropriate.

## 8    Fault diagnosis – driveshafts

| Symptom | Reason(s) |
|---|---|
| Vibration and/or noise on turns | Worn constant velocity outer joint(s) |
| Vibration when accelerating | Worn inner joint spiders<br>Dent or distorted driveshaft |
| Noise on taking up drive | Worn stub axle or driveshaft splines<br>Loose driveshaft retaining nut<br>Worn constant velocity joints or inner spiders |

*See also: Fault diagnosis – suspension and steering*

# Chapter 8 Braking system

*For modifications, and information applicable to later models, see Supplement at end of manual*

## Contents

## Specifications

### System type

Servo-assisted dual circuit hydraulic with pressure regulating valve in rear brake circuit. Cable-operated handbrake acting on rear wheels

### Front brakes

| | |
|---|---|
| Type | Disc with Bendix or Girling single piston sliding calipers |
| Disc diameter | 238 mm (9.37 in) |
| Disc thickness (new) | 12 mm (0.47 in) |
| Minimum disc thickness | 11 mm (0.43 in) |
| Maximum disc run-out (measured at 210 (8.27 in) diameter) | 0.07 mm (0.003 in) |
| Maximum variation of disc thickness (measured at 210 mm (8.27 in) diameter) | 0.01 mm (0.0004 in) |
| Minimum brake pad thickness (including backing) | 6.0 mm (0.24 in) |
| Brake caliper cylinder bore diameter | 48 mm (1.89 in) |

### Rear brakes

| | |
|---|---|
| Type | Self-adjusting Bendix or Girling single leading shoe drum |
| Drum diameter | 180.25 mm (7.10 in) |
| Maximum drum diameter | 181.25 mm (7.14 in) |
| Minimum brake shoe friction material thickness (including shoe) | 2.5 mm (0.098 in) |
| Wheel cylinder bore diameter | 17.5 or 22 mm (0.69 or 0.87 in) |

### General

| | |
|---|---|
| Master cylinder bore diameter | 19 mm (0.75 in) |
| Servo unit diameter | 152, 175 or 200 mm (6.0, 6.9 or 7.9 in) according to model and dual circuit layout |
| Hydraulic fluid type/specification | Hydraulic fluid to SAE J1703 F, DOT 3 or DOT 4 (Duckhams Universal Brake and Clutch Fluid) |

### Torque wrench settings

| | Nm | lbf ft |
|---|---|---|
| Master cylinder retaining nuts | 13 | 10 |
| Servo unit retaining nuts | 20 | 15 |
| Brake caliper to stub axle carrier (Bendix) | 100 | 74 |
| Caliper body to reaction frame (Bendix) | 60 | 44 |
| Guide pin bolts (Girling) | 35 | 26 |
| Carrier bracket to stub axle carrier (Girling) | 100 | 74 |
| Bleed screws | 10 | 7 |
| Wheel cylinder to backplate | 10 | 7 |
| Brake backplate to rear suspension trailing arm | 35 | 26 |
| Hydraulic pipe and hose unions | 13 | 10 |
| Rear hub nut | 160 | 118 |
| Roadwheel bolts | 80 | 59 |

## 1 General description

The braking system is of the servo-assisted, dual circuit hydraulic type with disc brakes at the front and drum brakes at the rear. According to model, the dual circuit hydraulic system may be split diagonally, whereby each circuit operates one front and one diagonally opposite rear brake, or front to rear in which one circuit operates the front brakes and the other circuit the rear brakes. Under normal conditions both circuits operate in unison; however, in the event of hydraulic failure in one circuit, full braking force will still be available at two wheels. On certain models a pressure regulating valve is incorporated in the rear brake hydraulic circuit. This valve regulates the pressure applied to the rear brakes, according to vehicle load and

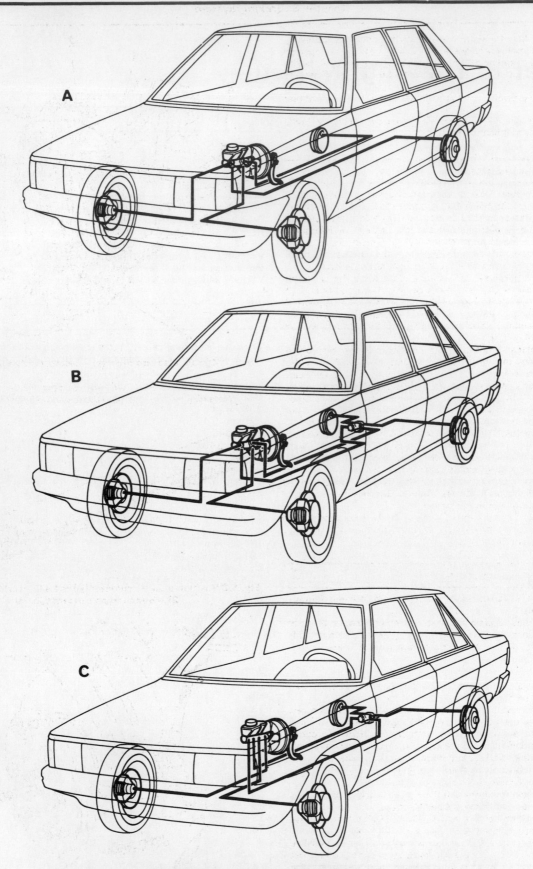

**Fig. 8.1 Braking system hydraulic circuit layouts (Sec 1)**

*A   Diagonally split dual circuit without pressure regulating valve*
*B   Diagonally split dual circuit with pressure regulating valve*
*C   Front to rear split dual circuit with pressure regulating valve*

reduces the possibility of the rear wheels locking under heavy braking.

The front disc brakes are operated by single piston sliding type calipers. At the rear, leading and trailing brake shoes are operated by twin piston wheel cylinders and are self-adjusting by footbrake application.

The handbrake provides an independent mechanical means of rear brake application.

Driver warning lights are provided for brake pad wear, low brake hydraulic fluid level and handbrake applied.

## 2   Maintenance and inspection

1   The brake hydraulic fluid should be checked weekly and, if necessary, topped up with the specified fluid to the MAX mark on the reservoir. To compensate for fluid displacement due to normal wear of brake pads and linings only a small amount of fluid, at infrequent intervals, should be needed to maintain the correct level in the reservoir. The addition of fluid regularly or in large quantities indicates a leak in the system which should be investigated immediately.

2   At the intervals specified in Routine maintenance the following service operations should be carried out on the braking system.

3   With the car raised on a hoist, over an inspection pit or supported on ramps or axle stands, carefully inspect all the hydraulic pipes, hoses and unions for chafing, cracks, leaks and corrosion. Details will be found in Section 14.

4   Remove the plugs over the inspection holes in the rear brake backplates and check the thickness of the brake linings. Renew the brake shoes if the linings have worn to the specified minimum thickness. Note that it is only possible to check the thickness of the brake shoe linings in one position when viewing through the inspection holes. To check the lining condition and the operation of the wheel cylinders, it is recommended that the rear brake drums be removed so that a thorough inspection can be carried out, as described in Section 6.

5   Check the operation of the handbrake on each rear wheel and lubricate the exposed cables and linkages under the car.

6   Remove the front wheels and check the thickness of the front brake pads. Renew the pads, as described in Section 3, if they are worn to the specified minimum thickness.

7   At less frequent intervals (see Routine maintenance) the brake servo air filter and non-return valve should also be renewed, using the procedure described in Section 22.

## 3   Front disc pads – inspection and renewal

1   Jack up the front of the car and support it on axle stands. Remove the front roadwheels.

2   View the brake pads end on and measure their thickness. If any of the pads is less than the specified minimum thickness, all four pads must be renewed as follows, according to brake caliper type.

### Bendix calipers

3   Remove the brake fluid reservoir cap. Disconnect the brake pad wear warning light wire at the connector.

4   Extract the small spring clip and then withdraw the retaining key.

5   Using a suitable blunt instrument, carefully lever between the disc and caliper so that the piston is pushed back sufficiently to allow removal of the pads. The action of retracting the piston will cause the brake fluid level to rise – anticipate this by syphoning some out.

6   Using pliers, if necessary, withdraw the pads from the caliper, and remove the anti-rattle spring from each pad.

7   With the pads removed, check that the caliper is free to slide along its mounting bolts, and that the rubber dust excluders around the piston and caliper guide sleeves are undamaged. If attention to these components is necessary refer to Section 4.

8   To refit the pads, move the caliper sideways as far as possible towards the centre of the car. Fit the anti-rattle spring to the innermost pad and locate the pad in position, with the backing plate against the piston.

9   Using a suitable blunt instrument between the caliper and disc, carefully lever the caliper away from the centre of the car. This will cause the piston to be retracted fully into its bore to allow the remaining new pad to be fitted. The action of retracting the piston will cause a quantity of brake fluid to be returned to the master cylinder

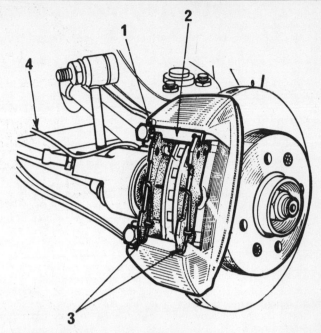

Fig. 8.2 Front disc pad renewal – Bendix type calipers (Sec 3)

1   Spring clip              3   Anti-rattle springs
2   Retaining key           4   Brake pad wear warning light wire

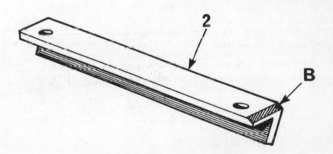

Fig. 8.3 Position of entry chamfer (B) to be filed on retaining key (2) – Bendix type calipers (Sec 3)

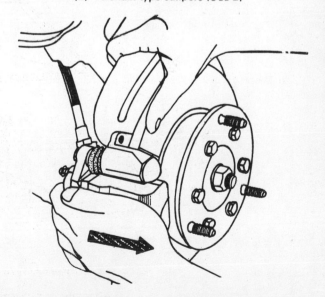

Fig. 8.4 Pull the caliper body outwards to retract the piston prior to removing the pads – Girling type calipers (Sec 3)

reservoir, so place some old rags around the reservoir to catch any fluid which might overflow.

10  Fit the anti-rattle spring to the outer pad and locate the pad in the caliper.

11  Slide the retaining key into place and refit the small spring clip. It may be necessary to file an entry chamfer on the edge of the retaining key to enable it to be fitted without difficulty.

12  Reconnect the brake pad wear warning light wire, refit the roadwheel and repeat the renewal procedures on the other front brake. On completion check the hydraulic fluid level and refit the reservoir cap, depress the footbrake two or three times to bring the pads into contact with the disc, refit the roadwheels and lower the car to the ground.

### Girling calipers

13  Remove the brake fluid reservoir cap. Grasp the caliper body and pull it outwards by hand away from the centre of the car. This will push the piston back into its bore to facilitate removal and refitting of the pads.

14  Disconnect the brake pad wear warning light wire at the connector (photo).

15  Undo the upper and lower guide pin bolts using a suitable spanner while holding the guide pins with a second spanner (photo).

16  With the guide pin bolts removed, lift the caliper off the brake pads and carrier bracket (photo), and tie it up from a convenient place under the wheel arch. Do not allow the caliper to hang unsupported on the flexible brake hose.

17  Withdraw the two brake pads from the carrier bracket (photo).

18  Before refitting the pads, check that the guide pins are free to slide in the carrier bracket and check that the rubber dust excluders around the guide pins are undamaged. Brush the dust and dirt from the caliper and piston but **do not** *inhale as it is injurious to health.* Inspect the dust excluder around the piston for damage and the piston for evidence of fluid leaks, corrosion or damage. If attention to any of these components is necessary, refer to Section 4.

19  To refit the pads, place them in position on the carrier bracket

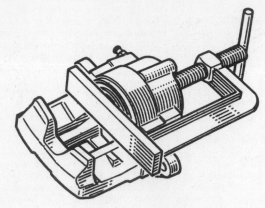

**Fig. 8.5 Retract the caliper piston with a G-clamp – Girling type calipers (Sec 3)**

noting that the pad with the warning light wire must be nearest to the centre of the car (photo).

20  Make sure that the caliper piston is fully retracted in its bore. If not, carefully push it in using a flat bar or screwdriver as a lever or preferably use a G-clamp. The action of retracting the piston will cause a quantity of brake fluid to be returned to the master cylinder reservoir, so place some old rags around the reservoir to catch any fluid which might overflow.

21  Place the caliper body over the pads and refit the guide pin bolts. Tighten the bolts to the specified torque.

22  Reconnect the brake pad wear warning light wire, refit the roadwheel and repeat the renewal procedures on the other front brake. On completion check the hydraulic fluid level and refit the reservoir cap, depress the footbrake two or three times to bring the pads into contact with the disc, then refit the roadwheels and lower the car to the ground.

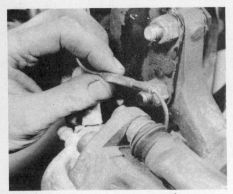

3.14 Disconnect the brake pad wear warning light wire

3.15 Using two spanners, undo the guide pin bolts

3.16 Lift the caliper off the carrier bracket ...

3.17 ... and withdraw the brake pads

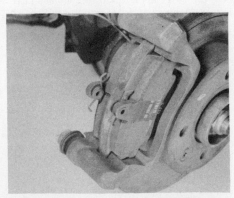

3.19 Refit the pads as shown so that the pad with the warning light wire is on the inside

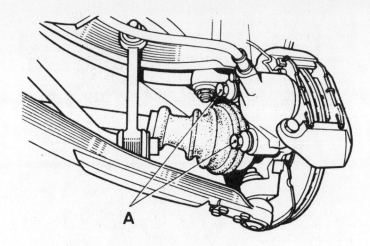

Fig. 8.6 Brake caliper-to-stub axle carrier retaining bolts (A) –
Bendix type calipers (Sec 4)

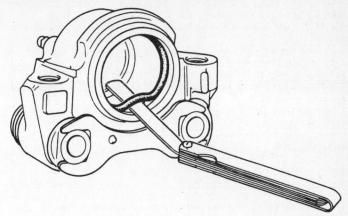

Fig. 8.7 Using a feeler blade to remove the caliper piston seal –
Bendix type calipers (Sec 4)

## 4 Front brake caliper – removal, overhaul and refitting

*Bendix calipers*

1 Jack up the front of the car and support it on axle stands. Remove the appropriate front roadwheel.
2 Remove the brake pads, as described in the previous Section.
3 Undo the two bolts securing the caliper assembly to the stub axle carrier and withdraw the caliper.
4 With the flexible brake hose still attached to the caliper, have an assistant very slowly depress the brake pedal until the piston has been ejected just over halfway out of its bore.
5 Using a brake hose clamp, or self-locking wrench with protected jaws, clamp the brake hose. This will minimise brake fluid loss during subsequent operations.
6 Slacken the brake hose-to-caliper body union, and then, while holding the hose, rotate the caliper to unscrew it from the hose. Lift away the caliper and plug or tape over the end of the hose to prevent dirt entry.
7 With the caliper on the bench wipe away all traces of dust and dirt, but *avoid inhaling the dust as it is injurious to health.*
8 Undo the two bolts securing the caliper body to the reaction frame and lift off the body.
9 Withdraw the partially ejected piston from the caliper body and remove the dust cover.
10 Using a suitable blunt instrument such as a knitting needle or a thick feeler blade, carefully extract the piston seal from the caliper bore.
11 Clean all the parts in methylated spirit or clean brake fluid, and wipe dry using a lint-free cloth. Inspect the piston and caliper bore for signs of damage, scuffing or corrosion, and if these conditions are evident renew the caliper body assembly. Inspect the condition of the dust excluders over the guide sleeves and renew these too if there is any sign of damage or deterioration.
12 If the components are in a satisfactory condition, a repair kit consisting of new seals and dust excluders should be obtained.
13 Thoroughly lubricate the components and piston seal with clean brake fluid and carefully fit the seal to the caliper bore.
14 Insert the piston into its bore, fit the new dust cover and then push the piston fully into its bore.
15 Place the caliper in position on the reaction frame and secure with the two bolts, tightened to the specified torque.
16 Where necessary fit the new seals and dust excluders to the caliper guide sleeves.
17 Hold the flexible brake hose and screw the caliper body back onto the hose.
18 Refit the two bolts securing the caliper assembly to the stub axle carrier and tighten the bolts to the specified torque.
19 Fully tighten the brake hose-to-caliper body union and remove the brake hose clamp.
20 Refit the brake pads, as described in Section 3, and bleed the

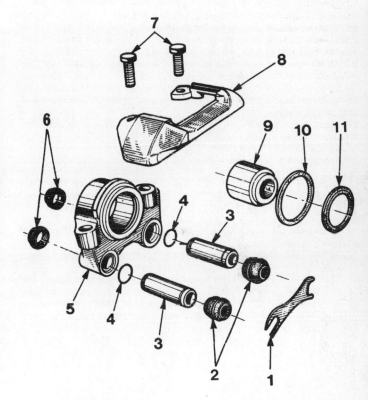

Fig. 8.8 Bendix type brake caliper components (Sec 4)

| | | | |
|---|---|---|---|
| 1 | Retaining strip | 7 | Reaction frame retaining |
| 2 | Guide sleeve inner dust | | bolts |
| | excluders | 8 | Reaction frame |
| 3 | Guide sleeves | 9 | Piston |
| 4 | Guide sleeve seals | 10 | Piston seal |
| 5 | Caliper body | 11 | Piston dust excluder |
| 6 | Guide sleeve outer dust | | |
| | excluders | | |

hydraulic system, as described in Section 15. Note that providing the precautions described were taken to minimise brake fluid loss, it should only be necessary to bleed the relevant front brake.
21 Refit the roadwheel and lower the car to the ground.

*Girling calipers*

22 Jack up the front of the car and support it on axle stands. Remove the appropriate front roadwheel.

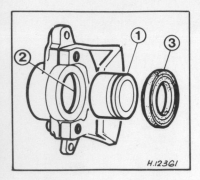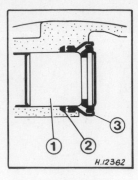

Fig. 8.9 Girling type brake caliper components (Sec 4)

1   Piston                        3   Dust cover
2   Piston seal

23 Using a suitable spanner, unscrew the guide pin bolts while holding the guide pins with a second spanner.

24 Disconnect the pad wear indicator wiring connector (right-hand side caliper only) and lift away the caliper body, leaving the disc pads and carrier bracket still in position. It is not necessary to remove the carrier bracket unless it requires renewal because of accident damage or severe corrosion.

25 With the flexible brake hose still attached to the caliper body, very slowly depress the brake pedal until the piston has been ejected just over halfway out of its bore.

26 Using a brake hose clamp or self-locking wrench with protected jaws, clamp the flexible brake hose. This will minimise brake fluid loss during subsequent operations.

27 Slacken the brake hose-to-caliper body union, and then, while holding the hose, rotate the caliper to unscrew it from the hose. Lift away the caliper and plug or tape over the end of the hose to prevent dirt entry.

28 With the caliper on the bench wipe away all traces of dust and dirt, but *avoid inhaling the dust as it is injurious to health*.

29 Withdraw the partially ejected piston from the caliper body and remove the dust cover.

30 Using a suitable blunt instrument, such as a knitting needle, carefully extract the piston seal from the caliper bore.

31 Clean all the parts in methylated spirit, or clean brake fluid, and wipe dry using a lint-free cloth. Inspect the piston and caliper bore for signs of damage, scuffing or corrosion and if these conditions are evident renew the caliper body assembly. Also renew the guide pins if bent or damaged.

32 If the components are in a satisfactory condition, a repair kit consisting of new seals and dust cover should be obtained.

33 Thoroughly lubricate the components and new seals with clean brake fluid and carefully fit the seal to the caliper bore.

34 Position the dust cover over the innermost end of the piston so

that the caliper bore sealing lip protrudes beyond the base of the piston. Using a blunt instrument, if necessary, engage the sealing lip of the dust cover with the groove in the caliper. Now push the piston into the bore until the other sealing lip of the dust cover can be engaged with the groove in the piston. Having done this, push the piston fully into its bore. Ease the piston out again slightly, and make sure that the cover lip is correctly seating in the piston groove.

35 Remove the guide pins from the carrier bracket and smear them with high melting-point brake grease. Fit new dust covers to the guide pins and refit them to the carrier bracket.

36 Hold the flexible brake hose and screw the caliper body back onto the hose.

37 With the piston pushed fully into its bore, refit the caliper and secure it with the guide pin bolts. Tighten the bolts to the specified torque.

38 Fully tighten the brake hose union and remove the clamp. Reconnect the pad warning light wiring connector.

39 Refer to Section 15 and bleed the brake hydraulic system, noting that if precautions were taken to minimise fluid loss, it should only be necessary to bleed the relevant front brake.

40 Refit the roadwheel and lower the car to the ground.

---

### 5   Front brake disc – inspection, removal and refitting

1   Jack up the front of the car and support it on axle stands. Remove the appropriate front roadwheel.

2   Rotate the disc by hand and examine it for deep scoring, grooving, or cracks. Light scoring is normal, but, if excessive, the disc must be renewed. Any loose rust and scale around the outer edge of the disc can be removed by lightly tapping it with a small hammer while rotating the disc.

3   To remove the disc, undo the two bolts securing the brake caliper assembly to the stub axle carrier. Withdraw the caliper, complete with pads, off the disc and support it to one side. Avoid straining the flexible brake hose.

4   Using a Torx type socket bit or driver, undo the two screws securing the disc to the hub and withdraw the disc. If it is tight, lightly tap its rear face with a hide or plastic mallet. If the disc still refuses to free, refer to Chapter 10, Section 3.

5   Refitting the disc is the reverse sequence to removal. Ensure complete cleanliness of the hub and disc mating faces and tighten all bolts to the specified torque.

---

### 6   Rear brake shoes – inspection and renewal

1   Jack up the rear of the car and support it on axle stands. Remove the rear roadwheels. Release the handbrake.

2   By judicious tapping and levering, remove the hub cap from the centre of the brake drum (photo).

3   Using a socket and long bar, undo the hub nut and remove the thrust washer (photos).

4   It should now be possible to withdraw the brake drum and hub

6.2 Remove the hub cap by tapping and levering

6.3A Undo and remove the hub nut (arrowed) ...

6.3B ... followed by the thrust washer (arrowed) ...

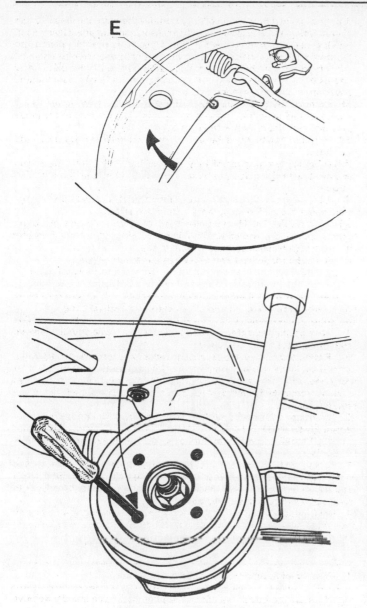

Fig. 8.10 Using a screwdriver inserted through the brake drum to release the handbrake operating lever (Sec 6)

*E  Handbrake operating lever peg*

Fig. 8.11 Remove the brake shoe steady spring cups (R) by depressing and turning through 90° while holding the pin from behind – Bendix brake assemblies (Sec 6)

6.4 ... then withdraw the brake drum

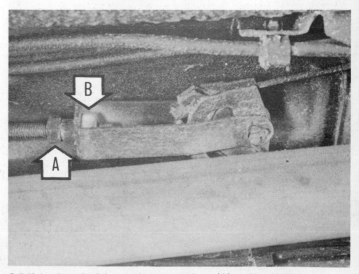

6.5 If the drum is tight, slacken the locknut (A) and back off the handbrake knurled adjuster (B) then release the brake shoes

bearing assembly from the stub axle by hand (photo). It may be difficult to remove the drum due to the tightness of the hub bearing on the stub axle, or due to the brake shoes binding on the inner circumference of the drum. If the bearing is tight, tap the periphery of the drum using a hide or plastic mallet, or use a universal puller, secured to the drum with the wheel bolts, to pull it off. If the brake shoes are binding, proceed as follows:

5   First ensure that the handbrake is fully off. From under the car slacken the locknut then back off the knurled adjuster on the primary rod (photo).

6   Refer to Fig. 8.10 and insert a screwdriver through one of the wheel bolt holes in the brake drum so that it contacts the handbrake operating lever on the trailing brake shoe. Push the lever until the peg slips behind the brake shoe web allowing the brake shoes to retract. The brake drum can now be withdrawn.

7   With the brake drum assembly removed, brush or wipe the dust from the drum, brake shoes, wheel cylinder and backplate. *Take great care not to inhale the dust as it is injurious to health.*

8   Measure the thickness of the friction material, including the shoe. If any of the brake shoes have worn down to the specified minimum

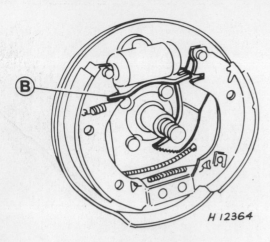

Fig. 8.12 Detach the operating link (B) from the adjusting arm after moving the arm toward the stub axle – Bendix brake assemblies (Sec 6)

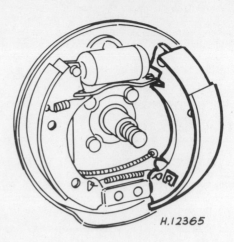

Fig. 8.13 Turn the brake shoes at right-angles to the backplate. Detach the handbrake cable and remove both shoes – Bendix brake assemblies (Sec 6)

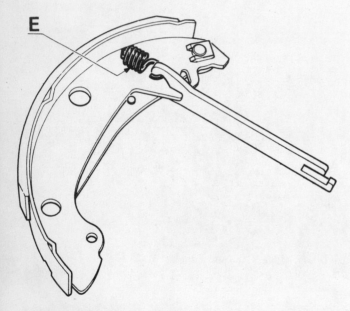

Fig. 8.14 Position the operating link and spring (E) as shown before refitting the brake shoes – Bendix brake assemblies (Sec 6)

Fig. 8.15 Adjusting link notch (A) must locate against the adjusting lever on the leading brake shoe – Girling brake assemblies (Sec 6)

thickness, all four brake shoes must be renewed. The shoes must also be renewed if any are contaminated with brake fluid or grease, or show signs of cracking or scoring. If contamination is evident, the cause must be traced and rectified before fitting new brake shoes. Contamination will be caused either by leaking fluid seals in the wheel cylinder or by a faulty hub bearing oil seal in the brake drum assembly.
9   Examine the internal surface of the brake drum for signs of scoring or cracks. If any deterioration of the surface finish is evident the drum may be skimmed to a maximum of 1.0 mm (0.04 in) on the internal diameter, otherwise renewal is necessary. If the drum is to be skimmed it will be necessary to have the work carried out on both drums to maintain a consistent internal diameter on both sides.
10  If the brake shoes and drum are in a satisfactory condition, proceed to paragraph 26. If the brake shoes are to be removed proceed as follows, according to type:

*Bendix brake assemblies*
11  Before proceeding, make a note of the position and fitted direction of the brake shoe return springs and components as a guide to reassembly.

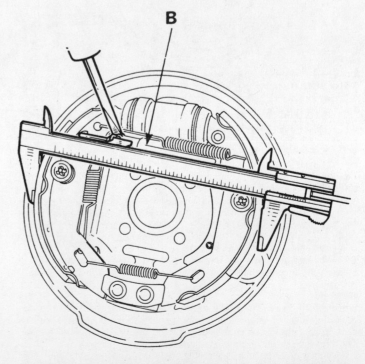

Fig. 8.16 Before refitting the brake drum, turn the toothed wheel on the adjusting link (B) to give a brake shoe diameter of between 178.7 and 179.2 mm (7.04 and 7.06 in) – Girling brake assemblies (Sec 6)

12 Using pliers, detach the upper shoe return spring from both brake shoes.

13 Again using pliers, depress the brake shoe steady spring cups while supporting the steady spring pin from the rear of the backplate with your finger. Turn each spring cup through 90° and withdraw it, together with the spring, from the pin. Withdraw the trailing shoe steady spring pin from the backplate, but note that it is not possible to withdraw the leading shoe pin due to the close proximity of the suspension trailing arm. Note also that there is a hole in the hollow suspension arm directly in line with the steady pin, and, if care is not taken, the pin will drop into the arm. Place a wooden wedge or other suitable packing between the backplate and suspension arm to stop this happening.

14 Ease the leading shoe away from the wheel cylinder at the top and move the serrated adjusting arm towards the stub axle.

15 Detach the operating link end from the adjusting arm and then return the adjusting arm to its original position.

16 Turn the leading shoe at right angles to the backplate and detach the lower return spring. Lift off the shoe.

17 Disconnect the handbrake cable from the operating lever on the trailing brake shoe and lift off the shoe complete with operating link.

18 Extract the spring clips and pivot pins and transfer the self-adjusting mechanism and handbrake lever to the new brake shoes. Also fit the operating link and spring to the new trailing shoe.

19 Before refitting the new brake shoes, clean off the backplate with a rag and apply a trace of silicone grease to the shoe contact areas and pivots on the backplate.

20 Engage the handbrake cable with the operating lever on the trailing shoe and position the shoe complete with operating link on the backplate.

21 Hook one end of the lower return spring into the hole in the trailing shoe and attach the other end to the leading shoe. Place the leading shoe in position on the backplate.

22 Move the leading shoe adjusting arm in towards the stub axle as far as possible and engage the notch on the operating link with the slot on the adjusting arm.

23 Move the serrated quadrant towards the stub axle and allow the adjusting arm to move back to the fully retracted position.

24 Refit the steady pins, springs and cups to both brake shoes, followed by the upper return spring.

25 Ensure that the adjusting arm is fully retracted and that the brake shoes are centrally positioned on the backplate.

26 Slide the brake drum onto the stub axle and refit the thrust washer and hub nut. Tighten the hub nut to the specified torque and then tap the hub cap into place.

27 Depress the footbrake several times to operate the self-adjusting mechanism.

28 The handbrake should now be adjusted, as described in Section 16, or after attending to the brake shoes on the other rear brake if this is being done.

29 On completion, refit the roadwheels and lower the car to the ground.

*Girling brake assemblies*

30 Before proceeding, make a note of the position and fitted direction of the brake shoe return springs and components as a guide to reassembly (photo).

31 Using pliers, detach the upper and lower brake shoe return springs from both brake shoes.

32 Again using pliers, depress the brake shoe steady spring cups while supporting the steady spring pin from the rear of the backplate with your finger. Turn each spring cup through 90° and withdraw it, together with the spring, from the pin. Withdraw the trailing shoe steady spring pin from the backplate, but note that it is not possible to withdraw the leading shoe pin due to the close proximity of the suspension trailing arm. Note also that there is a hole in the hollow suspension arm directly in line with the steady pin, and, if care is not taken, the pin will drop into the arm. Place a wooden wedge or other suitable packing between the backplate and suspension arm to stop this happening.

33 Lift off the leading shoe and the adjusting link, detach the handbrake cable from the trailing shoe operating lever and lift off the trailing shoe.

34 Detach the return spring and adjusting lever from the leading shoe and fit these components to the new leading shoe. Make sure that the spring is fitted correctly (photo).

6.30 Layout and position of the rear brake components prior to removal

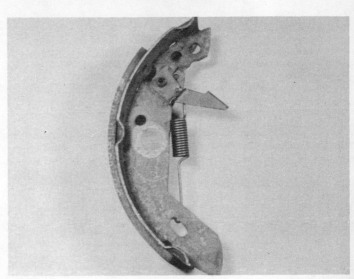

6.34 Correct fitting of the leading brake shoe adjusting lever and return spring

35 Before fitting the new brake shoes, clean off the backplate with a rag and apply a trace of silicone grease to the shoe contact areas and pivots on the backplate.

36 Engage the handbrake cable with the operating lever on the trailing shoe, position the shoe on the backplate and retain it in place with the steady pin, spring and cup (photos).

37 Lubricate the threads in the adjusting link and make sure it is free to turn. Note that the links are not interchangeable from side to side and are colour coded for identification. The link fitted to the left-hand side of the car has a silver coloured end, while the link fitted to the right-hand side has a gold coloured end.

38 Engage the adjusting link ends with both brake shoes (photo) ensuring that the notch on the threaded end locates against the adjusting lever on the leading shoe (photo).

39 Position the leading shoe on the backplate and retain it in place with the steady pin, spring and cup (photo).

40 Refit the upper and lower brake shoe return springs (photos).

41 Hold the adjusting lever clear and turn the toothed wheel on the adjusting link as necessary so that the overall diameter of the brake shoes is between 178.7 and 179.2 mm (7.04 and 7.06 in).

42 Refit the brake drum and complete the remainder of the reassembly, as described in paragraphs 26 to 29 inclusive.

6.35 Apply a trace of silicone grease to the areas arrowed before refitting the brake shoes

6.36A Engage the handbrake cable with the trailing shoe operating lever ...

6.36B ... then secure the shoe in place with the steady pin, spring and cup (arrowed)

6.38A Engage the adjusting link ends with both brake shoes ...

6.38B ... ensuring that the notch on the adjusting link locates against the adjusting lever (arrowed)

6.39 Secure the leading shoe in place with the steady pin, spring and cup (arrowed)

6.40A Refit the upper return spring in the holes (arrowed) ...

6.40B... followed by the lower return spring in the elongated slots (arrowed)

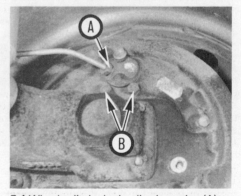

7.4 Wheel cylinder hydraulic pipe union (A) and retaining bolts (B)

## 7 Rear wheel cylinder – removal and refitting

1   Begin by removing the brake drum assembly, as described in Section 6, paragraphs 1 to 6 inclusive.

2   Using pliers, detach the brake shoe upper return spring from both brake shoes.

3   Using a brake hose clamp or self-locking wrench with protected jaws, clamp the flexible brake hose just in front of the rear suspension transverse member. This will minimise brake fluid loss during subsequent operations.

4   Wipe away all traces of dirt around the brake pipe union at the rear of the wheel cylinder (photo).

5   Unscrew the union nut securing the brake pipe to the wheel cylinder. Carefully ease out the pipe and plug or tape over its end to prevent dirt entry.

6   Undo the two bolts securing the wheel cylinder to the backplate.

Move the brake shoes apart at the top and withdraw the cylinder from between the two shoes.

7   To refit the wheel cylinder, spread the brake shoes and place the cylinder in position on the backplate.

8   Engage the brake pipe and screw in the union nut two or three turns to ensure that the thread has started.

9   Refit the two retaining bolts and tighten them to the specified torque. Now fully tighten the brake pipe union nut.

10  On models equipped with Bendix brakes, move the serrated quadrant of the self-adjusting mechanism towards the stub axle so that the adjusting arm moves back to the fully retracted position. Refit the upper brake shoe return spring. On models equipped with Girling brakes, refit the upper brake shoe return spring and turn the toothed wheel on the adjusting link as necessary so that the overall diameter of the brake shoes is between 178.7 and 179.2 mm (7.04 and 7.06 in).

11  Slide the brake drum over the stub axle, refit the thrust washer and

hub nut then tighten the hub nut to the specified torque. Tap the hub cap into place.

12 Remove the clamp from the brake hose and bleed the brake hydraulic system, as described in Section 15. Providing suitable precautions were taken to minimise loss of fluid, it should only be necessary to bleed the relevant rear brake.

13 After bleeding the system, depress the brake pedal several times to operate the self-adjusting mechanism. If it was necessary to slacken the handbrake linkage to remove the brake drum, adjust the handbrake, as described in Section 16.

14 Refit the roadwheel and lower the car to the ground.

## 8 Rear wheel cylinder – overhaul

1 Remove the wheel cylinder from the car, as described in the previous Section.

2 With the wheel cylinder on the bench, remove the dust covers, the two pistons, cup seals and spring. If necessary tap the end of the cylinder on a block of wood to eject the pistons. Unscrew the bleed screw from the cylinder body.

3 Thoroughly clean all the components in methylated spirits or clean brake fluid, and dry with a lint-free rag.

4 Carefully examine the surfaces of the pistons and cylinder bore for wear, score marks or corrosion and, if evident, renew the complete wheel cylinder. If the components are in a satisfactory condition, obtain a repair kit consisting of new seals and dust covers.

5 Dip the new seals and pistons in clean brake fluid and assemble them wet, as follows:

6 Insert one of the seals into one end of the cylinder with the flat face of the seal facing outwards. Insert the piston and fit the new dust cover.

7 From the other end of the cylinder, slide in the spring followed by the second seal, flat face outwards, then the piston and finally the dust cover.

8 Screw the bleed screw into the cylinder body and then refit the wheel cylinder to the car, as described in Section 7.

## 9 Rear brake backplate – removal and refitting

1 Begin by removing the rear brake shoes, as described in Section 6, and the wheel cylinder, as described in Section 7.

2 Slide the hub bearing inner spacer off the stub axle, undo the four retaining bolts and withdraw the backplate.

3 To refit the backplate, place it in position over the stub axle and refit the four bolts. Tighten the bolts to the specified torque.

4 Place the spacer over the stub axle and refit the wheel cylinder and brake shoes, as described in Sections 7 and 6 respectively.

5 Bleed the hydraulic system after the brake shoes and brake drum have been refitted using the procedure described in Section 15.

## 10 Master cylinder – removal and refitting

1 The master cylinder is located in a rather inaccessible position behind the engine on the right-hand side of the engine compartment bulkhead. To provide greater access, remove the air cleaner, as described in Chapter 3.

2 Working under the front of the car, remove the dust cover from the bleed screw on one of the front brake calipers. Obtain a plastic or rubber tube to fit snugly over the bleed screw and place the other end of the tube in a suitable receptacle. Connect a second tube in the same way to the bleed screw of the rear wheel cylinder on the same side of the car.

3 Open both bleed screws one complete turn and operate the brake pedal until the master cylinder reservoir is empty. Tighten the bleed screws and remove the tubes. Discard the expelled brake fluid.

4 Disconnect the wiring connectors from the master cylinder reservoir cap terminals.

5 If a heat shield is fitted around the end of the master cylinder, undo the two bolts securing the shield to the body and lift it away.

6 Suitably mark or label each of the brake pipe locations at the master cylinder to avoid confusion when refitting.

7 Unscrew the brake pipe union nuts and carefully withdraw the pipes from the master cylinder. Plug or tape over the ends of the pipes

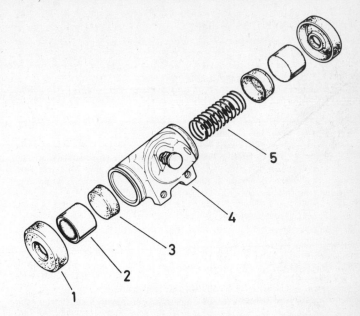

**Fig. 8.17 Exploded view of the rear wheel cylinder (Sec 8)**

1  Dust cover          4  Cylinder body
2  Piston              5  Spring
3  Cup seal

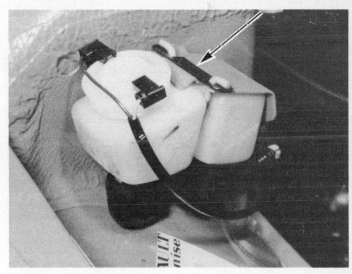

10.8 Remotely-mounted master cylinder reservoir locking plate (arrowed)

to prevent dirt entry and place rags under the master cylinder to protect the surrounding paintwork from dripping fluid.

8 On models having a remotely-mounted reservoir, release the metal locking plate by pushing it sideways to release it from the bracket. Remove the plate and lift the reservoir out of the bracket (photo).

9 Undo the two nuts and washers securing the master cylinder to the servo unit. Lift off the hose support bracket on the upper stud, withdraw the cylinder from the servo and remove it, complete with reservoir, from the car.

10 If the master cylinder is to be renewed, it will be necessary to remove the reservoir so that it can be fitted to the new unit which will be supplied without a reservoir. To do this, pull it upwards while moving it from side-to-side to release it from its rubber locating seals. If a remotely-mounted reservoir is fitted the two fluid feed tubes can be removed in the same way.

11  Refitting the master cylinder is the reverse sequence to removal, bearing in mind the following points:

   (a) *Tighten the master cylinder retaining nuts to the specified torque*
   (b) *Ensure that the brake pipes are refitted to their correct locations as noted during removal*
   (c) *Bleed the complete hydraulic system, as described in Section 15 after refitting*

## 11  Master cylinder – overhaul

1   Remove the master cylinder from the car, as described in the previous Section. Drain any fluid remaining in the reservoir and prepare a clean uncluttered working surface ready for dismantling. Proceed as follows according to master cylinder type:

### Teves master cylinder

2   Remove the reservoir, or fluid feed tubes, by pulling upwards and out of the rubber locating seals on the master cylinder body.
3   Mount the cylinder in a vice having protected jaws.
4   Using a blunt instrument, push the primary piston down slightly and undo the set bolt at the base of the cylinder body. Extract the snap-ring and washer from the end of the cylinder.
5   Release the primary piston assembly and withdraw it from the cylinder bore.
6   Remove the master cylinder from the vice and tap it on a block of wood to eject the secondary piston. If necessary apply low pressure air from a tyre foot pump to the outlet ports.
7   Clean the two piston assemblies and the cylinder body in methylated spirit or clean brake fluid and dry with a lint-free cloth.
8   Carefully examine the cylinder bore and the two piston assemblies for signs of wear ridges, scoring or corrosion. If these conditions are evident on the cylinder bore, a new master cylinder must be obtained. If the cylinder bore is serviceable it will be necessary to obtain a new primary and secondary piston assembly, as the rubber seals and piston components are not available separately.
9   Before reassembling, liberally lubricate all the parts in clean brake fluid and assemble them wet.
10  Refit the secondary piston assembly, followed by the primary piston assembly, to the cylinder bore.
11  Depress the primary piston and refit the washer and snap-ring, then the set bolt.
12  Locate the reservoir fluid feed tubes in the rubber seals and push firmly into place.
13  The assembled master cylinder can now be refitted to the car, as described in the previous Section.

### Bendix master cylinder

14  Remove the reservoir, or fluid feed tubes, by pulling upwards and out of the rubber locating seals on the master cylinder body.
15  To dismantle the master cylinder it will be necessary to make up a piston retaining tool from 6 mm diameter steel rod, as shown in Fig. 8.20.
16  Locate the retaining tool over the cylinder so that it holds the primary piston in place.
17  Place a 3.5 mm diameter twist drill in a vice and place the master cylinder over it so that the drill engages with the secondary piston retaining roll pin through the reservoir port. Turn the master cylinder round the drill and then pull it to extract the roll pin.
18  Extract the primary piston roll pin in the same way.
19  Release the retaining tool and withdraw the two piston assemblies by tapping the cylinder on a block of wood.
20  Clean, inspect and renew the master cylinder components, as described in paragraphs 7 and 8.
21  Before reassembling, liberally lubricate all the parts in clean brake fluid and assemble them wet.
22  Refit the secondary piston assembly followed by the primary piston assembly to the cylinder bore, ensuring that their slots align with the roll pin holes.
23  Refit the piston retaining tool and tap in the roll pins with their slots facing the mounting flange end of the cylinder body.
24  Remove the tool, locate the reservoir or fluid feed tubes in the rubber seals and push firmly into place.
25  The assembled master cylinder can now be refitted to the car, as described in the previous Section.

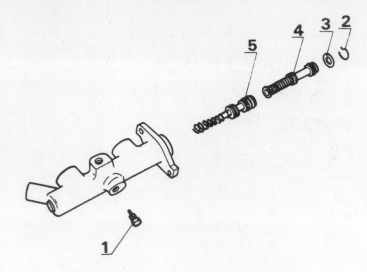

**Fig. 8.18 Exploded view of the Teves type master cylinder (Sec 11)**

| 1 | Set bolt | 4 | Primary piston assembly |
|---|----------|---|-------------------------|
| 2 | Snap-ring | 5 | Secondary piston assembly |
| 3 | Washer | | |

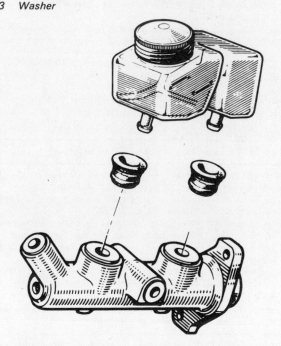

**Fig. 8.19 Master cylinder reservoir and locating seals – Bendix type (Sec 11)**

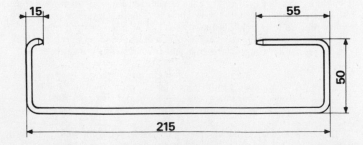

**Fig. 8.20 Piston retaining tool fabrication diagram – Bendix type master cylinder (Sec 11)**

*Note: all dimensions in millimetres*

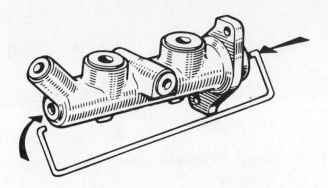

Fig. 8.21 Using the retaining tool to compress the master cylinder piston assemblies – Bendix type (Sec 11)

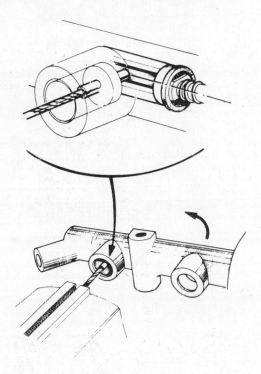

Fig. 8.22 Using a twist drill to extract the master cylinder piston roll pins – Bendix type (Sec 11)

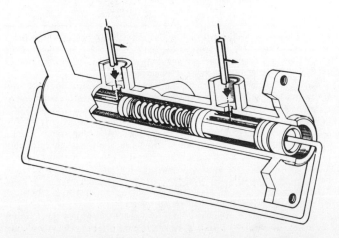

Fig. 8.23 Correct fitting of master cylinder piston roll pins with their slots facing the mounting flange – Bendix type (Sec 11)

## 12 Pressure regulating valve – description and testing

1    The pressure regulating valve is located under the car at the rear and is used to control the braking force available at the rear wheels. The valve is controlled by a linkage connected to the rear suspension and varies the fluid pressure to the rear brakes according to suspension travel. If the car is lightly loaded, the risk of the rear wheels locking under heavy braking is high, so the valve reduces rear brake hydraulic pressure accordingly. When the car is fully loaded, full braking power is necessary and there is less chance of the rear wheels locking. In this condition very little reduction in pressure is made by the valve.

2    The operation of the valve may be suspect if one or both rear wheels continually lock under heavy braking with the car lightly loaded. Should this fault occur it is essential to ensure that the problem does not lie with the brake shoe assemblies or wheel cylinders, and that adverse road conditions are also not responsible.

3    A certain degree of adjustment is possible on the valve and this should be checked if the valve operation is suspect. Adjustment entails the use of special pressure gauges and this work must be left to a Renault dealer.

4    In the event of confirmed valve failure, it will be necessary to renew the complete unit as it is a sealed assembly and cannot be dismantled.

## 13 Pressure regulating valve – removal and refitting

1    Jack up the rear of the car and support it on axle stands.

2    Unscrew the filler cap from the master cylinder reservoir and place it to one side, lay a piece of polythene over the filler neck and secure it tightly in place with a rubber band. This will minimise brake fluid loss during subsequent operations.

3    Working under the rear of the car clean away all traces of dirt, oil or grease from the brake pipe unions at the regulating valve.

4    Identify by marking, or labelling, each of the brake pipes at the regulating valve to avoid confusion during reassembly.

5    Unscrew the brake pipe union nuts and carefully withdraw the pipes from the valve. Plug or tape over each union after removal to prevent dirt entry and further loss of fluid.

6    Undo the two bolts securing the valve mounting plate to the underbody (photo). Slide the valve and mounting plate assembly off the operating rod and remove the unit from under the car. After removal, release the valve from the mounting plate.

7    Refitting is the reverse sequence to removal. On completion bleed the hydraulic system, as described in Section 15, and have the valve operation adjusted by a Renault dealer.

13.6 Pressure regulating valve mounting plate retaining bolts (arrowed)

## 14 Hydraulic pipes and hoses — inspection, removal and refitting

1   At the specified service intervals, carefully examine all brake pipes, hoses, hose connections and pipe unions.

2   First check for signs of leakage at the pipe unions. Then examine the flexible hoses for signs of cracking, chafing and fraying.

3   The brake pipes must be examined carefully and methodically. They must be cleaned off and checked for signs of dents, corrosion or other damage. Corrosion should be scraped off, and, if the depth of pitting is significant, the pipes renewed. This is particularly likely in those areas underneath the vehicle body where the pipes are exposed and unprotected.

4   If any section of the pipe or hose is to be removed, first unscrew the master cylinder reservoir filler cap and place a piece of polythene over the filler neck. Secure the polythene with an elastic band, ensuring that an airtight seal is obtained. This will minimise brake fluid loss when the pipe or hose is removed.

5   Brake pipe removal is usually quite straightforward. The union nuts at each end are undone, the pipe and union pulled out and the centre section of the pipe removed from the body clips. Where the union nuts are exposed to the full force of the weather they can sometimes be quite tight. As only an open-ended spanner can be used, burring of the flats on the nuts is not uncommon when attempting to undo them. For this reason a self-locking wrench is often the only way to separate a stubborn union.

6   To remove a flexible hose, wipe the unions and bracket free of dirt and undo the union nut from the brake hose end(s).

7   Next lift off the hose retaining spring clip and withdraw the end of the hose out of its serrated mounting (photo). If a front brake hose is being removed, it can now be unscrewed from the brake caliper.

8   Brake pipes with the end flares and union nuts in place can be obtained individually or in sets from Renault dealers or most accessory shops. The pipe is then bent to shape, using the old pipe as a guide, and is ready for fitting to the car.

9   Refitting the pipes and hoses is a reverse of the removal sequence. Make sure that the brake pipes are securely supported in their clips and ensure that the hoses are not kinked. Check also that the hoses are clear of all suspension components and underbody fittings and will remain clear during movement of the suspension or steering. Reposition one of the hose ends in its serrated mounting if necessary. After refitting, remove the polythene from the reservoir and bleed the brake hydraulic system, as described in Section 15.

## 15 Hydraulic system — bleeding

1   The correct functioning of the brake hydraulic system is only possible after removal of all air from the components and circuit; this is achieved by bleeding the system. Note that only clean unused brake fluid, which has remained unshaken for at least 24 hours, must be used.

2   If there is any possibility of incorrect fluid being used in the system, the brake lines and components must be completely flushed with uncontaminated fluid and new seals fitted to the components.

3   **Never** reuse brake fluid which has been bled from the system.

4   During the procedure, do not allow the level of brake fluid to drop more than halfway down the reservoir.

5   Before starting work, check that all pipes and hoses are secure, unions tight and bleed screws closed. Take great care not to allow brake fluid to come into contact with the car paintwork, otherwise the finish will be seriously damaged. Wash off any spilled fluid immediately with cold water.

6   If brake fluid has been lost from the master cylinder due to a leak in the system, ensure that the cause is traced and rectified before proceeding further.

7   If the hydraulic system has only been partially disconnected and suitable precautions were taken to prevent further loss of fluid, then it should only be necessary to bleed the brake concerned, or that part of the circuit 'downstream' from where the work took place.

8   If possible, one of the diy brake bleeding kits available from accessory shops should be used, particularly the type which pressurise the system, as they greatly simplify the task and reduce the risk of expelled air and fluid being drawn back into the system. Where one of these kits is being used, follow the manufacturer's instructions concerning their operation.

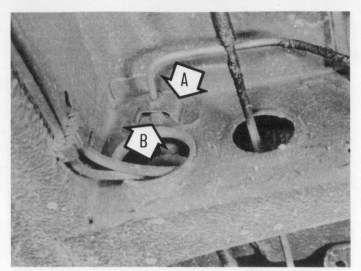

14.7 Rear brake hose retaining spring clip (A) and serrated mounting (B)

9   If a brake bleeding kit is not being used, the system may be bled in the conventional way as follows:

10  Obtain a clean glass jar, a suitable length of plastic or rubber tubing which is a tight fit over the bleed screws, a tin of the specified brake fluid and the help of an assistant.

11  Clean the area around the bleed screw and remove the rubber dust cap. If the complete system is to be bled, start at the right-hand rear brake first.

12  Fit the tube to the bleed screw, immerse the free end of the tube in the jar and pour in sufficient brake fluid to keep the end of the tube submerged. Open the bleed screw half a turn and have your assistant depress the brake pedal to the floor and then release it. Tighten the bleed screw at the end of each downstroke to prevent the expelled air and fluid from being drawn back into the system. Repeat the procedure until clean brake fluid, free from air bubbles, can be seen emerging from the tube then finally tighten the bleedscrew, remove the tube and refit the dust cap. Remember to periodically check the brake fluid level in the reservoir and keep it topped up.

13  Repeat this procedure on the other rear brake and then on the front brakes. When completed, recheck the fluid level in the reservoir, top up if necessary and refit the cap. Depress the brake pedal several times; it should feel firm and free from 'sponginess' which would indicate air is still present in the system.

## 16 Handbrake — adjustment

1   Jack up the rear of the car and support it on axle stands. Make sure that the handbrake is fully released.

2   Working under the car, slacken the primary rod locknut and slacken the knurled adjuster wheel until there is considerable slack in the cables (photo 6.5).

3   Fully depress the footbrake two or three times to ensure full operation of the self-adjusting mechanism on the brake shoes. This is particularly important if the brake drums have been recently removed.

4   Turn the knurled adjuster wheel until the brake shoes make light contact with the drums; so that the drums just drag as the wheels are turned.

5   Now back off the knurled adjuster wheel so that the shoes are clear of the drums and the wheels turn freely.

6   Turn the knurled adjuster wheel as necessary to give a minimum of 12 clicks on the handbrake lever ratchet before the rear wheels are fully locked.

7   After adjustment tighten the primary rod locknut and lower the car to the ground.

## 17 Handbrake cable – removal and refitting

1   Jack up the rear of the car and support it on axle stands. Remove the appropriate rear roadwheel.
2   Remove the brake drum, as described in Section 6, paragraphs 2 to 6 inclusive.
3   Remove the split pin, washer and clevis pin securing the compensator assembly to the primary rod yoke under the car. Now slip the cable end out of the compensator.
4   Disconnect the other end of the cable from the operating lever on the trailing brake shoe.
5   Undo the bolt and release the bracket securing the cable to the suspension trailing arm.
6   Tap the outer cable out of its location in the brake backplate and underbody support member, release the rear axle retaining clips and withdraw the cable out from under the car.
7   Refitting the handbrake cable is the reverse sequence to removal, bearing in mind the following points:

   (a)   Refit the brake drum, as described in Section 6, paragraphs 26 and 27
   (b)   Adjust the handbrake as described in Section 16, then refit the roadwheel and lower the car to the ground

## 18 Handbrake lever – removal and refitting

1   Jack up the rear of the car and support it on axle stands.
2   Working under the car, remove the split pin, washer and clevis pin securing the handbrake lever primary rod to the compensator assembly.
3   Disengage the primary rod from the support/guide block.

4   Undo the retaining bolts and remove the two seat belt flexible stalk anchorages.
5   Make a slit in the carpet just to the rear of the lever assembly to provide access to the lever mountings.
6   Spread the carpet and disconnect the warning light switch wires.
7   Undo the two bolts securing the lever to the floor and remove the assembly from inside the car.
8   Refitting is the reverse sequence to removal.

## 19 Footbrake pedal – removal and refitting

1   Working inside the car, detach the moulded plastic cover from the pedal bracket assembly beneath the facia.
2   If necessary the air duct at the base of the facia can be removed to provide greater access by detaching it from the heater unit and side vent tube.
3   Extract the split pin, washer and clevis pin securing the brake servo pushrod to the pedal.
4   Prise off the retaining clips on both ends of the pedal cross-shaft. Slide the shaft out of the pedal bracket, noting the position of any washers fitted between the clutch and brake pedals. With the cross-shaft removed, lift out the brake pedal.
5   Check the condition of the pedal bushes, and renew them if worn.
6   Refitting the brake pedal is the reverse sequence to removal.

## 20 Stop-lamp switch – removal, refitting and adjustment

1   The stop-lamp switch is electrically-operated and is mounted on the pedal bracket assembly beneath the facia.
2   To gain access to the switch remove the moulded plastic cover around the pedal bracket assembly (photos).

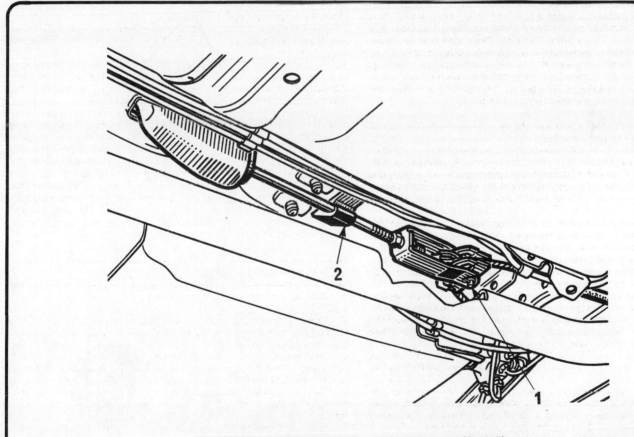

**Fig. 8.24 Handbrake lever primary rod attachments (Sec 18)**

*1   Clevis pin – primary rod yoke to compensator*
*2   Support/guide block*

20.2A Remove the plastic cover around the pedal bracket assembly ...

20.2B ... to gain access to the stop-lamp switch (arrowed)

3   The switch can be unscrewed from its location after disconnecting the wiring plug.
4   Refitting is the reverse of this procedure, but adjust the position of the switch so that the stop-lamps operate after approximately 6 mm (0.24 in) of pedal travel.

## 21 Vacuum servo unit – description

A vacuum servo unit is fitted into the brake hydraulic circuit in series with the master cylinder, to provide assistance to the driver when the brake pedal is depressed. This reduces the effort required by the driver to operate the brakes under all braking conditions.

The unit operates by vacuum obtained from the inlet manifold and comprises basically a booster diaphragm, control valve and a non-return valve.

The servo unit and hydraulic master cylinder are connected together so that the servo unit piston rod acts as the master cylinder pushrod. The driver's braking effort is transmitted through another pushrod to the servo unit piston and its built-in control system. The servo unit piston does not fit tightly into the cylinder, but has a strong diaphragm to keep its edges in constant contact with the cylinder wall, so assuring an airtight seal between the two parts. The forward chamber is held under vacuum conditions created in the inlet manifold of the engine and, during periods when the brake pedal is not in use, the controls open a passage to the rear chamber so placing it under vacuum conditions as well. When the brake pedal is depressed, the vacuum passage to the rear chamber is cut off and the chamber opened to atmospheric pressure. The consequent rush of air pushes the servo piston forward in the vacuum chamber and operates the main pushrod to the master cylinder.

The controls are designed so that assistance is given under all conditions and, when the brakes are not required, vacuum in the rear chamber is established when the brake pedal is released. All air from the atmosphere entering the rear chamber is passed through a small air filter.

## 22 Vacuum servo unit – servicing and testing

1   At the specified service intervals the servo unit air filter and non-return valve should be renewed, as follows:

### Air filter
2   Working inside the car, remove the moulded plastic cover around the pedal bracket assembly beneath the facia.
3   Ease the convoluted rubber cover off the servo end and move it up the pushrod.

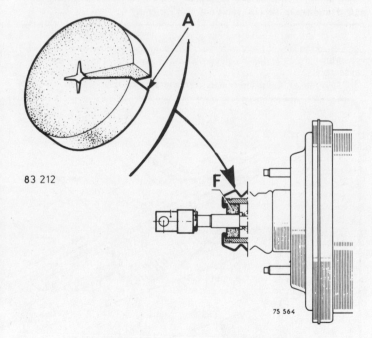

83 212

Fig. 8.25 Servo unit air filter renewal (Sec 22)

A   Cut in filter to facilitate fitting
F   Filter location in servo end

75 564

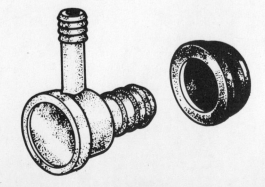

Fig. 8.26 Servo unit non-return valve and grommet (Sec 22)

4    Using a screwdriver or scriber, hook out the old air filter and remove it from the servo.
5    Make a cut in the new filter, as shown in Fig. 8.25, and place it over the pushrod and into position in the servo end.
6    Refit the rubber cover and moulded plastic cover.

### Non-return valve

7    Slacken the clip and disconnect the vacuum pipe from the non-return valve on the front face of the servo.
8    Withdraw the valve from its rubber sealing grommet by pulling and twisting.
9    Refit the new valve using the reverse of the removal sequence.

### Testing

10   If the operation of the servo is suspect, the following test can be carried out to determine whether the unit is functioning correctly.
11   Depress the footbrake several times then hold it down and start the engine. As the engine starts there should be a noticeable 'give' in the brake pedal. Allow the engine to run for at least two minutes and then switch it off. If the brake pedal is now depressed again it should be possible to detect a hiss from the unit as the pedal is depressed. After about four or five applications no further hissing will be heard and the pedal will feel noticeably firmer.
12   If the servo does not work as described, check the vacuum pipe condition and ensure that it is not kinked. Run the engine with the pipe disconnected at the servo and check that there is vacuum at the pipe end. If the servo air filter and non-return valve are in a satisfactory condition then the servo is faulty and renewal will be necessary.

### 23  Vacuum servo unit — removal and refitting

1    Disconnect the battery negative terminal.
2    Refer to Section 10 and remove the master cylinder.
3    Slacken the clip and disconnect the vacuum pipe at the servo non-return valve.
4    Working inside the car, remove the moulded plastic cover from around the pedal bracket assembly.
5    Extract the split pin, washer and clevis pin securing the servo unit pushrod to the brake pedal.
6    Undo the four nuts and remove the washers securing the servo to the bulkhead and withdraw the unit into the engine compartment.
7    Note that the servo cannot be dismantled for repair or overhaul and, if faulty, must be renewed.
8    Before refitting the servo, measure the length of the servo pushrod and output rod, ensuring that they are set to the specified length, as shown in Fig. 8.28. If necessary, slacken the locknuts and adjust the rod lengths. Tighten the locknuts after adjustment.
9    Refitting the servo unit is the reverse sequence to removal. Bleed the brake hydraulic system, as described in Section 15, after refitting the master cylinder.

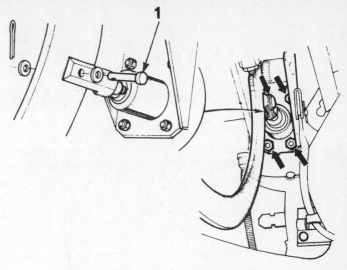

**Fig. 8.27 Servo unit removal (Sec 23)**

1    Pushrod-to-brake pedal clevis pin
Servo retaining nuts arrowed

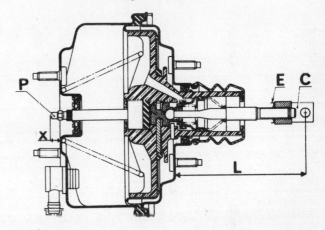

**Fig. 8.28 Sectional view of the vacuum servo unit (Sec 23)**

C    Pushrod collar              P    Output rod
E    Collar locknut              X    Output rod length = 9 mm
L    Pushrod length = 117 mm          (0.35 in)
     (4.61 in)

**24  Fault diagnosis – braking system**

| Symptom | Reason(s) |
| --- | --- |
| Excessive pedal travel | Rear brake self-adjusting mechanism inoperative<br>Air in hydraulic system<br>Faulty master cylinder |
| Brake pedal feels spongy | Air in hydraulic system<br>Faulty master cylinder |
| Judder felt through brake pedal or steering wheel when braking | Excessive run-out or distortion of front discs or rear drums<br>Brake pads or linings worn<br>Brake backplate or disc caliper loose<br>Wear in suspension or steering components or mountings – see Chapter 10 |
| Excessive pedal pressure required to stop car | Faulty servo unit, disconnected, damaged or insecure vacuum pipe<br>Wheel cylinder(s) or caliper piston seized<br>Brake pads or brake shoe linings worn or contaminated<br>Brake shoes incorrectly fitted<br>Incorrect grade of pads or linings fitted<br>Primary or secondary hydraulic circuit failure |
| Brakes pull to one side | Brake pads or linings worn or contaminated<br>Wheel cylinder or caliper piston seized<br>Seized rear brake self-adjust mechanism<br>Brake pads or linings renewed on one side only<br>Faulty pressure regulating valve<br>Tyre, steering or suspension defect – see Chapter 10 |
| Brakes binding | Wheel cylinder or caliper piston seized<br>Handbrake incorrectly adjusted<br>Faulty master cylinder |
| Rear wheels locking under normal braking | Rear brake shoe linings contaminated<br>Faulty pressure regulating valve |

# Chapter 9 Electrical system

*For modifications, and information applicable to later models, see Supplement at end of manual*

## Contents

## Specifications

**System type** ................................................... 12 volt, negative earth

### Battery
Type ................................................................... Low maintenance or maintenance-free 'sealed for life'
Capacity ............................................................. 35 amp hr, 40 amp hr, 50 amp hr, 65 amp hr or 70 amp hr according to model and optional equipment

### Alternator
Type .................................................................. Ducellier 516023 or 516030; Paris-Rhone A13N12 or A13N29
Maximum output:
    All except Ducellier 516030 ......................... 48 amps
    Ducellier 516030 ...................................... 68 amps

### Starter motor
Type .................................................................. Ducellier 534029 or 534031; Paris-Rhone D9E39, D9E52 or D10E85 – pre-engaged

### Wiper blades ................................................. Champion C-4101 (1982-on) and tailgate C-4501 (1983-on)

### Bulbs (typical)

| | Wattage |
|---|---|
| Headlamp: | |
|     Standard bulb | 45/50 |
|     Halogen bulb | 60/55 |
| Front foglamp | 55 |
| Front sidelight | 4 |
| Direction indicators | 21 |
| Stop/tail | 21/5 |
| Reversing lamp | 21 |
| Rear foglamp | 21 |
| Rear number plate lamp | 5 |
| Interior lamps | 10 |
| Switch and panel illumination | 1.2 or 2 |
| Warning lamps | 1.2 or 2 |

## 1   General description

The electrical system is of the 12 volt negative earth type, and consists of a battery, alternator, starter motor and related electrical accessories, components and wiring.

The battery, charged by the alternator which is belt-driven from the crankshaft pulley, provides a steady amount of current for the ignition, starting, lighting and other electrical circuits. The battery may be a low maintenance type or a maintenance-free 'sealed for life' type, according to model.

The starter motor is of the pre-engaged type incorporating an integral solenoid. On starting, the solenoid moves the drive pinion into engagement with the flywheel ring gear before the starter motor is energised. Once the engine has started, a one-way clutch prevents the motor armature being driven by the engine until the pinion disengages from the flywheel.

Further details of the major electrical systems are given in the relevant Sections of this Chapter.

**Caution:** *Before carrying out any work on the vehicle electrical system, read through the precautions given in Safety First! at the beginning of this manual and in Section 2 of this Chapter.*

## 2   Electrical system – precautions

It is necessary to take extra care when working on the electrical system to avoid damage to semiconductor devices (diodes and transistors), and to avoid the risk of personal injury. In addition to the precautions given in Safety First! at the beginning of this manual, observe the following items when working on the system.

1  *Always remove rings, watches, etc before working on the electrical system.* Even with the battery disconnected, capacitive discharge could occur if a component live terminal is earthed through a metal object. This could cause a shock or nasty burn.

2  *Do not reverse the battery connections.* Components such as the alternator or any other having semiconductor circuitry could be irreparably damaged.

3  If the engine is being started using jump leads and a slave battery, connect the batteries *positive to positive* and *negative to negative*. This also applies when connecting a battery charger.

4  Never disconnect the battery terminals, or alternator wiring when the engine is running.

5  The battery leads and alternator wiring must be disconnected before carrying out any electric welding on the car.

6  Never use an ohmmeter of the type incorporating a hand cranked generator for circuit or continuity testing.

## 3   Maintenance and inspection

1  At the intervals given in Routine maintenance the following service operations should be carried out on the electrical system components:

2  Check the operation of all the electrical equipment, ie wipers, washers, lights, direction indicators, horn etc. Refer to the appropriate Sections of this Chapter if any components are found to be inoperative.

3  Visually check all accessible wiring connectors, harnesses and retaining clips for security, or any signs of chafing or damage. Rectify any problems encountered.

4  Check the alternator drivebelt for cracks, fraying or damage. Renew the belt if worn or, if satisfactory, check and adjust the belt tension. These procedures are covered in Chapter 2.

5  Check the condition of the wiper blades and if they are cracked or show signs of deterioration, renew them, as described in Section 36 and other applicable Sections of this Chapter. Check the operation of the windscreen, tailgate and headlamp washers, as applicable, and adjust the nozzle setting if necessary.

6  Top up the battery, on models where this is necessary, using distilled water until the tops of the cell plates are just submerged. Clean the battery terminals and case and, if necessary, check the battery condition using the procedures described in Section 4.

7  Top up the washer fluid reservoir and check the security of the pump wires and water pipes.

8  It is advisable to have the headlamp aim adjusted using optical beam setting equipment.

9  While carrying out a road test, check the operation of all the instruments and warning lights and the operation of the direction indicator self-cancelling mechanism.

## 4   Battery – general

1  According to model the battery may be of the low maintenance type in which the cell covers may be removed to allow periodic topping-up in the conventional way, or of the maintenance-free type which do not require topping-up (photos). The maintenance-free battery has a sealed top cover which must not under any circumstances be removed. If the seals are broken the battery warranty will be invalidated.

2  On low maintenance batteries, periodically lift off the cover and check the electrolyte level. The tops of the cell plates should be just covered by the electrolyte. If not, add distilled or demineralized water until they are. Do not add extra water with the idea of reducing the

4.1A Low maintenance type battery ...

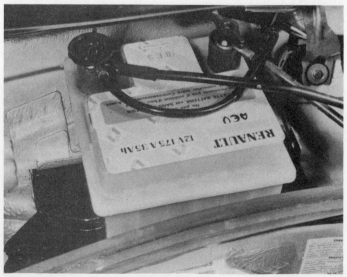

4.1B ... and maintenance-free 'sealed for life' type battery

intervals of topping-up. This will merely dilute the electrolyte and reduce charging and current retention efficiency.

3   If the electrolyte level needs an excessive amount of replenishment but no leaks are apparent, it could be due to over-charging as a result of the battery having been run down and then left to recharge from the vehicle rather than an outside source. If the battery has been heavily discharged for one reason or another, it is best to have it continuously charged at a low amperage for a period of many hours. If it is charged from the car's system under such conditions, the charging will be intermittent and greatly varied in intensity. This does not do the battery any good at all. If the battery needs topping-up frequently, even when it is known to be in good condition and not too old, then the voltage regulator should be checked to ensure that the charging output is being correctly controlled. An elderly battery, however, may need topping-up more than a new one, because it needs to take in more charging current. Do not worry about this, provided it gives satisfactory service.

4   Keep the battery clean and dry all over by wiping it with a dry cloth. A dirty or damp top surface could cause tracking between the two terminal posts with consequent draining of power.

5   Periodically remove the battery and check the support tray clamp and battery terminal connections for signs of corrosion — usually indicated by a whitish green crystalline deposit. Wash this off with clean water to which a little ammonia or washing soda has been added. Then treat the terminals with petroleum jelly and the battery mounting with suitable protective paint to prevent further corrosive action.

6   On maintenance-free batteries access to the cells is not possible and only the overall condition of the battery can be checked using a voltmeter connected across the two terminals. On the low maintenance type a hydrometer can be used to check the condition of each individual cell. The table in the following Section gives the hydrometer readings for the various states of charge. A further check can be made when the battery is undergoing a charge. If, towards the end of the charge, when the cells should be 'gassing' (bubbling), one cell appears not to be, this indicates the cell or cells in question are probably breaking down and the life of the battery is limited.

## 5   Battery – charging

1   In winter when a heavy demand is placed on the battery, such as when starting from cold and using more electrical equipment, it may be necessary to have the battery fully charged from an external source. *Note that both battery leads must be disconnected before charging in order to prevent possible damage to any semiconductor electrical components.*

2   The terminals of the battery and the leads of the charger must be connected *positive to positive* and *negative to negative*.

3   Charging is best done overnight at a 'trickle' rate of 1 to 1.5 amps. Alternatively, on low maintenance batteries, a 3 to 4 amp rate can be

used over a period of 4 hours or so. Check the specific gravity in the latter case and stop the charge when the reading is correct. Maintenance-free batteries should not be charged in this way due to their design and construction. It is strongly recommended that you seek the advice of a Renault dealer on the suitability of various types of charging equipment before using them on maintenance-free batteries.

4   The specific gravities for hydrometer readings on low maintenance batteries are as follows:

| Fully discharged | Electrolyte temperature | Fully charged |
|---|---|---|
| 1.098 | 38°C (100°F) | 1.268 |
| 1.102 | 32°C (90°F) | 1.272 |
| 1.106 | 27°C (80°F) | 1.276 |
| 1.110 | 21°C (70°F) | 1.280 |
| 1.114 | 16°C (60°F) | 1.284 |
| 1.118 | 10°C (50°F) | 1.288 |
| 1.122 | 4°C (40°F) | 1.292 |
| 1.126 | -1.5°C (30°F) | 1.296 |

## 6   Battery – removal and refitting

1   The battery is located on the right-hand side of the engine compartment adjacent to the bulkhead.

2   Lift up the battery cover, unscrew the negative terminal clamp and lift off the leads.

3   Unscrew the positive terminal clamp and lift off the leads.

4   Slacken the locknut and unscrew the battery tray clamp bolt (photo).

5   Withdraw the battery from the carrier tray.

6   Refitting is the reverse sequence to removal. Ensure that the positive terminal leads and clamps are fitted first and those of the negative terminal last.

## 7   Alternator – removal and refitting

1   Disconnect the battery negative terminal.

2   Make a note of the electrical lead locations at the rear of the alternator and disconnect them (photo).

3   On 1108 cc and 1397 cc engines slacken the alternator adjusting arm nut and bolt and the mounting nut and through-bolt, push the alternator towards the engine and slip off the drivebelt. On 1721 cc engines slacken the nut and bolt securing the alternator to the adjustment bracket and back off the two nuts on the adjustment rod until the belt can be slipped off the pulley.

4   Remove the alternator mounting and adjustment nuts and bolts then withdraw the alternator from the engine (photo).

5   Refitting is the reverse sequence to removal, but before tightening the adjustment and mounting bolts tension the drivebelt, as described in Chapter 2.

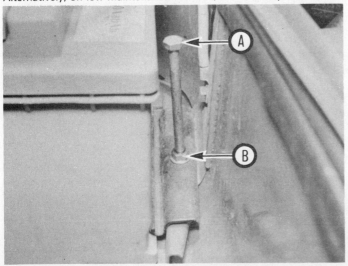

6.4 Battery tray clamp bolt (A) and locknut (B)

7.2 Electrical connections at the rear of the alternator

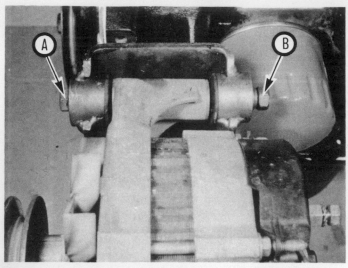

7.4 Alternator mounting through-bolt (A) and retaining nut (B)

fault and should be renewed or taken to an automobile electrician for testing and repair.

2   If the ignition warning lamp illuminates when the engine is running, ensure that the drivebelt is correctly tensioned (see Chapter 2), and that the connections on the rear of the alternator are secure. If all is so far satisfactory, check the alternator brushes and commutator, as described in Section 9. If the fault still persists, the alternator should be renewed, or taken to an automobile electrician for testing and repair.

3   If the alternator output is suspect even though the warning lamp functions correctly, the regulated voltage may be checked as follows:

4   Connect a voltmeter across the battery terminals and then start the engine.

5   Increase the engine speed until the reading on the voltmeter remains steady. This should be between 13.5 and 15 volts.

6   Switch on as many electrical accessories as possible and check that the alternator maintains the regulated voltage at between 13.5 and 15 volts.

7   If the regulated voltage is not as stated, the fault may be due to a faulty diode, a severed phase or worn brushes, springs or commutator. The brushes and commutator may be attended to, as described in Section 9, but if the fault still persists the alternator should be renewed, or taken to an automobile electrician for testing and repair.

## 8   Alternator – fault tracing and rectification

1   If the ignition warning lamp fails to illuminate when the ignition is switched on, first check the wiring connections at the rear of the alternator for security. If satisfactory, check that the warning lamp bulb has not blown and is secure in its holder. If the lamp still fails to illuminate check the continuity of the warning lamp feed wire from the alternator to the bulb holder. If all is satisfactory, the alternator is at

## 9   Alternator brushes – removal, inspection and refitting

Note: *Due to the specialist knowledge and equipment required to test and repair an alternator accurately, it is recommended that, if the performance is suspect, the alternator be taken to an automobile electrician who will have the facilities for such work. It is, however, a relatively simply task to attend to the brush gear and this operation is described below. The work may be carried out without removing the unit from the engine.*

1   Disconnect the battery negative terminal.

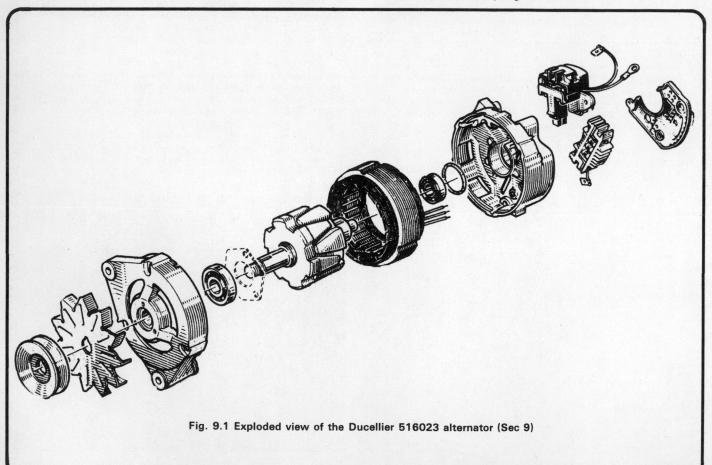

Fig. 9.1 Exploded view of the Ducellier 516023 alternator (Sec 9)

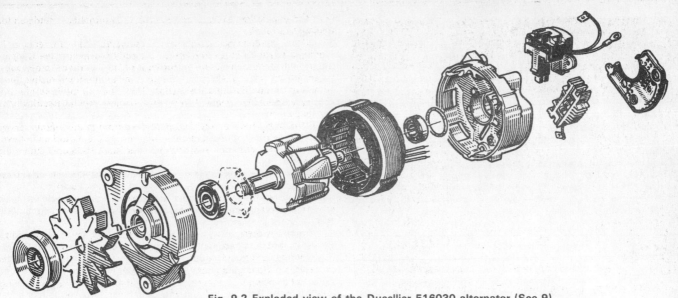

Fig. 9.2 Exploded view of the Ducellier 516030 alternator (Sec 9)

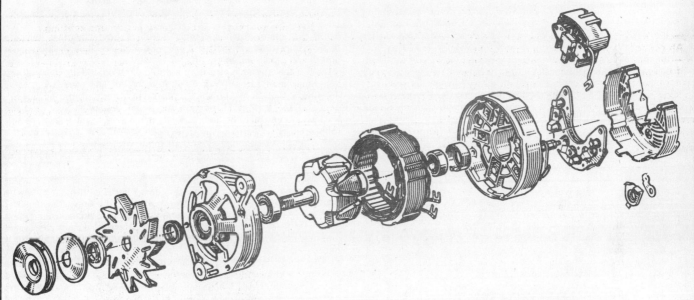

Fig. 9.3 Exploded view of the Paris-Rhone A13N12 alternator (Sec 9)

Fig. 9.4 Exploded view of the Paris-Rhone A13N29 alternator (Sec 9)

2   Note the locations of the wiring connectors and leads at the rear of the alternator and disconnect them.

3   Undo the two small bolts or nuts securing the regulator and brush box assembly to the rear of the alternator. Lift off the regulator and brush box, disconnect the electrical leads, noting their locations, then remove the regulator and brush box assembly from the alternator.

4   Check that the brushes stand proud of their holders and are free to move without sticking. If necessary clean them with a petrol-moistened cloth. Check that the brush spring pressure is equal for both brushes and gives reasonable tension. If in doubt about the condition of the brushes and springs compare them with new parts at a Renault parts dealer.

5   Clean the commutator with a petrol-moistened cloth, then check for signs of scoring, burning or severe pitting. If evident the commutator should be attended to by an automobile electrician.

6   Refitting the regulator and brush box assembly is the reverse sequence to removal.

## 10  Starter motor – testing in the car

1   If the starter motor fails to operate, first check the condition of the battery by switching on the headlamps. If they glow brightly then gradually dim after a few seconds, the battery is in an uncharged condition.

2   If the battery is satisfactory, check the starter motor main terminal and the engine earth cable for security. Check the terminal connections on the starter solenoid, located on top of the starter motor.

3   If the starter still fails to turn, use a voltmeter, or 12 volt test lamp and leads, to ensure that there is battery voltage at the solenoid main terminal (containing the cable from the battery positive terminal).

4   With the ignition switched on and the ignition key in position D check that voltage is reaching the solenoid terminal with the spade connector, and also the starter main terminal.

5   If there is no voltage reaching the spade connector there is a wiring or ignition switch faulty. If voltage is available, but the starter does not operate, then the starter or solenoid is likely to be at fault.

## 11  Starter motor – removal and refitting

1   Disconnect the battery negative terminal.

2   Refer to Chapter 3 and remove the air cleaner.

3   Disconnect the electrical leads at the starter solenoid terminals, noting their respective locations.

4   Undo the bolt securing the starter motor support bracket to the rear facing side of the cylinder block (photo).

5   Undo the three bolts securing the starter motor to the transmission bellhousing (photo) and withdraw the starter from the engine. Note the position of the locating dowel in the upper rear bellhousing bolt hole and make sure that it is in place when refitting (photo).

6   Refitting the starter motor is the reverse sequence to removal, but tighten the bellhousing bolts before the support bracket bolt.

## 12  Starter motor – overhaul

**Note:** *Overhaul of the starter motor is normally confined to inspection and, if necessary, renewal of the brush gear components. Due to the limited availability of replacement parts, any other faults occurring on the starter usually result in renewal of the complete motor. However, for those wishing to dismantle the starter motor, this Section may be used as a guide. The procedure is essentially similar for all motor types and any minor differences can be noted by referring to the accompanying illustrations.*

1   Remove the starter motor from the car, as described in the previous Section.

2   Undo the two nuts and remove the mounting support bracket from the rear of the motor.

3   Undo the nut and disconnect the lead from the solenoid terminal.

4   Where fitted, remove the cap plate on the rear cover and the bolt and washers between rear cover and armature.

5   Tap out the engaging lever pivot pin from the drive end housing.

6   Undo the nuts securing the solenoid to the drive end housing.

7   Undo the through-bolts and withdraw the yoke, armature, solenoid and engaging lever as an assembly from the drive end housing.

8   Withdraw the solenoid and engaging lever, remove the rear cover with brushes, then slide the armature out of the yoke.

9   Slip the brushes out of their brush holders to release the rear cover.

10  If the pinion/clutch assembly is to be removed, drive the stop collar up the armature shaft and extract the circlip. Slide the stop collar and pinion clutch assembly off the armature.

11  With the starter motor now completely dismantled, clean all the components with paraffin or a suitable solvent and wipe dry.

12  Check that all the brushes protrude uniformly from their holders and that the springs all provide moderate tension. Check that the brushes move freely in their holders and clean them with a petrol-moistened rag if there is any tendency to stick. If in doubt about the brush length or condition, compare them with new components and renew if necessary. Note that new field brushes must be soldered to their leads.

13  Check the armature shaft for distortion and the commutator for excessive wear, scoring or burrs. If necessary, the commutator may be lightly skimmed in a lathe and then polished with fine glass paper.

14  Check the pinion/clutch assembly, drive end housing, engaging lever and solenoid for wear or damage. Make sure that the clutch permits movement in one direction only and renew the unit if necessary.

15  Accurate checking of the armature, commutator and field coil windings and insulation requires the use of special test equipment. If the starter motor was inoperative when removed from the car and the previous checks have not highlighted the problem, then it can be assumed that there is a continuity or insulation fault and the unit should be renewed.

16  If the starter is in a satisfactory condition, or if a fault has been traced and rectified, the unit can be reassembled using the reverse of the dismantling procedure.

11.4 Starter motor support bracket-to-cylinder block retaining bolt (arrowed)

11.5A Undo the starter motor-to-bellhousing retaining bolts (arrowed) ...

11.5B ... and withdraw the starter. Note the position of the locating dowel (arrowed)

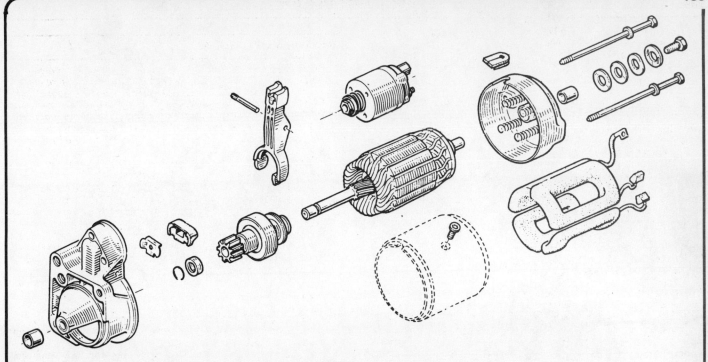

Fig. 9.5 Exploded view of the Ducellier 534029 and 534031 starter motors (Sec 12)

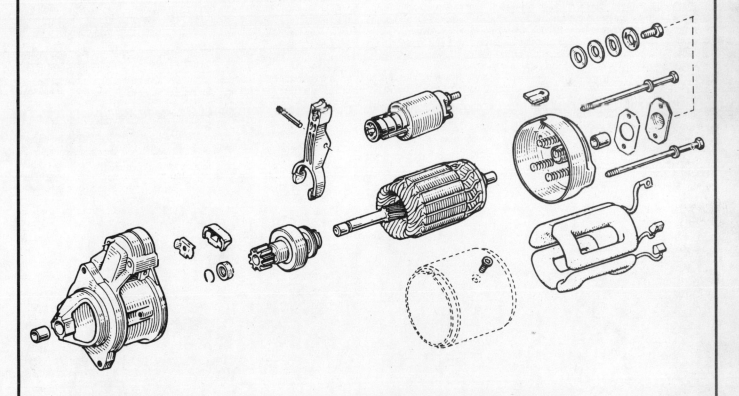

Fig. 9.6 Exploded view of the Paris-Rhone D9E39 and D9E52 starter motors (Sec 12)

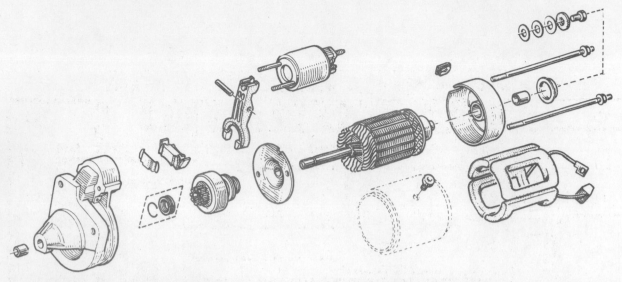

Fig. 9.7 Exploded view of the Paris-Rhone D1DE85 starter motor (Sec 12)

## 13 Fuses and relays – general

1   The fuses and relays are located on an accessory plate which is situated below the glovebox. To gain access to the plate, depress the two front catches and lower the plate down at the front (photo).

2   The fuses, relays and wiring connectors are plugged into the accessory plate printed circuit board (photo). The vehicle may be fitted with either a simplified or a comprehensive accessory plate. On Renault 9 models the simplified plate contains 10 fuse locations, and the comprehensive plate contains 19 fuse locations. On Renault 11 models the simplified and comprehensive plates contain 13 and 19 fuse locations respectively. The location of the fuses, relays and wiring connectors are shown in the accompanying illustrations.

3   To remove a fuse from its location simply lift it upwards and out (photo). The wire within the fuse is clearly visible and it will be broken if the fuse is blown.

4   Always renew a fuse with one of an identical rating. Never renew a fuse more than once without tracing the source of the trouble. The fuse rating is stamped on top of the fuse and spare fuses are located in a holder in the front of the accessory plate cover.

5   The various relays can be removed from their respective locations by carefully pulling them upwards and out.

6   If a system controlled by a relay becomes inoperative and the relay

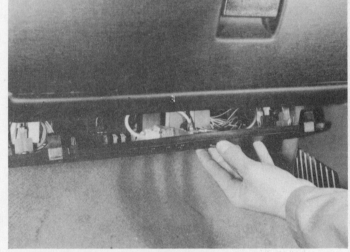

13.1 Accessory plate location beneath the glovebox

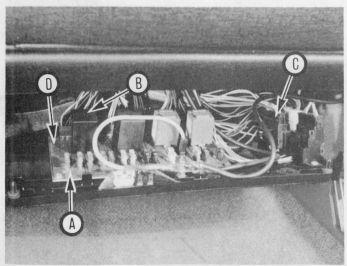

13.2 Fuses (A), relays (B), and connectors (C) on the accessory plate (D)

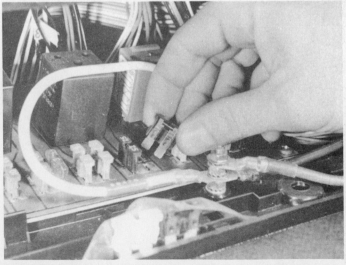

13.3 Remove the fuses by lifting upwards to free them from their locations (Renault 11 type show)

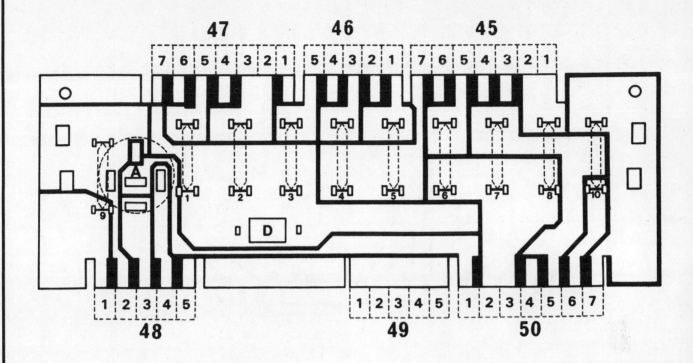

Fig. 9.8 Component layout on the Renault 9 simplified accessory plate (Sec 13)

**Connector 45**
1  Rear screen demister (+)
2  Reversing lights (+) windscreen wiper/washer (+)
3  Not used
4  Not used
5  Instrument panel (+)
6  Not used
7  Side, rear and number plate light fuses (+)

**Connector 46**
1  RH side and rear lights via rheostat
2  Not used
3  LH side and rear lights, identification plate illumination
4  Not used
5  Windscreen wiper/washer (+)

**Connector 47**
1  Not used
2  (+) Before ignition/starter switch and clock
3  Cigar lighter (−)
4  Not used
5  Windscreen wiper 'park'
6  Not used
7  Not used

**Connector 48**
1  Accessories (+)
2  Accessories, stop-lights, radio (+)
3  Direction indicators tell-tale
4  Direction indicators switch
5  Not used

**Connector 49 – any connection**
Side, rear and number plate lighting rheostat
Instrument panel illumination
Heater controls illumination
Clock illumination

**Connector 50**
1  Earth
2  (+) After ignition/starter switch
3  Not used
4  Not used
5  Heater fan motor
6  Rear foglamp
7  Rear foglamp

**Units**
A  Flasher unit
D  Current feed plate

| Fuse No | Rating | Unit |
| --- | --- | --- |
| 1 | 5A | Windscreen wiper 'park' |
| 2 | 8A | Interior light, cigar lighter |
| 3 | 16A | Windscreen wiper/washer switch |
| 4 | 5A | LH side and rear lights |
| 5 | 5A | RH side and rear lights |
| 6 | 5A | Instrument panel (+) |
| 7 | 16A | Heater fan motor |
| 8 | 16A | Reversing lights, rear screen demister |
| 9 | 8A | Flasher unit, stop lights, radio |
| 10 | 5A | Rear foglamp |

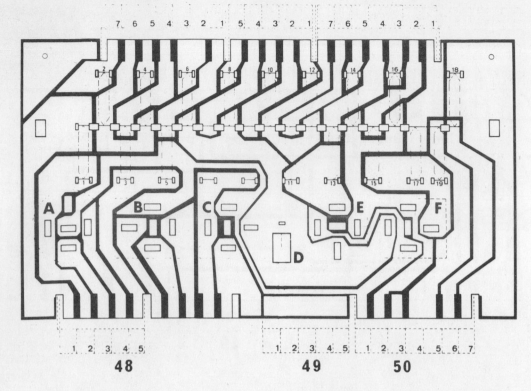

Fig. 9.9 Component layout on pre-1984 Renault 9 comprehensive accessory plate (Sec 13)

**Connector 45**
1   Rear screen demister
2   Reversing lights (+)
3   Automatic transmission
4   RH window winder
5   Instrument panel (+)
6   LH window winder
7   Side, rear and number plate fuses (+)

**Connector 46**
1   RH side and rear lights/rheostat
2   Not used
3   LH side and rear lights, identification plate illumination
4   Not used
5   Windscreen wiper/washer (+)

**Connector 47**
1   Accessories, radio (+)
2   (+) After ignition/starter switch/clock
3   Cigar lighter, interior light
4   Stop-lights, 'Normalur' cruise control
5   Windscreen wiper 'park'
6   Not used
7   Not used

**Connector 48**
1   Flasher unit
2   Not used
3   Direction indicators tell-tale
4   Direction indicators switch
5   Accessories (+)

**Connector 49 – any connection**
Side, rear and number plate lights/rheostat
Selector illumination
Instrument panel illumination
Heater controls illumination
Clock illumination

**Connector 50**
1   Earth
2   (+) After ignition/starter switch
3   Not used
4   Not used
5   Heater fan motor
6   Rear foglamp
7   Rear foglamp

**Units**
A   Flasher unit
B   Not used
C   Not used
D   Current feed to plate
E   Window motors relay
F   Relay after ignition/starter switch

| Fuse No | Rating | Unit |
| --- | --- | --- |
| 1 | 8A | Flasher unit |
| 2 | – | Not used |
| 3 | 5A | Stop-lights – 'Normalur' cruise control |
| 4 | 5A | Windscreen wiper 'park' |
| 5 | 5A | Radio |
| 6 | 8A | Interior light |
| 7 | – | Not used |
| 8 | 16A | Windscreen wiper/washer |
| 9 | – | Not used |
| 10 | 5A | LH side and rear lights |
| 11 | 10A | LH window |
| 12 | 5A | RH side and rear lights |
| 13 | 10A | RH window |
| 14 | 5A | Instrument panel (+) feed |
| 15 | 5A | Reversing lights |
| 16 | 1,5A | Automatic transmission |
| 17 | 16A | Rear screen demister |
| 18 | 16A | Heater fan motor |
| 19 | 5A | Rear foglamp |

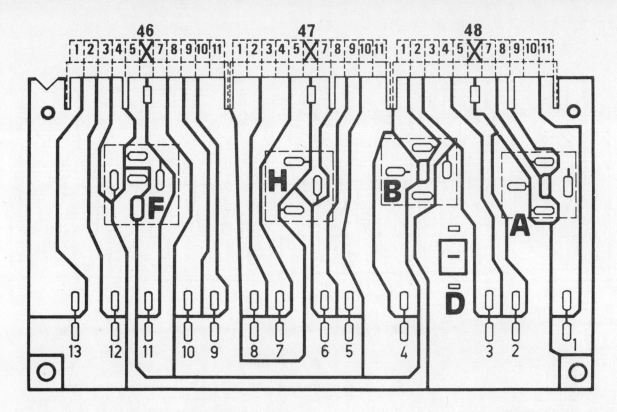

Fig. 9.10 Component layout on the Renault 11 simplified accessory plate (Sec 13)

**Connector 46 (Black)**
1  Accessories/radio (+)
2  Accessories (+)
3  Heater fan motor
4  Direction indicators switch
5  Direction indicators tell-tale
7  Flasher unit
8  Stop-lights/clock
9  Instrument panel (+)
10  (+) After ignition/starter switch
11  (+) After ignition/starter switch

**Connector 47 (Red)**
1  LH side and rear lights
2  Heater controls illumination
3  RH side and rear lights
4  Identification plates illumination
5  Side and rear lights fuses (+)
7  Lights 'on' buzzer
8  Reversing lights (+)/windscreen wiper/washer timer
9  Windscreen wiper/washer (+)
10  Rear screen demister
11  Rear screen demister

**Connector 48 (Yellow)**
1  Rear screen demister relay
2  Earth via starter solenoid
3  Interior light
4  Luggage compartment light/cigar lighter
5  Windscreen wiper 'park'
7  LH headlamp main beam

8  Earth
9  Feed to headlamp dipped beams
10  RH headlamp dipped beam
11  Rear foglamp

**Units**
A  Headlamp dipped beams relay
B  Rear screen demister relay
D  Feed to accessories plate
F  Flasher unit
H  Lights 'On' buzzer

| Fuse No | Rating | Unit |
|---|---|---|
| 1 | 7.5A | Rear foglamp |
| 2 | 5A | Windscreen wiper and rear screen wiper 'park' |
| 3 | 15A | Cigar lighter/clock/luggage compartment illumination |
| 4 | 20A | Rear screen demister |
| 5 | 7.5A | Windscreen wiper/washer/rear screen wiper |
| 6 | 5A | Reversing lights/windscreen wiper/washer timer |
| 7 | 5A | RH side and rear lights/instrument lighting rheostat |
| 8 | 5A | LH side and rear lights/identification plate illumination |
| 9 | 3A | Instrument panel |
| 10 | 10A | Stoplights/'Normalur' |
| 11 | 10A | Flasher unit |
| 12 | 7.5A | Heater fan motor |
| 13 | 3A | Radio |

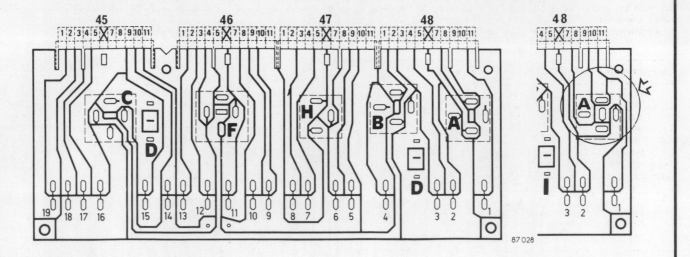

Fig. 9.11 Component layout on the 1984 Renault 9 and Renault 11 comprehensive accessory plate (Sec 13)

**Connector 45 (Clear)**
1   Not used
2   Not used
3   RH window winder
4   LH window winder
5   Not used
7   Air conditioning
8   Air conditioning
9   Door locks
10  Automatic transmission
11  Not used

**Connector 46 (Black)**
1   Accessories (+)/Radio
2   Accessories (+)
3   Not used
4   Direction indicators switch
5   Direction indicators tell-tale
7   Flasher unit
8   Stop-lights/clock
9   Instrument panel (+)
10  (+) After ignition/starter switch
11  (+) After ignition/starter switch

**Connector 47 (Red)**
1   LH side and rear lights
2   Identification plate illumination
3   RH side and rear lights
4   Lighting/clock
5   Sidelights and rear lights fuses (+)
7   Lights 'On' buzzer
8   Reversing lights/windscreen wiper/washer timer
9   Windscreen wiper/washer (+)
10  Rear screen demister
11  Rear screen demister

**Connector 48 (Yellow) (1st assembly)**
1   Rear screen demister relay
2   Earth via starter solenoid
3   Interior light
4   Luggage compartment light/cigar lighter
5   Windscreen wiper 'park'
7   LH headlamp main beam
8   Earth
9   Feed to headlamp dipped beams
10  RH headlamp dipped beam

11  Rear foglamp

**Connector 48 (Yellow) (2nd assembly – see inset)**

Connections are the same as those for 1st assembly with the exceptions listed below

4   Luggage compartment light
7   Dipped beam headlamp relay earth
8   LH dipped beam headlamp
10  RH main beam headlamp

**Units**
A   Headlamp dipped beams relay
B   Rear screen demister relay
C   Relay after ignition/starter switch
D   Feed to accessories plate
F   Flasher unit
H   Lights 'On' buzzer

| Fuse No | Rating | Unit |
| --- | --- | --- |
| 1 | 7.5A | Rear foglamp |
| 2 | 5A | Windscreen wiper and rear screen wiper 'park' |
| 3 | 15A | Cigar lighter/clock/luggage compartment illumination |
| 4 | 20A | Rear screen demister |
| 5 | 7.5A | Windscreen wiper/washer/rear screen wiper |
| 6 | 5A | Reversing lights/windscreen wiper/washer timer |
| 7 | 5A | RH side and rear lights/instrument lighting rheostat |
| 8 | 5A | LH side and rear lights/identification plate illumination |
| 9 | 3A | Instrument panel |
| 10 | 10A | Stop-lights/'Normalur' |
| 11 | 10A | Flasher unit |
| 12 | 7.5A | Heater fan motor |
| 13 | 3A | Radio |
| 14 | 2A | Automatic transmission |
| 15 | 15A | Door locks |
| 16 | 25A | Air conditioning/sunroof |
| 17 | 25A | LH window winder |
| 18 | 25A | RH window winder |
| 19 | – | Not used |

is suspect, operate the system and if the relay is functioning it should be possible to hear it click as it is energized. If this is the case the fault lies with the components or wiring of the system. If the relay is not being energized then the relay is not receiving a main supply voltage or a switching voltage, or the relay itself is faulty.

## 14 Accessory plate – removal and refitting

1    Disconnect the battery negative terminal.
2    Depress the two front catches and lower the accessory plate down at the front.
3    Release the clip on the side bracket and move the plate towards the left to release it from the rear pivots.
4    Make a careful note of all the wiring plug locations and disconnect them from the printed circuit board and from their support clips. The accessory plate can now be removed.
5    To remove the printed circuit board, undo the retaining screws, release the catches and remove the board. If the board is to be renewed, transfer the fuses and relays to the new unit.
6    Refitting is the reverse sequence to removal.

## 15 Direction indicator and hazard flasher system – general

1    The flasher unit is located on the accessory plate situated below the glovebox (see Section 13).
2    Should the flashers become faulty in operation, check the bulbs for security and make sure that the contact surfaces are not corroded. If one bulb blows or is making a poor connection due to corrosion, the system will not flash on that side of the car.
3    If the flasher unit operates in one direction and not the other, the fault is likely to be in the bulbs, or wiring to the bulbs. If the system will not flash in either direction, operate the hazard flashers. If these function, check the appropriate fuse and renew it if blown. If the fuse is satisfactory, renew the flasher unit.

## 16 Instrument panel – removal and refitting

### Renault 9 models
1    Disconnect the battery negative terminal.
2    Undo the two screws, one each side, securing the instrument panel trim surround to the facia at the front.
3    Press the side of the trim surround inwards to release the catches and lift it upwards and off the facia (photo).
4    Depress the two metal tags at the top of the instrument panel (photo), tip the panel towards the steering wheel and lift it slightly to release the lower locating tangs.
5    Reach behind the panel, disconnect the speedometer cable and multi-plug connectors (photo), then remove the instrument panel from the car.
6    Refitting is the reverse sequence to removal.

### Renault 11 models
7    Disconnect the battery negative terminal.
8    Using a small screwdriver, depress the four clips securing the cover panel to the underside of the facia (photo). Lift off the cover panel.
9    Depress the two metal tags at the top of the instrument panel (photo), tip the panel towards the steering wheel and lift it slightly to release the lower locating tags.
10    Reach behind the panel, disconnect the speedometer cable and multi-plug connectors, then remove the instrument panel from the car.
11    Refitting is the reverse sequence to removal.

## 17 Instrument panel – dismantling and reassembly

1    Remove the instrument panel from the car, as described in the previous Section.

16.3 Press the Renault 9 instrument panel trim surround inwards to release the catches (arrowed)

16.4 Renault 9 instrument panel retaining tags (arrowed)

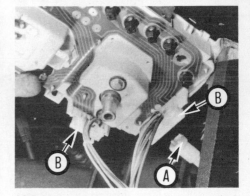
16.5 After releasing the panel disconnect the speedometer cable (A) and multi-plug connectors (B) from the rear

16.8 Remove the cover panel on Renault 11 models by depressing the four clips

16.9 Free the two tags (arrowed) to release the instrument panel

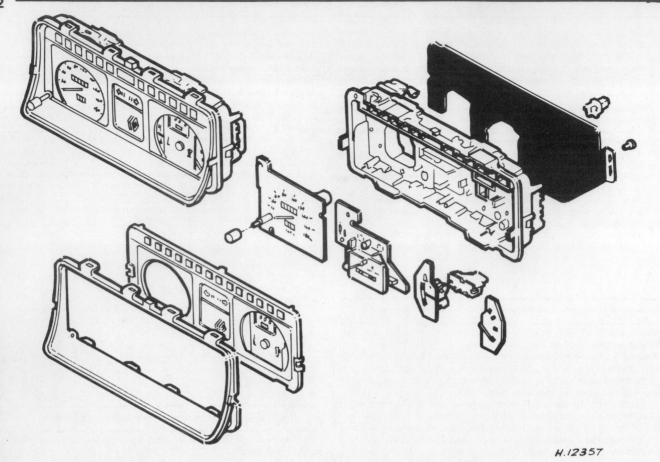

H.12357

Fig. 9.12 Typical Renault 9 instrument panel layout (Sec 17)

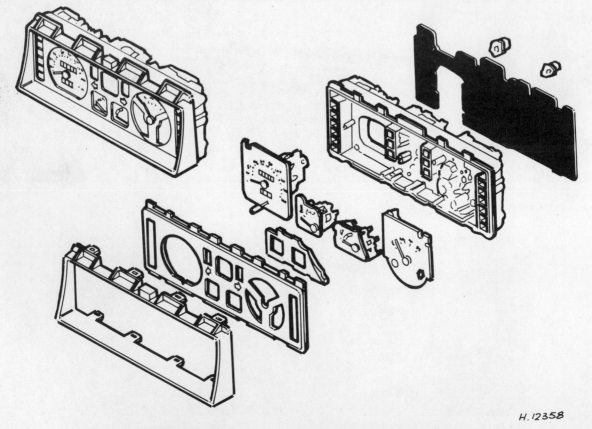

H.12358

Fig. 9.13 Typical Renault 11 instrument panel layout (Sec 17)

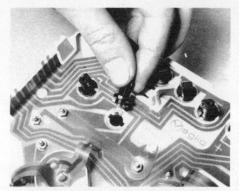

17.2 Removing the instrument panel bulb holders

17.4 Lift the catches (arrowed) to remove the lens and facing plate from the instrument panel body

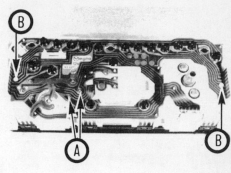

17.9 Two of the instrument retaining nuts (A) and printed circuit pegs (B) at the rear of the instrument panel

### Panel illumination and warning lamp bulbs

2    The bulb holders are secured to the rear of the instrument panel by a bayonet fitting. Turn the bulb holder anti-clockwise to remove, and then withdraw the push-fit bulbs (photo).
3    Refit the bulb holders by turning clockwise slightly.

### Instruments

4    Remove the instrument panel lens by carefully lifting the catches around its periphery (photo).
5    Lift off the facing plate from the panel body.
6    Undo the retaining screws and nuts securing the relevant instrument to the panel body and to the printed circuit on the back. Release the catches, where applicable, and lift out the instrument.
7    Refit the instrument using the reverse of the removal procedure.

### Printed circuit

8    Remove the illumination and warning lamp bulb holders from the rear of the instrument panel.
9    Undo the nuts securing the instruments to the panel body and printed circuit at the rear (photo).
10    Release the printed circuit from the locating pegs and from the multi-plug connector posts, then carefully withdraw the circuit from the instrument panel.
11    Refitting the printed circuit is the reverse of the removal procedure.

### 18 Steering column switches – removal and refitting

1    Disconnect the battery negative terminal.
2    Undo the retaining screws securing the lower half of the steering column shroud to the column, facia and shroud upper half as applicable (photo). Release the retaining catches and lift off the lower shroud half (photo). Place the shroud to one side but avoid straining the wiring connections, where fitted.

3    Undo the screws securing the upper column shroud to the steering column, but do not remove it.
4    If the combination lighting and direction indicator switch is to be removed, undo the two retaining screws, lift the upper shroud to provide clearance and withdraw the switch. Disconnect the wiring multi-plugs and remove the switch.
5    If the combination windscreen wiper and washer switch is to be removed, undo the screws securing the switch to the upper shroud (photo), lift the shroud to provide clearance and withdraw the switch. Disconnect the wiring multi-plugs and remove the switch.
6    Both the combination switches are sealed assemblies and cannot be repaired. If the switches are faulty they must be renewed.
7    If any of the switches or components on the steering column shrouds are to be removed (according to model and options fitted), this can be done by disconnecting the wiring connectors or multi-plugs and then releasing the retaining catches or screws, as applicable.
8    Refitting the switches, components and shrouds is the reverse sequence to removal.

### 19 Facia and centre console switches – removal and refitting

1    The majority of interior switches and control fittings on Renault 9 and 11 models are retained by plastic locating tags and are simple to remove.
2    Before removing a switch or control, disconnect the battery negative terminal.
3    To remove a rocker switch or push-push switch, ease the switch out of its location using a thin blunt instrument (photo).
4    Disconnect the wiring multi-plug at the rear and remove the switch (photo).
5    Refitting is simply a matter of reconnecting the multi-plug and pushing the switch back into its location.
6    On Renault 11 models an additional small switch panel is located on the facia to the right of the steering column. To remove this panel,

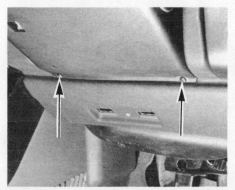

18.2A Undo the screws securing the shroud to the steering column and facia (arrowed) ...

18.2B ... then withdraw the shroud lower half

18.5 Combination switch-to-shroud upper half retaining screws (arrowed)

19.3 The facia and console switches are retained by small tags at the top (arrowed) ...

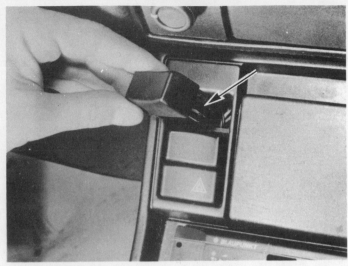

19.4 ... or at the side (arrowed), and have a multi-plug wiring connector at the rear

undo the two screws and lower it to release the upper catches. The components on the panel can now be removed from the rear as necessary.
7    Refitting the panel is the reverse sequence to removal.
8    The remainder of the controls and fittings on the facia and centre console are dealt with under their main headings in this Chapter and Chapter 11.

## 20 Ignition switch – removal and refitting

1    Disconnect the battery negative terminal.
2    Undo the retaining screws securing the lower half of the steering column shroud to the column, facia and shroud upper half, as applicable. Release the retaining catches and lift off the shroud lower half. Place the shroud to one side, but avoid straining the wiring connections, where fitted.
3    Slide the ignition switch trim facing plate out of the column shroud upper half.
4    Insert the ignition key and turn the switch to position G. Remove the key.
5    Disconnect the ignition switch wiring at the multi-plug connector.
6    Undo the small screw securing the switch to the column, depress the retaining pin with a scriber or thin rod, then withdraw the switch from the column.
7    To remove the switch from the lock barrel, insert the key, turn it to the ST position then remove it.
8    Undo the screw at the back, depress the three locating tags around the side, and slide the switch out of the lock barrel.
9    Reassembling and refitting follows the reverse of this procedure.

## 21 Clock – removal and refitting

1    On both the Renault 9 and 11 models the clock is a push-fit in its location and is retained by plastic catches.
2    To remove the clock first disconnect the battery negative terminal.
3    Carefully ease the clock from its location using a thin blunt instrument.
4    Disconnect the wiring connections and remove the clock from the car.
5    Refitting is the reverse sequence to removal.

## 22 Cigarette lighter – removal and refitting

1    Disconnect the battery negative terminal.
2    Pull out the cigarette lighter element and then turn the lighter

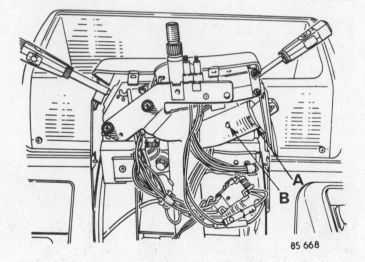

Fig. 9.14 Ignition switch-to-steering column retaining screw (A) and retaining pin (B) (Sec 20)

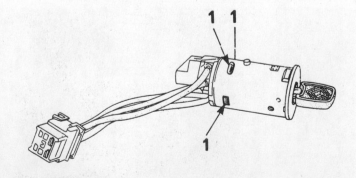

Fig. 9.15 Ignition switch-to-lock barrel locating tags (1) (Sec 20)

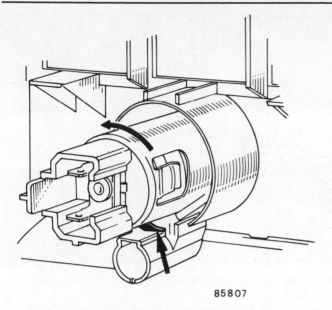

85807

**Fig. 9.16 Cigarette lighter removal (Sec 22)**

*Turn lighter body in direction of upper arrow to remove. Lower arrow indicates illumination bulb earthing strip*

body a few degrees clockwise to disengage the retaining tags. Do not turn the body too far or the illumination bulb earthing strip will be damaged.

3    With the tags released, withdraw the lighter body, disconnect the wiring multi-plug and remove the unit.

4    Refitting is the reverse sequence to removal.

## 23 Courtesy lamp pillar switches – removal and refitting

1    Disconnect the battery negative terminal.

2    Open the door and locate the front courtesy lamp switch on the door pillar.

3    Remove the retaining screw and withdraw the switch.

4    Disconnect the supply wire and tie a loose knot in it to prevent it dropping into the pillar. Remove the switch.

5    The above procedure is also applicable for the switches operated by the boot or tailgate.

6    Refitting is the reverse sequence to removal.

## 24 Headlamp bulb – renewal

### Renault 9 models

1    From within the engine compartment disconnect the wiring connector at the rear of the bulb (photo).

2    For greater access, lift off the rubber cover around the bulb and lens assembly (photo).

3    If conventional bulbs are fitted, spring back the two wire retaining clips (photo). If halogen bulbs are fitted release the ends of the wire retaining clip and pivot the clip clear.

4    The bulb can now be withdrawn from its location in the lens assembly (photo). Take care not to touch the bulb glass with your fingers; if touched, clean the bulb with methylated spirits.

5    Refit the bulb, ensuring that it engages properly with the lens assembly, slip the retaining clip(s) into place then refit the rubber cover and wiring connector.

### Renault 11 models

6    From within the engine compartment, lift off the rubber cover around the bulb and lens assembly (photo).

7    Disconnect the electrical leads on the bulb and lens assembly.

8    Release the ends of the wire retaining clip and pivot the clip clear.

24.1 Disconnect the wiring connector (arrowed) on the Renault 9 headlamp ...

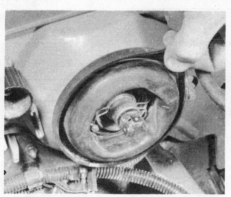

24.2 ... lift off the rubber cover ...

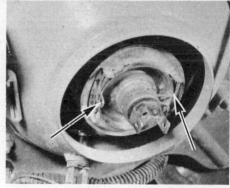

24.3 ... release the wire retaining clips (arrowed) ...

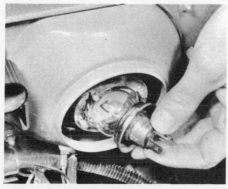

24.4 ... and lift out the bulb

24.6 On Renault 11 headlamps, lift off the rubber cover first to gain access to the wiring and bulb

9   The bulb can now be withdrawn from its location in the lens assembly. Take care not to touch the bulb glass with your fingers; if touched, clean the bulb with methylated spirits.
10  Refit the bulb ensuring that it engages properly with the lens assembly. Slip the retaining clip into place, reconnect the wiring and refit the rubber cover.

## 25  Front sidelight bulb – renewal

1   From within the engine compartment withdraw the sidelight bulb holder from the lens assembly. On Renault 9 models the bulb holder is a push fit (photo) and on Renault 11 models a bayonet fitting is used.
2   On all models the bulb has a bayonet fitting in the holder and is removed by turning anti-clockwise and lifting out.
3   Refit the new bulb to the holder and secure the holder in the lens assembly.

## 26  Front direction indicator bulb – renewal

### Renault 9 models
1   Remove the bulb holder from the lens assembly by turning it anti-clockwise and withdrawing it to the rear (photo).
2   Turn the bulb anti-clockwise and remove it from the holder.
3   Refit the bulb and holder using the reverse of this procedure.

### Renault 11 models
4   Remove the lens assembly from the front bumper by inserting a thin blade down one side to release the retaining catch (photo).
5   Withdraw the assembly from the bumper, spread the two tabs and release the lens to gain access to the bulb (photo).
6   Remove the bulb by turning anti-clockwise.
7   Refit the bulb and lens, then push the assembly into the bumper until the retaining catches engage.

## 27  Front foglamp bulb – renewal

1   Undo the two screws securing the lens glass to the lamp body and carefully withdraw the lens.
2   Disconnect the two wires at the bulb holder terminals, release the retaining spring clip and lift out the bulb holder.
3   Lift and pull the bulb to remove it from the holder.
4   Refit the bulb and lens assembly using the reverse of this procedure. Ensure that the new bulb is held with a piece of cloth or tissue paper and clean the bulb glass with methylated spirit if it is touched with the fingers.

25.1 The sidelight bulb holders are located in the headlamp lens assembly

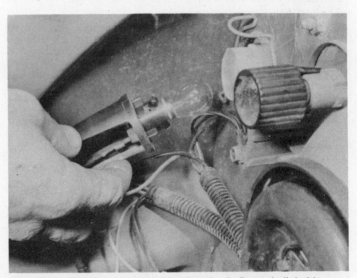

26.1 On Renault 9 models, turn the direction indicator bulb holder anti-clockwise to remove it for access to the bulb

26.4 On Renault 11 models remove the direction indicator lens assembly using a thin blunt instrument

26.5 With the direction indicator assembly removed, spread the tabs and lift off the lens for access to the bulb

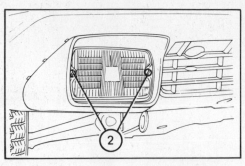
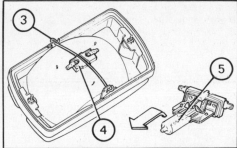

**Fig. 9.17 Front foglamp components (Sec 27)**

2   Lens glass retaining screws
3   Bulb holder retaining spring clip

4   Bulb holder
5   Bulb

## 28 Headlamp lens assembly – removal and refitting

### Renault 9 models

1   Remove the direction indicator lens assembly, as described in Section 29.
2   Disconnect the wiring connector at the rear of the headlamp bulb and remove the sidelight bulb holder from the lens assembly.
3   Undo the four nuts and remove the washers securing the lens assembly to the front body panel. Close the bonnet and withdraw the unit from the front of the car.
4   Refitting is the reverse sequence to removal.

### Renault 11 models

5   Disconnect the two wiring multi-plug and socket connectors located between the two lamp units.
6   Refer to Chapter 11 and remove the radiator grille.
7   Undo the retaining screw located under the headlamp nearest to the side of the car and unhook the tension spring.
8   Withdraw the unit from the front of the car.
9   Refitting is the reverse sequence to removal.

## 29 Front direction indicator lens assembly – removal and refitting

### Renault 9 models

1   Remove the direction indicator bulb holder by turning it anti-clockwise and withdrawing to the rear (photo).
2   Pull the wire retaining clip loop upwards to release the lens assembly and remove the unit from the front of the car (photos).
3   Refitting is the reverse sequence to removal.

### Renault 11 models

4   Removal of the lens assembly is covered as part of the bulb renewal procedure, and reference should be made to Section 26.

## 30 Front foglamp lens assembly – removal and refitting

1   From within the engine compartment disconnect the two wires at the connectors and slacken the nut securing the lens assembly to the mounting bracket.
2   From the front of the car free the clips and remove the plastic casing.
3   Remove the securing nut and washer, then withdraw the unit from the front of the car.
4   Refitting is the reverse sequence to removal. Adjust the position of the foglamp beam before tightening the securing nut.

## 31 Headlamp aim – adjustment

1   Accurate adjustment of the headlamp aim can only be done using optical beam setting equipment and this work should therefore be carried out by a Renault dealer or service station with the necessary facilities. For reference, the location of the beam adjusting screws are shown in the photos.
2   Additionally a two position adjuster is provided to allow the headlamps to be moved up or down to compensate for vehicle load. According to model this adjustment may be carried out from inside the car by turning a knob on the facia, or at the headlamp units by moving a knob or lever. On Renault 9 models the adjustment at the headlamp units is by a knob (photo). When viewed from within the engine compartment, turning the knob clockwise raises the headlamps,

29.1 Remove the direction indicator bulb holder ...

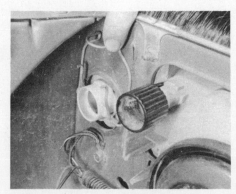

29.2A ... lift the wire retaining clip loop ...

29.2B ... then withdraw the direction indicator lens assembly

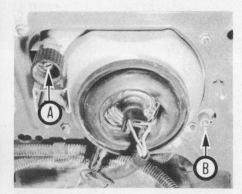

31.1A Renault 9 headlamp vertical adjustment screw (A) and horizontal adjustment screw (B)

31.1B Renault 11 headlamp horizontal adjustment screws (A), vertical adjustment screws (B) and two position height adjuster (C)

31.2 Two position height adjuster knob (arrowed) on Renault 9 headlamp

turning it anti-clockwise lowers them. On Renault 11 models adjustment is by a lever situated between each pair of headlamps (photo 31.1B). Moving the lever down raises the headlamps and moving it up lowers them. Always ensure that both headlamps are set at the same position.

3   Holts Amber Lamp is useful for temporarily changing the headlight colour to conform with the normal usage on Continental Europe.

## 32  Rear lamp cluster bulbs – renewal

### Renault 9 models
1   Press the two plastic locating arms towards each other and withdraw the lamp cluster assembly into the luggage compartment (photo).
2   The bulbs may be removed by turning them anti-clockwise and

withdrawing them from their holders (photo).
3   Refit the bulb and cluster assembly, ensuring that it is securely held by the locating arms.

### Renault 11 models
4   Release the upper and lower retaining catches and withdraw the lamp cluster assembly into the luggage compartment (photo).
5   The bulbs may be removed by turning them anti-clockwise and withdrawing them from their holders (photo).
6   Refit the bulb and cluster assembly, ensuring that it is securely located in the retaining catches.
7   The rear foglamp bulb is housed in a separate bulb holder. This is removed by turning anti-clockwise and withdrawing (photo). The bulb is removed in the same way.
8   Refit the bulb and turn the holder clockwise to lock it in the lens unit.

32.1 On Renault 9 models press the two locating arms (arrowed) together then withdraw the rear lamp cluster

32.2 The bulbs can then be removed by turning anti-clockwise

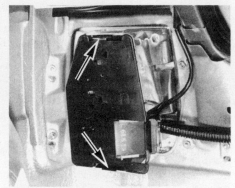

32.4 On Renault 11 models release the upper and lower catches (arrowed) then withdraw the rear lamp cluster

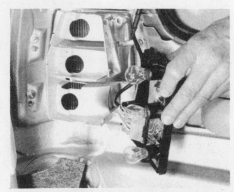

32.5 The bulbs can then be removed by turning anti-clockwise

32.7 The Renault 11 rear foglamp bulb is housed in a separate holder

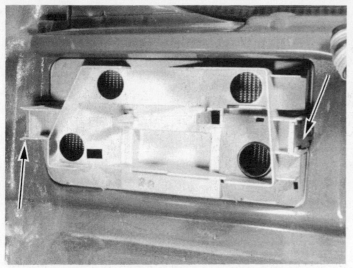

33.2A Depress the two spring retaining clips (arrowed) ...

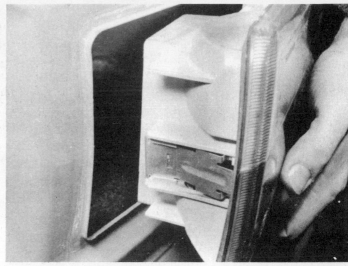

33.2B ... to remove the Renault 9 rear lamp lens assembly

## 33 Rear lamp lens assembly – removal and refitting

### Renault 9 models

1   Remove the lamp cluster, as described in the previous Section.
2   Depress the two spring retaining clips on the side of the lens assembly and withdraw the unit from the rear of the car (photos).
3   Refitting is the reverse of this procedure.

### Renault 11 models

4   Remove the lamp cluster and rear foglamp bulb holder, as described in the previous Section.
5   Undo the two nuts and remove the washers securing the foglamp lens assembly to the rear body panel and withdraw the unit from the rear.
6   Undo the four nuts and remove the washers securing the rear lamp lens assembly to the body and withdraw the unit from the rear.
7   Refitting is the reverse of this procedure.

## 34 Rear number plate lamp bulb – renewal

1   Undo the two lamp body retaining screws and withdraw the body lens and bulb assembly (photo).
2   The festoon type bulb can now be slipped from between the two contacts (photo).
3   Refitting is the reverse sequence to removal.

## 35 Facia, switch and heater control illumination bulbs – renewal

1   According to model and equipment fitted, illumination of the various controls, switches and accessories is provided by bulbs in or around the component concerned.
2   Access to the switch and instrument panel bulbs is gained after removal of the unit, and this is described in the relevant Section of this Chapter.
3   To gain access to the heater control illumination bulbs and certain components on the centre console, reference should be made to Chapter 11.

## 36 Wiper blades and arms – removal and refitting

### Wiper blades

1   The wiper blades should be renewed when they no longer clean the windscreen or where fitted, the tailgate window effectively.
2   Lift the wiper arm away from the window.

34.1 Undo the retaining screws ...

34.2 ... to gain access to the rear number plate lamp bulb

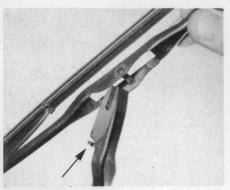

36.3 Wiper blade retaining catch (arrowed) on the arm

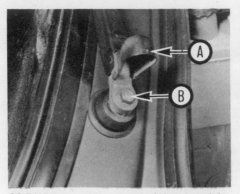

36.5 Wiper arm hinged cover (A) and retaining nut (B)

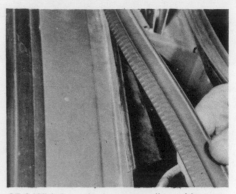

37.2 Withdraw the bonnet sealing rubber ...

3    Release the catch on the arm, turn the blade through 90° and withdraw the blade from the arm fork (photo).
4    Insert the new blade into the arm, making sure it locates securely.

*Wiper arms*
5    To remove a wiper arm, lift the hinged cover and unscrew the retaining nut (photo).
6    Using a screwdriver, carefully prise the arm off the spindle.
7    Before refitting the arm switch the wipers on and off, allowing them to return to the 'park' position.

8    Refit the arm to the spindle, with the arm and blade positioned at the bottom edge of the screen in the normal 'parked' position.
9    Refit and tighten the retaining nut and close the hinged cover.

**37  Windscreen wiper motor and linkage – removal and refitting**

1    Remove the wiper arms, as described in the previous Section.
2    Carefully withdraw the bonnet sealing rubber at the base of the windscreen (photo).

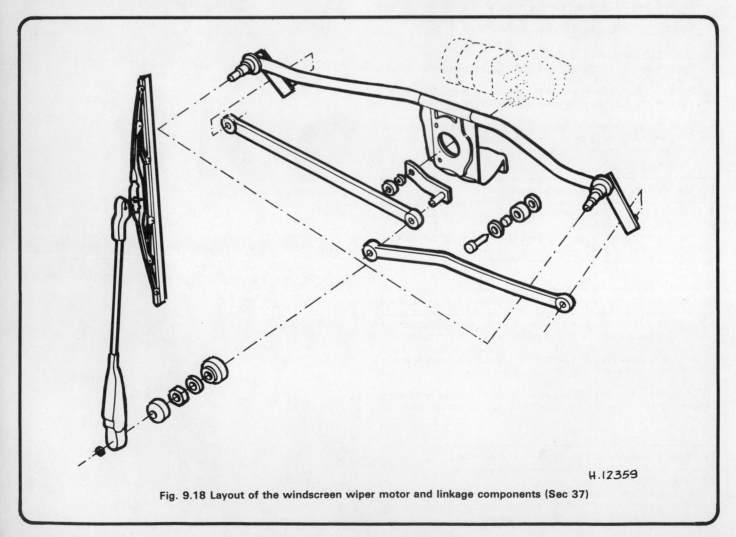

H.12359

Fig. 9.18 Layout of the windscreen wiper motor and linkage components (Sec 37)

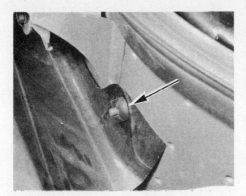

37.3 ... undo the wing nuts (arrowed) and lift off the cover tray to gain access to the windscreen wiper motor and linkage

37.5 Wiper motor mounting bracket retaining bolt (arrowed)

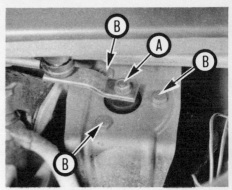

38.3 Wiper motor crank arm retaining nut (A) and motor-to-mounting bracket retaining bolts (B)

3   Unscrew the retaining wing nuts and lift off the cover tray over the motor and linkage (photo).
4   At the wiper arm spindles, withdraw the rubber washer, undo the nut and remove the second washer.
5   Undo the bolt and washer securing the motor mounting bracket to the bulkhead (photo).
6   Disconnect the motor wiring multi-plug, push the spindles through to the inside then withdraw the wiper motor and linkage from the car. Note the number and position of washers and spacers remaining on the spindles and ensure that they are in place when refitting.
7   Refitting is the reverse sequence to removal.

## 38 Windscreen wiper motor – overhaul

1   Remove the wiper motor and linkage from the car, as described in the previous Section.
2   Remove the crank arm from the motor by undoing the nut then lifting the washer and arm off the motor spindle.
3   Undo the three bolts securing the motor to the mounting bracket and remove the motor (photo).
4   Undo the screws securing the gear cover plate to the casing and remove the cover plate and gasket.

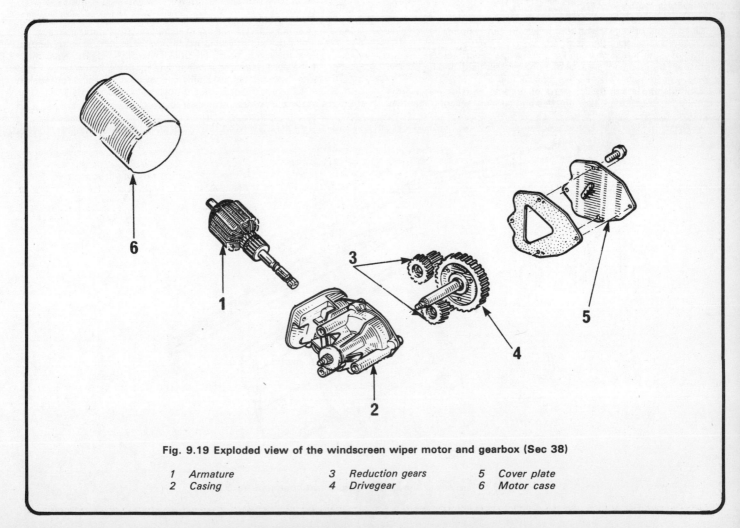

Fig. 9.19 Exploded view of the windscreen wiper motor and gearbox (Sec 38)

| | | | |
|---|---|---|---|
| 1 | Armature | 3 | Reduction gears | 5 | Cover plate |
| 2 | Casing | 4 | Drivegear | 6 | Motor case |

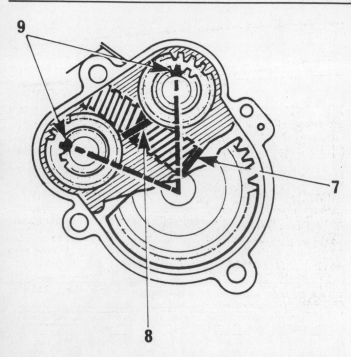

**Fig. 9.20 Wiper motor armature and reduction gear alignment (Sec 38)**

7  Armature assembly shim       9  Assembly marks on reduction
8  Armature worm gear              gears

5   Lift out the drivegear and the reduction gears, noting which side the coloured reduction gear is fitted.
6   Remove the motor case and withdraw the armature.
7   Inspect the gears for wear or damage to their teeth and for scoring or excessive free play of the drivegear spindle.
8   Examine the armature for signs of burning and for wear of the commutator. Check the motor brushes and springs, ensuring that they

are of reasonable length, free to slide and equally tensioned by the springs.
9   The gears and motor brushes are available as replacement parts, but if any of the other components are worn or damaged renewal of the complete unit will be necessary. If the brushes are to be renewed, it will be necessary to re-solder the leads.
10   With the new parts obtained as necessary, begin reassembly as follows:
11   Obtain a shim or packing piece 1.8 mm (0.071 in) thick, then insert the armature and shim into the casing with the shim positioned as shown in Fig. 9.20.
12   Lubricate the gears with multi-purpose grease then fit the coloured reduction gear so that its assembly mark is in line with the reduction gear and drivegear centres (Fig. 9.20).
13   Fit the plain reduction gear so that its assembly mark is aligned in the same way.
14   Remove the shim, but hold the armature securely so that it doesn't move. Now fit the drivegear into mesh with the reduction gears.
15   Refit the gasket and gear cover plate followed by the motor case.
16   Refit the motor to the mounting bracket and secure with the three bolts.
17   Before refitting the crank arm to the motor spindle, refit the motor and linkage assembly to the car, as described in the previous Section. Turn the windscreen wiper switch on and then off again so that the motor stops in its 'park' position. Move the linkage so that the linkage arm and crank arms are all parallel to each other then, in this position, refit the crank arm, washer and nut.

## 39  Tailgate wiper motor – removal and refitting

1   Remove the wiper arm, as described in Section 36.
2   Open the tailgate and remove the cover panel to gain access to the motor.
3   Lift off the rubber washer, then undo the nut securing the motor spindle to the tailgate. Lift off the remaining washers and spacers.
4   Disconnect the motor wiring multi-plug, undo the retaining bolts and withdraw the motor assembly from inside the tailgate. Note the location of the earth lead under one of the retaining bolts.
5   The motor and gearbox assembly cannot be dismantled for repair or overhaul as replacement parts are not available separately.
6   Refitting is the reverse sequence to removal.

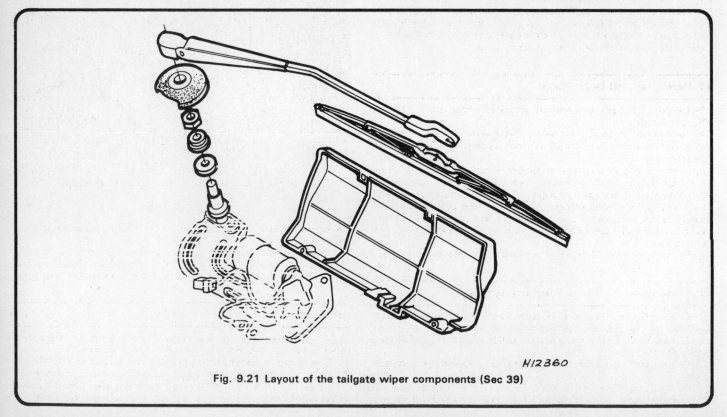

H12360

**Fig. 9.21 Layout of the tailgate wiper components (Sec 39)**

### 40 Headlamp wash/wipe components – removal and refitting

1 According to model a headlamp cleaning system consisting of washers or washers and wipers may be fitted as standard or optional equipment. The various components of the system may be removed as follows:

#### Wiper blades and arms

2 To remove a blade, release the locking clip and withdraw the blade from the arm.
3 New blades are refitted by placing them in position and locking with the clip.
4 To remove a wiper arm, undo the retaining nut and ease the arm off the motor spindle.
5 Position the arm so that it is in the 'parked' position at the bottom of the headlamp before fitting.

#### Wiper motor

6 Remove the wiper arms, as described previously, then refer to Chapter 11 and remove the radiator grille.
7 Disconnect the motor wiring multi-plug, and undo the bolt at the front securing the motor bracket to the body member.
8 Slacken the motor bracket side-mounting bolt and remove the motor assembly from the car.
9 The motor and gearbox assembly cannot be dismantled for repair or overhaul as replacement parts are not available separately.
10 Refitting is the reverse sequence to removal.

#### Washer jets

11 Remove the front bumper assembly, as described in Chapter 11.
12 With the bumper removed, ease the pipe elbow out of the washer, undo the retaining nut and lift off the washer jet assembly.
13 Refitting is the reverse sequence to removal. Adjust the jet nozzles using a pin after refitting.

#### Pump and reservoir

14 The pump and reservoir assembly is combined with the windscreen washer reservoir and is located under the cooling system expansion tank. To remove it, release the expansion tank strap and move the tank to one side. Disconnect the wiring and washer pipes and lift the reservoir from its location.
15 The washer pumps are retained in position either by a tight push-fit in their rubber sealing washers or by a slotted retaining sleeve which can be unscrewed with a screwdriver from inside the tank.
16 Refitting is the reverse sequence to removal.

### 41 Horn – removal and refitting

1 The horn is located in the engine compartment on the right-hand side of the radiator.
2 To remove the horn disconnect the electrical lead, undo the mounting bracket retaining bolt and remove the horn and bracket (photo).
3 If the horn is inoperative, check for a supply voltage to it by connecting a test bulb between the electrical lead and a good earth. With the ignition switched on, depress the horn button and the test bulb should light. If the bulb fails to light, check for a blown fuse. If the fuse is satisfactory there is a fault in the wiring or multi-function switch. If the bulb lights, the horn is faulty and the horn will have to be renewed.
4 Refitting the horn is the reverse sequence to removal.

### 42 Speedometer cable – removal and refitting

1 Refer to Section 16, and remove the instrument panel sufficiently to allow the speedometer cable to be disconnected.
2 Release the bulkhead grommet and pull the cable through into the engine compartment.
3 Release the cable from its retaining clips in the engine compartment.
4 At the rear of the transmission, withdraw the shaped wire clip securing the cable to the transmission through the engine mounting

Fig. 9.22 Headlamp wiper motor retaining bolt locations (1 and 2) (Sec 40)

41.2 Horn electrical lead (A) and mounting bracket retaining bolt (B)

bracket. Withdraw the cable and remove it from the engine compartment.
5 Refitting is the reverse sequence to removal, but ensure that the transmission retaining clip is located through the holes in the mounting bracket and gearbox with its shaped end in the lower hole.

### 43 Engine oil level indicator – general

1 On models so equipped, a gauge is provided on the instrument panel to inform the driver of the level of oil in the sump.
2 The gauge is controlled by an electronic circuit located in the instrument panel which receives information from a sensor located in the sump. The sensor contains a high resistance wire whose thermal conductivity alters according to its depth of immersion in the oil.

3  If the engine develops a fault the following test can be carried out to isolate the component concerned.

4  Remove the sensor from the sump by disconnecting the two wires and unscrewing the unit from its mounting (photo).

5  Using an ohmmeter, check the resistance across the sensor terminals. A reading on the ohmmeter should be shown. If not, the sensor is faulty and should be renewed.

6  If the sensor is satisfactory, remove the instrument panel, as described in Section 16, and check the continuity of the wires from the sensor wiring connectors to the appropriate terminals in the instrument panel multi-plug. If there is no continuity, trace the wiring until the break or poor connection is found and make the necessary repair.

7  If the wiring is satisfactory the fault lies with the indicator gauge or the electronic circuit and these can only accurately be checked by substitution.

8  Refit any removed components using the reverse of the removal sequence.

## 44 Electro-mechanical door locks – general

1  An electric or electro-mechanical door locking system may be fitted as standard or optional equipment to certain Renault 9 and 11 models. The system enables all four doors (and on some versions the tailgate) to be locked or unlocked from the outside by locking or unlocking either of the front doors. By depressing a switch on the centre console, all the doors can be locked or unlocked from the inside. The rear doors may be unlocked manually from the inside by operating the door lock button or rocker switch.

2  Each lock is operated by a solenoid on early models, or by an electric motor on later models, connected to the lock mechanism inside each door. A safety device consisting of an inertia switch and thermal cut-out automatically unlocks all the doors in the event of impact or heat build-up. These components are located in the steering column shroud lower half. A reset button is also provided in the shroud to enable the system to be reset in the event of a malfunction.

3  Removal and refitting of the door locks is basically the same as for conventional locks, and full details will be found in Chapter 11.

4  On some versions the door locks are operated by remote control using a small hand held infra-red transmitter. The transmitter signal is decoded by a receiver mounted above the interior rear view mirror and this activates the electro-mechanical system to lock or unlock the doors.

5  The transmitter is powered by three 1.5 volt alkaline type batteries which have a life of approximately 12 months. The batteries can be renewed after undoing the transmitter case screws and opening the case to gain access.

6  In the event of a fault occurring in the system it is recommended that you seek the advice of a dealer as specialist knowledge and equipment are necessary for accurate fault diagnosis.

## 45 Electrically-operated windows – general

1  Electrically-operated windows are provided on certain versions as standard or optional equipment, and are controlled by switches located in the front door armrests or centre console.

2  Removal and refitting of the window motors is basically the same as for manually-operated windows, and full details of both types will be found in Chapter 11.

## 46 Radio – installation

1  On most Renault 9 and 11 models, 'pre-radio' equipment consisting of an aerial, positive and negative leads and speaker wiring is in position ready for connection to a suitable receiver and loudspeakers.

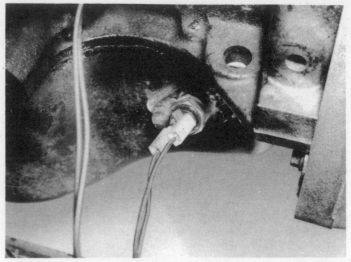

43.4 Engine oil level indicator sensor and wiring location on the side of the sump

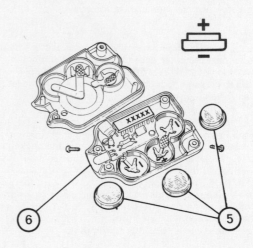

Fig. 9.23 Electro-magnetic door lock infra-red transmitter (Sec 44)

5   Batteries                    6   Transmitter case

2  Provision for the radio receiver is made in the centre console and, after releasing the blanking plate, the wires will be found ready for connection. The actual receiver purchased will dictate whether or not a fitting kit is required and this can be obtained from a Renault dealer whose advice should be sought.

3  On Renault 9 models two speaker grilles are provided in the facia and provision is also made in the rear shelf for two additional speakers. The speaker wires will be found behind the grilles. On Renault 11 models two speaker grilles and the appropriate wiring are located in the driver's and passenger's footwells.

4  On models that are not equipped with 'pre-radio' equipment the fitting of the aerial and wiring should be carried out in accordance with the component maker's instructions.

5  All models are fully suppressed in respect of ignition and charging system interference and further suppression should not be necessary.

## 47 Fault diagnosis – electrical system

| Symptom | Reason(s) |
| --- | --- |
| Starter fails to turn engine | Battery discharged or defective |
| | Battery terminal and/or earth leads loose |
| | Starter motor connections loose |
| | Starter solenoid faulty |
| | Starter brushes worn or sticking |
| | Starter commutator dirty or worn |
| | Starter field coils earthed |
| Starter turns engine very slowly | Battery discharged |
| | Starter motor connections loose |
| | Starter brushes worn or sticking |
| Starter spins but does not turn engine | Pinion or flywheel ring gear teeth broken or badly worn |
| Starter noisy | Pinion or flywheel ring gear teeth badly worn |
| | Mounting bolts loose |
| Battery will not hold charge for more than a few days | Battery defective internally |
| | Battery terminals loose |
| | Alternator drivebelt slipping |
| | Alternator or regulator faulty |
| | Short circuit |
| Ignition light stays on | Alternator faulty |
| | Alternator drivebelt broken |
| Ignition light fails to come on | Warning bulb blown |
| | Indicator light open circuit |
| | Alternator faulty |
| Fuel or temperature gauge gives no reading | Wiring open circuit |
| | Sender unit faulty |
| Fuel or temperature gauge give maximum reading all the time | Wiring short circuit |
| | Gauge faulty |
| Lights inoperative | Bulb blown |
| | Fuses blown |
| | Battery discharged |
| | Switch faulty |
| | Wiring open circuit |
| | Bad connection due to corrosion |
| Failure of component motor | Commutator dirty or burnt |
| | Armature faulty |
| | Brushes sticking or worn |
| | Armature bearings dry or misaligned |
| | Field coils faulty |
| | Fuse blown |
| | Wiring loose or broken |
| Failure of an individual component | Wiring loose or broken |
| | Fuse blown |
| | Bad circuit connection |
| | Switch faulty |
| | Component faulty |

# Chapter 10 Suspension and steering

*For modifications, and information applicable to later models, see Supplement at end of manual*

## Contents

## Specifications

### Front suspension

Type ............................................................. Independent by MacPherson struts with coil springs, integral telescopic shock absorbers and anti-roll bar

Anti-roll bar diameter ....................................... 23 or 24 mm (0.91 or 0.94 in), according to model

Front underbody height (H1 minus H2; see Section 25) .......... $75 \text{ mm} \begin{array}{c} +10 \\ -5 \end{array}$ ($2.95 \text{ in} \begin{array}{c} +0.4 \\ -0.2 \end{array}$)

### Rear suspension

Type ............................................................. Independent by trailing arms with transverse torsion bars, telescopic shock absorbers and anti-roll bar

Anti-roll bar diameter ....................................... 15 or 16 mm (0.59 or 0.63 in), according to model
Torsion bar diameter ......................................... 18.5 mm (0.73 in)
Torsion bar length ........................................... 645 mm (25.4 in)

Rear underbody height (H4 minus H5; see Section 25) .......... $20 \text{ mm} \begin{array}{c} +10 \\ -5 \end{array}$ ($0.79 \text{ in} \begin{array}{c} +0.4 \\ -0.2 \end{array}$)

Rear wheel camber angle .................................... -0° 20' to -1° 20'
Rear wheel toe setting ...................................... 0° to 0° 30' (0 to 3 mm) toe-in

### Steering

Type ............................................................. Rack and pinion
Turns lock to lock ........................................... 4
Camber angle ................................................. -0° 20' to +0° 40'
Castor angle at specified underbody height (H5 minus H2; see Section 25)
    10 mm (0.39 in) ..................................... 2° 30'
    30 mm (1.18 in) ..................................... 2°
    50 mm (1.97 in) ..................................... 1° 30'
    65 mm (2.56 in) ..................................... 1°
    85 mm (3.35 in) ..................................... 0° 30'
Steering axis inclination .................................... 12° 30' to 13° 30'
Toe setting ................................................... Parallel to 0° 20' (0 to 2 mm) toe-out

### Roadwheels

Type ............................................................. Pressed steel or aluminium alloy according to model
Size ............................................................. 4½Jx13, 5½Jx13 or 5½Bx13
Maximum wheel run-out (measured at rim side) ............ 1.2 mm (0.047 in)

## Tyres
Tyre size ...................................................................   145SR13, 155SR13 or 175/70SR13
Tyre pressures (cold):
   Front ................................................................   1.8 bar (26 lbf/in²)
   Rear .................................................................   2.0 bar (29 lbf/in²)

### Torque wrench settings

| | Nm | lbf ft |
|---|---|---|
| **Front suspension** | | |
| Driveshaft retaining nut | 210 | 155 |
| Lower arm balljoint to stub axle carrier | 60 | 44 |
| Balljoint to lower arm | 75 | 55 |
| Lower arm to subframe | 80 | 59 |
| Suspension strut to stub axle carrier | 80 | 59 |
| Strut upper mounting to inner wing turret | 27 | 20 |
| Strut upper mounting nut to piston rod | 60 | 44 |
| Anti-roll bar to clamp bolts | 30 | 22 |
| **Rear suspension** | | |
| Trailing arm mounting brackets to body | 70 | 52 |
| Hub bearing retaining nut | 160 | 118 |
| Anti-roll bar to trailing arm | 45 | 33 |
| Shock absorber to trailing arm | 80 | 59 |
| Shock absorber to body | 25 | 18 |
| **Steering** | | |
| Steering gear to subframe | 60 | 44 |
| Steering arm balljoint to stub axle carrier | 35 | 26 |
| Steering arm inner balljoint to rack | 40 | 30 |
| Steering wheel retaining nut: | | |
|    Up to August 1983 | 65 | 48 |
|    August 1983 on | 45 | 33 |
| Steering column intermediate shaft universal joint clamp and retaining bolts | 25 | 18 |
| **Roadwheels** | | |
| Wheel bolts | 80 | 59 |

## 1  General description

The independent front suspension is of the MacPherson strut type, incorporating coil springs and integral telescopic shock absorbers. Lateral and longitudinal location of each strut assembly is by pressed-steel lower suspension arms utilizing rubber inner mounting bushes and incorporating a balljoint at their outer ends. The two lower suspension arms are interconnected by an anti-roll bar which is attached to the rear of the front subframe via rubber bushes. The front stub axle carriers, which house the wheel bearings, brake calipers and the hub/disc assemblies are bolted to the MacPherson struts and connected to the lower suspension arms via the balljoints.

The independent rear suspension is of the trailing arm type utilizing transverse torsion bars and telescopic double-acting shock absorbers. An anti-roll bar is also used at the rear, interconnecting the two trailing arms. The integral rear hub and brake drum assemblies rotate on the trailing arm stub axles via double row roller bearings.

The steering gear is of the conventional rack and pinion type located behind the front wheels. Movement of the steering wheel is transmitted to the steering gear through a steering column shaft and collapsible intermediate shaft containing two universal joints. The front stub axle carriers are connected to the steering gear by steering arms, each having an inner and outer balljoint.

## 2  Maintenance and inspection

1   At the intervals given in Routine maintenance a thorough inspection of all suspension and steering components should be carried out, using the following procedure as a guide.

### Front suspension and steering
2   Apply the handbrake, jack up the front of the car and support it securely on axle stands.
3   Visually inspect the lower balljoint dust covers and the steering rack and pinion rubber bellows for splits, chafing, or deterioration. Renew the rubber bellows or the balljoint assembly, as described in Sections 20 and 19 respectively, if any damage is apparent.

4   Grasp the roadwheel at the 12 o'clock and 6 o'clock positions and try to rock it. Very slight free play may be felt, but if the movement is appreciable further investigation is necessary to determine the source. Continue rocking the wheel while an assistant depresses the footbrake. If the movement is now eliminated or significantly reduced, it is likely that the hub bearings are at fault. If the free play is still evident with the footbrake depressed, then there is wear in the suspension joints or mountings. Pay close attention to the lower balljoint and lower arm mounting bushes. Renew any worn components, as described in the appropriate Sections of this Chapter.
5   Now grasp the wheel at the 9 o'clock and 3 o'clock positions and try to rock it as before. Any movement felt now may again be caused by wear in the hub bearings or the steering arm inner or outer balljoints. If the outer balljoint is worn the visual movement will be obvious. If the inner joint is suspect it can be felt by placing a hand over the rack and pinion rubber bellows and gripping the joint. If the wheel is now rocked, movement will be felt at the inner joint if wear has taken place. Repair procedures are described in Section 19 and 21 respectively.
6   Using a large screwdriver or flat bar check for wear in the anti-roll bar mountings and lower arm mountings by carefully levering against these components. Some movement is to be expected, as the mountings are made of rubber, but excessive wear should be obvious. Renew any bushes that are worn.
7   With the car standing on its wheels, have an assistant turn the steering wheel back and forth about one eighth of a turn each way. There should be no lost movement whatever between the steering wheel and roadwheels. If this is not the case, closely observe the joints and mountings previously described, but in addition check the intermediate shaft universal joints for wear and also the rack and pinion steering gear itself. Any wear should be visually apparent and must be rectified, as described in the appropriate Sections of this Chapter.

### Rear suspension
8   Chock the front wheels, jack up the rear of the car and support it securely on axle stands.
9   Visually inspect the rear suspension components, attachments and linkages for any visible signs of wear or damage.
10   Grasp the roadwheel at the 12 o'clock and 6 o'clock positions and

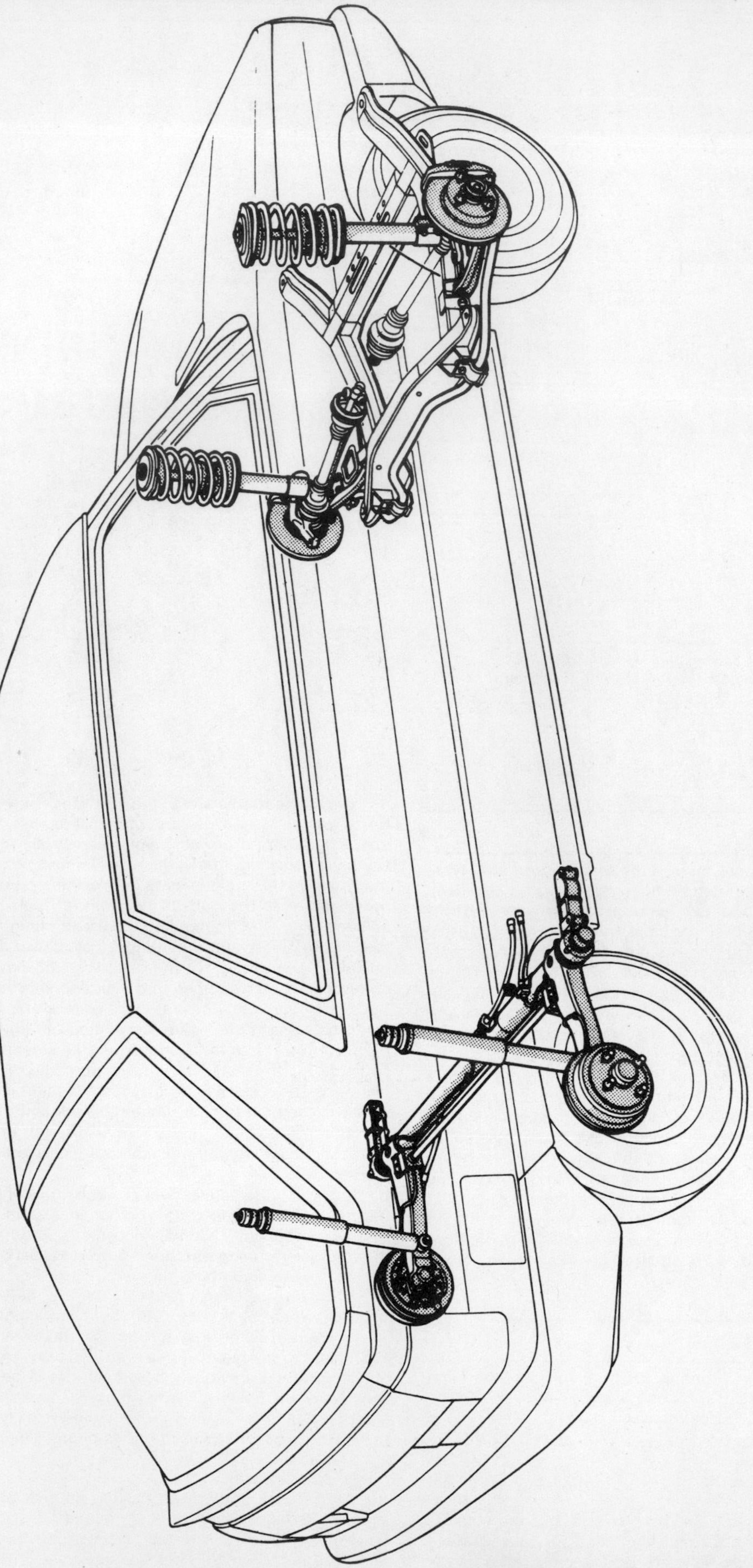

Fig. 10.1 Front and rear suspension assembly layout (Sec 1)

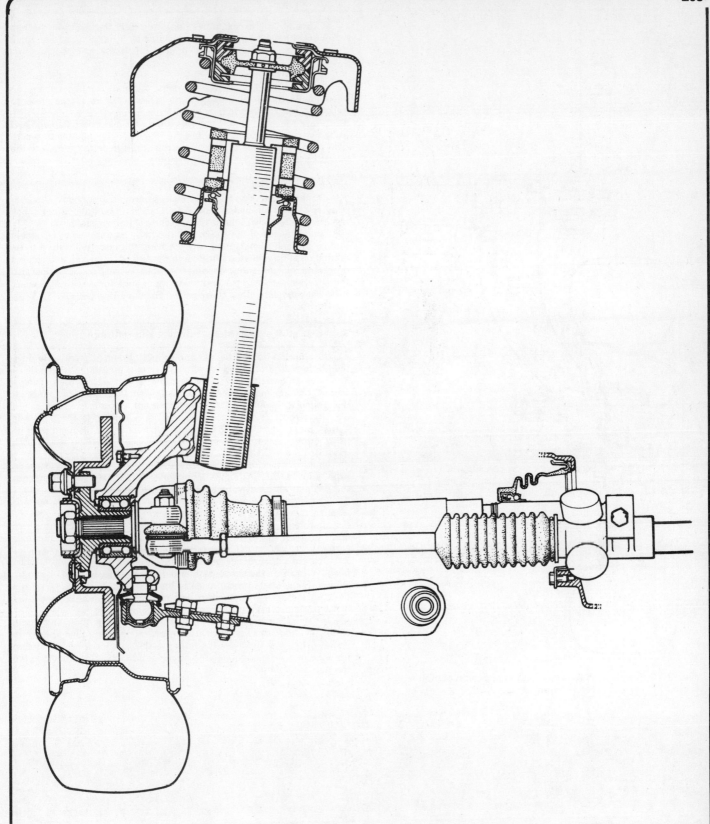

Fig. 10.2 Sectional view of the front suspension and steering components (Sec 1)

try to rock it. Any excess movement here indicates wear in the hub bearings which may also be accompanied by a rumbling sound when the wheel is spun. Renewal procedures are described in Section 10.

### Wheels and tyres

11  Carefully inspect each tyre, including the spare, for signs of uneven wear, lumps, bulges or damage to the sidewalls or tread face. Refer to Section 27 for further details.
12  Check the condition of the wheel rims for distortion, damage and excessive run-out. Also make sure that the balance weights are secure with no obvious signs that they are missing. Check the torque of the wheel nuts and check the tyre pressures.

### Shock absorbers

13  Check for any signs of fluid leakage around the shock absorber body or around the piston rod. Should any fluid be noticed the shock absorber is defective internally and renewal is necessary.
14  The efficiency of the shock absorber may be checked by bouncing the car at each corner. Generally speaking the body will return to its normal position and stop after being depressed. If it rises and returns on a rebound, the shock absorber is probably suspect. Examine also the shock absorber upper and lower mountings for any sign of wear. Renewal procedures are contained in Sections 6 and 11.

### 3  Front stub axle carrier – removal and refitting

1  Jack up the front of the car and support it on axle stands. Remove the appropriate front roadwheel.
2  Have an assistant firmly depress the footbrake and then, using a socket and long knuckle bar, undo the driveshaft retaining nut. Recover the dished thrust plate fitted behind the nut (photo).
3  Undo the two bolts securing the brake caliper to the stub axle carrier. Slide the caliper, complete with pads, off the disc and tie it up using string or wire from a convenient place under the wheel arch (photo).
4  Undo the locknut securing the steering arm balljoint to the stub axle carrier. Using a suitable extractor tool (see Section 19), release the balljoint and move the steering arm to one side.
5  At the base of the stub axle carrier, undo and remove the nut and washer, then withdraw the balljoint clamp bolt (photo).
6  Undo and remove the nuts and washers, then withdraw the two bolts securing the suspension strut to the upper part of the stub axle carrier.
7  Release the stub axle carrier from the strut and then lift it, while pushing down on the suspension arm, to disengage the lower balljoint. Withdraw the stub axle carrier from the driveshaft and remove it from the car (photo). If the driveshaft is a tight fit in the hub bearings, tap it out using a plastic mallet, or use a suitable puller.
8  If the stub axle carrier is being removed for attention to the hub bearings, undo the two Torx type screws securing the disc to the hub flange using a splined key (photo). The disc can now be withdrawn from the hub. If it is tight, lay the disc over two blocks of wood and tap the hub out (photos).

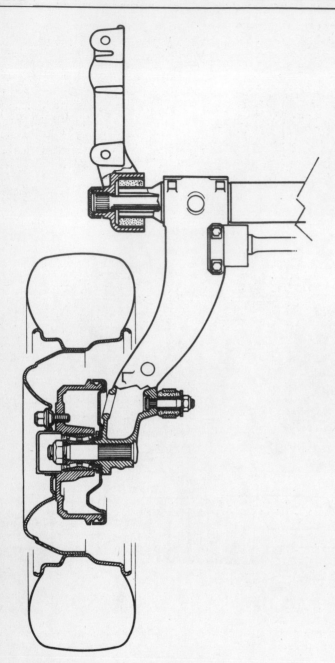

Fig. 10.3 Sectional view of the rear suspension components (Sec 1)

3.2 Remove the dished washer after undoing the driveshaft retaining nut

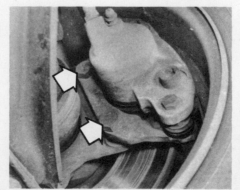

3.3A Undo the brake caliper retaining bolts (arrowed) ...

3.3B ... and withdraw the caliper, complete with pads

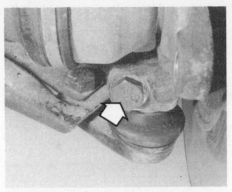

3.5 Undo and remove the nut and washer, then withdraw the balljoint clamp bolt (arrowed)

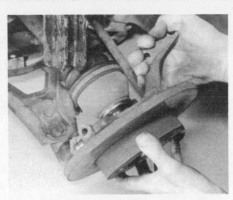

3.7 Disengage the stub axle carrier from the balljoint then withdraw the assembly from the driveshaft

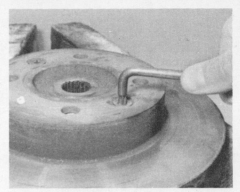

3.8A Undo the two Torx type screws securing the disc to the hub flange using a splined key ...

3.8B ... then lift off the disc

3.8C If the disc is tight, support it on blocks and drive out the hub

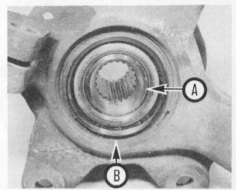

4.2 Hub flange inner end (A) and bearing retaining circlip (B) in the stub axle carrier

9    Refitting is the reverse sequence to removal, bearing in mind the following points:

   (a)    *Ensure that the mating faces of the disc and hub flange are clean and flat before refitting the disc*
   (b)    *Tighten all nuts and bolts to the specified torque*

## 4    Front hub bearings – renewal

**Note**: *The front hub bearings should only be removed from the stub axle carrier if they are to be renewed. The removal procedure renders the bearings unserviceable and they must not be reused.*

1    Remove the stub axle carrier from the car, as described in the previous Section.
2    Support the stub axle carrier securely on blocks or in a vice. Using a tube of suitable diameter in contact with the inner end of the hub flange (photo), drive the hub flange out of the bearing.
3    The bearing will come apart as the hub flange is removed and one of the bearing inner races will remain on the hub flange. To remove it, support the flange in a vice and lever off the inner race using two tyre levers with packing pieces, or preferably use a two- or three-legged puller. Recover the thrust washer from the hub flange after removal of the inner race.
4    Extract the bearing retaining circlip from the inner end of the stub axle carrier.
5    Support the stub axle carrier on blocks or in a vice so that the side nearest the roadwheel is uppermost.
6    Place the previously removed inner race back in position over the ball cage. Using a tube of suitable diameter in contact with the inner race, drive the complete bearing assembly out of the stub axle carrier.
7    Before fitting the new bearing, remove the plastic covers protecting the seals at each end.
8    Support the stub axle carrier so that the side away from the roadwheel is uppermost, and place the new bearing squarely in position.

9    Using a tube of suitable diameter in contact with the bearing outer race, drive the bearing into the stub axle carrier. Ensure that the bearing does not tip slightly and bind as it is being fitted. If this happens the outer race may crack so take great care to keep it square.
10    With the bearing in position, lubricate the lips of the two seals with multi-purpose grease. Remove the retaining sleeve.
11    Place the thrust washer over the hub flange and lay it on the bench, flat face down.
12    Locate the stub axle carrier and bearing inner race over the hub flange and drive the bearing onto the flange using a tube in contact with the bearing inner race.
13    Fit a new bearing retaining circlip to the stub axle carrier and then refit the assembly to the car, as described in the previous Section.

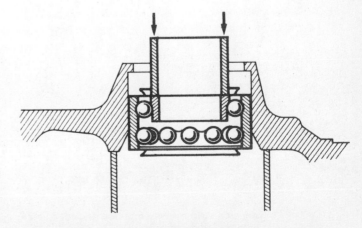

**Fig. 10.4 Using a tube of suitable diameter in contact with the bearing inner race to remove the bearing from the stub axle (Sec 4)**

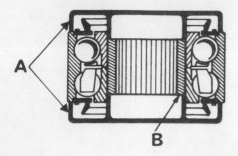

Fig. 10.5 Remove the plastic protective covers (A) before fitting the new bearing. The retaining sleeve (B) should be left in place until the bearing is fitted (Sec 4)

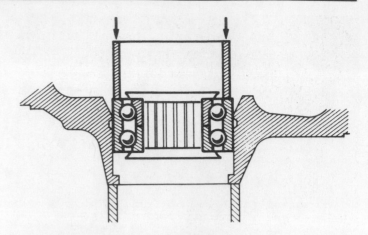

Fig. 10.6 Using a tube in contact with the bearing outer race to fit the bearing to the stub axle carrier (Sec 4)

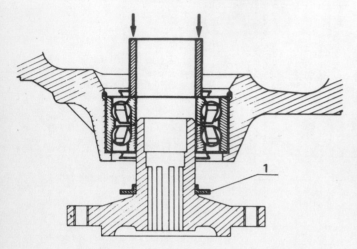

Fig. 10.7 Refitting the hub flange using a tube in contact with the bearing inner race. Ensure that the thrust washer (1) is in position (Sec 4)

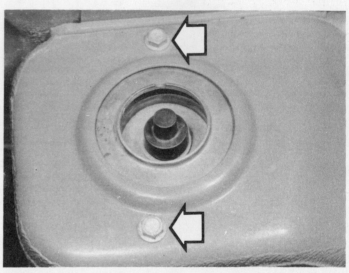

5.3 Front suspension strut-to-mounting turret upper retaining bolts (arrowed)

Straight spring          Inclined spring

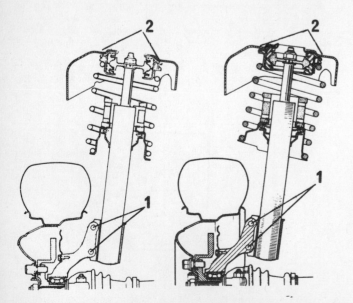

Fig. 10.8 Front suspension strut mounting details and spring type identification (Secs 5 and 6)

1   Strut-to-stub axle carrier retaining bolts
2   Upper mounting bolts

## 5   Front suspension strut – removal and refitting

1   Jack up the front of the car and support it on axle stands. Remove the appropriate front roadwheel.
2   Undo the nuts and remove the two bolts and washers securing the suspension strut to the upper part of the stub axle carrier.
3   From within the engine compartment undo the two bolts securing the strut upper mounting to the turret (photo).
4   Release the strut from the stub axle carrier and withdraw it from under the wheel arch.
5   Refitting the strut is the reverse sequence to removal. Ensure that the strut-to-stub axle carrier bolts are fitted with the nuts facing the front of the car and tighten all the retaining bolts to the specified torque.

## 6   Front suspension strut – dismantling and reassembly

Note: *Before attempting to dismantle the front suspension strut, a tool to hold the coil spring in compression must be obtained. The shape of the spring and lower seat is such that a conventional coil spring compressor cannot be used, and only the Renault special tools shown in the illustrations and described in the text are suitable. If these tools*

6.5 With the spring compressed, undo the strut upper mounting nut (A) while holding the piston rod (B) with an Allen key

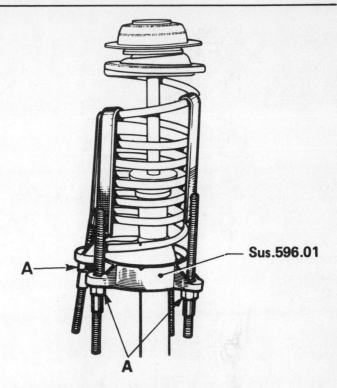

Fig. 10.9 Renault tool in position holding the front spring compressed (Sec 6)

A Tool tightening nuts

*cannot be borrowed or hired, then the work must be left to a Renault dealer. Any attempt to dismantle the strut without these special tools is likely to result in damage or personal injury.*

1    Begin by removing the front suspension strut from the car, as described in the previous Section.

2    As stated in the introductory note at the beginning of this Section, a special tool will be needed to compress the coil spring before dismantling can begin. The spring may be mounted on the strut in one of two ways and this mounting arrangement determines the special tool type needed for removal. View the strut assembly end on as if looking at it from the front of the car (Fig. 10.8). If the spring runs parallel with the strut tube then a straight spring is fitted. If the spring is offset in relation to the strut tube so that it leans in at the top and out at the bottom, then an inclined spring is fitted.

3    If a straight spring is fitted, tool Sus.596.01 will be needed for removal. If an inclined spring is fitted, Sus.863 and the spring cup from Sus.864 will be needed. In both cases, if the spring is to be renewed, Sus.594 and Sus.594.02 will also be required, but will not be needed if the original spring is to be refitted.

4    Having obtained the necessary tools, mount the strut in a vice and fit the tool over the spring and strut, as shown in Fig. 10.9. Compress the spring until all tension is relieved on the spring upper mounting.

5    Withdraw the plastic cap over the strut upper mounting nut, hold the strut piston with an Allen key and undo the nut with a ring spanner (photo).

6    Lift off the washer, upper mounting and spring seat assembly followed by the spring and compressor tool. Do not remove the tool from the spring unless the spring is to be renewed. Finally withdraw the pivot bearing from the strut, and the bump stop from the centre of the spring.

7    With the strut assembly now completely dismantled, examine all the components for wear, damage or deformation and check the bearing for smoothness of operation. Renew any of the components as necessary.

8    Examine the strut for signs of fluid leakage. Check the strut piston for signs of wear or pitting along its entire length and check the strut body for signs of damage or elongation of the mounting bolt holes. Test the operation of the strut, while holding it in an upright position, by moving the piston through a full stroke and then through short strokes of 50 to 100 mm (2 to 4 in). In both cases the resistance felt should be smooth and continuous. If the resistance is jerky, or uneven, or if there is any visible sign of wear or damage to the strut, renewal is necessary.

9    If the original spring is to be refitted proceed to paragraph 12. If spring renewal is necessary, this is done as follows: Clamp the base of tool Sus.594 in a vice and place the spring assembly over it. Position the washer (Sus.594.02) over the spring, fit the rest of the tool and tighten it until the first tool, Sus.596.01 or Sus.863, can be removed. Now release tool Sus.594 slowly until the spring reaches its fully free length, then remove the spring and lower seat from the tool.

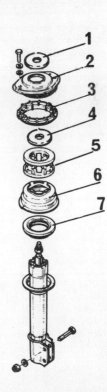

Fig. 10.10 Front spring and strut mounting components (Sec 6)

| | | | |
|---|---|---|---|
| 1 | Washer | 5 | Bump stop |
| 2 | Upper mounting | 6 | Lower spring seat |
| 3 | Upper spring seat | 7 | Pivot bearing |
| 4 | Washer | | |

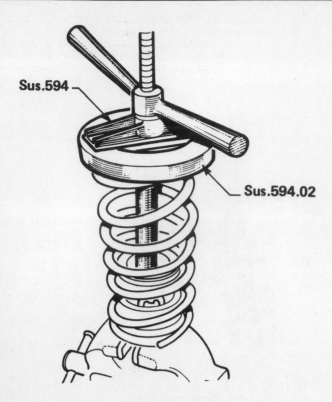

Sus.594

Sus.594.02

Fig. 10.11 If the spring is to be renewed after removal a Renault tool will be required to compress the spring and allow the removal tool to be withdrawn (Sec 6)

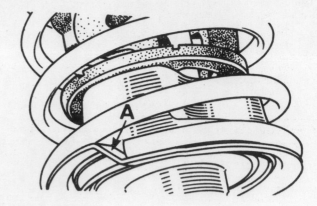

A

Fig. 10.12 When refitting the spring, the coil end must abut the stop (A) in the spring lower seat (Sec 6)

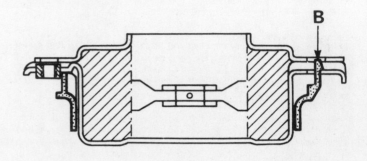

B

Fig. 10.13 Correct location of spring upper seat peg (B) in the upper mounting (Sec 6)

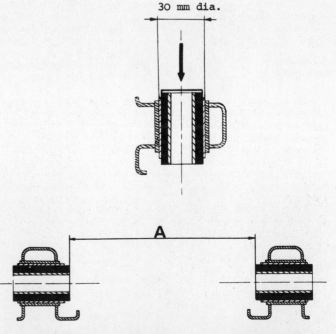

30 mm dia.

A

Fig. 10.14 Lower suspension arm bush renewal (Sec 7)

*Use a tube of 30 mm (1.18 in) to remove and refit the bushes Dimension A between the bush inner edges must be maintained at 146.5 to 147.5 mm (5.77 to 5.81 in)*

10  Place the new spring in position over the lower seat so that the coil end (marked with a red dab of paint) abuts the stop in the lower seat. Lubricate the coil end and lower seat with molybdenum disulphide grease.

11  Compress the spring and seat assembly as before using tool Sus.594 and Sus.594.02 until it is possible to refit tool Sus.596.01 or Sus.863 back over the spring. Now remove tool Sus.594.

12  Position the pivot bearing over the stud, followed by the compressed spring assembly. Ensure that the peg on the upper spring seat is correctly located in the upper mounting, as shown in Fig. 10.13, fit the bump stop, pull the strut piston rod out as far as it will go and refit the upper mounting.

13  Place the washer over the piston rod, then refit and fully tighten the upper mounting nut.

14  Refit the plastic cap to the nut, remove the spring compressor tool and refit the strut assembly to the car, as described in the previous Section.

## 7  Front lower suspension arm – removal and refitting

1  Jack up the front of the car and support it on axle stands. Remove the front roadwheels.

2  Undo and remove the nut, bolt and washer securing the anti-roll bar clamps to each lower suspension arm (photo 9.1). Disengage the clamps from the slots in the arms and pivot the anti-roll bar down and well clear of the suspension arms.

3  Undo and remove the nut and washer then withdraw the clamp bolt securing the lower suspension arm balljoint to the stub axle carrier (photo 8.2).

4  Undo and remove the two nuts, washers and pivot bolts securing the arm to the subframe.

5  Pull the arm down to disengage the balljoint then lever it out of its inner pivot mountings. Recover the balljoint washer.

6  If the inner pivot bushes are to be renewed this can be done using suitable lengths of tube and a press or wide-opening vice. Renew the bushes one at a time so that the distance between the bush inner edges is maintained at 146.5 to 147.5 mm (5.77 to 5.81 in).

7    Refitting the lower suspension arm is the reverse sequence to removal bearing in mind the following points:

    (a)  *Ensure that the plastic washer is in position over the balljoint shank before refitting the balljoint to the stub axle carrier*
    (b)  *Tighten all nuts and bolts to the specified torque, but do not tighten the pivot bolts and anti-roll bar clamp bolts until the car has been lowered to the ground and rolled back and forth to settle the suspension*

## 8    Front lower suspension arm balljoint – removal and refitting

1    Jack up the front of the car and support it on axle stands. Remove the appropriate front roadwheel.
2    Undo and remove the nut, washer and clamp bolt securing the balljoint to the stub axle carrier (photo).
3    Undo and remove the two nuts, washers and bolts securing the balljoint to the suspension arm, pull the joint down to disengage it from the stub axle carrier and remove it from the car. Remove the washer over the balljoint shank.
4    Refitting is the reverse sequence to removal, ensuring that the retaining bolts are tightened to the specified torque.

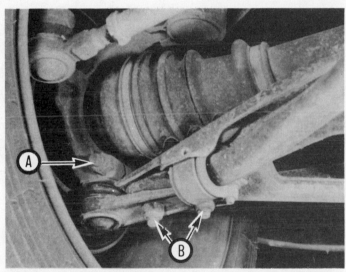

8.2 Suspension arm balljoint clamp bolt (A) and balljoint retaining bolts and nuts (B)

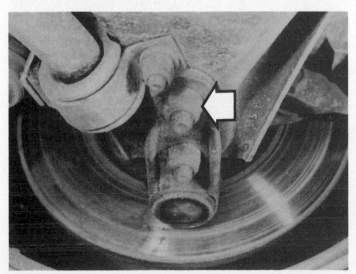

9.1 Anti-roll bar-to-suspension arm clamp nut, washer and bolt (arrowed)

## 9    Front anti-roll bar – removal and refitting

**Note:** *For this operation the front suspension must be kept in a laden condition. If a vehicle lift or inspection pit are not available, it will be necessary to drive the front of the car up on ramps.*
1    Undo and remove the nut, bolt and washer securing the anti-roll bar clamps to each lower suspension arm (photo). Remove the clamps after disengaging their tags from the slots in the arms.
2    Undo and remove the two bolts securing the anti-roll bar clamps to the subframe (photo). Remove the clamps after disengaging their tags from the slots in the subframe.
3    Manipulate the anti-roll bar to clear the exhaust and gear selector linkage and withdraw the car sideways from under the car.
4    If the rubber bushes are in need of renewal, slide them off the bar and place new ones in position after lubricating liberally with rubber grease.
5    Refitting is the reverse sequence to removal, but ensure that the mounting bolts are tightened to the specified torque.

## 10   Rear hub bearings – renewal

1    Jack up the rear of the car and support it on axle stands. Remove the appropriate rear roadwheel.
2    By judicious tapping and levering, remove the hub cap from the centre of the brake drum.
3    Using a socket and knuckle bar, undo the hub nut and remove the thrust washer.
4    Make sure that the handbrake is released and then withdraw the brake drum and hub assembly from the stub axle. It may be difficult to remove the drum and hub assembly due to the tightness of the hub bearing on the stub axle, or due to the brake shoes binding on the inner circumference of the drum. If the bearing is tight, but the drum will still turn, tap the periphery of the drum with a hide or plastic mallet or use a universal puller secured to the drum with the wheel bolts to pull it off. If the drum binds on the brake shoes and cannot be removed, refer to the procedure given in Chapter 8, Section 6, to retract the brake shoes.
5    With the hub and drum assembly removed, extract the bearing retaining circlip. Drive out the bearing using a tube of suitable diameter inserted through the inside of the hub and in contact with the bearing outer race.
6    Place the new bearing in the hub and drive it fully home, again using a tube in contact with the bearing outer race. Take great care to keep the bearing square as it is installed, otherwise it may jam in the hub bore which could crack the outer race.
7    With the bearing in position, refit the retaining circlip.
8    Make sure that the inner thrust washer is in place on the stub axle,

9.2 Anti-roll bar to subframe clamp bolt (arrowed)

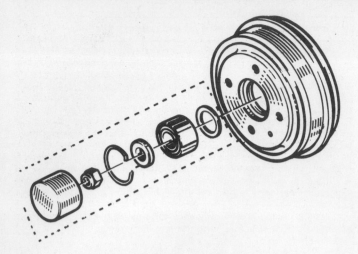

Fig. 10.15 Rear hub bearing components (Sec 10)

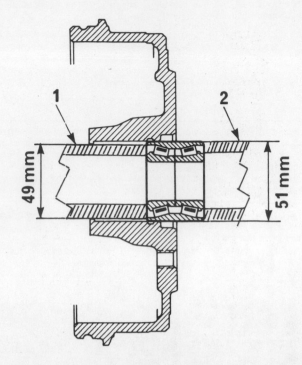

refit the hub and drum assembly followed by the outer thrust washer and hub nut.

9   Tighten the hub nut to the specified torque and tap the hub cap back into place.

10  If it was necessary to slacken the handbrake to enable the hub and drum assembly to be removed, adjust the handbrake, as described in Chapter 8, Section 16.

11  On completion, refit the roadwheel and lower the car to the ground.

## 11  Rear shock absorber – removal and refitting

1   Jack up the rear of the car and support it on axle stands. Place a jack beneath the suspension trailing arm on the appropriate side of the car. Using the jack, raise the trailing arm slightly. Supplement the jack with an axle stand or blocks if necessary – ensure that the trailing arm is securely supported.

2   Working in the luggage compartment, lift off the rubber cover over the shock absorber upper mounting (photo).

3   Undo the upper mounting retaining nut while holding the flats on the end of the shock absorber piston rod with a small spanner or self-locking wrench (photo).

4   Lift off the upper mounting thrust washers and rubber bush.

5   From under the car undo the nut and thrust washer securing the lower end of the shock absorber to the mounting stud on the suspension trailing arm (photo).

6   Slide the shock absorber off the stud and withdraw it down and out from under the wheel arch. Remove the remaining upper mounting washer, rubber bush and sleeve noting their arrangement, then remove the outer top cover and rubber bump stop.

Fig. 10.16 Tube diameter necessary to remove and refit the rear hub bearing (Sec 10)

1   Removal                                2   Refitting

7   Examine the shock absorber body for signs of damage or corrosion, and for any trace of fluid leakage. Check the piston rod for distortion, wear, pitting or corrosion along its entire length. Test the operation of the shock absorber, while holding it in an upright position, by moving the piston rod through a full stroke and then through short strokes of 50 to 100 mm (2 to 4 in). In both cases the resistance felt should be smooth and continuous. If the resistance is jerky or uneven, or if there is any sign of wear or damage to the unit, renewal is necessary. Also check the condition of the upper and lower mounting bushes and renew them if there are any signs of deterioration or swelling of the rubber. Note that new shock absorbers are supplied complete with mounting bushes.

8   To refit the shock absorber first place the rubber bump stop and outer top cover over the piston rod (unless a new shock absorber is being fitted), followed by the sleeve, rubber bush and thrust washer.

9   Locate the shock absorber in position and fit the lower thrust washer and retaining nut to the trailing arm stud. Tighten the nut to the specified torque.

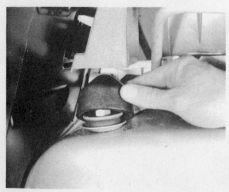

11.2 Withdraw the rubber cover to gain access to the rear shock absorber upper mounting

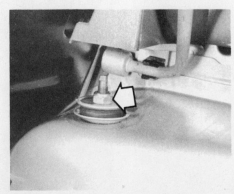

11.3 Shock absorber upper mounting retaining nut (arrowed)

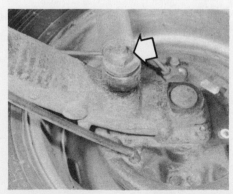

11.5 Shock absorber lower mounting retaining nut on the trailing arm (arrowed)

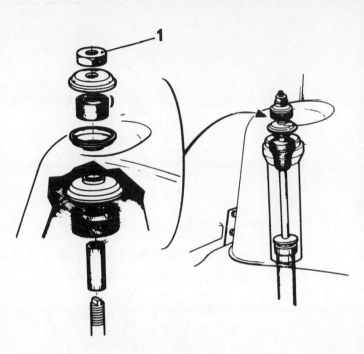

**Fig. 10.17 Rear shock absorber upper mounting details (Sec 11)**

*1   Upper retaining nut*

12.2 Handbrake cable retaining clips on the rear anti-roll bar (arrowed)

10   Pull the piston rod up through the mounting hole and fit the thrust washer, rubber bush, second thrust washer and retaining nut. Tighten the retaining nut securely, then refit the rubber cover.
11   Remove the supports under the trailing arm and lower the car to the ground.

## 12  Rear anti-roll bar – removal and refitting

1   Jack up the rear of the car and support it on axle stands.
2   Release the two handbrake cable retaining clips from the anti-roll bar (photo).
3   Undo the two bolts each side securing the anti-roll bar to the suspension trailing arms and withdraw the bar from under the car (photo).
4   Refitting is the reverse sequence to removal, but tighten the retaining bolts to the specified torque. Ensure that the handbrake cable guide clips are fitted under the bolt heads each side and that the offset edges of the anti-roll bar brackets face the front of the car.

## 13  Rear torsion bar – removal and refitting

1   Jack up the rear of the car and support it on axle stands. Remove the appropriate rear roadwheel.
2   Remove the anti-roll bar, as described in Section 12, and the shock absorber on the side concerned, as described in Section 11.
3   Slowly lower the jack used to support the trailing arm during removal of the shock absorber until the trailing arm is hanging unsupported.
4   Prise off the cap (where fitted) on the outer face of the trailing arm mounting bracket (photo).
5   The torsion bar can now be withdrawn outwards using a slide hammer such as Renault tool Emb.880 or a suitable alternative. It is possible to improvise by screwing a long bolt with a flat washer into the torsion bar and placing the jaws of a spanner against the washer. Striking the spanner sharply with a hammer should free the torsion bar.
6   Once the splines of the torsion bar are free, the bar can be withdrawn completely from its location. Note that the torsion bars are not interchangeable from side to side and are marked with symbols on

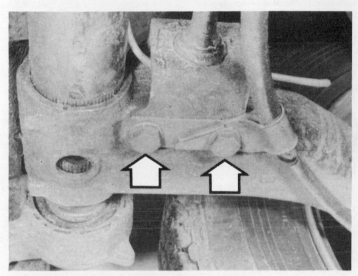

12.3 Rear anti-roll bar retaining bolts (arrowed) and handbrake cable guide clip on the trailing arm

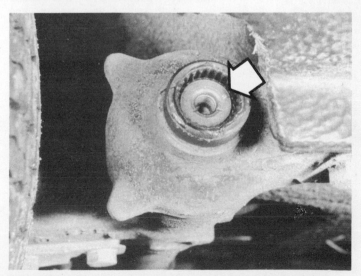

13.4 Trailing arm mounting bracket showing torsion bar location (arrowed)

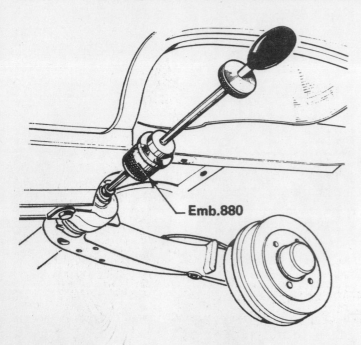

Fig. 10.18 Renault tool shown, or a suitable alternative slide hammer, will be needed to remove the rear torsion bars (Sec 13)

L.H. torsion bar: 2 symbols

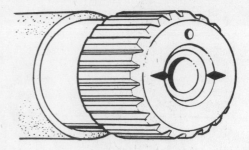

R.H. torsion bar: 3 symbols

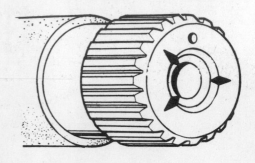

Fig. 10.19 Rear torsion bar identification markings (Sec 13)

their ends for identification. Bars with two symbols are fitted to the left-hand side and bars with three symbols are fitted to the right hand side.

7    Before refitting the torsion bar it is necessary to position the trailing arm so that the correct underbody height of the car is obtained when it is lowered onto its wheels. This is done as follows:

8    Measure the distance from the centre of the shock absorber lower mounting stud on the trailing arm to the shock absorber upper mounting contact point under the wheel arch. Move the trailing arm up or down as necessary until the distance is exactly 620 mm (24.41 in). If it was necessary to move the arm up to achieve the setting support it in this position using a jack. If it was necessary to pull the arm down, support it with a length of wood cut to length and small packing pieces. Take care over this procedure as this is a critical dimension and will determine the success of subsequent operations.

9    With the trailing arm supported in this position, lubricate the torsion bar splines with molybdenum disulphide grease and insert it into its location. Jiggle the bar as necessary until the inner and outer splines engage, check that the trailing arm setting dimension, as previously described, is still correct then tap the bar fully home using a hammer and soft metal drift. Refit the cap over the outer face of the trailing arm mounting bracket.

10  Refit the shock absorber, as described in Section 11, and the anti-roll bar, as described in Section 12.

11  Refit the roadwheel and lower the car to the ground.

12  Roll the car back and forth and then bounce the body to settle the suspension. If the trailing arm was positioned correctly, as described in paragraph 8, the car should now be standing level and at the correct height (see Section 25). If this is not the case then the setting procedure will have to be repeated, noting that a deviation of 3 mm (0.12 in) either side of the specified dimension will alter the torsion bar position by one spline. This will have a corresponding affect on the underbody height; increasing or decreasing it by 3 mm (0.12 in).

## 14  Rear suspension trailing arm – removal and refitting

1    Jack up the rear of the car and support it on axle stands. Remove the appropriate rear roadwheel.

2    Remove the anti-roll bar and the shock absorber, as described in Sections 12 and 11 respectively. Remove the torsion bar on the side concerned, as described in Section 13.

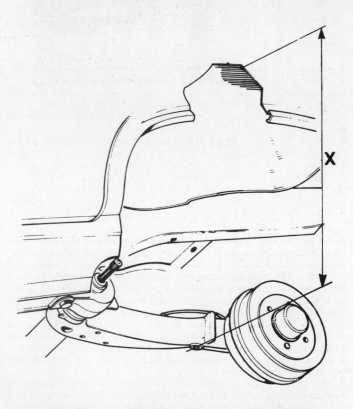

Fig. 10.20 Rear trailing arm setting dimension (Sec 13)

X = 620 mm (24.41 in)

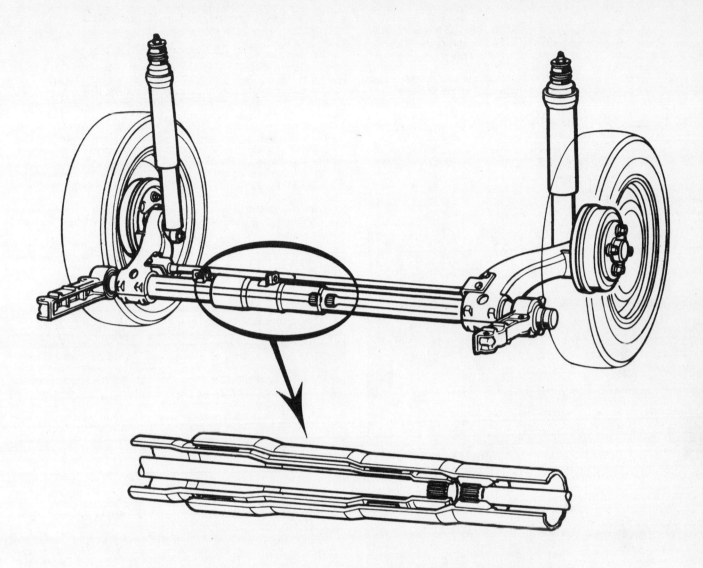

Fig. 10.21 Rear suspension assembly and trailing arm transverse member details (Sec 14)

3 Refer to Chapter 8, Section 6 and remove the brake drum and hub assembly.

4 With the drum removed, detach the handbrake cable from the operating lever on the trailing brake shoe and withdraw the cable from the brake backplate.

5 Using a brake hose clamp or self-locking wrench with protected jaws, clamp the appropriate flexible brake hose just in front of the union on the rear suspension transverse member. This will minimise brake fluid loss during subsequent operations.

6 Wipe clean the area around the brake pipe-to-flexible hose union on the suspension transverse member, and unscrew the pipe union. Carefully withdraw the pipe, slip off the hose retaining clip and withdraw the hose from the bracket. Plug or tape over the pipe and hose ends to prevent dirt entry.

7 If the right-hand trailing arm is being removed, release the retaining clip and withdraw the brake pressure regulating valve operating rod from the bracket on the suspension transverse member (photo).

8 Position a jack under the trailing arm on the side to be removed, beneath the anti-roll bar mounting bolt holes. Raise the jack until it contacts the arm.

9 Refer to Chapter 11 and remove the rear seat cushion and side mouldings to gain access to the trailing arm mounting bracket nuts.

14.7 Brake pressure regulating valve operating rod clip (arrowed)

10 Hold the nuts from above and unscrew the mounting bracket bolts from below (photo).

11 Lower the jack until the mounting bracket is clear of the sill. Hold the arm and transverse member firmly and pull it sideways to remove. Tap the arm sharply with a soft-faced mallet if tight.

12 The assembly can be further dismantled, if necessary, by removing the brake pipe from its clips and then undoing the four bolts securing the brake backplate to the trailing arm. Withdraw the backplate and brake pipe, noting the positioning of the thrust washer on the stub axle.

13 Renew the trailing arm bushes if required, as described in Section 15.

14 To refit the trailing arm, slide it into position and align the mounting bracket and body retaining bolt holes. Support the assembly

14.10 Trailing arm mounting bracket retaining bolts (arrowed)

on the jack and refit the retaining nuts and bolts tightened to the specified torque.

15 Refit the interior trim side mouldings and rear seat, as described in Chapter 11.

16 Fit the brake backplate to the trailing arm and secure with the retaining bolts, tightened to the specified torque. Refit the thrust washer to the stub axle and locate the brake pipe in its clips.

17 Reconnect the flexible brake hose and brake pipe, ensuring that the hose is not kinked or twisted and is retained in its bracket with the clip. Remove the hose clamp.

18 Refit the brake pressure regulating valve operating rod to the valve lever and suspension member bracket. Secure the rod with the clip.

19 Refit the handbrake cable to the brake backplate and operating lever on the trailing brake shoe.

20 Position the self-adjusting mechanism on the brake shoes and refit the hub and drum assembly using the procedure given in Chapter 8, Section 6.

21 Refit the torsion bar, as described in Section 13, followed by the shock absorber and anti-roll bar, as described in Sections 11 and 12 respectively.

22 Bleed the brake hydraulic system, as described in Chapter 8, noting that it should only be necessary to bleed the relevant rear brake providing the hose was clamped as described.

23 Finally refit the roadwheel and lower the car to the ground.

## 15 Rear suspension trailing arm bushes – renewal

**Note:** *The rear suspension trailing arms pivot on outer bushes, one located in each mounting bracket, and on two inner bushes situated in the left-hand part of the suspension transverse member. If the inner bushes are to be renewed the left-hand trailing arm must be removed. If the outer are to be renewed, the trailing arm on the side concerned must be removed. The outer bushes are an integral part of the mounting bracket and, if renewal is necessary, the complete bracket and bush assembly must be obtained.*

1 Remove the appropriate trailing arm, as described in the previous Section.

### Inner bushes

2 To remove the bushes it will be necessary to obtain the Renault tool shown in Fig. 10.23 or make up a similar tool using the Renault tool as a pattern, as follows:

3 Obtain a threaded rod long enough to reach the inner bush, a tube of suitable diameter as shown, one washer of diameter equal to that of the bushes, a washer of diameter greater than the tube and two nuts. Cut two sides off the smaller washer so that just a flat strip with a hole in the centre remains. This will form the swivelling end part shown on the Renault tool. Pass the threaded rod through the hole in the strip and screw on a nut. Feed the strip and rod through the bush so that the strip locates behind the bush. Place the tube over the rod and in contact with the edge of the transverse member. Place the large washer over the end of the tube and then screw on the remaining nut. Hold the rod with grips and tighten the nut to draw out the bush, then repeat this operation to remove the remaining bush.

4 Lubricate the new bushes and fit them using tubes of suitable

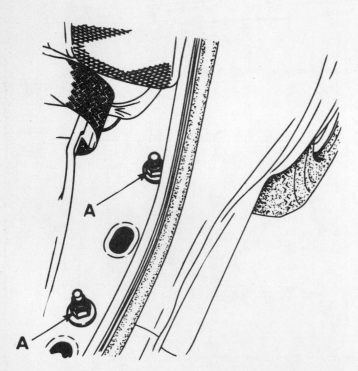

Fig. 10.22 Trailing arm mounting bracket upper retaining nuts (A) (Sec 14)

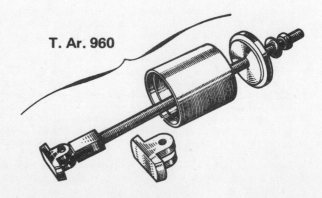

T. Ar. 960

Fig. 10.23 Trailing arm inner bush removal tool (Sec 15)

diameter. Make sure that the bushes are positioned as shown in Fig. 10.24.

5   The trailing arm can now be refitted, as described in Section 14.

*Outer bushes*

6   Liberally coat the bush in the trailing arm mounting bracket with clean brake fluid and allow it to soak in. This will soften the bush rubber and facilitate removal.

7   Using a two- or three-legged puller, draw the mounting bracket off the trailing arm. Note that the bracket will not come off cleanly, but the rubber of the bush will tear.

8   Using a hacksaw, very carefully cut through the rubber and metal backing of the bush remaining on the trailing arm. Take care not to cut the arm itself. After splitting the bush prise it off the trailing arm using a screwdriver.

9   Align the new mounting bracket and bush assembly with the trailing arm so that the arm is at an angle of 7° to the bracket and the alignment marks on the bracket and arm are as shown in Fig. 10.28. Make sure that the bracket and arm are the right way up as well.

10  Hold the two components in this position and press or drive the mounting bracket onto the trailing arm until the end of the arm is flush with the end of the bush.

11  The trailing arm assembly can now be refitted to the car, as described in Section 14.

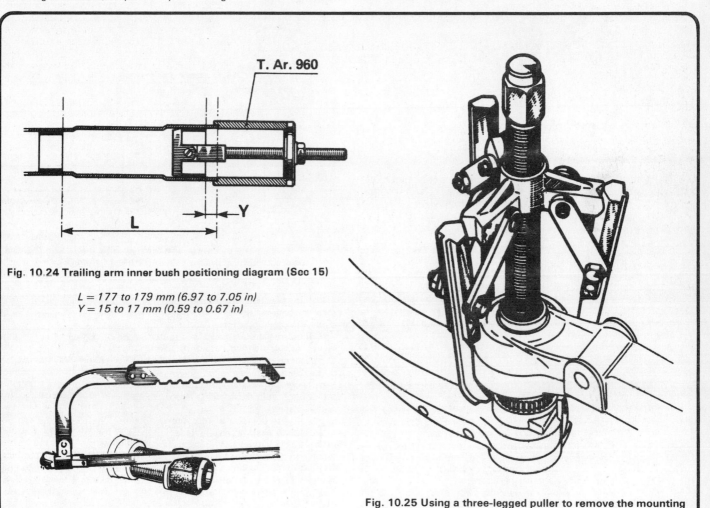

**Fig. 10.24 Trailing arm inner bush positioning diagram (Sec 15)**

*L = 177 to 179 mm (6.97 to 7.05 in)*
*Y = 15 to 17 mm (0.59 to 0.67 in)*

**Fig. 10.26 The remains of the old bush must be cut off after removing the trailing arm from the mounting bracket (Sec 15)**

**Fig. 10.25 Using a three-legged puller to remove the mounting bracket from the trailing arm (Sec 15)**

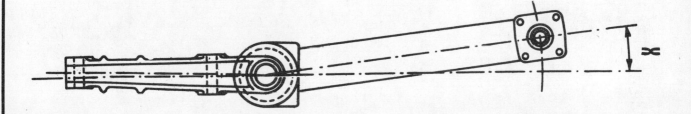

**Fig. 10.27 Correct alignment of the trailing arm and mounting bracket prior to assembly (Sec 15)**

*X = 7°*

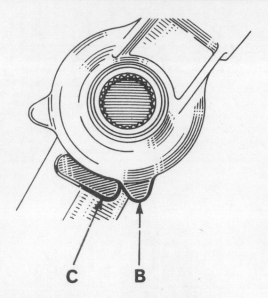

Fig. 10.28 With the arm and bracket correctly positioned the projection on the bracket (B) should be aligned as shown with the casting mark (C) on the arm (Sec 15)

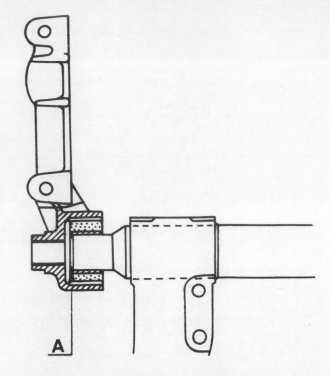

Fig. 10.29 The end of the trailing arm must be flush with the end of the mounting bracket bush (A) after fitting (Sec 15)

## 16  Steering wheel – removal and refitting

1  Set the front wheels in the straight-ahead position.
2  Ease off the steering wheel pad to provide access to the retaining nut (photo).
3  Using a socket and knuckle bar undo and remove the retaining nut and lockwasher.
4  Mark the steering wheel and steering column shaft in relation to each other and withdraw the wheel from the shaft splines. If it is tight, tap it upwards near the centre, using the palm of your hand. Refit the steering wheel retaining nut two turns before doing this, for obvious reasons.
5  Refitting is the reverse of removal, but align the previously made marks and tighten the retaining nut to the specified torque.

## 17  Steering column assembly – removal, overhaul and refitting

1  Disconnect the battery negative terminal.
2  Remove the steering wheel, as described in the previous Section.
3  Undo the retaining screws, release the catches and withdraw the steering column lower shroud (photo). Lay the shroud to one side, but avoid straining the cowl switch electrical connections.

4  Undo the two screws securing the wiper/washer switch to the steering column upper shroud. Undo the screws securing the upper shroud in place and lift it off the column.
5  Undo the two screws securing the lighting/direction indicator switch to the steering column bracket.
6  Disconnect the ignition switch, lighting/direction indicator switch and any accessory switch wiring harnesses at their multi-plug connectors. Label each connector to avoid confusion when refitting. Release the wiring cable clips from the steering column and move the wires and switches clear.
7  Mark the position of the steering column shaft in relation to the intermediate shaft upper universal joint. Undo the nut and remove the clamp bolt securing the shaft to the universal joint.
8  Undo the steering column bracket upper retaining bolts and small screws, and slacken the lower bolts (photo). Pull the column upwards to disengage the column shaft from the universal joint, and the lower mounting bracket from the bolts, then remove the assembly from the car.
9  To remove the steering column bushes, extract the snap-ring located at the top of the column.

16.2 Access to the steering wheel retaining nut (arrowed) is gained after lifting off the trim pad

17.3 Steering column lower shroud removal

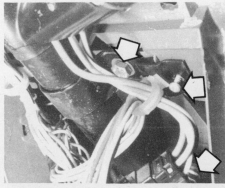

17.8 Steering column right-hand side retaining bolts and screw (arrowed)

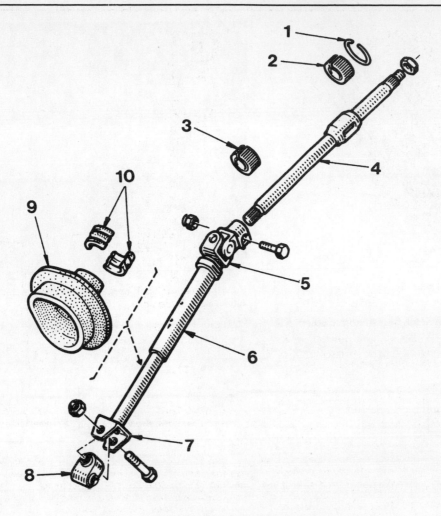

**Fig. 10.30 Steering column shaft components (Sec 17)**

1  Snap ring
2  Column upper bush
3  Column lower bush
4  Steering column shaft

5  Intermediate shaft upper universal joint
6  Intermediate shaft
7  Intermediate shaft yoke

8  Lower universal joint
9  Bulkhead rubber bellows
10  Bellows bearing

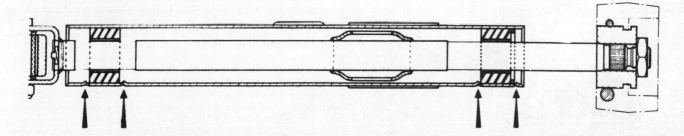

**Fig. 10.31 Steering column bush locating indents (arrowed) (Sec 17)**

10  Refit the steering wheel temporarily and screw on the retaining nut finger tight.

11  Sharply pull the steering wheel upwards to free the shaft and release the upper bush. Make sure that the ignition key is in the switch and the steering lock released before doing this.

12  Tilt the shaft and push in the steering wheel to release the lower bush. Remove the steering wheel and withdraw the shaft and bushes from the column.

13  Lubricate the new lower bush and fit it to the column using a tube of suitable diameter. Slide the shaft into position and then fit the upper bush in the same way. Ensure that both bushes locate between the indents in the column. Refit the retaining snap-ring to the top of the column.

14  The steering column can now be refitted using the reverse procedure to removal, but bearing in mind the following points:

(a)  Ensure that the flat on the steering column shaft splined end is towards the clamp bolt in the universal joint when engaging the shaft

(b)  Tighten the column upper retaining bolts first, followed by the lower bolts

(c)  Refit the steering wheel, as described in Section 16

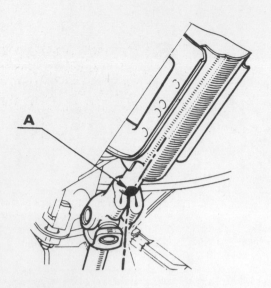

18.5 Intermediate shaft universal joint retaining bolt (A) and bulkhead rubber bellows (B)

Fig. 10.32 Correct positioning of the flat (A) on the steering column shaft (Sec 17)

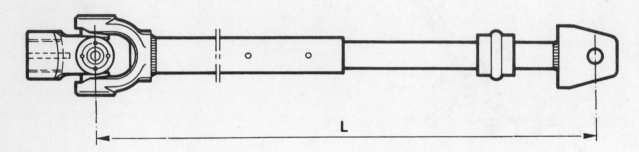

Fig. 10.33 Intermediate shaft length checking dimension (Sec 18)

*L = 399 to 401 mm (15.71 to 15.79 in); 400 to 402 mm (15.75 to 15.83 in) for models 1983 onwards*

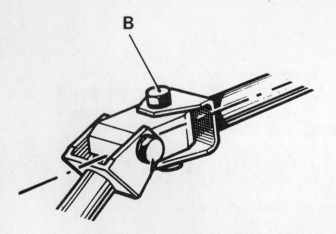

Fig. 10.34 Intermediate shaft universal joint must be positioned as shown when tightening bolt B (Sec 18)

### 18 Steering column intermediate shaft – removal and refitting

1   Jack up the front of the car and support it on axle stands. Disconnect the battery negative terminal.

2   Working inside the car, undo the retaining screws, release the catches and withdraw the steering column lower shroud. Lay the

shroud to one side, but avoid straining the cowl switch electrical connections.

3   Turn the steering wheel so that the roadwheels are in the straight-ahead position and the steering wheel spokes are in the normal driving position.

4   Undo the nut and remove the clamp bolt securing the steering column shaft to the intermediate shaft upper universal joint.

5   From under the front of the car undo the nut and remove the bolt securing the intermediate shaft yoke to the upper part of the lower universal joint. Separate the yoke from the joint (photo).

6   Release the rubber bellows from the bulkhead, pull the intermediate shaft down to disengage it from the upper universal joint then withdraw the shaft and bellows from inside the car.

7   With the shaft removed, check the bellows for any signs of splits or deterioration of the rubber and renew, if necessary.

8   Check the shaft for deformation or damage and check the security of the two parts of the shaft where they join at the impact absorbing collapsible section. Measure the length of the shaft, as shown in Fig. 10.33 and renew it if its length is less than specified.

9   Refitting the intermediate shaft is the reverse sequence to removal, bearing in mind the following points:

(a)   Ensure that the roadwheels and steering wheel are in the straight-ahead position before fitting

(b)   The flat on the end of the steering column must face the clamp bolt hole in the intermediate shaft upper universal joint

(c)   Tighten the upper universal joint clamp bolt first, followed by the lower joint clamp bolt. Ensure that the lower universal joint is positioned as shown in Fig. 10.34 before fully tightening the clamp bolt

## 19 Steering arm outer balljoint – removal and refitting

1 Jack up the front of the car and support it on axle stands. Remove the appropriate front roadwheel.
2 Using a suitable spanner, slacken the balljoint locknut on the steering arm by a quarter of a turn (photo). Hold the steering arm with a second spanner engaged with the flats at its inner end to prevent it from turning.
3 Undo and remove the locknut securing the balljoint to the stub axle carrier and then release the tapered shank using a balljoint separator tool (photo).
4 Count the number of exposed threads between the end of the balljoint and the locknut and record this figure.
5 Unscrew the balljoint from the steering arm and unscrew the locknut from the balljoint.
6 Screw the locknut onto the new balljoint and position it so that the same number of exposed threads are visible as was noted during removal.
7 Screw the balljoint onto the steering arm until the locknut just contacts the arm. Now tighten the locknut while holding the steering arm as before.
8 Engage the shank of the balljoint with the stub axle carrier and refit the locknut. Tighten the locknut to the specified torque. If the

balljoint shank turns while the locknut is being tightened, place a jack under the balljoint and raise it sufficiently to push the tapered shank fully into the stub axle carrier. The tapered fit of the shank will lock it and prevent rotation as the nut is tightened.
9 On completion, remove the jack, refit the roadwheel and lower the car to the ground.
10 Check the front wheel alignment, as described in Section 26.

## 20 Steering gear rubber bellows – removal and refitting

1 Remove the steering arm outer balljoint, as described in the previous Section.
2 Release the retaining wire or unscrew the retaining clip screws and slide the bellows off the rack and pinion housing and steering arm.
3 Lubricate the inner ends of the new bellows with rubber grease and position it over the housing and steering arm.
4 Using new clips, or two or three turns of soft iron wire, secure the bellows in position.
5 Refit the outer balljoint, as described in the previous Section.

## 21 Steering arm and inner balljoint – removal and refitting

1 Remove the outer balljoint and rubber bellows, as described in Sections 19 and 20 respectively.
2 Hold the thrust washer with grips to prevent the rack turning and unscrew the inner balljoint housing with a small stilson wrench. Remove the balljoint housing and steering arm assembly from under the wheel arch.
3 With the components on the bench for inspection, identify the assembly type fitted by referring to Fig. 10.35. Note that the early type steering arm and balljoint assembly must be renewed after each dismantling whereas the later type may be refitted providing that it is in a satisfactory condition and that the balljoint serrations are undamaged. In both cases the lockplate and thrust washer must be renewed before refitting.
4 With new components of the correct type obtained, as necessary, reassemble as follows:
5 Refit the thrust washer and lockplate to the rack, ensuring that the two tabs on the lockplate are in line with the two flats on the end of the rack.
6 Apply a drop of locking compound to the threads of the balljoint and screw the balljoint housing and steering arm assembly into position. Tighten the housing securely.
7 Refit the rubber bellows and outer balljoint, as described in Sections 20 and 19 respectively.

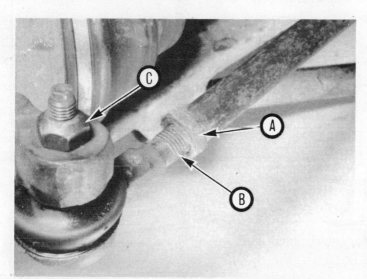

19.2 Outer balljoint-to-steering arm locknut (A), balljoint exposed threads (B) and balljoint-to-stub axle retaining locknut (C)

## 22 Steering rack support bearing – removal and refitting

1 Remove the left-hand side steering arm outer balljoint, steering gear rubber bellows and the steering arm and inner balljoint, as described in Sections 19, 20 and 21 respectively.
2 Turn the steering onto full left-hand lock so that the rack is clear of the bearing.
3 Working under the wheel arch, extract the bearing from the rack and pinion housing by prising it out with a screwdriver.
4 Clean the rack, and rack and pinion housing, and then lubricate both with molybdenum disulphide grease. Liberally lubricate the new bearing also.
5 Carefully insert the new bearing into the housing and position it so that each of the three bearing tags enter their slots in the housing.
6 Move the steering onto full right-hand then left-hand lock to settle the bearing and distribute the grease.
7 Refit the steering arm and inner balljoint, the rubber bellows and outer balljoint, as described in Sections 21, 20 and 19.

## 23 Steering gear – removal and refitting

1 Jack up the front of the car and support it on axle stands. Remove both front roadwheels.
2 Unscrew the locknuts securing the steering arm outer balljoints to the stub axle carriers then release them using a balljoint separator tool.

19.3 Using a balljoint separator tool to release the balljoint from the stub axle carrier

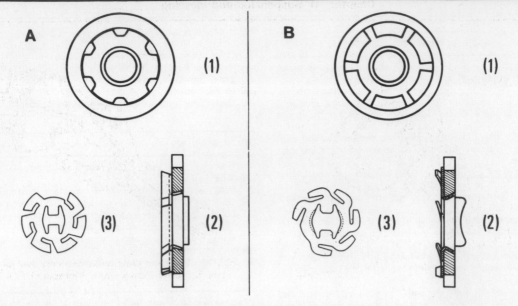

**Fig. 10.35 Steering arm inner balljoint assemblies (Sec 21)**

A Early type
B Later type
1 End view of balljoint assembly
2 Side view of assembled thrust washer and lockplate
3 Lockplate

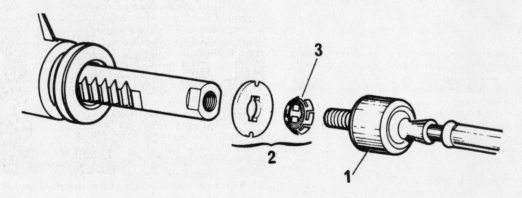

**Fig. 10.36 Steering arm balljoint attachment components (Sec 21)**

1 Inner balljoint and steering arm assembly    2 Thrust washer and lockplate    3 Lockplate showing direction of fitting

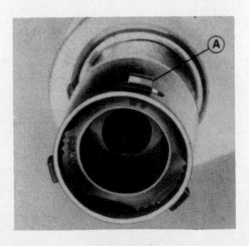

Fig. 10.37 Using a screwdriver to extract the steering rack support bearing (Sec 22)

Fig. 10.38 The three tags in the bearing (A) must be engaged with the slots in the rack housing after fitting (Sec 22)

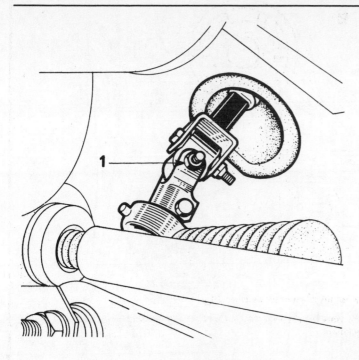

Fig. 10.39 Steering gear yoke-to-universal joint retaining bolt (1)
(Sec 23)

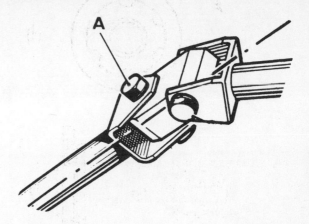

Fig. 10.40 Steering gear yoke and universal joint must be
positioned as shown when tightening bolt A (Sec 23)

23.5 Steering gear-to-subframe retaining bolts (arrowed)

3   Mark the position of the intermediate shaft lower universal joint in relation to the rack and pinion housing and also the two halves of the universal joint in relation to each other.
4   Undo the nut and remove the ball securing the lower part of the universal joint to the steering gear yoke.
5   Undo the two nuts and bolts securing the steering gear to the subframe (photo), separate the universal joint and withdraw the steering gear sideways from under the wheel arch.
6   Refitting the steering gear is the reverse sequence to removal, bearing in mind the following points.

(a)  Tighten all nuts and bolts to the specified torque
(b)  When refitting the universal joint and steering gear yoke, align the marks made during removal. If no marks are present due to component renewal, set the steering wheel and steering gear to the straight-ahead position before fitting
(c)  Tighten the universal joint retaining bolt with the joint positioned as shown in Fig. 10.40
(d)  If the steering arms or outer balljoints have been removed, or their positions altered, check and adjust the front wheel alignment, as described in Section 26.

## 24  Steering gear – overhaul

**Note:** *Overhaul of the steering gear is limited as only certain parts are available separately. Renewal of the steering arm balljoints, steering arms, rack support bearing and the rubber bellows may be carried out with the steering gear either in or out of the car, and these operations are covered in previous Sections of this Chapter. The only other repair possible is renewal and/or adjustment of the rack damper plunger. To carry out this work the steering gear must be removed from the car and the procedure is then as follows:*
1   With the steering gear on the bench, unlock the damper adjusting nut by straightening the tabs around the periphery of the nut.
2   Using a suitable Allen key or hexagon socket bit, unscrew the adjusting nut and remove it from the rack and pinion housing.
3   Lift out the washer, spring and damper plunger.
4   Inspect the damper plunger and renew it if there is any sign of excessive scoring or wear of its contact face.
5   Lubricate the plunger and housing with molybdenum disulphide grease, then refit the plunger, spring, washer and adjusting nut.

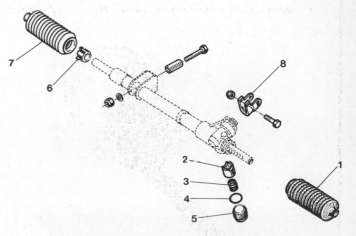

Fig. 10.41 Steering gear components (Sec 24)

| | | | |
|---|---|---|---|
| 1 | Rubber bellows | 5 | Adjusting nut |
| 2 | Rack damper plunger | 6 | Rack support bearing |
| 3 | Spring | 7 | Rubber bellows |
| 4 | Washer | 8 | Yoke |

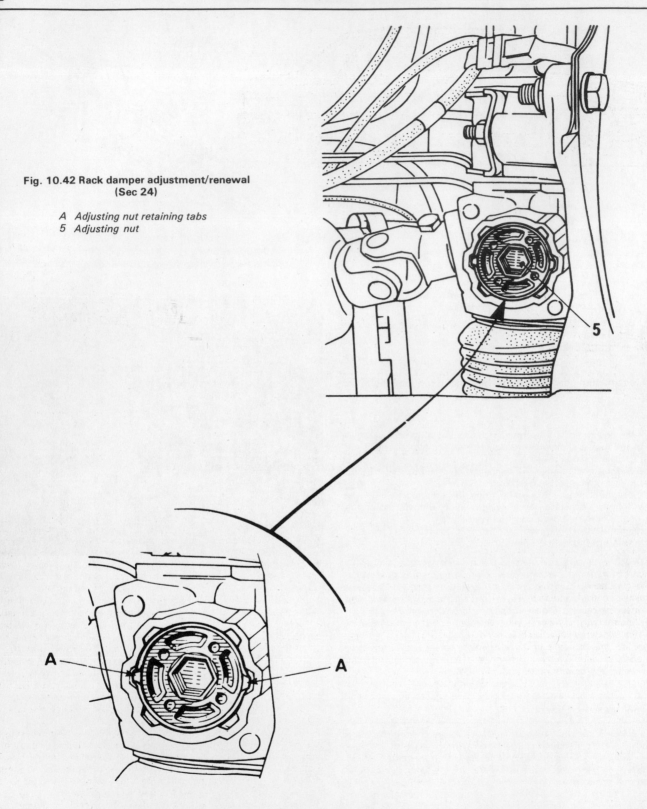

**Fig. 10.42 Rack damper adjustment/renewal (Sec 24)**

A  *Adjusting nut retaining tabs*
5  *Adjusting nut*

6    To adjust the plunger, tighten the adjusting nut using a hexagon socket bit and torque wrench to a torque of 10 Nm (7.9 lbf ft). Now back off the nut by a quarter of a turn.

7    Move the rack from lock to lock by turning the pinion yoke and check for any tight spots. If any are felt, slacken the adjusting nut further by a small amount until the rack will turn smoothly from lock to lock. Note that the rack will feel tight, but as long as the tightness is uniform over the entire length of travel, all is well.

8    After adjustment, secure the adjusting nut by bending the tabs down into the recesses in the housing.

9    The steering gear can now be refitted to the car, as described in Section 23.

## 25  Vehicle underbody height – checking and adjustment

1    Before carrying out the following checks, ensure that the fuel tank is full, the tyres are correctly inflated and the car is standing on level ground.

2    Refer to Fig. 10.43 and take measurements at the points shown,

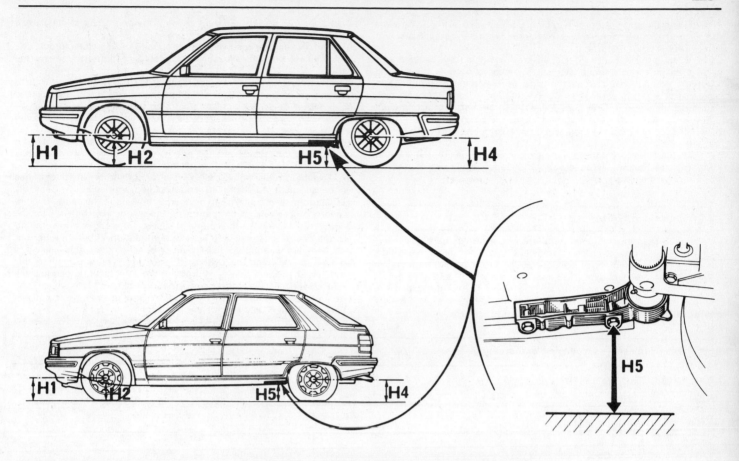

Fig. 10.43 Vehicle underbody height measuring points (Sec 25)

noting that H1 is from the front hub centreline, H2 is the distance from the bottom of the sill to the ground measured in line with the wheel centres, H4 is from the rear hub centreline and H5 is the distance from the trailing arm mounting bracket rear bolt to the ground.

3   After taking the measurements, the differences between the respective dimensions obtained should be as given in the Specifications. When calculated, the underbody heights should not vary from one side of the car to the other by more than 10 mm (0.4 in).

4   Only the rear underbody height is adjustable, and this is achieved by repositioning the rear torsion bars in their mounting bracket splines. Repositioning the torsion bars by one spline either way from their original position will alter the height on the side concerned by 3 mm (0.12 in). The procedure for doing this is described in Section 13.

5   If the front underbody height is not within the specified tolerance, this will be caused by a weakening of the front coil springs. If this is the case renewal is necessary and, to maintain the side to side tolerance, the springs should be renewed in pairs. This procedure is covered in Section 6.

6   If any alteration to the rear underbody height is made, it will be necessary to adjust the headlamp aim, as described in Chapter 9, and to have the brake pressure regulating valve (where fitted) adjusted by a Renault dealer.

## 26  Front wheel alignment and steering angles

1   Accurate front wheel alignment is essential to provide positive steering and prevent excessive tyre wear. Before considering the steering/suspension geometry, check that the tyres are correctly inflated, the front wheels are not buckled and the steering linkage and suspension joints are in good order, without slackness or wear.

2   Wheel alignment consists of four factors: **Camber** is the angle at which the front wheels are set from the vertical when viewed from the front of the car. 'Positive camber' is the amount (in degrees) that the

wheels are tilted outward at the top from the vertical. **Castor** is the angle between the steering axis and a vertical line when viewed from each side of the car. 'Positive castor' is when the steering axis is inclined rearward. **Steering axis inclination** is the angle (when viewed from the front of the car) between the vertical and an imaginary line drawn between the suspension strut upper mounting and the lower suspension arm balljoint. **Toe setting** is the amount by which the distance between the front inside edges of the roadwheels (measured at hub height) differs from the diametrically opposite distance measured between the rear inside edges of the front roadwheels.

3   With the exception of the toe setting all other steering angles are set during manufacture and no adjustment is possible. It can be assumed, therefore, that unless the car has suffered accident damage all the preset steering angles will be correct. Should there be some doubt about their accuracy it will be necessary to seek the help of a Renault dealer, as special gauges are needed to check the steering angles.

4   Two methods are available to the home mechanic for checking the toe setting. One method is to use a gauge to measure the distance between the front and rear inside edges of the roadwheels. The other method is to use a scuff plate in which each front wheel is rolled across a movable plate which records any deviation, or scuff, of the tyre from the straight-ahead position as it moves across the plate. Relatively inexpensive equipment of both types is available from accessory outlets to enable these checks, and subsequent adjustments to be carried out at home.

5   If, after checking the toe setting using whichever method is preferable, it is found that adjustment is necessary, proceed as follows.

6   Turn the steering wheel onto full left lock and record the number of exposed threads on the right-hand steering arm. Now turn the steering onto full right lock and record the number of threads on the left-hand arm. If there are the same number of threads visible on both arms then subsequent adjustments can be made equally on both sides. If there are more threads visible on one side than the other it will be

necessary to compensate for this during adjustment. *After adjustment there must be the same number of threads visible on each steering arm. This is most important.*

7   To alter the toe-setting slacken the locknut on the steering arm and turn the arm, using a self-grip wrench to achieve the desired setting. When viewed from the side of the car, turning the arm clockwise will increase the toe-in, turning it anti-clockwise will increase the toe-out. Only turn the arms by a quarter of a turn each time and then recheck the setting using the gauges, or scuff plate. Note that turning the steering arm by one complete turn will alter the toe-in or toe-out by 30' or 3 mm (0.12 in).

8   After adjustment tighten the locknuts and reposition the steering gear rubber bellows, if necessary, to remove any twist caused by turning the steering arms.

## 27  Wheels and tyres

1   Check the tyre pressures regularly when the tyres are cold.

2   Frequently inspect the tyre walls and treads for damage and pick out any stones which have become trapped in the tread pattern.

3   In the interests of extending tread life, the wheels and tyres can be moved between front and rear on the same side of the car. If the wheels have previously been balanced on the car, it may be necessary to have them rebalanced after rotation.

4   Never mix tyres of different construction, or very dissimilar tread patterns.

5   Always keep the roadwheels tightened to the specified torque, and if the wheel bolt holes become elongated or flattened, renew the wheel.

6   Occasionally clean the inner faces of the roadwheels and if there is any sign of rust or corrosion, paint them with metal preservative paint. **Note:** *Corrosion on aluminium alloy wheels may be evidence of a more serious problem which could lead to wheel failure. If corrosion is evident, consult your dealer for advice.*

7   Before removing a roadwheel which has been balanced on the car, always mark one wheel and hub bolt hole, so that the roadwheel may be refitted in the same relative position to maintain the balance.

8   Should unexpected excessive wear be noticed on any of the tyres its cause must be identified and rectified immediately. Generally speaking the wear pattern can be used as a guide to the cause. If a tyre is worn excessively in the centre of the tread face, but not on the edges, over inflation is indicated. Similarly if the edges are worn, but not the centre, this may be due to under inflation. If both the front or rear tyres are wearing on their inside or outside edges, this is likely to be due to incorrect toe setting. If only one tyre is exhibiting this tendency then there may be a problem with the steering geometry, a worn steering or suspension component, or a faulty tyre. Wheel and tyre imbalance is indicated by irregular and uneven wear patches appearing periodically around the tread face.

## 28  Fault diagnosis – suspension and steering

**Note:** *Before diagnosing steering or suspension faults, be sure that the trouble is not due to incorrect tyre pressures, a mixture of tyre types or binding brakes*

| Symptom | Reason(s) |
| --- | --- |
| Vehicle pulls to one side | Incorrect wheel alignment<br>Wear in suspension or steering components<br>Faulty tyre<br>Accident damage to steering or suspension components |
| Steering stiff or heavy | Lack of steering gear lubricant<br>Seized balljoint<br>Wheel alignment incorrect<br>Steering rack or column bent or damaged |
| Excessive play in steering | Worn steering or suspension joints<br>Wear in intermediate shaft universal joints<br>Worn rack and pinion assembly<br>Worn or incorrectly adjusted rack damper |
| Wheel wobble and vibration | Roadwheels out of balance<br>Roadwheels buckled or distorted<br>Faulty or damaged tyre<br>Worn steering or suspension joints<br>Wheel bolts loose<br>Worn rack and pinion assembly |
| Tyre wear uneven | Wheel alignment incorrect<br>Worn steering or suspension components<br>Wheels out of balance<br>Accident damage |

# Chapter 11 Bodywork and fittings

*For modifications, and information applicable to later models, see Supplement at end of manual*

## Contents

## Specifications

### Torque wrench settings

| | Nm | lbf ft |
|---|---|---|
| Seat belt anchorage and mounting bolts | 20 | 15 |

## 1  General description

The bodyshell and underframe is of all-steel welded construction, incorporating progressive crumple zones at the front and rear and a rigid centre safety cell. The assembly and welding of the main body unit is completed by computer-controlled robots, and is checked for dimensional accuracy using computer and laser technology.

The front and rear bumpers are of collapsible cellular construction to minimise minor accident damage and the front wings are bolted in position to facilitate accident damage repair.

## 2  Maintenance – bodywork and underframe

1  The general condition of a vehicle's bodywork is the one thing that significantly affects its value. Maintenance is easy but needs to be regular. Neglect, particularly after minor damage, can lead quickly to further deterioration and costly repair bills. It is important also to keep watch on those parts of the vehicle not immediately visible, for instance the underside, inside all the wheel arches and the lower part of the engine compartment.

2  The basic maintenance routine for the bodywork is washing – preferably with a lot of water, from a hose. This will remove all the loose solids which may have stuck to the vehicle. It is important to flush these off in such a way as to prevent grit from scratching the finish. The wheel arches and underframe need washing in the same way to remove any accumulated mud which will retain moisture and tend to encourage rust. Paradoxically enough, the best time to clean the underframe and wheel arches is in wet weather when the mud is thoroughly wet and soft. In very wet weather the underframe is usually cleaned of large accumulations automatically and this is a good time for inspection.

3  Periodically, except on vehicles with a wax-based underbody protective coating, it is a good idea to have the whole of the underframe of the vehicle steam cleaned, engine compartment included, so that a thorough inspection can be carried out to see what minor repairs and renovations are necessary. Steam cleaning is available at many garages and is necessary for removal of the accumulation of oily grime which sometimes is allowed to become thick in certain areas. If steam cleaning facilities are not available, there are one or two excellent grease solvents available such as Holts Engine Cleaner or Holts Foambrite which can be brush applied. The dirt can then be simply hosed off. Note that these methods should not be used on vehicles with wax-based underbody protective coating or the coating will be removed. Such vehicles should be inspected annually, preferably just prior to winter, when the underbody should be washed down and any damage to the wax coating repaired using Holts Undershield. Ideally, a completely fresh coat should be applied. It would also be worth considering the use of such wax-based protection for injection into door panels, sills, box sections, etc, as an additional safeguard against rust damage where such protection is not provided by the vehicle manufacturer.

4  After washing paintwork, wipe off with a chamois leather to give an unspotted clear finish. A coat of clear protective wax polish, like the many excellent Turtle Wax polishes, will give added protection against chemical pollutants in the air. If the paintwork sheen has dulled or oxidised, use a cleaner/polisher combination such as Turtle Extra to restore the brilliance of the shine. This requires a little effort, but such dulling is usually caused because regular washing has been neglected. Care needs to be taken with metallic paintwork, as special non-abrasive cleaner/polisher is required to avoid damage to the finish. Always check that the door and ventilator opening drain holes and pipes are completely clear so that water can be drained out. Bright work should be treated in the same way as paint work. Windscreens and windows can be kept clear of the smeary film which often appears, by the use of a proprietary glass cleaner like Holts Mixra. Never use any form of wax or other body or chromium polish on glass.

## 3  Maintenance – upholstery and carpets

Mats and carpets should be brushed or vacuum cleaned regularly to keep them free of grit. If they are badly stained remove them from the vehicle for scrubbing or sponging and make quite sure they are dry before refitting. Seats and interior trim panels can be kept clean by wiping with a damp cloth and Turtle Wax Carisma. If they do become stained (which can be more apparent on light coloured upholstery) use a little liquid detergent and a soft nail brush to scour the grime out of the grain of the material. Do not forget to keep the headlining clean in the same way as the upholstery. When using liquid cleaners inside the vehicle do not over-wet the surfaces being cleaned. Excessive damp could get into the seams and padded interior causing stains, offensive odours or even rot. If the inside of the vehicle gets wet accidentally it is worthwhile taking some trouble to dry it out properly, particularly where carpets are involved. *Do not leave oil or electric heaters inside the vehicle for this purpose.*

### 4  Minor body damage – repair

*The colour bodywork repair photographic sequences between pages 32 and 33 illustrate the operations detailed in the following sub-sections.*
Note: *For more detailed information about bodywork repair, the Haynes Publishing Group publish a book by Lindsay Porter called The Car Bodywork Repair Manual. This incorporates information on such aspects as rust treatment, painting and glass fibre repairs, as well as details on more ambitious repairs involving welding and panel beating.*

#### Repair of minor scratches in bodywork

If the scratch is very superficial, and does not penetrate to the metal of the bodywork, repair is very simple. Lightly rub the area of the scratch with a paintwork renovator like Turtle Wax New Color Back, or a very fine cutting paste like Holts Body + Plus Rubbing Compound, to remove loose paint from the scratch and to clear the surrounding bodywork of wax polish. Rinse the area with clean water.

Apply touch-up paint, such as Holts Dupli-Color Color Touch or a paint film like Holts Autofilm, to the scratch using a fine paint brush; continue to apply fine layers of paint until the surface of the paint in the scratch is level with the surrounding paintwork. Allow the new paint at least two weeks to harden; then blend it into the surrounding paintwork by rubbing the scratch area with a paintwork renovator or a very fine cutting paste, such as Holts Body + Plus Rubbing Compound or Turtle Wax New Color Back. Finally, apply wax polish from one of the Turtle Wax range of wax polishes.

Where the scratch has penetrated right through to the metal of the bodywork, causing the metal to rust, a different repair technique is required. Remove any loose rust from the bottom of the scratch with a penknife, then apply rust inhibiting paint, such as Turtle Wax Rust Master, to prevent the formation of rust in the future. Using a rubber or nylon applicator fill the scratch with bodystopper paste like Holts Body + Plus Knifing Putty. If required, this paste can be mixed with cellulose thinners, such as Holts Body + Plus Cellulose Thinners, to provide a very thin paste which is ideal for filling narrow scratches. Before the stopper-paste in the scratch hardens, wrap a piece of smooth cotton rag around the top of a finger. Dip the finger in cellulose thinners, such as Holts Body + Plus Cellulose Thinners, and then quickly sweep it across the surface of the stopper-paste in the scratch; this will ensure that the surface of the stopper-paste is slightly hollowed. The scratch can now be painted over as described earlier in this Section.

#### Repair of dents in bodywork

When deep denting of the vehicle's bodywork has taken place, the first task is to pull the dent out, until the affected bodywork almost attains its original shape. There is little point in trying to restore the original shape completely, as the metal in the damaged area will have stretched on impact and cannot be reshaped fully to its original contour. It is better to bring the level of the dent up to a point which is about ⅛ in (3 mm) below the level of the surrounding bodywork. In cases where the dent is very shallow anyway, it is not worth trying to pull it out at all. If the underside of the dent is accessible, it can be hammered out gently from behind, using a mallet with a wooden or plastic head. Whilst doing this, hold a suitable block of wood firmly against the outside of the panel to absorb the impact from the hammer blows and thus prevent a large area of the bodywork from being 'belled-out'.

Should the dent be in a section of the bodywork which has a double skin or some other factor making it inaccessible from behind, a different technique is called for. Drill several small holes through the

metal inside the area – particularly in the deeper section. Then screw long self-tapping screws into the holes just sufficiently for them to gain a good purchase in the metal. Now the dent can be pulled out by pulling on the protruding heads of the screws with a pair of pliers.

The next stage of the repair is the removal of the paint from the damaged area, and from an inch or so of the surrounding 'sound' bodywork. This is accomplished most easily by using a wire brush or abrasive pad on a power drill, although it can be done just as effectively by hand using sheets of abrasive paper. To complete the preparation for filling, score the surface of the bare metal with a screwdriver or the tang of a file, or alternatively, drill small holes in the affected area. This will provide a really good 'key' for the filler paste.

To complete the repair see the Section on filling and re-spraying.

#### Repair of rust holes or gashes in bodywork

Remove all paint from the affected area and from an inch or so of the surrounding 'sound' bodywork, using an abrasive pad or a wire brush on a power drill. If these are not available a few sheets of abrasive paper will do the job just as effectively. With the paint removed you will be able to gauge the severity of the corrosion and therefore decide whether to renew the whole panel (if this is possible) or to repair the affected area. New body panels are not as expensive as most people think and it is often quicker and more satisfactory to fit a new panel than to attempt to repair large areas of corrosion.

Remove all fittings from the affected area except those which will act as a guide to the original shape of the damaged bodywork (eg headlamp shells etc). Then, using tin snips or a hacksaw blade, remove all loose metal and any other metal badly affected by corrosion. Hammer the edges of the hole inwards in order to create a slight depression for the filler paste.

Wire brush the affected area to remove the powdery rust from the surface of the remaining metal. Paint the affected area with rust inhibiting paint like Turtle Wax Rust Master; if the back of the rusted area is accessible treat this also.

Before filling can take place it will be necessary to block the hole in some way. This can be achieved by the use of aluminium or plastic mesh, or aluminium tape.

Aluminium or plastic mesh or glass fibre matting, such as the Holts Body + Plus Glass Fibre Matting, is probably the best material to use for a large hole. Cut a piece to the approximate size and shape of the hole to be filled, then position it in the hole so that its edges are below the level of the surrounding bodywork. It can be retained in position by several blobs of filler paste around its periphery.

Aluminium tape should be used for small or very narrow holes. Pull a piece off the roll and trim it to the approximate size and shape required, then pull off the backing paper (if used) and stick the tape over the hole; it can be overlapped if the thickness of one piece is insufficient. Burnish down the edges of the tape with the handle of a screwdriver or similar, to ensure that the tape is securely attached to the metal underneath.

#### Bodywork repairs – filling and re-spraying

Before using this Section, see the Sections on dent, deep scratch, rust holes and gash repairs.

Many types of bodyfiller are available, but generally speaking those proprietary kits which contain a tin of filler paste and a tube of resin hardener are best for this type of repair, like Holts Body + Plus or Holts No Mix which can be used directly from the tube. A wide, flexible plastic or nylon applicator will be found invaluable for imparting a smooth and well contoured finish to the surface of the filler.

Mix up a little filler on a clean piece of card or board – measure the hardener carefully (follow the maker's instructions on the pack) otherwise the filler will set too rapidly or too slowly. Alternatively, Holts No Mix can be used straight from the tube without mixing, but daylight is required to cure it. Using the applicator apply the filler paste to the prepared area; draw the applicator across the surface of the filler to achieve the correct contour and to level the filler surface. As soon as a contour that approximates to the correct one is achieved, stop working the paste – if you carry on too long the paste will become sticky and begin to 'pick up' on the applicator. Continue to add thin layers of filler paste at twenty-minute intervals until the level of the filler is just proud of the surrounding bodywork.

Once the filler has hardened, excess can be removed using a metal plane or file. From then on, progressively finer grades of abrasive paper should be used, starting with a 40 grade production paper and finishing with 400 grade wet-and-dry paper. Always wrap the abrasive paper around a flat rubber, cork, or wooden block – otherwise the surface of the filler will not be completely flat. During the smoothing of the filler surface the wet-and-dry paper should be periodically rinsed in water. This will ensure that a very smooth finish is imparted to the filler at the final stage.

At this stage the 'dent' should be surrounded by a ring of bare metal, which in turn should be encircled by the finely 'feathered' edge of the good paintwork. Rinse the repair area with clean water, until all of the dust produced by the rubbing-down operation has gone.

Spray the whole repair area with a light coat of primer, either Holts Body+Plus Grey or Red Oxide Primer – this will show up any imperfections in the surface of the filler. Repair these imperfections with fresh filler paste or bodystopper, and once more smooth the surface with abrasive paper. If bodystopper is used, it can be mixed with cellulose thinners to form a really thin paste which is ideal for filling small holes. Repeat this spray and repair procedure until you are satisfied that the surface of the filler, and the feathered edge of the paintwork are perfect. Clean the repair area with clean water and allow to dry fully.

The repair area is now ready for final spraying. Paint spraying must be carried out in a warm, dry, windless and dust free atmosphere. This condition can be created artificially if you have access to a large indoor working area, but if you are forced to work in the open, you will have to pick your day very carefully. If you are working indoors, dousing the floor in the work area with water will help to settle the dust which would otherwise be in the atmosphere. If the repair area is confined to one body panel, mask off the surrounding panels; this will help to minimise the effects of a slight mis-match in paint colours. Bodywork fittings (eg chrome strips, door handles etc) will also need to be masked off. Use genuine masking tape and several thicknesses of newspaper for the masking operations.

Before commencing to spray, agitate the aerosol can thoroughly, then spray a test area (an old tin, or similar) until the technique is mastered. Cover the repair area with a thick coat of primer; the thickness should be built up using several thin layers of paint rather than one thick one. Using 400 grade wet-and-dry paper, rub down the surface of the primer until it is really smooth. While doing this, the work area should be thoroughly doused with water, and the wet-and-dry paper periodically rinsed in water. Allow to dry before spraying on more paint.

Spray on the top coat using Holts Dupli-Color Autospray, again building up the thickness by using several thin layers of paint. Start spraying in the centre of the repair area and then work outwards, with a side-to-side motion, until the whole repair area and about 2 inches of the surrounding original paintwork is covered. Remove all masking material 10 to 15 minutes after spraying on the final coat of paint.

Allow the new paint at least two weeks to harden, then, using a paintwork renovator or a very fine cutting paste such as Turtle Wax New Color Back or Holts Body+Plus Rubbing Compound, blend the edges of the paint into the existing paintwork. Finally, apply wax polish.

## 5  Major body damage – repair

Where serious damage has occurred, or large areas need renewal due to neglect, it means that completely new sections or panels will need welding in, and this is best left to professionals. If the damage is due to impact, it will also be necessary to completely check the alignment of the bodyshell structure. Due to the principle of construction, the strength and shape of the whole car can be affected by damage to one part. In such instances the services of an accident repair specialist or Renault dealer with specialist checking jigs are essential. If a body is left misaligned, it is first of all dangerous, as the car will not handle properly, and secondly uneven stresses will be imposed on the steering, engine and transmission, causing abnormal wear or complete failure. Tyre wear may also be excessive.

## 6  Maintenance – hinges and locks

1   Oil the hinges of the bonnet, boot or tailgate and door with a drop or two of light oil at regular intervals (see Routine maintenance).
2   At the same time, lightly oil the bonnet release mechanism and all door locks.
3   Do not attempt to lubricate the steering lock.

## 7  Door rattles – tracing and rectification

1   Check first that the door is not loose at the hinges, and that the latch is holding the door firmly in position. Check also that the door lines up with the aperture in the body. If the door is out of alignment, adjust it, as described in Sections 22 and 23 or 28 and 29.
2   If the latch is holding the door in the correct position, but the latch still rattles, the lock mechanism is worn and should be renewed.
3   Other rattles from the door could be caused by wear in the window operating mechanism, interior lock mechanism, or loose glass channels.

## 8  Bonnet – removal, refitting and adjustment

1   Open the bonnet and support it in the open position using the stay.
2   Using a suitable drill, drill the head off the rivet securing the safety wire to the bonnet. Tap out the remains of the rivet with a punch and remove the wire.
3   Disconnect the windscreen washer hose at the pump outlet or T connector.

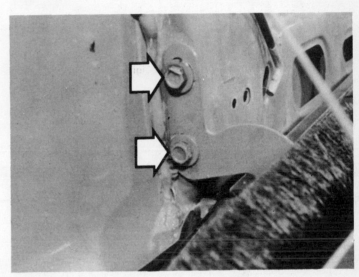

8.4 Bonnet hinge and retaining bolts (arrowed)

4   Mark the outline of the hinges with a soft pencil, then loosen the four retaining bolts (photo).
5   With the help of an assistant, remove the stay, unscrew the four bolts and lift the bonnet off the car.
6   Refitting is the reverse sequence to removal. Position the bonnet hinges within the outline marks made during removal, but alter its position as necessary to provide a uniform gap all round. Adjust the height of the lock mechanism if necessary, as described in Section 9.

## 9  Bonnet lock and release cable – removal, refitting and adjustment

### Bonnet lock
1   With the bonnet open, disconnect the cable eye from the lock lever and withdraw the cable from the lock.
2   Undo the two retaining bolts and remove the lock from the car.
3   Refitting is the reverse sequence to removal, but adjust the lock height so that the bonnet line is flush with the front wings and shuts securely without force.

### Release cable
4   With the bonnet open, disconnect the cable eye from the lock lever and withdraw the cable from the lock.
5   From inside the car undo the two bolts securing the release handle to the side panel under the facia.

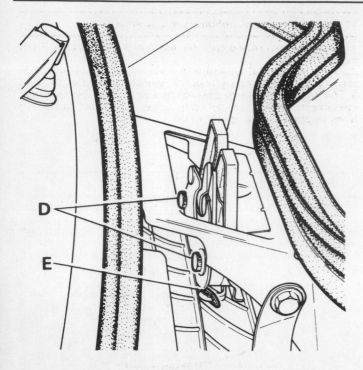

Fig. 11.1 Bonnet lock retaining bolts (D) and cable eye fitting (E) (Sec 9)

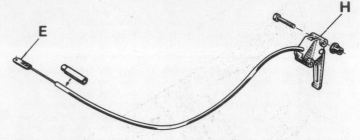

Fig. 11.2 Bonnet release cable and handle assembly (Sec 9)

E  Cable eye                    H  Handle assembly

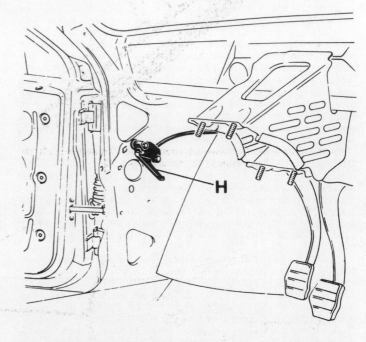

Fig. 11.3 Bonnet release handle location (H) under facia (Sec 9)

6   Release the cable from its engine compartment clips, pull the cable through the bulkhead and remove the complete assembly from inside the car.
7   Refitting is the reverse sequence to removal.

## 10  Radiator grille – removal and refitting

1   Open the bonnet and undo the three screws securing the grille to the body panel.
2   On Renault 11 models undo the two screws at the front, one each side, securing the grille to its support bracket (photo).
3   Close the bonnet, tip the grille forwards at the top and release the two side arms from the slots in the support brackets. Remove the grille from the car.
4   Refitting is the reverse sequence to removal.

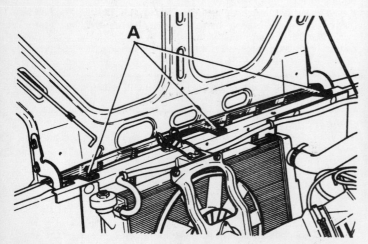

Fig. 11.4 Radiator grille-to-body panel retaining screws (A) (Sec 10)

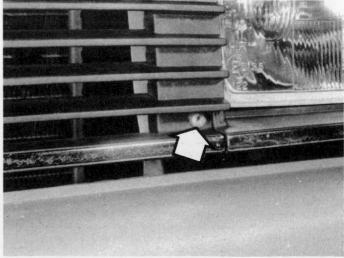

10.2 Renault 11 radiator grille retaining screw (arrowed)

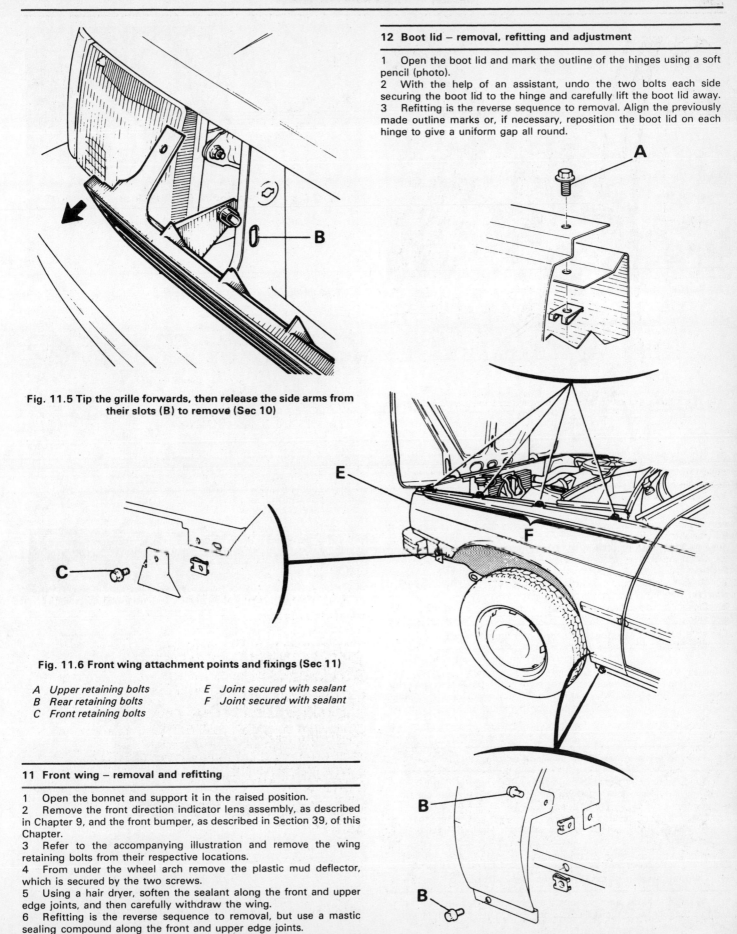

Fig. 11.5 Tip the grille forwards, then release the side arms from
their slots (B) to remove (Sec 10)

Fig. 11.6 Front wing attachment points and fixings (Sec 11)

A   Upper retaining bolts        E   Joint secured with sealant
B   Rear retaining bolts         F   Joint secured with sealant
C   Front retaining bolts

## 12 Boot lid – removal, refitting and adjustment

1   Open the boot lid and mark the outline of the hinges using a soft
pencil (photo).
2   With the help of an assistant, undo the two bolts each side
securing the boot lid to the hinge and carefully lift the boot lid away.
3   Refitting is the reverse sequence to removal. Align the previously
made outline marks or, if necessary, reposition the boot lid on each
hinge to give a uniform gap all round.

## 11 Front wing – removal and refitting

1   Open the bonnet and support it in the raised position.
2   Remove the front direction indicator lens assembly, as described
in Chapter 9, and the front bumper, as described in Section 39, of this
Chapter.
3   Refer to the accompanying illustration and remove the wing
retaining bolts from their respective locations.
4   From under the wheel arch remove the plastic mud deflector,
which is secured by the two screws.
5   Using a hair dryer, soften the sealant along the front and upper
edge joints, and then carefully withdraw the wing.
6   Refitting is the reverse sequence to removal, but use a mastic
sealing compound along the front and upper edge joints.

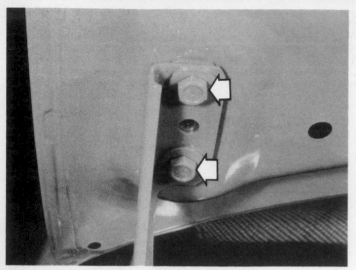

12.1 Renault 9 boot lid hinge retaining bolts (arrowed)

13.1 Boot lid lock retaining nuts (arrowed)

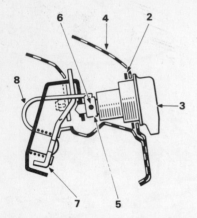

**Fig. 11.7 Boot lid lock assembly diagram (Secs 13 and 14)**

| 2 | Private lock retaining clip | 5 | Locking finger |
|---|---|---|---|
| | | 6 | Locking finger pin |
| 3 | Private lock | 7 | Lock mechanism |
| 4 | Boot lid | 8 | Spring wire |

## 13 Boot lid lock – removal, refitting and adjustment

1  Open the boot lid, undo the two retaining nuts (photo) and withdraw the lock from the boot lid.
2  Refitting is the reverse sequence to removal, but ensure that the spring wire locates over the locking finger on the private lock. Adjust the striker plate (photo) so that the boot lid shuts and locks without force.

## 14 Boot lid private lock – removal and refitting

1  Open the boot lid, reach through one of the apertures in the lid and withdraw the private lock retaining clip. Remove the private lock from the boot lid.
2  Refitting is the reverse sequence to removal, but ensure that the spring wire on the boot lid locates over the locking finger on the private lock.

## 15 Tailgate support struts – removal and refitting

1  With the tailgate open, unhook the parcel shelf support cords and support the tailgate in the raised position using a stout length of wood, or an assistant.

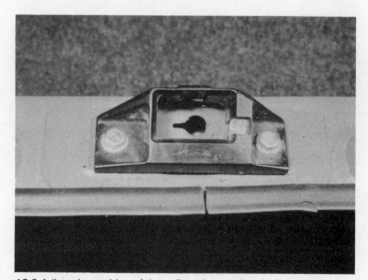

13.2 Adjust the position of the striker plate so that the boot lid shuts and locks without force

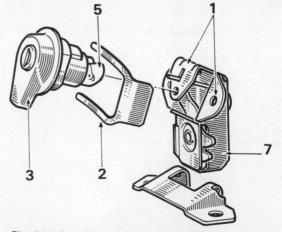

**Fig. 11.8 Boot lid lock and private lock components (Secs 13 and 14)**

| 1 | Lock mechanism retaining stud holes | 3 | Private lock |
|---|---|---|---|
| 2 | Retaining clip | 5 | Locking finger |
| | | 7 | Lock mechanism |

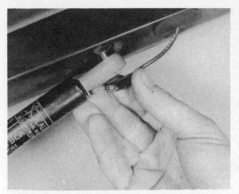

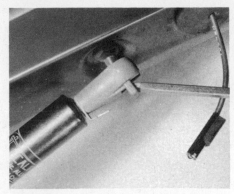

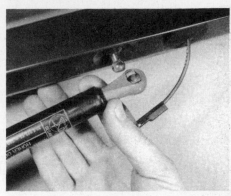

15.2 Disconnect the electrical leads at the tailgate support strut terminals

15.3 Lever out the locking retainer with a screwdriver ...

15.4 ... and remove the strut from the ball peg

2    Disconnect the electrical leads at the strut terminals (photo).
3    Using a screwdriver, carefully lever out the locking retainer at the strut ball end fittings (photo).
4    Withdraw the strut from the ball pegs and remove it from the car (photo).
5    Refitting is the reverse sequence to removal.

## 16  Tailgate – removal and refitting

1    Remove the support struts from the tailgate ball pegs, as described in the previous Section.
2    Disconnect the tailgate wiper electrical connections (where fitted).
3    Using a socket and extension bar, undo the tailgate hinge retaining nuts, accessible through an aperture on each side of the interior headlining (photo).
4    With the help of an assistant, remove the tailgate from the car.
5    Refitting is the reverse sequence to removal. Adjust the tailgate by means of the lock striker plate, as described in Section 17.

## 17  Tailgate lock – removal, refitting and adjustment

1    Open the tailgate and undo the two lock retaining bolts. Manipulate the lock by turning it anti-clockwise until the lock lever can be withdrawn from the tailgate aperture.
2    Refitting is the reverse sequence to removal. Adjust the striker plate by slackening the retaining bolt and moving the striker plate as necessary until the tailgate is a flush fit all round.

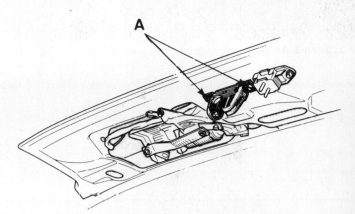

LOCK POSITION 1

LOCK POSITION 2

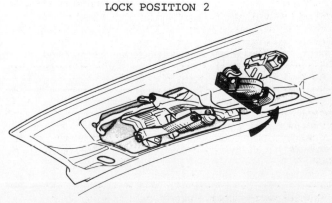

16.3 Tailgate hinge retaining nut, accessible through an aperture in the headlining after removal of a cover plate

Fig. 11.9 Tailgate lock removal sequence (Sec 17)

A  Lock retaining bolts
Turn the lock anti-clockwise to positions 1 and 2 to release the lock

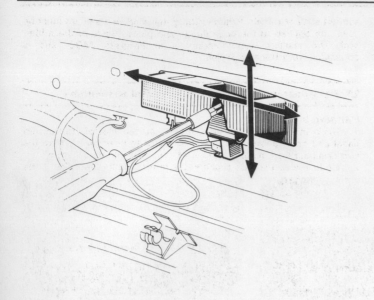

Fig. 11.10 Tailgate lock striker plate adjustment (Sec 17)

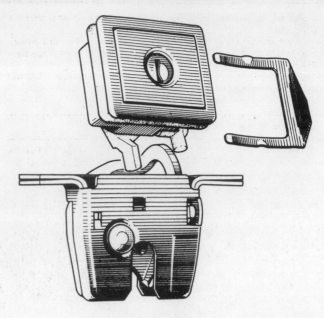

Fig. 11.11 Tailgate lock and private lock components
(Secs 17 and 18)

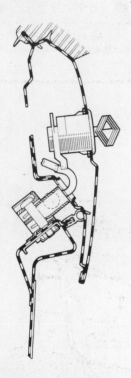

Fig. 11.12 Tailgate lock assembly diagram (Secs 17 and 18)

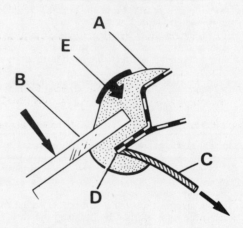

Fig. 11.13 Windscreen rubber seal and embellisher arrangement
(Sec 19)

A  Rubber seal          D  Body flange
B  Windscreen           E  Embellisher
C  Cord for fitting seal

## 18  Tailgate private lock – removal and refitting

1   Open the tailgate, reach in through one of the apertures and
withdraw the private lock retaining clip. Remove the private lock from
the tailgate.
2   Refitting is the reverse sequence to removal.

## 19  Windscreen – removal and refitting

1   Remove the interior trim mouldings around the windscreen, as
described in Section 36, and the wiper arms, as described in Chapter
9.

2   Cover the bonnet with a blanket to protect the paintwork and
similarly cover the top of the facia.
3   From inside the car turn the lip of the rubber seal over the body
flange using a blunt tool; starting at the top.
4   When the seal has been released at the top and sides, sit in the
front seat, place the soles of your shoes against the top of the
windscreen and push the glass out. Have an assistant support it as it
comes free.
5   Thoroughly clean the sealing edges of the body flange and also the
windscreen if the original screen is to be refitted.
6   Fit a new rubber seal around the glass and place a suitable length
of strong cord in the body flange groove of the seal. The cord ends
should overlap at the bottom right-hand corner. Where applicable, refit
the seal embellisher at this stage.
7   With the help of an assistant, place the windscreen in position
from the outside, engage the lower right-hand corner of the seal with
the body flange and allow the cords to hang down on the inside.
8   Start to pull one end of the cord from the inside while your
assistant pushes firmly on the glass from the outside. Pull the string at

right-angles to the seal and the cord will lift the lip of the seal over the body flange.

9    When the top centre of the screen is reached with one cord, repeat the procedure with the second cord until the seal lip is in place over the body flange all the way round.

10   Refit the interior trim mouldings, as described in Section 36, and the wiper arms, as described in Chapter 9.

## 20 Tailgate window – removal and refitting

1    The procedure is the same as described in the previous Section for the windscreen, but first disconnect the heater element wires at the

support strut terminals. When refitting the window a sealant must be used and applied to the body flange and glass groove of the rubber seal. The sealant recommended is Impermastic 1438, and is obtainable from Renault dealers.

## 21 Front door interior trim panel – removal and refitting

### Renault 9 models

1    Undo the screw at the bottom securing the door bin to the trim panel and door (photo). Lift the bin upwards to disengage it from the two retaining buttons and remove the bin from the door (photo).

2    Undo the two screws securing the armrest to the door and, if the

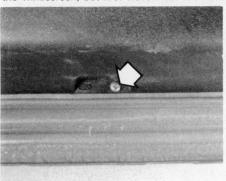

21.1A Undo the screw (arrowed) securing the door bin at the bottom ...

21.1B ... then lift the bin upwards to disengage the retaining buttons

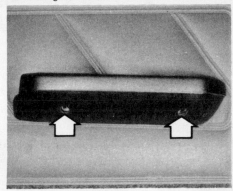

21.2 Remove the armrest by undoing the retaining screws (arrowed)

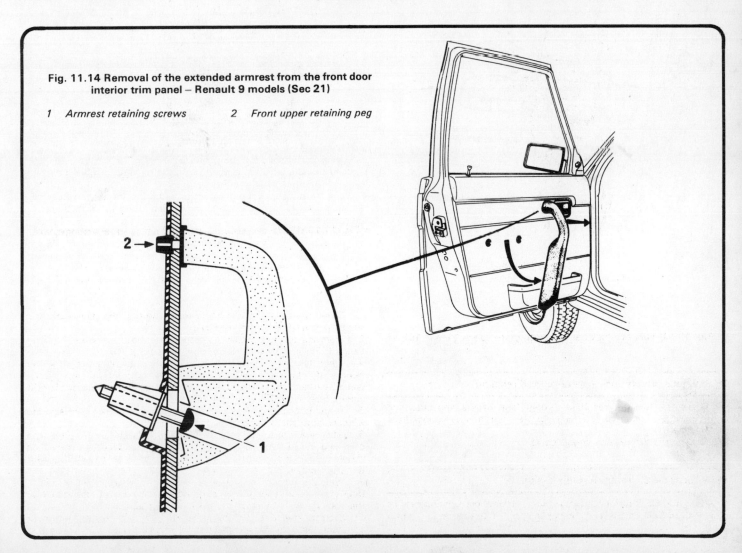

Fig. 11.14 Removal of the extended armrest from the front door interior trim panel – Renault 9 models (Sec 21)

1    Armrest retaining screws          2    Front upper retaining peg

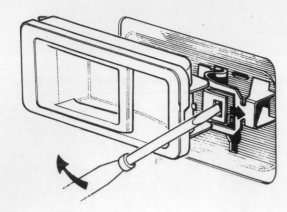

Fig. 11.15 Removal of the front door remote control handle
(Sec 21)

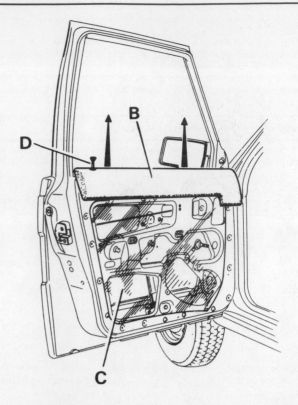

Fig. 11.16 Removal of the front door top moulding – Renault 9
models (Sec 21)

B   Top moulding                    D   Interior lock button
C   Plastic sheet

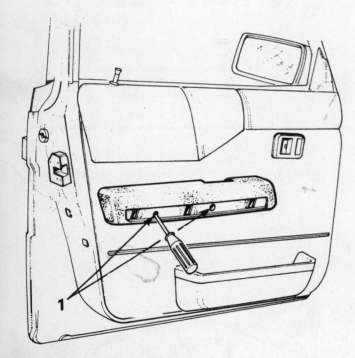

Fig. 11.17 Removal of the armrest from the front door interior trim
panel – Renault 11 models (Sec 21)

standard armrest is fitted, lift it off (photo). If the extended armrest is
fitted, pivot the armrest down at the rear to disengage the front upper
retaining peg.

3   Using a suitable flat blade as a lever, prise off the window
regulator handle which is a push fit on the regulator spindle (photo).
Withdraw the handle trim surround.

4   Ease the door lock remote control handle to the rear to free the
retaining catches then disengage the operating rod (photo). Remove
the handle.

5   Starting at one corner, prise the trim panel away from the door
using a thin flat blade, to release the retaining buttons (photo). When
all the buttons have been released, remove the panel by lowering it at
the top to free it from the top moulding (where fitted).

6   Where a top moulding is fitted this can be removed by first

21.3 Carefully prise off the window regulator
handle using a suitable flat blade if necessary

21.4 Disengage the remote control handle
from the operating rod

21.5 Using a thin flat blade ease the trim panel
from the door to release the retaining buttons

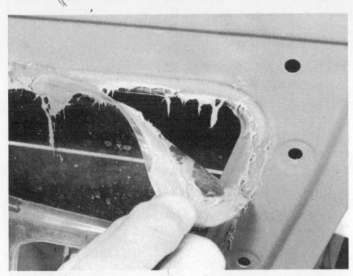

21.7 Peel back the plastic sheet to gain access to the door internal components

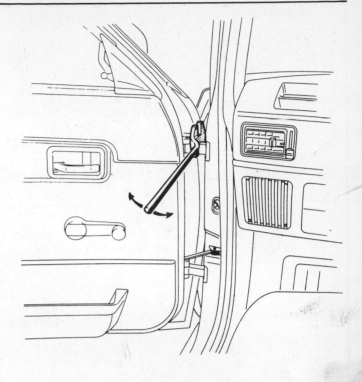

Fig. 11.18 Using a slotted bar to adjust the door hinges (Sec 22)

unscrewing the interior lock button, then easing the moulding out at the bottom and up at the top.

7   If the trim panel has been removed for access to the door internal components, peel back the plastic sheet as necessary (photo).

8   Refitting is the reverse sequence to removal.

### Renault 11 models

9   Undo the screw at the bottom securing the door bin to the trim panel and door. Lift the bin upwards to disengage it from the two retaining buttons and remove the bin from the door.

10   On two-door models, undo the two lower retaining screws and lift off the armrest. On four-door models, carefully prise off the armrest trim strip using a small screwdriver to gain access to the armrest retaining screws. Undo the screws and withdraw the armrest. Disconnect the electric window switch wiring multi-plug, where fitted, and remove the armrest.

11   Using a suitable flat blade as a lever, prise off the window regulator handle which is a push fit on the regulator spindle. Withdraw the handle trim surround.

12   Ease the door lock remote control handle to the rear to free the retaining catches then disengage the operating rod. Remove the handle.

13   Unscrew the interior lock button then, starting at one corner, prise the trim panel away from the door using a thin flat blade to release the retaining buttons. When all the buttons have been released, lift the panel to free the upper moulding catches and remove the panel from the door.

14   If the trim panel has been removed for access to the door internal components, peel back the plastic sheet as necessary.

15   Refitting is the reverse sequence to removal.

---

## 22 Front door – removal and refitting

1   On models having electrically-operated windows or electro-mechanical door locks, remove the interior trim panel, as described in Section 21, and disconnect the wiring multi-plug connectors. Remove the wiring harness from the door.

2   Release the door check strap by driving out the retaining pin with a drift (photo).

3   Support the door on blocks or with the help of an assistant.

4   Prise out the two caps covering each hinge pin, using a screwdriver.

5   Using a cranked metal rod of suitable diameter as a drift, drive out the upper and lower hinge pins. Note that the hinge pins are removed towards each other, ie downwards for the upper pin, and upwards for the lower pin.

6   With the hinge pins removed, carefully lift off the door.

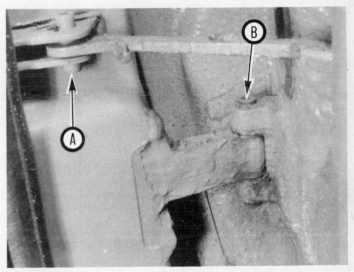

22.2 Door check strap retaining pin (A) and hinge pin protective caps (B)

7   Refitting is the reverse sequence to removal.

8   If the door is not a flush fit with the aperture, adjustment is carried out by bending the hinge arms as necessary. A slotted bar, as shown in Fig. 11.18, can be used for this purpose.

---

## 23 Front door lock – removal, refitting and adjustment

1   Open the door and wind the window fully up.

2   Remove the interior trim panel, as described in Section 21.

3   If the car is fitted with electro-mechanical door locks, reach inside the door and disconnect the wiring connector from the lock solenoid or motor. If manual locks are fitted, unscrew the interior lock button.

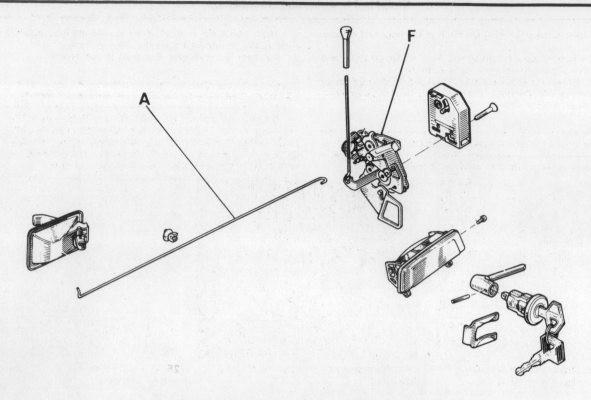

**Fig. 11.19 Manual front door lock components (Sec 23)**

A   Remote control handle rod        F   Lock mechanism

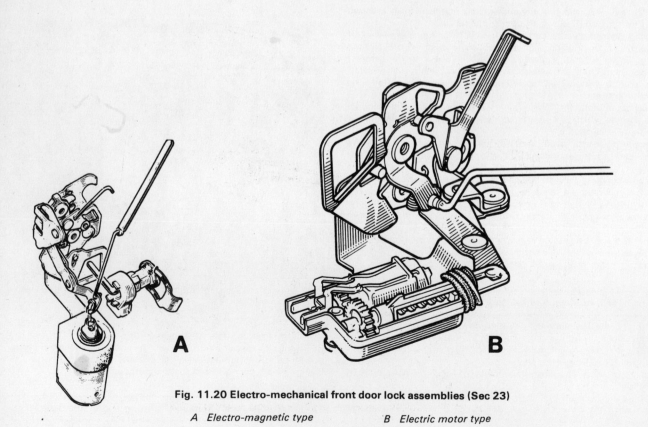

**Fig. 11.20 Electro-mechanical front door lock assemblies (Sec 23)**

A   Electro-magnetic type        B   Electric motor type

4 Undo the three screws securing the latch to the door and remove the latch.
5 Release the remote control handle rod from its support clip and withdraw the lock assembly from the door aperture.
6 Refitting is the reverse sequence to removal. Adjust the position of the striker (photo) so that the door shuts and locks without slamming, and is a flush fit all round.

### 24 Front door private lock – removal and refitting

1 Remove the interior trim panel, as described in Section 21.

2 From inside the door withdraw the private lock retaining clip and remove the private lock from the door (photo).
3 Refitting is the reverse sequence to removal.

### 25 Front door exterior handle – removal and refitting

1 On the side of the door, undo the retaining screw in the centre of the fixing spacer and then turn the fixing spacer half a turn to release it. On some models a retaining screw only is used (photo).
2 Slide the handle forwards to release the retaining lugs on the handle from the door, then tip the handle out at the top.

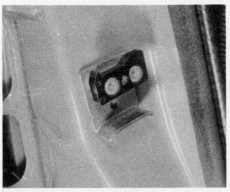

23.6 Adjust the striker position so that the door is flush and locks without slamming

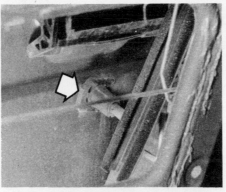

24.2 Front door private lock retaining clip (arrowed)

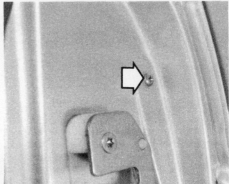

25.1 Front door exterior handle side retaining screw (arrowed)

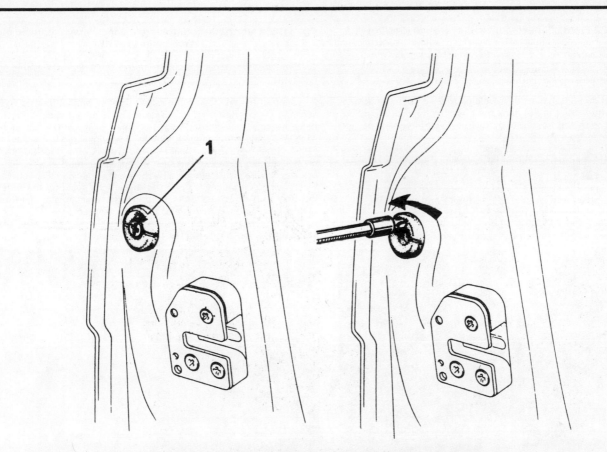

Fig. 11.21 Front door exterior handle side attachment (Sec 25)

1   Retaining screw in centre of fixing spacer        Arrow indicates fixing spacer direction of removal

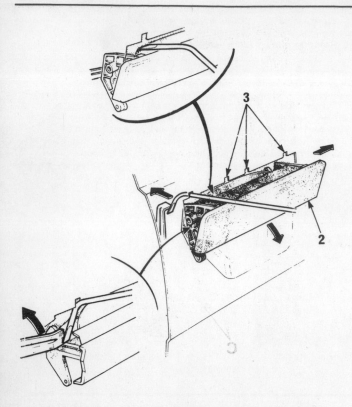

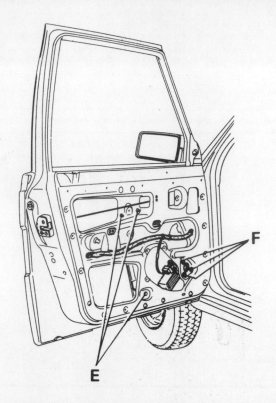

**Fig. 11.22 Front door exterior handle removal (Sec 25)**

*2    Exterior handle        3    Retaining lug slots in door*

*Inset shows tool being used to release door lock lever*

**Fig. 11.23 Electrically-operated front window regulator and motor attachments (Sec 26)**

*E    Regulator mechanism retaining bolts        F    Motor retaining bolts*

3    Insert a thin metal rod, such as a welding rod with a flattened end, through the rearmost slot in the door and push the door lock lever out of engagement with the handle (Fig. 11.22). Withdraw the rod and remove the handle from the door.

4    Refitting is the reverse sequence to removal, but keep the door lock lever raised when using the metal rod as the handle is inserted.

### 26 Front door glass and regulator – removal and refitting

1    Open the door and wind the window fully up.
2    Remove the interior trim panel, as described in Section 21.

3    Support the window in the raised position and undo the two bolts securing the window bottom frame to the regulator slide (photo). The bolts are accessible through the two holes in the inner door panel.

4    On models with manually-operated windows, undo the four bolts securing the regulator mechanism and cable to the door (photo) and manipulate the regulator out of the door aperture.

5    On models with electrically-operated windows, disconnect the motor wiring connectors, undo the three bolts securing the motor to the door and the three bolts securing the mechanism to the door. Manipulate the assembly out of the door aperture.

6    If the window is to be removed, withdraw the two rubber sealing strips on the top of the door by pulling them upwards.

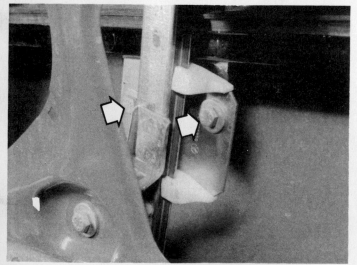

26.3 Door glass bottom frame-to-regulator slide retaining bolts (arrowed)

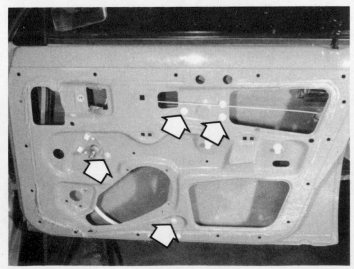

26.4 Window regulator mechanism retaining bolt locations (arrowed)

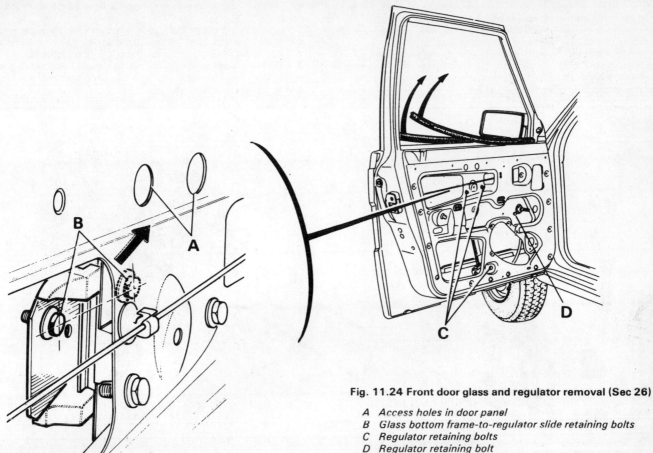

Fig. 11.24 Front door glass and regulator removal (Sec 26)

   A   *Access holes in door panel*
   B   *Glass bottom frame-to-regulator slide retaining bolts*
   C   *Regulator retaining bolts*
   D   *Regulator retaining bolt*
      *Arrows show rubber sealing strip removal direction*

7    Tilt the window to free it from the channels and lift it out from the outside.
8    Refitting is the reverse sequence to removal, but tighten all retaining bolts finger tight initially until all the components are fitted. Centralize the glass in the fully closed position before finally tightening the window bottom frame to regulator slide retaining bolts.

## 27 Rear door interior trim panel – removal and refitting

1    Undo the two retaining screws and remove the armrest.
2    Using a suitable flat blade as a lever, prise off the window regulator handle which is a push fit on the regulator spindle. Withdraw the handle trim surround.
3    Undo the retaining screw, ease the door lock remote control handle to the rear to free the retaining catches, then disengage the operating rod. Remove the handle.
4    Starting at one corner, prise the trim panel away from the door, using a thin flat blade to release the retaining buttons. When all the buttons have been released, pull the panel away from the door at the bottom and lower it to free it from the top moulding. Remove the panel.
5    To remove the top moulding, unscrew the interior lock button then ease the moulding out at the bottom, up at the top and off the door.
6    If the trim panel has been removed for access to the door internal components, peel back the plastic sheet as necessary.
7    Refitting the door trim is the reverse sequence to removal.

## 28 Rear door – removal and refitting

1    The procedure is the same as for the front doors, and reference should be made to Section 22.

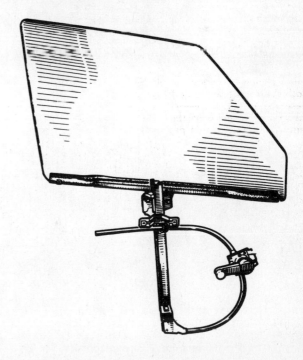

Fig. 11.25 Front door glass and regulator assembly (Sec 26)

## 29 Rear door lock – removal, refitting and adjustment

1    Open the door and wind the window fully up.
2    Remove the interior trim panel, as described in Section 27.
3    Unscrew the interior lock button or, if electro-mechanical locks are fitted, reach inside the door and disconnect the wiring connector from the lock solenoid or motor.

4    Undo the three screws securing the latch to the door and remove the latch.
5    Release the remote control handle rod from its support clip and the interior lock button rod from its support clip and bellcrank.
6    Withdraw the lock assembly from the door aperture.
7    Refitting is the reverse sequence to removal. Adjust the position of the striker plate so that the door shuts and locks without slamming, and is a flush fit all round.

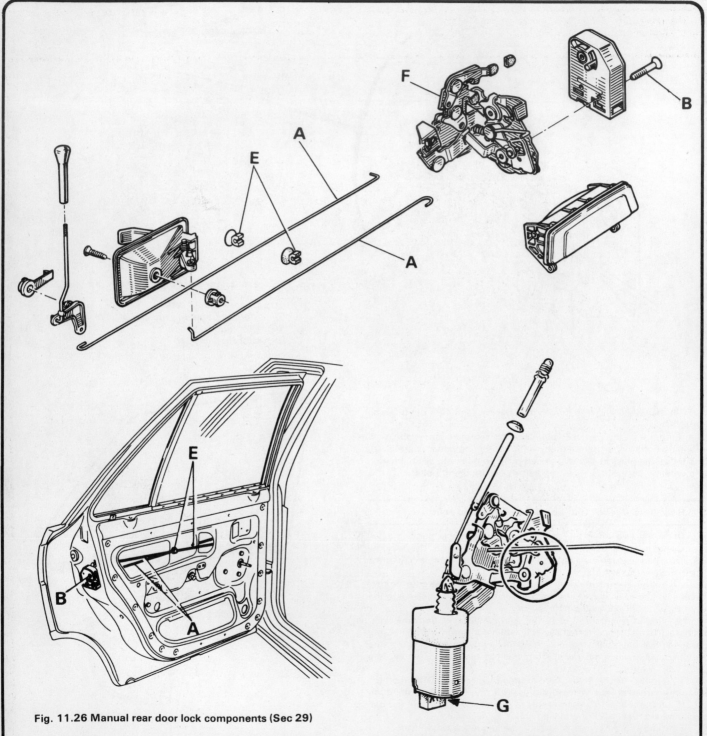

**Fig. 11.26 Manual rear door lock components (Sec 29)**

A    Control rods
B    Lock retaining screw
E    Control rod support clips
F    Lock mechanism

**Fig. 11.27 Electro-mechanical rear door lock assembly (Sec 29)**

G    Wiring plug connector on solenoid

## 30 Rear door private lock – removal and refitting

1   The procedure is the same as described previously for the front door. Remove the interior trim panel as described in Section 27, then refer to Section 24.

## 31 Rear door exterior handle – removal and refitting

1   The procedure is the same as described previously for the front doors, and reference should be made to Section 25.

## 32 Rear door glass and regulator – removal and refitting

1   Remove the interior trim panel, as described in Section 27.
2   Temporarily refit the handle and position the window so that its top edge is approximately 200 mm (7.9 in) from the top edge of the door. Support the glass in this position.
3   Undo the three bolts securing the regulator mechanism to the door, push the regulator into the door and detach the regulator arm roller from the glass lower channel. Withdraw the regulator from the door aperture.
4   To remove the glass, allow it to rest in the fully open position then

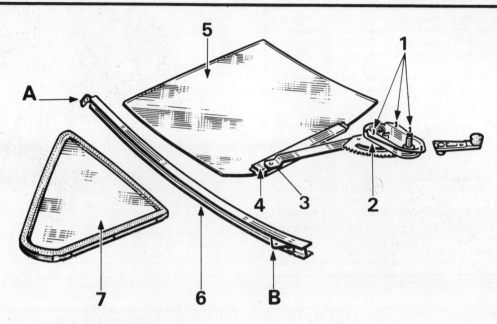

Fig. 11.28 Rear door glass and regulator components (Sec 32)

1   Regulator retaining studs
2   Regulator assembly
3   Regulator arm roller
4   Glass lower channel
5   Moving window
6   Rear guide channel
7   Fixed window
A   Rear guide channel attachment
B   Rear guide channel attachment

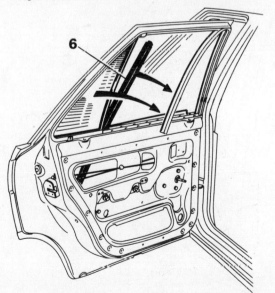

Fig. 11.29 Rear door glass removal – initial sequence (Sec 32)

*Detach rear guide channel (6), remove rubber guide channel from its location and remove fixed window*

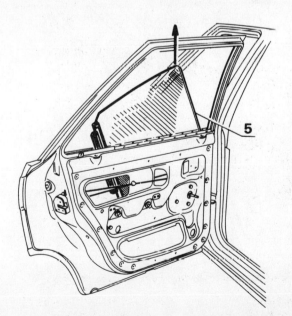

Fig. 11.30 Rear door glass removal – final sequence (Sec 32)

*Remove rear guide channel then lift out moving window (5)*

remove the two upper sealing strips from the top edge of the door by pulling upwards.
5  Undo the upper and lower screws securing the window rear guide channel to the door.
6  Remove the rubber guide channel from the door frame.
7  Tilt the rear guide channel towards the front and withdraw the fixed window from its location. Now remove the rear guide channel from the door.
8  Tip the window forwards and lift it up and out of the door.
9  Refitting is the reverse sequence to removal.

---

### 33  Interior rear view mirror – removal and refitting

**Note**: *It is not possible to remove the mirror base, which is bonded to the windscreen with adhesive, without breaking the mirror. However, if the mirror should become detached, or if a new mirror is being fitted to a new windscreen, the following procedure should be used for fitting.*
1  Clean the inside of the windscreen and the base of the mirror with trichlorethylene or a similar solvent and allow to air dry.
2  Apply a strip of adhesive tape to the outside of the windscreen so that its top edge is 45 mm (1.77 in) below the seal lower edge. Measure the width of the windscreen and then mark its centre on the tape. The base of the mirror should be positioned centrally, with the tape mark as a reference, and with its top edge level with the top edge of the tape.
3  Obtain a quantity of Loctite 312 from a Renault dealer and then spray the activator onto the inside of the glass in the bonding zone.
4  Allow the activator to dry, then apply the adhesive to the mirror base. Immediately place the mirror base against the glass and hold it firmly for at least one minute. The adhesive will be fully set after approximately one hour.

---

### 34  Exterior rear view mirror – removal and refitting

#### Standard mirror
1  Unclip and remove the door trim strip.
2  Carefully ease off the triangular facing panel to gain access to the mirror retaining screws.
3  Undo the three screws and remove the mirror from the door.
4  Refitting is the reverse sequence to removal.

#### Remote control mirror
5  Unclip and remove the door trim strip.
6  Undo the retaining screw at the base of the triangular facing panel.
7  Wind the window down and undo the screw securing the remote control mechanism to the facing panel and lift off the panel.
8  Push the rubber grommet in the centre of the mirror mount through, using a screwdriver.
9  Undo the three screws and remove the mirror and control mechanism from the door.
10  Refitting is the reverse sequence to removal.

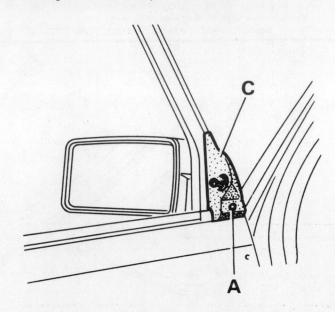

Fig. 11.31 Exterior rear view mirror facing panel (C) and panel retaining screw (A) (Sec 34)

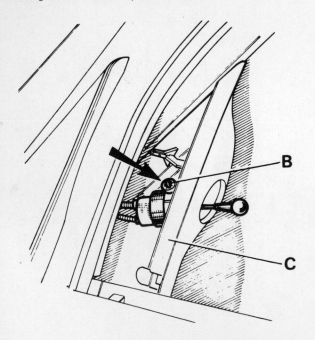

Fig. 11.32 Exterior rear view mirror remote control mechanism attachment (B) to facing panel (C) (Sec 34)

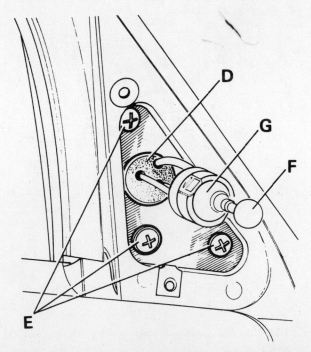

Fig. 11.33 Exterior rear view mirror rubber grommet (D), mount retaining screws (E), ball end (F) and ball socket (G) (Sec 34)

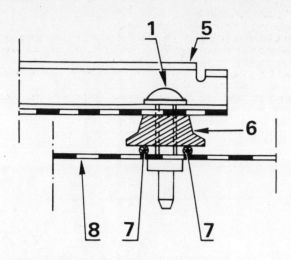

**Fig. 11.34 Front seat rail mounting arrangement (Sec 35)**

| 1 | Retaining bolt | 7 | Seal |
|---|---|---|---|
| 5 | Seat rail | 8 | Floorpan |
| 6 | Spacer | | |

---

**35 Front and rear seats – removal and refitting**

*Front seat – all models*

1   Slide the seat forwards as far as it will go and undo the two bolts securing the seat rails to the floor at the rear.

2   Now slide the seat fully back and undo the two seat rail retaining bolts at the front.
3   Remove the seat from the car and recover the spacers and seals fitted between the rails and the floor.
4   Refitting is the reverse sequence to removal.

*Rear seat – Renault 9*

5   To remove the seat cushion, withdraw the two tabs at the front securing the cushion tubular legs to the locating plates on the floor.
6   Lift the cushion at the front to release the legs from the plates and remove the cushion from the car.
7   To remove the seat back, simply lift it upwards to disengage the tongues at the back from their locating slots.
8   Refitting is the reverse sequence to removal, but push the cushion well in at the back then push it down firmly at the front so that the legs enter the locating plates. Ensure that the tabs locate properly over the cushion legs.

*Rear seat – Renault 11*

9   To remove the seat cushion, tip it forwards, undo the bolts securing the cushion to the hinge and withdraw the cushion.
10  To remove the seat back, tip the cushion forwards and release the seat back catch.
11  Undo the bolts securing the seat back to the floor and remove it from the car.
12  Refitting is the reverse sequence to removal.

---

**36 Interior trim mouldings – removal and refitting**

*Windscreen frame side trim*

1   Undo the two screws securing the grab handle above the door and remove the handle.

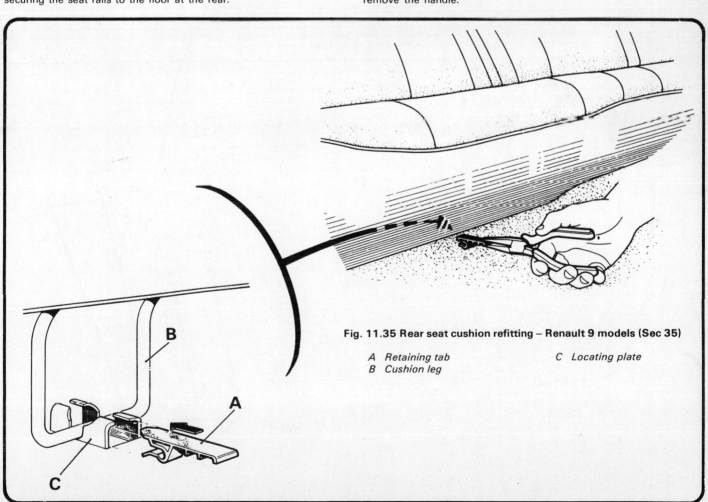

**Fig. 11.35 Rear seat cushion refitting – Renault 9 models (Sec 35)**

| A | Retaining tab | C | Locating plate |
|---|---|---|---|
| B | Cushion leg | | |

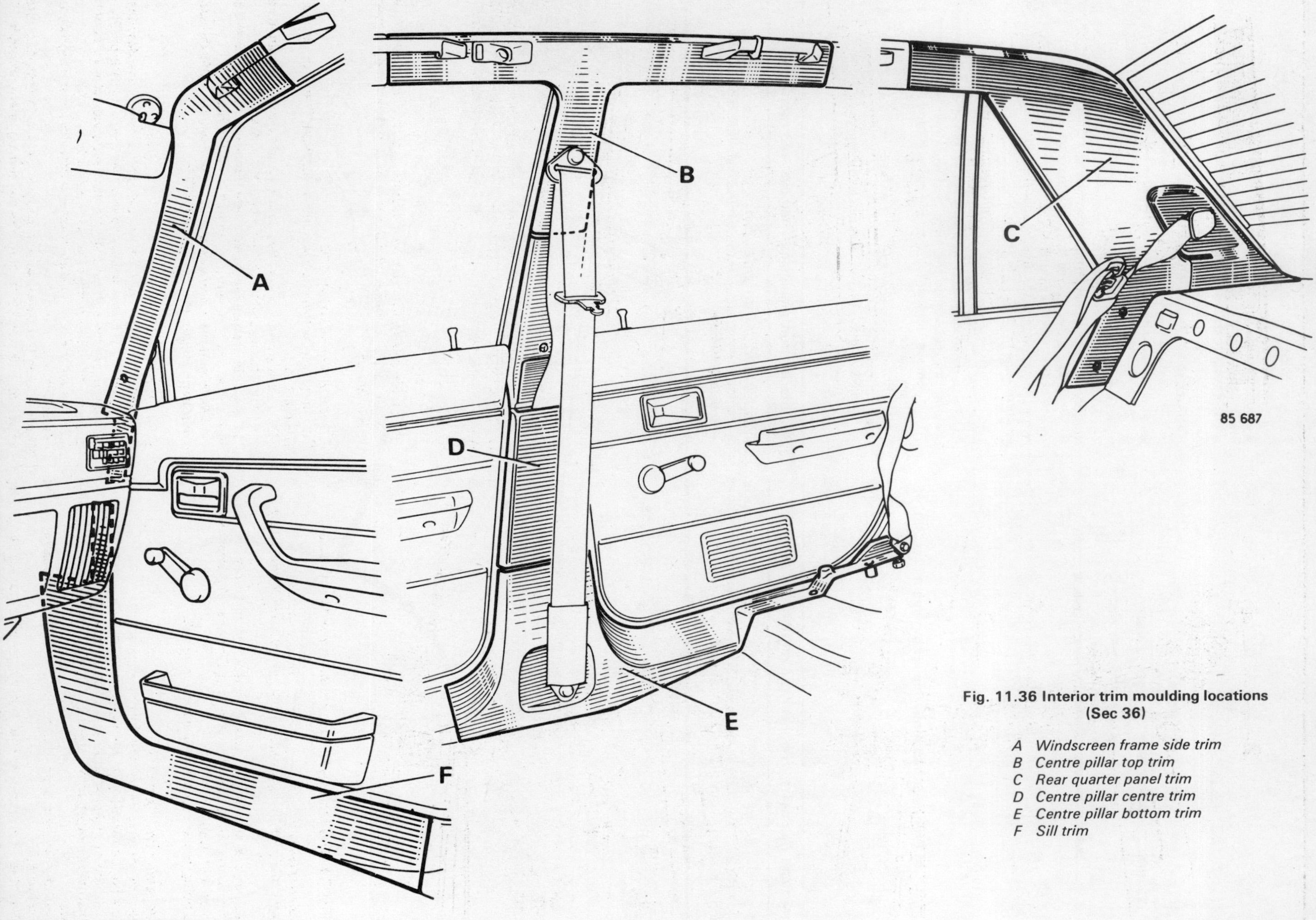

85 687

Fig. 11.36 Interior trim moulding locations (Sec 36)

A  Windscreen frame side trim
B  Centre pillar top trim
C  Rear quarter panel trim
D  Centre pillar centre trim
E  Centre pillar bottom trim
F  Sill trim

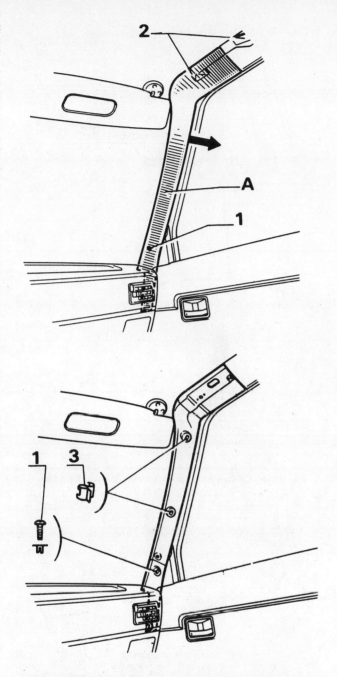

Fig. 11.37 Windscreen frame side trim details (Sec 36)

1  Trim retaining screw              3  Retaining clips
2  Grab handle retaining screws      A  Windscreen frame side trim

2   Release the trim button over the side trim retaining screw and
undo the screw. Slide the trim to the rear to release the retaining clips
and remove it from the pillar.
3   Refitting is the reverse sequence to removal.

## Centre pillar top trim
4   Disconnect the battery negative terminal.
5   Remove the windscreen frame side trim, as previously described.
6   Undo the retaining screws and remove the grab handle.
7   Undo the seat belt upper mounting bolt, referring to Section 38 if
necessary.
8   Ease the interior lamp out of its location and disconnect the
electrical leads.
9   Move the trim to the rear to disengage the two retaining clips,
then remove the trim from the pillar.

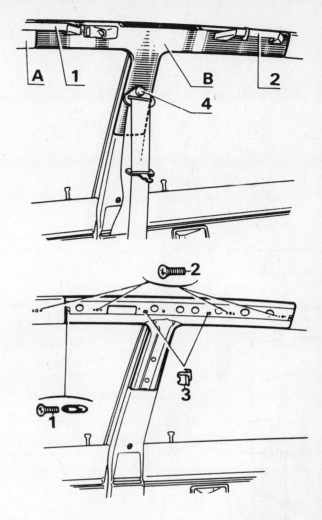

Fig. 11.38 Centre pillar top trim details (Sec 36)

1  Grab handle and retaining screws   4  Seat belt upper mounting
2  Grab handle and retaining screws   A  Windscreen frame side trim
3  Retaining clips                    B  Centre pillar top trim

10  Refitting is the reverse sequence to removal, but ensure that the
seat belt upper mounting components are correctly fitted, as described
in Section 38.

## Centre pillar centre trim
11  Undo the seat belt upper and lower mountings, as described in
Section 38.
12  Lift the lower edge of the centre pillar top trim to gain access to
the centre trim retaining screw and undo the screw.
13  Undo the remaining screw, pass the seat belt through the slot in
the centre trim and remove the trim from the pillar.
14  Refitting is the reverse sequence to removal, but refit the seat belt
mountings, as described in Section 38.

## Centre pillar bottom trim
15  Remove the centre pillar centre trim, as previously described.
16  Remove the rear seat cushion, as described in Section 35.
17  Undo the two screws at the top and two screws at the rear
securing the trim to the pillar and rear floor.
18  Manipulate the trim to release it from the retaining clips, then
remove it from the car.
19  Refitting is the reverse sequence to removal. Transfer the retaining
clips from the body to the trim by turning them through 90° to
remove. Now slide them into their slots in the trim.

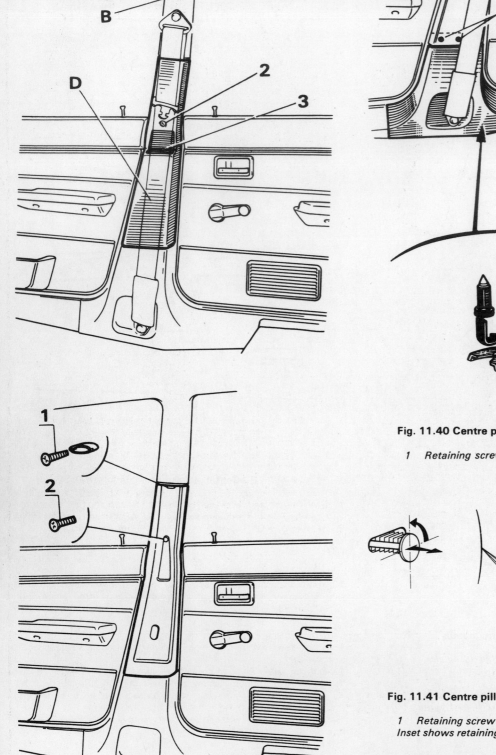

**Fig. 11.39 Centre pillar centre trim details (Sec 36)**

1  Retaining screws          B  Centre pillar top trim
2  Retaining screws          D  Centre pillar centre trim
3  Seat belt slot in trim

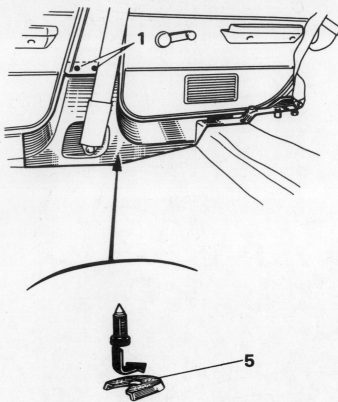

**Fig. 11.40 Centre pillar bottom trim details (Sec 36)**

1   Retaining screws          5   Retaining clip

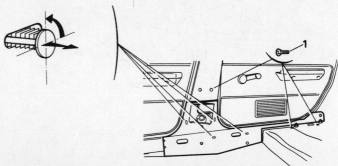

**Fig. 11.41 Centre pillar bottom trim attachments (Sec 36)**

1   Retaining screw locations
Inset shows retaining clip locations and removal sequence

*Rear quarter panel trim*
20  Remove the centre pillar top trim, as previously described.
21  On Renault 11 models remove the side parcel shelves, as described later in this Section, and on two-door models the seat side panel, by easing it out to free the retaining clips.
22  On Renault 9 models remove the rear seat, as described in Section 35.
23  Undo the single upper and two lower screws securing the trim to the body.

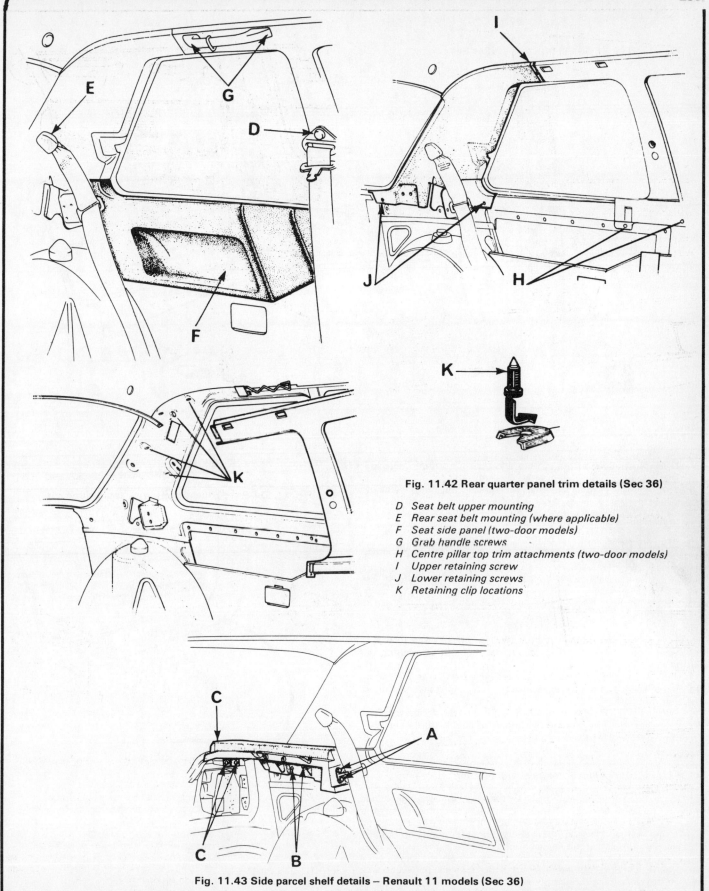

**Fig. 11.42 Rear quarter panel trim details (Sec 36)**

D  Seat belt upper mounting
E  Rear seat belt mounting (where applicable)
F  Seat side panel (two-door models)
G  Grab handle screws
H  Centre pillar top trim attachments (two-door models)
I  Upper retaining screw
J  Lower retaining screws
K  Retaining clip locations

**Fig. 11.43 Side parcel shelf details – Renault 11 models (Sec 36)**

A  Seat back striker plate retaining bolts     B  Retaining screw locations     C  Retaining screw locations

**Fig. 11.44 Sill trim details (Sec 36)**

1  *Rear retaining screws*
5  *Retaining clip locations*

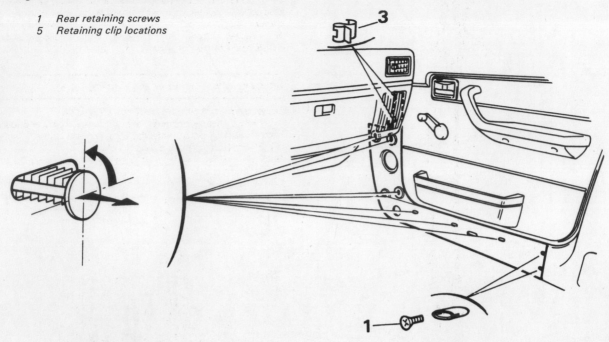

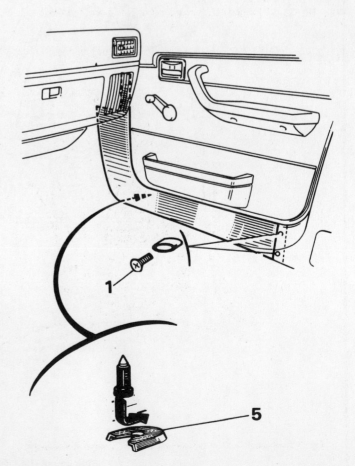

24  Pull the panel out at the bottom and then forwards to release it from the retaining clips. Remove the trim from the car.
25  Refitting is the reverse sequence to removal. Transfer the retaining clips from the body to the trim by turning them through 90° to remove. Now slide them into their slots in the trim.

*Side parcel shelves*
26  Undo the two seat back striker plate bolts and remove the striker plate.
27  Undo the five screws securing the shelf to the body and remove the shelf.
28  Refitting is the reverse sequence to removal.

*Sill trim*
29  Remove the centre pillar bottom trim, as previously described.
30  Remove the two bonnet release handle bolts, if working on the left-hand sill trim.
31  Undo the two screws at the rear securing the trim to the body.
32  Pull the trim to the rear to release the retaining clips and remove the trim from the car.
33  Refitting is the reverse sequence to removal. Transfer the peg type retaining clips from the body to the trim by turning them through 90° to remove. Now slide them into their slots in the trim.

## 37  Exterior trim panels – removal and refitting

1  The exterior trim panels consist of the side protective mouldings fitted to the doors of certain Renault 11 models, the thinner trim strip fitted to the doors and wings of Renault 9 models, the trim panel behind the rear side fixed window and the boot lid or tailgate spoiler.
2  The side protective mouldings are held at the top by spring clips engaging with welded rivets and by screws along the bottom. To remove a moulding, undo the screws and then slide the panel upwards and off the clips. Take care not to scratch the paintwork by pushing a sheet of thin card down behind the moulding before moving it upwards. If any of the clips require renewal, have your dealer do this as a special gun is needed to fit the welded rivets.
3  The door and wing trim strips are retained by clips. Carefully lift

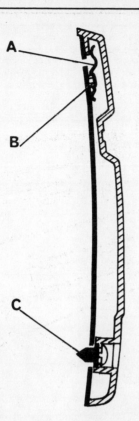

**Fig. 11.45 Exterior trim panel side protective moulding attachments (Sec 37)**

A  *Spring clip*      C  *Retaining screw*
B  *Welded rivet*

the bottom of the strip using a screwdriver to free it from the clips, then lift upwards to remove.

4  The side window trim panel is secured by welded rivets which must be drilled out to remove the panel. If removal is necessary leave this to your dealer as a special gun is needed to fit the new welded rivets.

5  The rear spoiler is retained by bolts and clips accessible from inside the boot lid or tailgate.

## 38 Seat belts – removal and refitting

### Side belt and inertia reel mechanism

1  Lift off the trim buttons, then undo the upper and lower side seat belt anchorage bolts. Note the arrangement of the spacers, washers and distance sleeves at each anchorage.

2  Refer to Section 36 and remove the centre pillar bottom trim and centre pillar centre trim.

3  With the trim removed, undo the bolt securing the inertia reel to

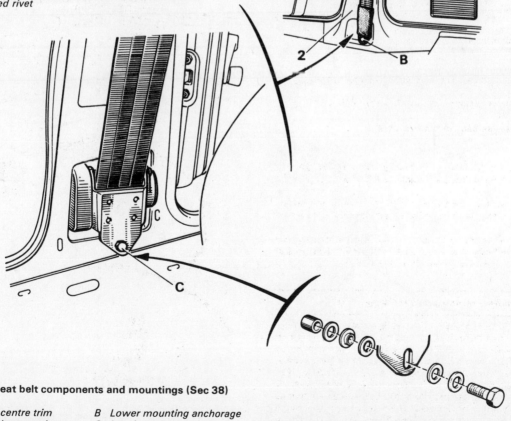

**Fig. 11.46 Seat belt components and mountings (Sec 38)**

1  *Centre pillar centre trim*      B  *Lower mounting anchorage*
2  *Centre pillar bottom trim*      C  *Inertia reel mounting*
A  *Upper mounting anchorage*

the base of the door pillar and remove the seat belt assembly from the car.

4   Refitting is the reverse sequence to removal, but ensure that the spacers, washers and sleeve are fitted as shown in Fig. 11.46, and tighten the anchorage bolts to the specified torque.

### Centre flexible stalks

5   Access to the centre stalks is rather limited as the one-piece carpet covers the retaining bolts. Lift the carpet at the rear and remove any trim panels as necessary until it is possible to reach the retaining bolts.

6   Undo the bolts with a socket or spanner and withdraw the stalk through the hole in the carpet.

7   Refitting is the reverse sequence to removal, but tighten the retaining bolt to the specified torque.

## 39 Front bumper – removal and refitting

1   Remove the radiator grille, as described in Section 10 and, where fitted, the front foglamps, as described in Chapter 9. On Renault 11 models remove the front direction indicator lens assemblies, also as described in Chapter 9.

2   Where fitted, partly release the trim moulding or prise out the plastic caps to gain access to the side retaining screws. Undo the Torx screws using a suitable splined key (photo).

3   Working under the wheel arch, undo the bolts securing the bumper to the front wings.

4   From underneath the bumper, undo the two bolts securing it to the front subframe (photo).

5   Prise out the clips securing the bumper impact-absorbing element to the body in the radiator grille aperture.

39.2 Front bumper side retaining screw

39.4 Front bumper-to-subframe retaining bolt

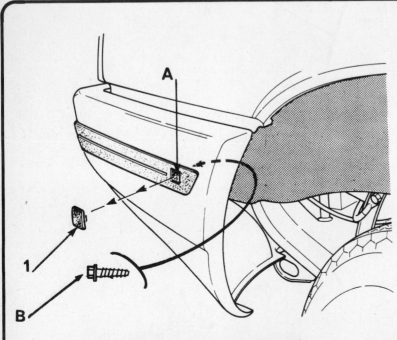

**Fig. 11.47 Front bumper side mounting (Sec 39)**

1   *Plastic cap*                          B   *Retaining screw*
A   *Retaining screw location*

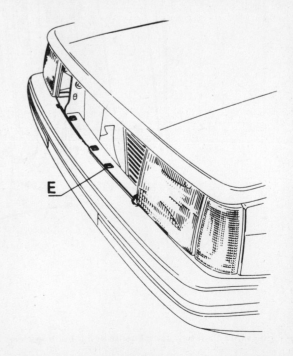

**Fig. 11.48 Front bumper retaining clips (E) (Sec 39)**

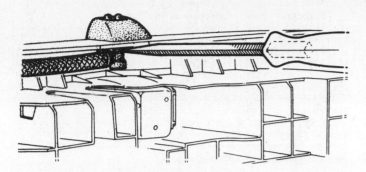

**Fig. 11.49 Removal of the washer pipes from the front bumper headlamp washer jet union (Sec 39)**

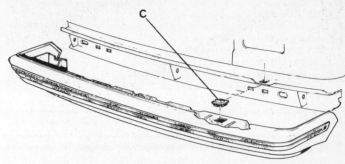

**Fig. 11.50 Renault 11 rear bumper upper retaining clips (C) must be renewed after bumper removal (Sec 40)**

6   Withdraw the bumper assembly from the car and, where fitted, ease the headlamp washer pipes from the washer jet union, using a screwdriver.

7   Refitting is the reverse sequence to removal.

### 40 Rear bumper – removal and refitting

1   Where fitted, partly release the trim moulding or prise out the plastic caps to gain access to the side retaining screws. Undo the Torx type screws using a suitable splined key.

2   On Renault 9 models, lift up the carpet in the luggage compartment and prise out the four clips at the rear (photo). Withdraw the bumper from the car.

3   On Renault 11 models, firmly pull the bumper to the rear to release the four upper retaining clips and remove the bumper from the car.

4   Refitting is the reverse sequence to removal. On Renault 11 models it will be necessary to renew the four upper retaining clips as the old ones will be damaged during removal.

### 41 Centre console – removal and refitting

1   Disconnect the battery negative terminal.

2   Withdraw the console oddments trays by tipping them sideways and removing from their apertures (photo).

3   Withdraw the console switches by carefully prising out the side or the top to release the retaining catches, withdraw the multi-plug connector and remove the switch (photo). If a clock is fitted to the console, this is removed in the same way.

4   On Renault 9 models, press the heater control panel on the right-hand side then, using a thin screwdriver or feeler blade, release the catches on the left-hand side (photo).

40.2 Renault 9 rear bumper retaining clip in luggage compartment

41.2 Withdraw the centre console oddments trays

41.3 Release the switches and disconnect the wiring multi-plugs

41.4 Push the heater control panel in and release the catches using a screwdriver or thin blade

41.6 Undo the two retaining screws around the gear lever housing (arrowed)

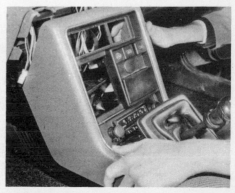

41.8 Release the catches at the top and lift out the console

5   Remove the cigarette lighter, if fitted, as described in Chapter 9.
6   Lift up the gear lever gaiter and undo the two screws securing the console to the gear lever housing (photo).
7   Reach through the console top apertures and release the catches securing the console to the facia.
8   Lift the console up at the rear and free it from the facia. Disconnect the radio wiring, where applicable, lift the console over the gear lever and remove it from the car (photo).
9   Refitting is the reverse sequence to removal.

## 42 Facia – removal and refitting

1   Referring to the appropriate Sections of Chapter 9 remove the instrument panel, facia switches, as applicable, and the accessory plate from its location under the glovebox.

2   Refer to Chapter 10 and remove the steering wheel.
3   Refer to Chapter 3 and remove the choke cable.
4   Refer to Section 41 of this Chapter and remove the centre console.
5   On Renault 11 models, release the heater control panel by pressing it on the right-hand side and releasing the catches on the left-hand side with a thin screwdriver or feeler blade.
6   Undo the screws securing the steering column lower shroud half to the steering column, facia and upper shroud half. Lift off the shroud, disconnect the electrical wiring, as applicable, and remove the shroud.
7   Undo the shroud upper half retaining screws, disconnect the windscreen wiper/washer switch wiring and remove the switch.
8   Undo the retaining screws, disconnect the wiring, and remove the lighting/direction indicator switch.
9   Refer to Figs 11.51 or 11.52 and undo the facia retaining screws at the positions shown.

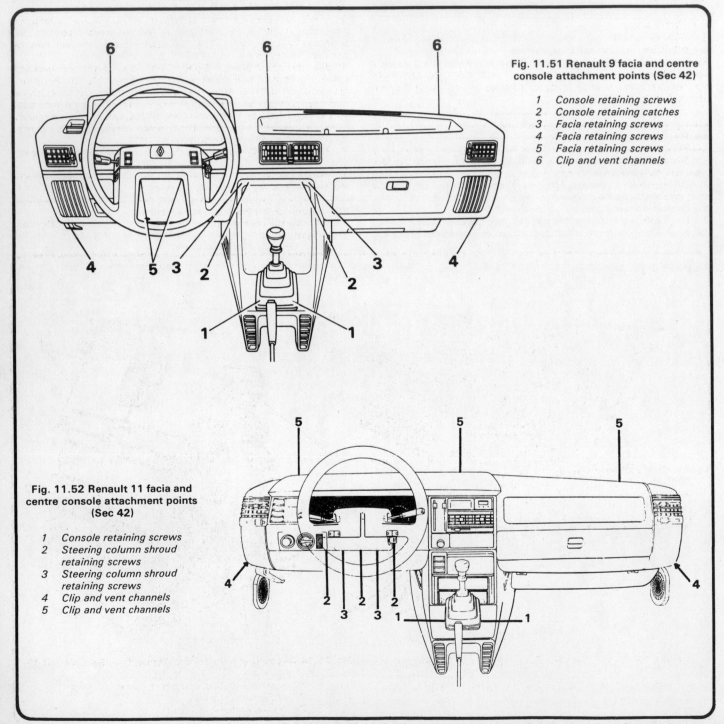

Fig. 11.51 Renault 9 facia and centre console attachment points (Sec 42)

1   Console retaining screws
2   Console retaining catches
3   Facia retaining screws
4   Facia retaining screws
5   Facia retaining screws
6   Clip and vent channels

Fig. 11.52 Renault 11 facia and centre console attachment points (Sec 42)

1   Console retaining screws
2   Steering column shroud retaining screws
3   Steering column shroud retaining screws
4   Clip and vent channels
5   Clip and vent channels

10 Disconnect any additional wiring according to vehicle optional equipment, lift the facia to free the upper clips and vent channels and remove it from the car.

11 Refitting is the reverse sequence to removal, but ensure that the vent channels locate correctly as the facia is fitted.

## 43 Heater control – adjustments

*Temperature control*

1 Move the temperature control knob on the heater control panel down to the cold position.

2 From under the facia, check that the warm/cold air flap lever on the side of the heater is closed. If not, release the clip securing the operating cable in position, move the cable until the flap is closed, then refit the clip.

*Air distribution*

3 Slide the air distribution knob on the heater control panel down to the side window distribution position.

4 From under the facia check that the operating lever on the side of the heater has closed both air distribution flaps. If not, release the clip securing the operating cable in position, move the cable until the flaps are closed, then refit the clip.

## 44 Heater – removal and refitting

**Note:** *The following procedure describes the removal of the complete heater assembly. It is, however, possible to remove the fan motor individually without disturbing the heater, and this operation is described in Section 46.*

1 Remove the facia, as described in Section 42.

2 From within the engine compartment, clamp the two heater hoses using self-locking wrenches or suitable clamps. Slacken the hose clips

and detach the hoses from the matrix outlets. Plug the outlets to prevent coolant spillage in the car.

3 Disconnect the fan motor wiring at the harness connectors.

4 Undo the four screws securing the heater to the bulkhead and remove the heater from the car.

5 Refitting is the reverse sequence to removal. Top up the cooling system after refitting and, if the heater control cables were disturbed, adjust them, as described in Section 43.

## 45 Heater – dismantling and reassembly

1 With the heater removed, as described in the previous Section, withdraw the fan and motor by pulling it upwards to release the retaining clips.

2 At the side of the heater, bend up the tabs securing the matrix in position and slide the matrix out of the heater casing.

3 If it is wished to dismantle the heater further, remove the retaining clips around the casing joint and in the fan motor aperture, and separate the two halves. The flap valves and levers can now be removed as necessary.

4 Examine the matrix for signs of leaks and, if any are apparent, renew the matrix. If the matrix appears serviceable, brush off any accumulation of dirt or debris from the fins and then reverse-flush the core. Inspect the remaining heater components for any sign of damage or distortion. Note that only the motor, matrix, wiring and controls are available as separate components, all other parts are supplied only as part of a complete heater assembly.

5 Reassemble the heater using the reverse sequence to removal.

## 46 Heater fan – removal and refitting

1 Disconnect the battery negative terminal.

2 Remove the bonnet rubber seal from the body flange at the base of the windscreen

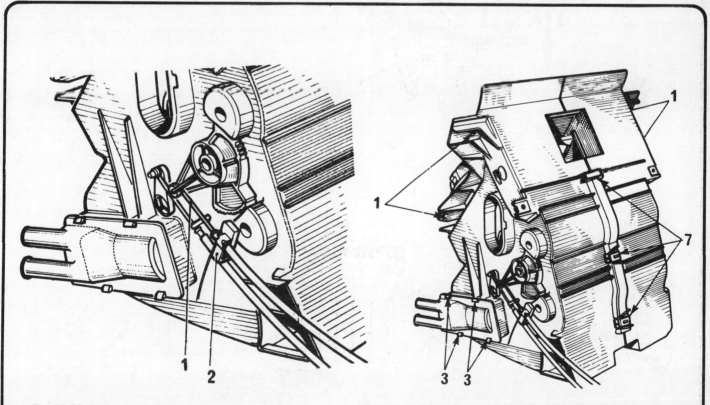

**Fig. 11.53 Heater control adjustment points (Sec 43)**

*1   Operating cable          2   Cable retaining clip*

**Fig. 11.54 Heater unit removal and dismantling (Secs 44 and 45)**

*1   Heater-to-bulkhead retaining screw locations*
*3   Matrix retaining tabs*
*7   Heater casing joint clips*

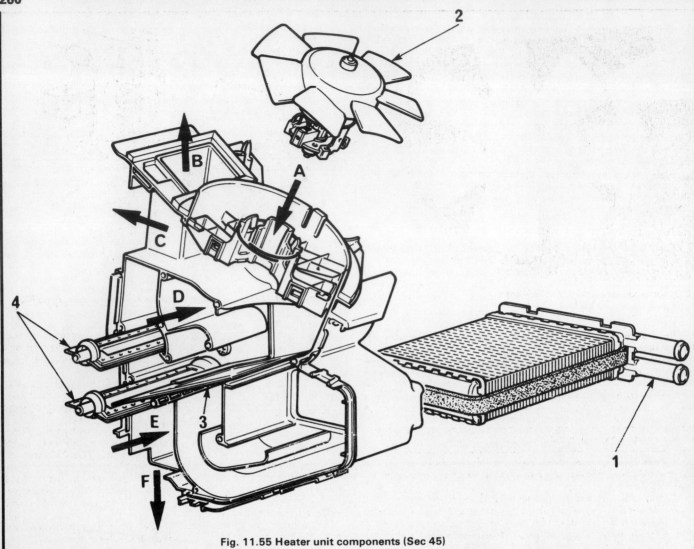

**Fig. 11.55 Heater unit components (Sec 45)**

| | | |
|---|---|---|
| 1 Matrix | 4 Air distribution flaps | C Air to centre ventilator | E Air to bottom ventilators |
| 2 Fan assembly | A Air intake | D Air to side ventilators | F Air to console ventilators |
| 3 Air temperature control flap | B Air to windscreen demister | | |

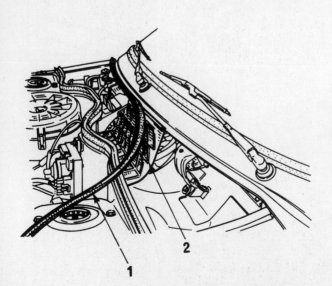

**Fig. 11.56 Bonnet rubber seal (1) and heater fan cover panel (2) (Sec 46)**

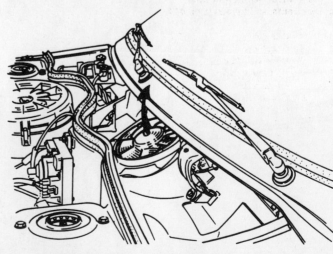

**Fig. 11.57 Heater fan removal (Sec 46)**

46.3 Heater fan location in front bulkhead

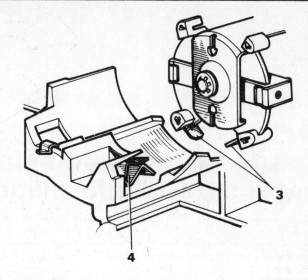

Fig. 11.58 Heater fan locating tabs (3) and retaining clips (4) (Sec 46)

3   Undo the wing nuts and lift out the cover panel to gain access to the fan assembly (photo).
4   Lift the motor and fan assembly upwards to release it from the retaining clips, disconnect the motor wiring and remove the assembly from the car.
5   Refitting is the reverse sequence to removal, but ensure that the tabs on the motor case locate in the clips on the housing.

## 47  Air conditioner – general

1   The following general points should be considered when operating, or working on, models equipped with air conditioning as a factory-fitted option.
2   During winter when the air conditioner is not in use, operate it for a few minutes each week to keep it lubricated and in good order.
3   At regular intervals inspect the refrigerant through the sight glass of the receiver dryer. The appearance of bubbles in the glass for the first few minutes of operation is normal, but if they continue to be visible, the refrigerant level is low and should be topped up by your dealer. Keep the compressor belt tensioned to give a deflection of 4 mm (0.16 in) on the longest run of the belt using moderate finger pressure.
4   The refrigerant used is Freon 12 which is odourless, non-poisonous, non-inflammable and non-corrosive, except when it comes into contact with a naked flame when a poison gas is created. Avoid contacting the refrigerant with the skin or eyes.
5   On cars equipped with an air conditioner, components of the system (compressor, condensor etc) may be unbolted and moved within the limits of travel of their flexible connecting hoses in order to facilitate engine overhaul.
6   **Never** disconnect any part of the system yourself, but if this is essential for access to parts being worked on, have the system discharged by your dealer or refrigeration engineer and recharged again on completion of the work.
7   It is important that all disconnected components of the system are sealed pending reconnection to prevent the entry of moisture.
8   Occasionally clean the fins of the condenser free of dirt and flies.

**Fig. 11.59 Air conditioner components and layout (Sec 47)**

1  Compressor
2  Condenser
3  Receiver/dryer
4  Reducing valve
5  Evaporator
6  Fan assembly
A  High pressure bleed
B  Low pressure bleed

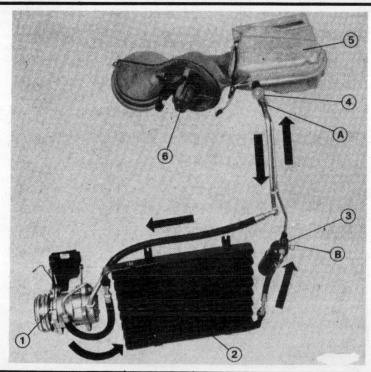

# Chapter 12 Supplement:
# Revisions and information on later models

## Contents

## 1  Introduction

This Supplement contains information which is additional to, or a revision of, material given in the first eleven Chapters. It contains mainly information on modifications and model changes introduced since approximately 1984 including the introduction of Turbo models.

The Sections in the Supplement follow the same order as the Chapters to which they relate. The Specifications are grouped together for convenience, but they too follow Chapter order.

It is recommended that before any particular operation is undertaken, reference be made to the appropriate Section(s) of the Supplement, in order to establish any changes to procedure or components in the main Chapters.

### Project vehicle

The vehicle used in the preparation of the Supplement, and appearing in many of the photographic sequences, was a 1988 model Renault 11 Turbo.

## 2  Specifications

*The Specifications given below are supplementary to, or revisions of, those given at the beginning of the preceding Chapters.*

### Engine – 1108 cc (1986 on)

**Cylinder head**
Minimum height after resurfacing ............................................................... 69.65 mm

### Engine  1237 cc
*Specifications as for the 1397 cc engine in Chapter 1, except for the following:*

**General**
Designation ................................................................................................... C1G-710
Bore ............................................................................................................... 71.5 mm

**Cylinder head**
Cylinder head height..................................................................................... 70.60 mm
Minimum height after resurfacing ............................................................... 70.10 mm
Maximum permitted warp............................................................................. 0.05 mm

### Engine – 1397 cc non-Turbo (1986 on)

**Cylinder head**
Minimum height after resurfacing ............................................................... 71.70 mm

### Engine – 1397 cc Turbo
*Specifications as for 1397 cc engine given in Chapter 1, except for the following:*

**General**
Designation:
    Pre-October 1986 models................................................................... C1J-L7-60
    October 1986-on models.................................................................... C1J-770
Compression ratio:
    Pre-October 1986 models................................................................... 8.0 : 1
    October 1986-on models.................................................................... 7.9 : 1
Lubrication system pressure:
    At 750 rpm.......................................................................................... 1.3 bar (19 lbf/in$^2$)
    At 4000 rpm........................................................................................ 3.2 bar (46 lbf/in$^2$)
Oil filter.......................................................................................................... Champion F124 (1984 to 1988)

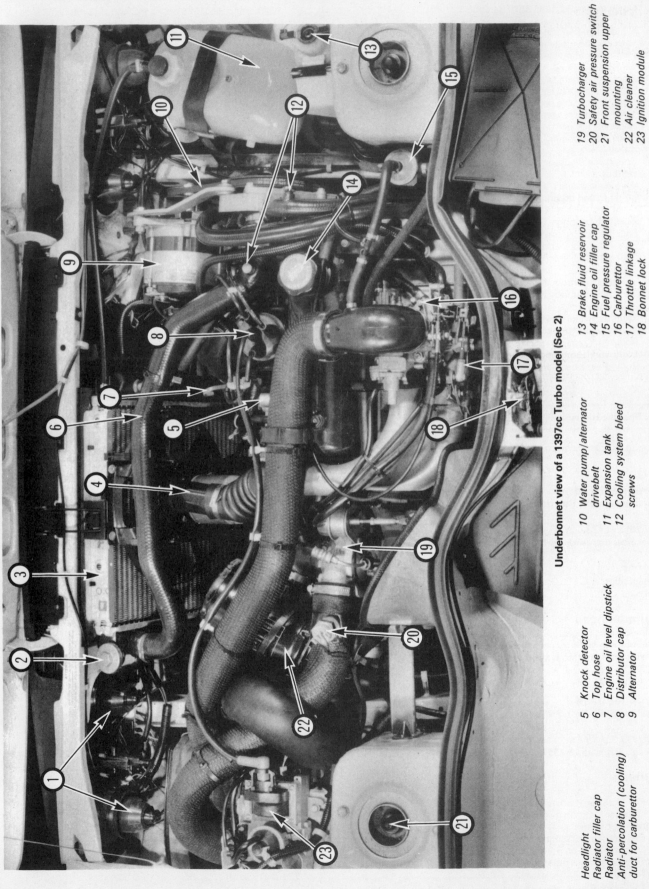

**Underbonnet view of a 1397cc Turbo model (Sec 2)**

| | | | |
|---|---|---|---|
| 1 Headlight | 5 Knock detector | 10 Water pump/alternator | 13 Brake fluid reservoir | 19 Turbocharger |
| 2 Radiator filler cap | 6 Top hose | drivebelt | 14 Engine oil filler cap | 20 Safety air pressure switch |
| 3 Radiator | 7 Engine oil level dipstick | 11 Expansion tank | 15 Fuel pressure regulator | 21 Front suspension upper |
| 4 Anti-percolation (cooling) | 8 Distributor cap | 12 Cooling system bleed | 16 Carburettor | mounting |
| duct for carburettor | 9 Alternator | screws | 17 Throttle linkage | 22 Air cleaner |
| | | | 18 Bonnet lock | 23 Ignition module |

## Cylinder head
Cylinder head height (no resurfacing allowed)................................................ 73.5 mm

## Valves
Valve spring free length.............................................................................. 46.9 mm
Inlet valve guide fitted height..................................................................... 27.5 mm
Valve clearances (cold):
    Inlet.......................................................................................................... 0.20 mm (0.008 in)
    Exhaust..................................................................................................... 0.25 mm (0.010 in)

## Crankshaft
Crankshaft endfloat..................................................................................... 0.07 to 0.23 mm

## *Cooling system*
## General
Thermostatic switch for electric cooling fan:
    Switch-on temperature............................................................................. 88°C (190°F)
    Switch-off temperature............................................................................ 79°C (174°F)
System capacity (including heater):
    1237 cc engine......................................................................................... 5.8 litres (10.2 Imp pints)
    1721 cc engine......................................................................................... 6.5 litres (11.4 Imp pints)

## *Fuel and exhaust systems (non-Turbo models)*
## Carburettor data
Zenith 32 1F 2:
    Type identification number........................................................................ **V 10506**
    Venturi..................................................................................................... 24
    Main jet................................................................................................... 132
    Idling jet................................................................................................... 59
    Air compensating jet................................................................................ 90 x 200
    Pneumatic enrichment jet ........................................................................ 100
    Accelerator pump stroke.......................................................................... 27.8
    Accelerator pump jet................................................................................ 50
    Accelerator pump delivery tube setting .................................................... 60
    Fuel needle valve ..................................................................................... 1.25
    Float height.............................................................................................. 13.55 to 13.75
    Auxiliary jet.............................................................................................. 120
    Auxiliary tube height................................................................................. 6.0 mm
    Defuming valve setting............................................................................. 2.0 mm
    Initial throttle opening.............................................................................. 0.80 mm
    Pneumatic part opening setting ............................................................... 2.9 mm
    Idling speed............................................................................................. 600 to 650 rpm
    CO mixture .............................................................................................. 0.5 to 1.5%

Weber 32 DRT:

| Type identification number | 101/201 | | 2 | | 3 | |
|---|---|---|---|---|---|---|
| | **1st** | **2nd** | **1st** | **2nd** | **1st** | **2nd** |
| Venturi | 23 | 24 | 23 | 24 | 23 | 24 |
| Main jet | 105 | 110 | 107 | 107 | 107 | 107 |
| Air compensating jet | 240 | 160 | 220 | 135 | 220 | 135 |
| Idling jet | 45 | 60 | 52 | 70 | 52 | 70 |
| Mixture centralizer | 4R | 4R | 4 | 4R | 4 | 4R |
| Emulsifier | F58 | F56 | F58 | F56 | F58 | F56 |
| Enrichment | 55 | | 55 | | 55 | |
| Needle valve | 1.75 | | 1.75 | | 1.75 | |
| Float level | 8.00 mm | | 8.00 mm | | 8.00 mm | |
| Float travel | 13.0 mm | | 13.0 mm | | 13.0 mm | |
| Accelerator pump jet | 50 | | 40 | | 40 | |
| Initial throttle opening | 1.00 mm | | 0.75 mm | | 0.9 mm | |
| Pneumatic part opening setting | 4.0 mm | | 3.5 mm | | 3.5 mm | |
| Defuming valve | 0.3 mm | | 0.3 mm | | 0.3 mm | |
| Idling speed | 625 to 675 rpm | | 675 to 725 rpm | | 575 to 625 rpm | |
| CO mixture | 1.0 to 2.0% | | 1.0 to 2.0% | | 0.5 to 1.5% | |

Weber 32 DRT:
    Type identification number........................................................................ **100**
    As 101/201 except for the following:
    Float travel.............................................................................................. 5.0 mm
    Initial throttle opening.............................................................................. 0.9 mm
    Pneumatic part opening setting ............................................................... 8.0 mm

Solex 32 BIS:

| | | |
|---|---|---|
| Type identification number | **797** | **829-829C** |
| Venturi | 23 | 24 |
| Main jet | 110 | 117.5 |
| Idling jet | 38 | 43 |
| Air compensating jet | 150 | 155 |

## Carburettor data (Solex 32 BIS) (continued)

| | 797 | 829-829C |
|---|---|---|
| Enrichment | 45 | 60 |
| Needle valve | 1.3 | 1.8 |
| Accelerator pump jet | 45 | 40 |
| Initial throttle opening | 0.65 mm | 0.75 mm |
| Defuming valve | 2.5 to 3.5 m | 2.5 to 3.5 mm |
| Accelerator pump clearance | 1.8 mm | 1.5 mm |
| Idling speed | 625 to 675 rpm | 600 to 650 rpm |
| CO mixture | 0.5 to 1.5% | 0.5 to 1.5% |

### Solex 32 BIS:

| | 918 |
|---|---|
| Type identification number | **918** |
| Venturi | 24 |
| Main jet | 115 |
| Idling jet | 115 |
| Air compensating jet | 155 |
| Enrichment device | 50 |
| Needle valve | 1.3 |
| Accelerator pump jet | 40 |
| Initial throttle opening | 0.70 mm |
| Defuming valve travel | 2.5 to 3.5 mm |
| Accelerator pump clearance | Cam type |
| Idling speed | 625 to 675 rpm |
| CO mixture | 1.0 to 2.0% |

### Solex 28-34 Z10:

| | 920 | |
|---|---|---|
| Identification number | **920** | |
| | **1st** | **2nd** |
| Venturi | 20 | 27 |
| Main jet | 102 | 145 |
| Idling jet | 47 | 50 |
| Air compensating jet | 210 | 190 |
| Econostat | – | 120 |
| Enrichner | 50 | – |
| Accelerator pump injector | 40 | 35 |
| Needle valve | 1.8 | |
| Float level | 33.5 mm | |
| Initial throttle opening (fast idle) | 1.0 mm to 35° 30′ | |
| Defuming valve setting | 2.0 mm | |
| Pneumatic part-opening setting | 2.0 to 2.4 mm | |
| Idle speed | 700 ± 50 rpm | |
| Fast idling speed* | 1050 ± 50 rpm | |
| CO mixture | 1.5 ± 0.5% | |

* Models equipped with power steering

### Solex 28-34 Z10:

| | 943 | |
|---|---|---|
| Identification number | **943** | |
| As for 920 except for the following: | **1st** | **2nd** |
| Main jet | 97.5 | 145 |
| Idling jet | 46 | 50 |
| Air compensating jet | 200 | 190 |
| Idle speed | 800 ± 50 rpm | |

### Solex 32-34 Z13:

| | 928 | |
|---|---|---|
| Identification number | **928** | |
| | **1st** | **2nd** |
| Venturi | 24 | 27 |
| Main jet | 115 | 137.5 |
| Idling jet | 43 | 50 |
| Econostat | – | 120 |
| Enrichner | 50 | – |
| Accelerator pump injector | 40 | 35 |
| Needle valve | 1.8 | |
| Float level | 33.5 mm | |
| Initial throttle opening (fast idle) | 0.75 mm or 22° 30′ | |
| Defuming valve setting | 0.3 mm | |
| Pneumatic part-opening setting | 3.5 mm | |
| Idle speed | 800 ± 50 rpm | |
| Fast idle speed* | 1050 ± 50 rpm | |
| CO mixture | 1.5 ± 0.5% | |

* Models equipped with power steering

## Fuel and exhaust systems (Turbo models with the C1J-L7-60 engine)

### Air cleaner

| | |
|---|---|
| Type | Automatic air temperature control type with renewable paper element. Champion W109 |
| Air temperature control range | 26 to 32°C (79 to 90°F) |

## Anti-percolation system
Fan switch control range ........................................................... 84 to 90°C (183 to 194°F)
Timed relay period .................................................................... 14 minutes

## Turbocharger
Type ........................................................................................ Garrett T2

## Intercooler
Type ........................................................................................ Air-to-air matrix
Air temperature control range .................................................. 43 to 47°C (109 to 117°F)
Safety switch operating pressure ............................................. 900 to 1000 mbar

## Electric fuel pump delivery ................................................ 60 litre/hr at a pressure of 2.5 bar (36.3 lbf/in$^2$)

## Carburettor data
Solex 32 DIS:
    Type identification number ................................................ **804**
    Venturi ............................................................................... 25
    Main jet ............................................................................. 117.5
    Air compensating jet ......................................................... 125
    Idling jet ............................................................................ 44
    Enrichner ........................................................................... 110
    Fuel needle valve .............................................................. 1.7
    Accelerator pump jet ......................................................... 40
    Accelerator pump stroke checking gauge .......................... 5.0 mm rod
    Cold start initial throttle opening ....................................... 0.75 mm
    Pneumatic initial throttle opening ..................................... 9.0 mm
    Fuel level (non-adjustable) ................................................ 1.0 mm
    Idling speed ...................................................................... 600 to 700 rpm
    CO mixture ........................................................................ 1.0 to 1.5%

## *Fuel and exhaust systems (Turbo models with C1J-770 engine)*
*As above except for following:*

## Anti-percolation system
Fan switch control range ........................................................... 89 to 95°C (192 to 203°F)

## Turbocharger
Type ........................................................................................ Garrett T2 with water cooling circuit
Boost pressure:
    At 3500 rpm ...................................................................... 680 ± 30 mbar
    At 5500 rpm ...................................................................... 700 ± 30 mbar
Safety switch operating pressure ............................................. 1100 ± 50 mbar

## Carburettor data
Solex 32 DIS:
    Type identification number ................................................ **912**
    Venturi ............................................................................... 25
    Main jet ............................................................................. 120
    Air compensation jet ......................................................... 125
    Idling jet ............................................................................ 44
    Enrichner ........................................................................... 100
    Fuel needle valve .............................................................. 1.7
    Accelerator pump jet ......................................................... 40
    Accelerator pump stroke checking gauge .......................... 5.0 mm rod
    Pneumatic initial throttle opening ..................................... 6.4 mm (full choke)
    Fuel level (non-adjustable) ................................................ 1.0 mm
    Idling speed ...................................................................... 625 to 675 rpm
    CO mixture ........................................................................ 1.0 to 2.0%

## *Ignition system (electronic)*
## Ignition timing (checking only)
*At engine idle speed with vacuum pipe disconnected*
Ignition module reference number*:

| | **Degrees advance BTDC** |
|---|---|
| RE 019 ..................................................... | 12 to 14 |
| RE 037 (Turbo) ........................................ | 7 to 9 |
| RE 249 ..................................................... | 7 to 9 |
| RE 026 ..................................................... | 5 to 7 |
| RE 254 ..................................................... | 7 to 9 |
| RE 250 ..................................................... | 5 to 9 |
| RE 208 ..................................................... | 7 to 9 |
| RE 450 ..................................................... | 5 to 7 |
| RE 256 ..................................................... | 5 to 7 |
| RE 007 ..................................................... | 3 to 5 |

*\* Refer to Section 7 for identification*

**Spark plugs (1397 cc Turbo)**
Type........................................................................................ Champion N3G
Electrode gap ...................................................................... 0.55 to 0.65 mm (0.022 to 0.026 in)

*Clutch*

**Clutch disc diameter**
Turbo models ....................................................................... 200.0 mm (7.874 in)

*Manual gearbox*

**Designation**
Later four-speed unit............................................................ JB4
Later five-speed unit............................................................. JB5

**Gearbox ratios**
JB3 (fitted to Turbo models):
    1st ................................................................................. 3.091 : 1
    2nd................................................................................. 1.842 : 1
    3rd.................................................................................. 1.320 : 1
    4th.................................................................................. 0.967 : 1
    5th.................................................................................. 0.758 : 1
    Reverse .......................................................................... 3.545 : 1
JB4 and JB5 .......................................................................... As JB0 and JB1

**Final drive ratios**
JB3 (Turbo models) .............................................................. 4.067 : 1
JB4 and JB5 .......................................................................... As JB0 and JB1

**Lubrication**
Capacity:
    JB4 (with steel filler plug) .............................................. 3.25 litres (5.72 Imp pts)
    JB4 (with dipstick) .......................................................... 2.75 litres (4.84 Imp pts)
    JB5 (with steel filler plug) .............................................. 3.40 litres (5.98 Imp pts)
    JB5 (with dipstick) .......................................................... 2.90 litres (5.10 Imp pts)
Lubricant type/specification (Turbo models) ....................... Gear oil, viscosity SAE 75W/90 (Duckhams Hypoid 75W/90S)

| **Torque wrench setting** | **Nm** | **lbf ft** |
| --- | --- | --- |
| Differential nut (taper bearings) | 130 | 96 |

*Automatic transmission*

| **Torque wrench settings** | **Nm** | **lbf ft** |
| --- | --- | --- |
| Monobloc oil cooler | 40 | 30 |
| Torque converter nuts: | | |
|     9.0 mm | 25 | 18 |
|     8.0 mm | 19 | 14 |
| Driveplate to crankshaft | 65 | 48 |

*Braking system (Turbo models)*

**Front disc brakes**
Disc thickness (new)............................................................. 20.0 mm (0.79 in)
Minimum disc thickness........................................................ 18.0 mm (0.71 in)

**Rear disc brakes**
Disc diameter ....................................................................... 238.0 mm (9.37 in)
Disc thickness (new)............................................................. 8.0 mm (0.31 in)
Minimum disc thickness........................................................ 7.0 mm (0.28 in)
Brake pad thickness (including backing)............................... 11.0 mm (0.43 in)
Minimum brake pad thickness (including backing) ............... 5.0 mm (0.20 in)

**Brake vacuum servo pushrod**
Dimension L.......................................................................... 117 mm (4.61 in)
Dimension X ......................................................................... 22.3 mm (0.88 in)

| **Torque wrench settings** | **Nm** | **lbf ft** |
| --- | --- | --- |
| *Rear disc brakes* | | |
| Caliper bracket bolts | 100 | 74 |
| Caliper bolts | 100 | 74 |
| Wheel hub nut | 160 | 118 |
| Wheel bolts | 80 | 59 |

*Electric system*

**Battery**
Capacity (later models) ....................................................... 30 amp hr, 36 amp hr or 45 amp hr

### Alternator
Regulated voltage:
Ducellier 516023 .................................................................... 13.5 to 15.0 volt at 3000 rpm
Ducellier 8371A .................................................................... 13.9 to 14.3 volt at 2500 rpm

### Starter motor
Type (later models) .................................................................. Ducellier 6231 pre-engaged

## *Suspension and steering*

### Front suspension (Turbo models)
Underbody height (H1 minus H2) ........................................... 120.0 mm (4.72 in)

### Rear suspension (Turbo models with tubular axle)
Rear wheel camber angle ........................................................ –1°15' to –0°45'
Rear wheel toe ........................................................................ –0°30' to 0°70' (toe-in)

### Rear suspension (four-bar type)
Anti-roll bar diameter ............................................................. 26.5 mm (1.04 in)
Torsion bar diameter .............................................................. 23.0 mm (0.91 in)
Torsion bar length .................................................................. 653 mm (25.7 in)
Rear wheel camber angle ........................................................ –1°20' to –0° 20'

### Rear suspension underbody height
H4 minus H5 – up to 1986 (H5 taken from suspension mounting
bracket bolt):
All models except Turbo ...................................................... 20.0 mm (0.79 in)
Turbo models with tubular axle ........................................... 55.0 mm (2.16 in)
H4 minus H5 – 1986 on (H5 taken from centre of torsion bar):
All except Turbo and 1721 cc engine models ...................... –15.0 mm (–0.59 in)
Turbo models with four-bar suspension .............................. 30.0 mm (1.18 in)
1721 cc engine models with four-bar suspension................ –4.0 mm (–0.15 in)
Dimension X:
All models except Turbo ...................................................... 620.0 mm (24.4 in)
Turbo models ...................................................................... 600.0 mm (23.6 in)
**Note**: *A tolerance of + 10 and –5 mm ( + 0.4 and –0.2 in) is allowed on all underbody height dimensions*

### Steering
Castor angle (later models, non-adjustable) at
H5 minus H2 = 100.0 mm (3.94 in) ...................................... Zero
Toe setting (Turbo models) ..................................................... 0°30' to 0°50' (3.0 to 5.0 mm) toe-out

### Roadwheels
Size:
Turbo models......................................................................... 5½J x 14 or 6J x 15
1237 cc engine models ......................................................... 5½J x 13

### Tyres
Size:
Turbo models ........................................................................ 175/65 R 14H or 195/50 VR 15
1237 cc engine models.......................................................... 165/70 SR or 155 SR 13

### Tyre pressures
Turbo models (with tubular rear axle):
Front..................................................................................... 1.8 bar (26.1 lbf/in²)
Rear ..................................................................................... 2.0 bar (29.0 lbf/in²)
Turbo models (with four-bar suspension):
Front and rear....................................................................... 2.1 bar (30.5 lbf/in²)
1237 cc engine models:
Front ..................................................................................... 1.9 bar (27.5 lbf/in²)
Rear ..................................................................................... 2.1 bar (30.5 lbf/in²)

### Torque wrench setting

| | Nm | lbf ft |
|---|---|---|
| Steering wheel retaining nut (August 1983 on) ........................... | 45 | 33 |

## *General dimensions and weights (October 1986 on)*

### Dimensions
Wheelbase ............................................................................... 2483 mm (97.8 in)
Overall length:
Renault 9 .............................................................................. 4132 mm (162.0 in)
Renault 11 ............................................................................ 4047 m (159.4 in)
Overall width ........................................................................... 1666 mm (65.6 in)
Overall height .......................................................................... 1410 mm (55.5 in)

## Dimensions (continued)
Front track:
Renault 9 ...................................................................... 1400 mm (55.1 in)
Renault 11 .................................................................... 1410 mm (55.5 in)
Rear track ...................................................................... 1357 mm (53.0 in)
Turning circle (between kerbs) ...................................... 9750 mm (384 in)

## Kerb weights
Renault 9:
TC ................................................................................ 830 kg (1830 lb)
TL ................................................................................ 840 kg (1852 lb)
GTL .............................................................................. 850 kg (1874 lb)
Automatic ..................................................................... 865 kg (1907 lb)
Turbo ........................................................................... 905 kg (1995 lb)
Renault 11 – as above except for:
GTL .............................................................................. 870 kg (1918 lb)
Automatic ..................................................................... 885 kg (1951 lb)
TXE .............................................................................. 925 kg (2039 lb)

### 3   Routine maintenance

As from January 1st 1985 the maintenance intervals have been changed, as shown in the following list. The engine oil change and adjustments are carried out every 6000 miles (10 000 km) with general overhaul procedures at 30 000 miles (50 000 km).

*Every 6000 miles (10 000 km) or 6 months – whichever occurs first*
Renew the engine oil (Chapter 1)
Check gearbox/final drive oil level (Chapter 6)
Adjust idling speed (Chapter 3)
Check alternator drivebelt condition and tension (Chapter 2)
Check levels of windscreen/rear screen washers, brake fluid, coolant and battery electrolyte, where applicable.
Check tyre condition and pressures (Chapter 10)
Visually check operation of all equipment
Check bodywork condition (Chapter 11)

*Every 12 000 miles (20 000 km) or 12 months – whichever occurs first*
Renew the oil filter (Chapter 1)

Renew the air filter (Chapter 3)
Check the valve clearances (Chapter 1)
Check the spark plugs and renew if necessary (Chapter 4)
Check the contact breaker points (Chapter 4)

*Ever 30 000 miles (50 000 km)*
Renew the gearbox/final drive oil or automatic transmission fluid (Chapter 6) – see note below
Renew the fuel filter, if fitted (Chapter 3)
Check condition of brake pads and rear linings (Chapter 8)
Renew the brake hydraulic fluid and check for leakage (Chapter 8)
Check suspension and steering components for condition and play (Chapter 10)
Check for front wheel alignment (Chapter 10)
Renew the brake vacuum servo air filter (Chapter 8)

*Every 40 000 miles (60 000 km)*
Renew the coolant/antifreeze solution (Chapter 2)

**Note:** *From October 1986 on, all Turbo models have their gearboxes lubricated with a new 'high temperature' oil (see* Recommended lubricants and fluids *at the beginning of this Manual). This new oil is also to be used on all older Turbo models, at the time of the next gearbox oil renewal. Gearbox oil renewal intervals for all Turbo models filled with the new oil is 30 000 miles (50 000 km).*

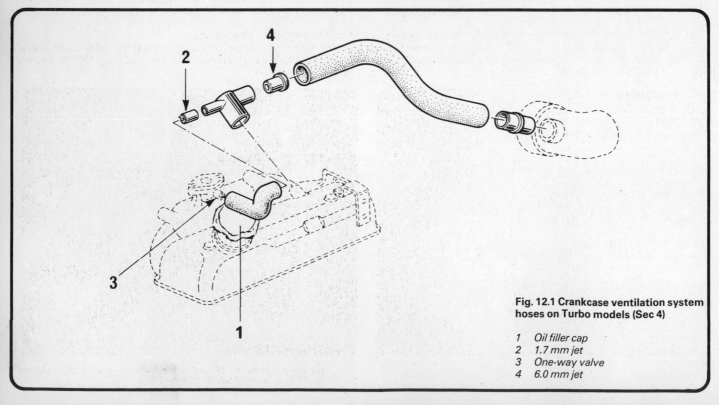

**Fig. 12.1 Crankcase ventilation system hoses on Turbo models (Sec 4)**

1   *Oil filler cap*
2   *1.7 mm jet*
3   *One-way valve*
4   *6.0 mm jet*

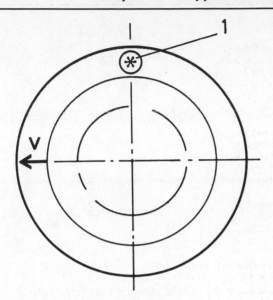

Fig. 12.2 Identification marks stamped on piston crowns of De Colmar pistons (Sec 4)

V    *Direction of fitting*        1    *Diameter*

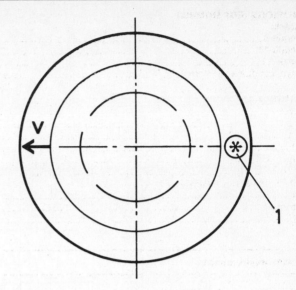

Fig. 12.3 Identification marks stamped on piston crowns of SMM pistons (Sec 4)

V    *Direction of fitting*        1    *Diameter*

## 4 Engine

### *1397 cc Turbo engine – removal and refitting (general)*

1    On Turbo models, the turbocharger can remain in position when removing and refitting the engine. The angled exhaust downpipe from the turbocharger to the support plate can also remain in position, and the exhaust disconnected at the spring tensioned flange. Refer to Section 6 of this Chapter when reconnecting the exhaust.

2    Additionally, the air intake ducting for the anti-percolation system must also be disconnected (see Section 6).

### *Crankcase ventilation system (Turbo models) – description*

3    The crankcase ventilation system for Turbo models is shown in Fig. 12.1.

4    Crankcase fumes from the rocker cover are drawn through hoses to the inlet side of the turbocharger and also to the inlet manifold just below the carburettor. When the turbocharger pressurizes the inlet air, however, the valve on the inlet manifold closes.

### *Pistons (1721 cc engine) – general*

5    Pistons from two manufacturers (SMM and De Colmar) were fitted to early 1721 cc engines. The variations in weight between the two types make it essential that all four pistons fitted to any one engine are from the same manufacturer. The two types must never be mixed.

6    Later models are fitted exclusively with SMM pistons, which may have different markings to those shown in Fig. 12.3. Ensure that the markings on all four pistons are identical.

### *Engine lubrication (Turbo models) – description*

7    On Turbo models an oil cooler is incorporated into the right-hand tank of the radiator (photo). The feed and return hoses are taken from an adaptor located beneath the oil filter.

8    The oil supply for the turbocharger is taken from the oil pressure sender unit location on the cylinder block (photo). Return oil is taken by hose to an inlet on the front of the sump.

### *1237 cc engine – description*

9    The Broadway models introduced in late 1985 may be fitted with a 1237 cc engine. The engine is essentially identical to the 1397 cc version but with a smaller bore.

4.7 Oil cooler union on the radiator (Turbo models)

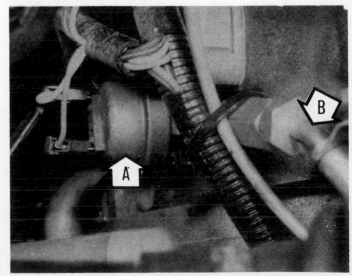

4.8 Oil pressure sender unit (A) and turbocharger oil supply pipe (B) on the front of the cylinder block (Turbo models)

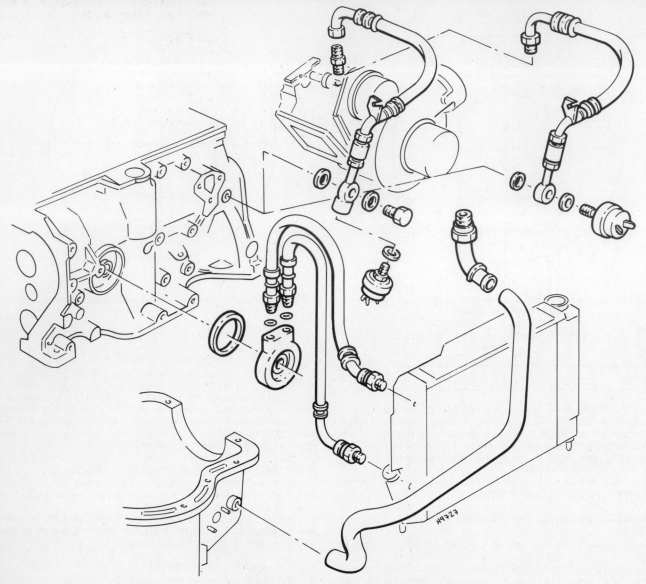

**Fig. 12.4 Turbocharger and oil cooler hoses (Sec 4)**

## 5   Cooling system

### Cooling system (Turbo models) – general

1    There are two systems in use, an early version, shown in Fig. 12.5, and the later version (Fig. 12.6), which is a development of the earlier system.

2    Both systems incorporate a 'hot' type expansion tank, where there is a continuous flow of coolant through the tank.

3    This arrangement helps to reduce the amount of air in the coolant, and prevents the accumulation of air pockets in the cylinder head.

4    For this reason there is no heater water valve in the car interior heater circuit, as the heater matrix plays a part in engine cooling, and the heater piping must not be obstructed.

5    The later system also incorporates a de-aeration chamber between the water pump and expansion tank, which also helps in removing air from the coolant (photo).

6    Also on the later system, the turbine bearing is cooled by the system, the supply of coolant being drawn from the carburettor base heating circuit, the coolant flowing around the turbine bearing and back to the pump (photo).

### Cooling system (Turbo models) – bleeding

7    If they have been removed for draining, check the tightness of the cylinder block drain plug and the radiator bottom hose.

8    Open all bleed screws and remove the radiator and expansion tank caps.

9    Fill the system slowly through the expansion tank.

10    As soon as coolant starts to flow from them, close the bleed screws and refit the radiator cap.

11    Continue filling until the coolant level reaches the MAX mark on the expansion tank.

12    Refit the expansion tank cap.

13    Run the engine at 1500 rpm for at least 15 minutes. **Do not** open any bleed screws while the engine is running.

14    Allow the system to cool completely, then check the coolant level in the expansion tank and top up as necessary. Refit the cap on completion.

### Cooling system (all models) – filling

15    When running the engine to normal operating temperature (Chapter 2, Section 5, paragraph 8) it is recommended that the engine speed is increased to 1500 rpm. This will help dislodge any trapped air bubbles in the cooling system and ensure a more accurate cold level check.

### Radiator bottom hose (1721 cc engine) – checking

16    On 1721 cc engines the radiator bottom hose should be periodically checked; particularly if engine overheating is experienced. The hose, which incorporates a tee-piece for water from the heater, may collapse if deteriorated. This is especially noticeable when the engine is cold and the thermostat shut.

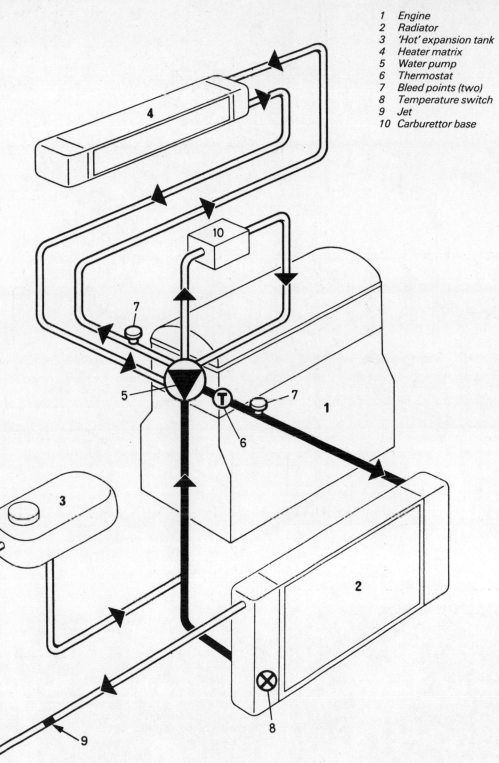

**Fig. 12.5 Diagram of the cooling system on early Turbo models (Sec 5)**

1  Engine
2  Radiator
3  'Hot' expansion tank
4  Heater matrix
5  Water pump
6  Thermostat
7  Bleed points (two)
8  Temperature switch
9  Jet
10  Carburettor base

**Fig. 12.6 Diagram of the cooling system on later Turbo models (Sec 5)**

1  Engine
2  Radiator
3  'Hot' expansion tank
4  Heater matrix
5  Water pump
6  Thermostat
7  Bleed points (three)
8  Temperature switch
9  Jet
10  Inlet manifold
11  Carburettor base heating
12  De-aeration chamber
13  Turbocharger

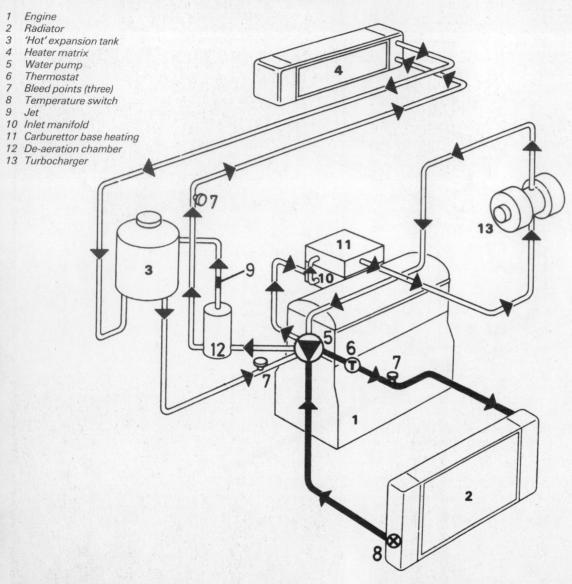

5.5 De-aeration chamber on later cooling systems (Turbo models)

5.6 Coolant connection (arrowed) on the later turbocharger

6.4A Solex Z10 carburettor

1   Fast idle actuator (power steering)
2   Idle cut-off solenoid
3   Choke vacuum actuator
4   Heater

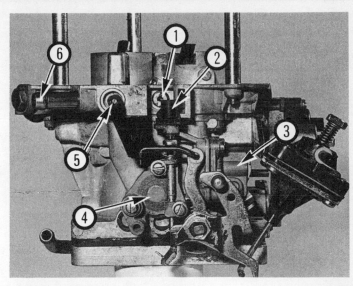

6.4B Solex Z10 carburettor (continued)

1   Idle jet
2   Idle speed adjusting screw
3   Accelerator pump
4   Enrichment device
5   Defuming valve
6   Float chamber vent

6.4C Solex Z10 carburettor (continued)

1   Fuel inlet strainer
2   Fuel inlet
3   Crankcase ventilation connection

17   If suspect, the hose should be removed and inspected. The heater tee-piece section can be checked by passing a 14.0 mm (0.551 in) diameter ball through it. Renew the hose if necessary.

## 6   Fuel and exhaust systems

### General information

1   The following paragraphs give information on developments to the fuel and exhaust systems. These include information on later carburettor types, the introduction of an anti-percolation system and the turbocharger system.

6.4D Solex Z10 carburettor (continued)

1   Idle mixture adjustment screw
2   Fast idle adjustment screw
3   Secondary throttle stop screw (do not touch)

2   In general, information on carburettors was sparse at the time of writing, but that which was available is given. This is particularly true of the Solex 28-34 Z10 and 32-34 Z13 carburettors fitted to the later 1721 cc models.

3   In some cases, only the specifications for later carburettors are given, as shown in the Specifications. Generally, the overhaul procedures for these carburettors (and those mentioned in the text) are as described in Chapter 3, using the Specifications at the beginning of this Supplement.

### Solex carburettor (later 1721 cc engines) – description

4   The Solex carburettor fitted to later 1721 cc engines is a twin throat downdraught unit, with sequential operation of the throttle valves. It is

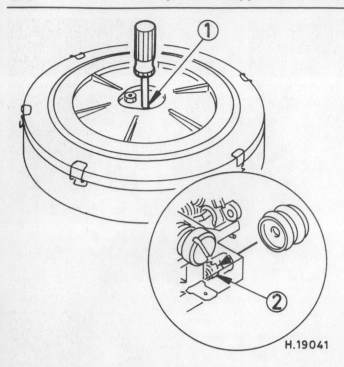

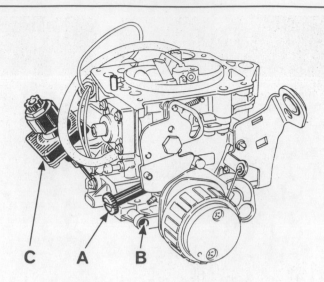

Fig. 12.7 Adjustment points on the Solex 28-34 Z10 carburettor
(Sec 6)

1    Idle speed        2    CO/Mixture

Fig. 12.8 Adjustment points on Solex 32-34 Z13 carburettor (Sec 6)

A    Idle speed           C    Fast idle actuator (models
B    CO/Mixture                with power steering)

very similar in operation to the earlier Weber carburettor described in
Chapter 3, Section 13 (photos).
5    All versions of the carburettor have an idle cut-off solenoid valve
which interrupts the idle mixture circuit when the ignition is switched
off, so preventing running-on. If this valve is disconnected or defective,
the engine will idle roughly or not at all.

6    The idle mixture circuit also incorporates an electrical heater to
improve fuel vaporization when cold. This system supersedes the
coolant heating of the carburettor base found on other models.
7    Later 32-34 Z13 versions of the carburettor have the opening of the
secondary throttle valve controlled by a vacuum diaphragm instead of
mechanically as on the 28-34 Z10 version.

### Solex carburettor (later 1721 cc engines) – idle speed and mixture adjustment

8    Refer to Chapter 3, Section 14, for the procedure. The locations of
the idle speed and mixture screw are as shown in Fig. 12.7 or 12.8 (as
applicable).

6.10 Disconnecting the idle cut-off solenoid

6.11 Unclipping the throttle link

6.12A Disconnecting the choke control inner
cable ...

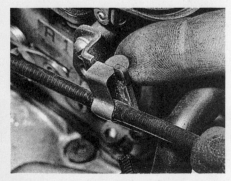

6.12B ... and unclipping the outer cable

6.13 Disconnecting the fuel inlet hose

6.14 Carburettor vacuum hoses

6.15 Disconnecting the crankcase ventilation hose

6.16 Four Allen screws (arrowed) which secure the carburettor

6.17 Removing the carburettor

6.20 Removing the fuel inlet strainer

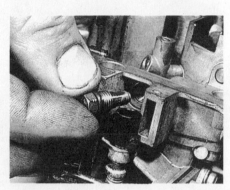

6.21 Removing the idling jet

6.22A Remove the screw and plate ...

6.22B ... and withdraw the heater assembly

6.23 Disconnecting the defuming valve link

## Solex carburettor (later 1721 cc engines) – removal and refitting

9  Disconnect the battery negative terminal and remove the air cleaner housing.
10  Disconnect the wiring from the carburettor heater and the idle cut-off solenoid (photo).
11  Unclip the throttle link rod balljoint (photo).
12  Disconnect the choke cable (photos).
13  Slacken the retaining clip and disconnect the fuel inlet hose; plug the hose end to minimise fuel loss (photo).
14  Identify and disconnect the vacuum hoses from the carburettor (photo).
15  Disconnect the crankcase ventilation hose from the base of the carburettor (photo).
16  Remove the four Allen screws and washers from the top of the carburettor (photo).
17  Lift off the carburettor and recover the gasket from the manifold (photo).
18  Refit by reversing the removal operations, using a new gasket.

## Solex carburettor (later 1721 cc engines) – overhaul

**Note:** *The carburettor seen in the photographs is a Solex 28-34 Z10. The 32-34 Z13 fitted to later models is very similar, the main difference being that the secondary throttle valve is opened by a vacuum diaphragm instead of mechanically.*

19  With the carburettor removed from the engine, thoroughly clean it externally with paraffin or a degreasing solvent.
20  Unscrew and remove the fuel inlet strainer (photo).
21  Unscrew the idling jet from the carburettor cover (photo).
22  Remove the heater securing plate screw. Carefully remove the plate and withdraw the roll pin with the insulator, the terminal and the heater disc; note that it is fragile (photos).
23  Prise the defuming valve link rod out of the plastic bush (photo).
24  Remove the five screws which secure the carburettor cover. Lift off the cover with the floats and choke vacuum actuator attached (photos).
25  Remove the float pivot pin. Remove the floats, the needle valve and gasket (photo).

6.24A Five screws (arrowed) which secure the cover

6.24B Removing the carburettor cover

26    Remove the idle circuit filter from the carburettor body (photo).
27    Pull the accelerator pump injector assembly from the body (photo).
28    Unscrew and remove the air correction jet/emulsion tube assemblies (photo).
29    Remove the main jets from the bottom of the emulsion tube wells by unscrewing them (photos).
30    If a complete overhaul is being undertaken, remove the various diaphragm covers so that the diaphragm can be checked for damage such as splits and, if necessary, renewed.
31    Clean out any sediment from the float chamber, and blow through all passages with low-pressure compressed air.
32    Reassemble in the reverse order to dismantling, using new gaskets, O-rings, etc., and carrying out the adjustment described in the following paragraphs (when appropriate). Pay attention to the correct fitting of the heater components – if the insulator is misplaced there is a risk of a short circuit.

**Float level adjustment**
33    With the carburettor cover reassembled (including the gasket) invert the cover and measure the distance from the gasket to the furthest point of the floats (photo). If necessary, adjust by carefully bending the float arms.

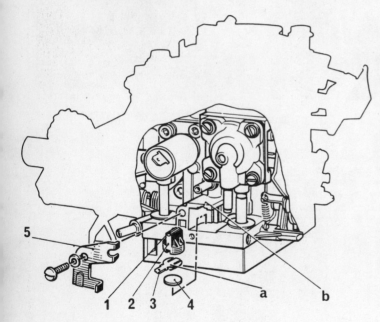

Fig. 12.9 Components of the electrical heating system – Solex 28-34 Z10 carburettor (Sec 6)

| | | | |
|---|---|---|---|
| 1 | Roll pin | 5 | Securing plate |
| 2 | Insulator | a | Tongue |
| 3 | Terminal | b | Roll pin slot |
| 4 | Heater disc | | |

**Defuming valve adjustment**
34    Invert the reassembled carburettor. Open the throttle until the defuming valve just closes. In this position, the throttle valve opening should be as given in the Specifications. If necessary adjust at the point shown in Fig. 12.10 or 12.11 (as appropriate).

**Initial throttle opening (fast idle)**
35    With the carburettor still inverted, operate the choke linkage to close the choke valve. Measure the throttle valve opening, which should be as specified. Adjust if necessary by turning the screw which bears on the fast idle cam (photo).

6.25 Removing the float pivot pin

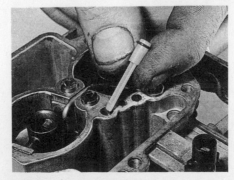

6.26 Removing the idle circuit filter

6.27 Removing the accelerator pump injector

6.28 Removing an air correction jet/emulsion tube assembly

6.29A Unscrewing a main jet

6.29B Removing a main jet from the well

6.33 Checking the float level

6.35 Fast idle adjustment screw

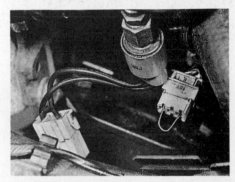
6.40 Bridging the pressure switch connector terminals with a paper clip

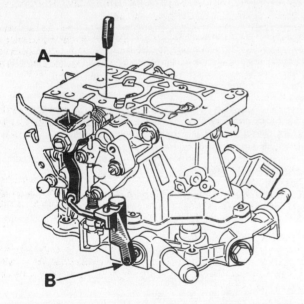

Fig. 12.10 Defuming valve adjustment – Solex 28-34 Z10 carburettor (Sec 6)

  A  Gauge rod (measuring throttle valve gap)
  B  Adjustment screw

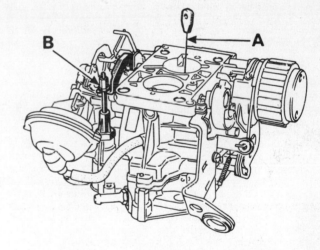

Fig. 12.11 Defuming valve adjustment – Solex 32-34 Z13 carburettor (Sec 6)

  A  Gauge rod          B  Adjustment screw

### Choke pneumatic part-opening adjustment

36   Operate the choke linkage to close the choke valve. Push the operating rod as far as it will go into the choke vacuum actuator. In this position measure the choke valve opening, which should be as specified. If necessary, adjust by means of the screw in the centre of the vacuum actuator.

### Secondary throttle link adjustment – 32-34 Z13 carburettor only

37   The rod between the throttle vacuum actuator and the secondary throttle lever should be adjusted so that there is a small amount of play ('A' in Fig. 12.12) in both the fully closed and fully open positions.

### Fast-idle actuator (models equipped with power steering) – description and adjustment

38   On models equipped with power steering, a vacuum-operated actuator raises the idle speed if the steering is turned to full lock, so preventing stalling. The vacuum feed to the actuator is via a solenoid valve which is controlled by a pressure operated switch in the high-pressure hydraulic pipe.

39   Before commencing adjustment, warm the engine up to normal operating temperature and adjust the idle speed and mixture settings.

40   With the engine idling and the steering in the straight-ahead

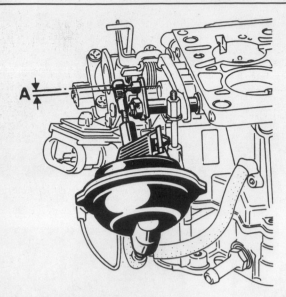

**Fig. 12.12 Throttle actuator link rod adjustment – Solex 32-34 Z13 carburettor (Sec 6)**

*A   See text*

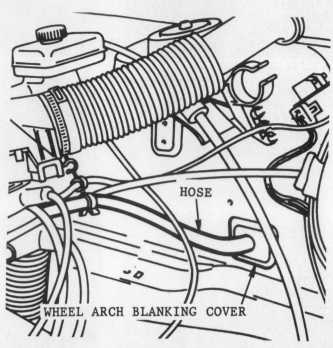

**Fig. 12.13 Carburettor venting hose – Solex 28-34 Z10 carburettor (Sec 6)**

position, unplug the wiring connector from the pressure switch. Bridge the terminals of the wiring connector with a split pin or short length of wire. Do not allow the bridge to earth on the vehicle (photo).
41   With the terminals bridged, idle speed should rise to the value given in the Specifications. If necessary, adjust by means of the adjusting screw on the fast idle actuator – see Fig. 12.8 (photo).
42   When adjustment is complete, stop the engine and reconnect the wiring connector to the switch.

### Solex 28-34 Z10 carburettor – fuel smells in the passenger compartment
43   Under some conditions, fuel smells may be noticed in the engine compartment on later 1721 cc models fitted with the above carburettor. The smell is caused by vapour escaping from the carburettor venting system, and may be remedied as follows.
44   Drill a 12 mm hole in the left-hand wheel arch blanking cover (see Fig. 12.13) and acquire suitable hose (Part Number 77 05 026 086) approximately 750 mm long. Fit the tubing to the carburettor float chamber. The tubing must run smoothly downwards, with no kinks or bends, noting that there should be at least 50 mm of hose behind the blanking cover.
45   Note that early (pre-October 1987) versions of the carburettor are not fitted with a suitable external vent to which the hose can be attached, in which case the carburettor must be renewed. Consult a Renault dealer for further information.

### Solex 28-34 Z10 carburettor – flat spot noted on acceleration
46   On models equipped with this carburettor several cases have been noted of a flat spot occurring under acceleration; this is caused by a lack of fuel as the carburettor changes from the primary to secondary throttle valve. Renault have overcome this problem by manufacturing a modified feed tube for the secondary valve idling circuit. However, fitting of the tube is a complex, fiddly task and it is therefore recommended that it is entrusted to a Renault dealer. Refer to your Renault dealer for further information.

### Weber DRT carburettor – engine regularly refusing to return to specified idle speed
47   On models equipped with this carburettor several cases have been noted of the engine regularly refusing to return to its specified idle speed; this is caused by the secondary throttle valve sticking open. To overcome this problem Renault introduced a modification consisting of

a teflon-coated secondary throttle valve spindle (of a smaller diameter than the original), a modified mounting bolt and a shim which is fitted between the carburettor and manifold. Refer to your Renault dealer for further information.

### Solex 32 BIS 918 carburettor – general description
48   Fitted to the 1237 cc engine, the Solex 32 BIS 918 carburettor is a development of earlier Solex carburettors fitted to the range. The basic procedure for idle and mixture setting and overhaul are similar to those described in Chapter 3, using the Specifications given in this Supplement.

### Solex 32 DIS carburettor – general description
49   The Solex 32 DIS carburettor is fitted to Turbo models.
50   It is a single-barrel, downdraught type carburettor, and is completely sealed (in respect of atmospheric air), operating downstream of the turbocharger. All internal jets and passages are subject to turbocharged air pressure.
51   To ensure pressure integrity, the carburettor features a reinforced cover gasket, throttle and choke spindle seals, adjustment screw seals, idling jet seals, improved accelerator pump and enrichener diaphragms, and a magnesium body and cover.

### Solex 32 DIS carburettor – idle speed and mixture adjustment
52   The procedure is identical to that described in Chapter 3. However, before starting, all the air hoses should be checked for condition and security. Note that the hoses must be completely dry when assembling them and the clips must be fully tightened.
53   An idle speed screw is fitted to this Solex carburettor and not a volume control screw as fitted to the Solex carburettor described in Chapter 3 (photo).

### Solex 32 DIS carburettor – overhaul
54   The procedure is similar to that described in Chapter 3 with reference also to the information given in the Specifications.
55   Note that on these carburettors the fuel level is non-adjustable. The thickness of the seal under the jet should be as given in the Specifications.

### Anti-percolation system – general description
56   From July 1987 on, an anti-percolation system is fitted to all 1721 cc and Turbo models.

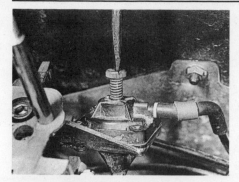

6.41 Adjusting the fast idle actuator

6.53 Idle speed screw (A) and mixture screw (B) on Solex DIS carburettor

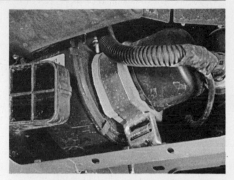

6.60A View of the anti-percolation system motor-driven fan with radiator grille removed ...

6.60B ... and looking down in the engine bay

6.60C Carburettor and fuel line cooling duct (arrowed)

6.61 Anti-percolation system solenoid valve

57    The function of the system is to improve hot starting.
58    On 1721 cc engines, the system consists simply of an anti-percolation chamber fitted between the fuel pump and the carburettor.
59    On Turbo models the system is more complex, and is described in more detail in the following paragraphs.

### Anti-percolation system (Turbo models) – description

60    On Turbo models, the anti-percolation system consists of a motor-driven fan, which supplies fresh air to a duct in which the fuel line to the carburettor is encased. The duct also directs cool air onto the carburet-

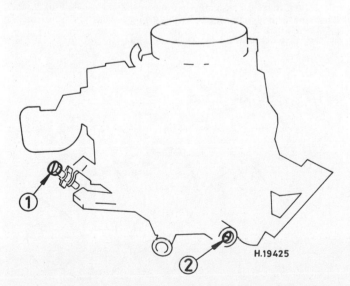

**Fig. 12.14 Adjustment points on the Solex 32 BIS carburettor (Sec 6)**

   *1   Idle speed*        *2   CO/Mixture*

tor. The motor is located low down in the front of the engine bay, behind the radiator grille (photos).
61    Also in the system are a thermal switch, mounted on the inlet manifold, and a solenoid valve, located just behind the right-hand headlamp unit (photo). These components control a fresh air bypass system between the carburettor air intake and the anti-percolation system air inlet duct.
62    With the ignition switched on, power is supplied to the motor-driven fan via the thermal switch. If the temperature at the switch is higher than that specified (see Specifications), the switch allows power to the motor, which delivers fresh air to the system.
63    With the ignition switched off and the temperature above the specified value, power is supplied to the solenoid valve via a relay (on the central accessories plate) which opens the bypass system, allowing fresh air from the carburettor air intake to the anti-percolation ducting (photo).

### Turbocharger – general description and precautions

64    The turbocharger consists of a centre shaft and two turbines. One of the turbines is located in the exhaust gas flow at the outlet of the exhaust manifold, and the other is in the airflow to the carburettor. The flow of exhaust gases causes the exhaust turbine to rotate, which turns the inlet turbine, pressurising the incoming air.
65    On later versions, the turbine bearings are water-cooled (see Section 5).
66    A sealed-type Solex 32 DIS carburettor is used in conjunction with the turbocharger, and the fuel pressure is regulated according to the air inlet pressure.
67    To prevent fuel percolation on early models, the carburettor is cooled by air ducting from the electric fan on the radiator, activated by a thermal switch on the inlet manifold by the carburettor.
68    On later models, the anti-percolation system is more complex, and is described in the previous sub-Section.
69    The temperature of the inlet air is regulated both by a control flap in the air cleaner assembly, and an air-to-air intercooler downstream of the turbocharger.
70    Fuel supply to the carburettor is via an electric pump located beneath the rear of the vehicle. An in-line fuel filter is located next to the fuel pump outlet.

6.63 Anti-percolation system bypass air connection

6.75A Turbocharger-to-carburettor air hose and rubber strap

6.75B Turbocharger with air hoses disconnected

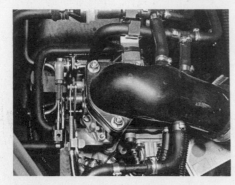

6.75C Turbocharger control system hose connections at the carburettor on later Turbo models

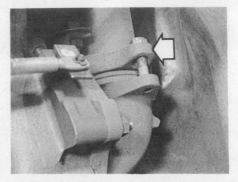

6.78 Exhaust downpipe elbow flange at the turbocharger

71    The turbocharger incorporates a control system, consisting of a vacuum capsule and a bypass valve (or wastegate). This system controls the speed of the exhaust turbine and therefore the pressure of the inlet air. On later models the control system has been modified, receiving more reference pressures than the early system.

**Precautions**
72    The turbocharger must not be operated with any of the hoses or ducts disconnected. After disconnecting the oil pipes for whatever reason, the oil circuit must first be primed before starting the engine. When stopping the engine, it should be allowed to idle for approximately 30 seconds before switching off the ignition. This is necessary to allow the turbines to slow down, otherwise bearing failure may result due to the turbine shaft rotating without an adequate oil supply from the engine.

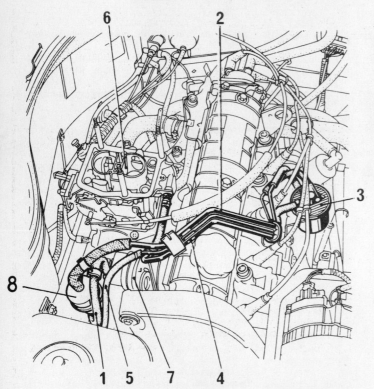

**Fig. 12.15 Anti-percolation system on non-Turbo models (Sec 6)**

1   Fuel inlet hose
2   Hose between fuel pump and anti-percolation chamber
3   Anti-percolation chamber
4   Hose between anti-percolation chamber and carburettor
5   Fuel return hose (to tank)
6   Carburettor
7   Fuel pump
8   Filter

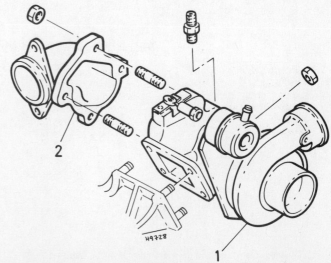

**Fig. 12.16 Turbocharger (1) and exhaust outlet elbow (2) (Sec 6)**

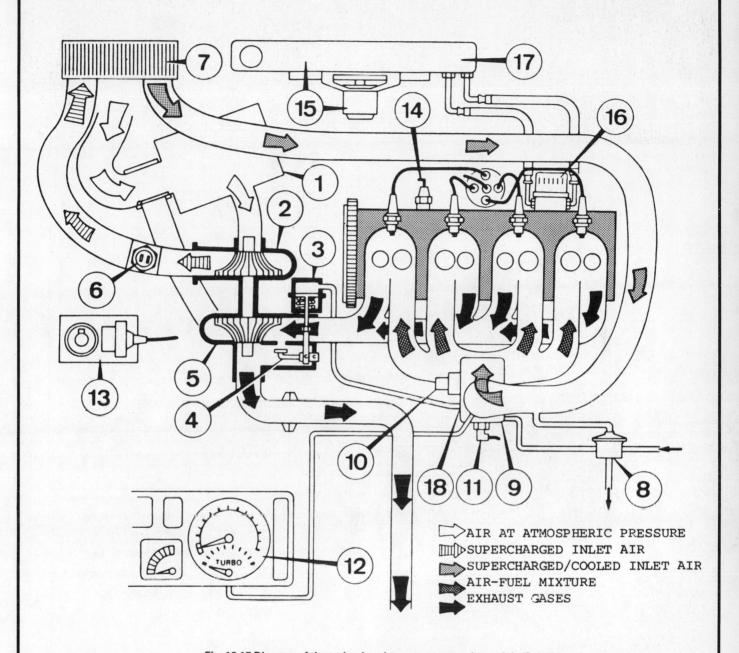

**Fig. 12.17 Diagram of the turbocharging system on early models (Sec 6)**

1  Air filter and temperature control unit
2  Inlet turbine
3  Air pressure regulator capsule
4  Wastegate
5  Exhaust turbine
6  Safety pressure switch
7  Intercooler with thermostatic valve
8  Fuel pressure regulator
9  'Sealed' carburettor
10 Choke
11 Temperature switch for carburettor cooling
12 Boost pressure gauge
13 Electronic ignition computer module
14 Knock detector
15 Radiator and electric cooling fan
16 Oil filter
17 Oil cooler
18 Wastegate pressure tapping

AIR AT ATMOSPHERIC PRESSURE
SUPERCHARGED INLET AIR
SUPERCHARGED/COOLED INLET AIR
AIR-FUEL MIXTURE
EXHAUST GASES

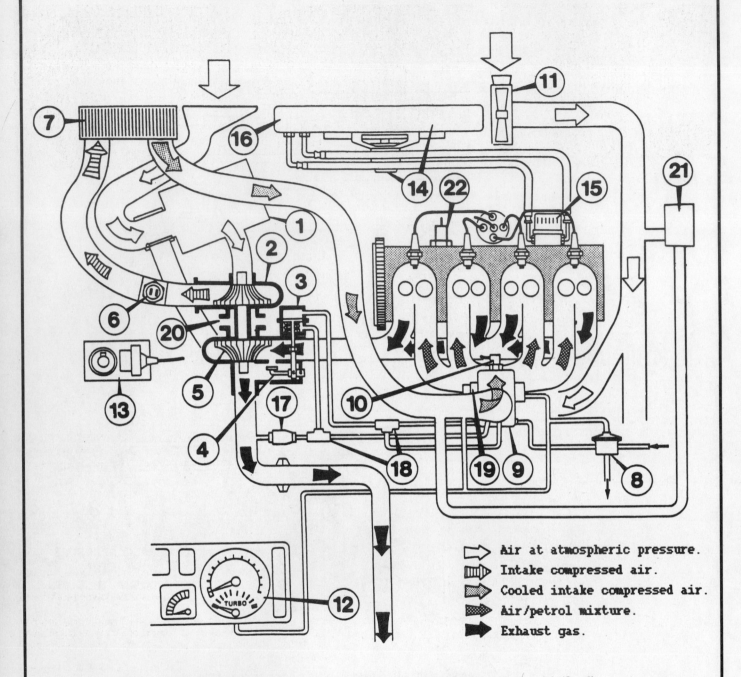

**Fig. 12.18 Diagram of the water-cooled turbocharging system on later models (Sec 6)**

Air at atmospheric pressure.
Intake compressed air.
Cooled intake compressed air.
Air/petrol mixture.
Exhaust gas.

| | | | |
|---|---|---|---|
| 1 Air filter and temperature control unit | 7 Intercooler with thermostatic valve | 12 Pressure gauge in instrument panel | 19 Enrichment device on carburettor |
| 2 Inlet turbine | 8 Fuel pressure regulator | 13 Ignition computer module | 20 Water-cooled turbocharger shaft and bearings |
| 3 Air pressure regulator capsule | 9 Sealed carburettor | 14 Radiator cooling fan | 21 Anti-percolation system bypass solenoid |
| 4 Wastegate | 10 Anti-percolation system thermal switch | 15 Oil filter | 22 Knock detector |
| 5 Exhaust turbine | 11 Anti-percolation system motor-driven fan | 16 Oil cooler | |
| 6 Safety pressure switch | | 17 Non-return valve | |
| | | 18 T-piece unions | |

6.79 Oil supply pipe on the turbocharger

6.80A Pressure regulator capsule and control rod on an early turbocharger

6.80B Later turbochargers have two connections

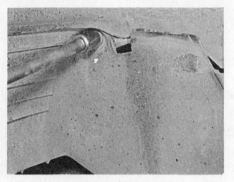

6.89 Intercooler with air hoses disconnected showing rubber strap

6.91 Removing the splash guard

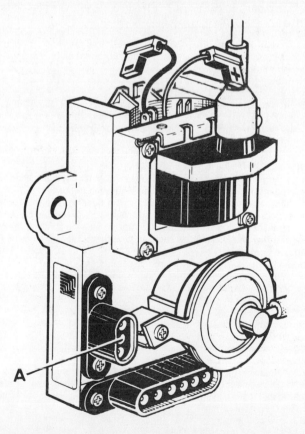

Fig. 12.19 Disconnect the three-pin plug from socket 'A' when priming the oil circuit (Sec 6)

73    The electric cooling fan operates independently from the ignition switch up to a maximum of 14 minutes after switching off the engine, therefore it is recommended that the battery negative lead is disconnected when working on a hot engine.

*Turbocharger – removal and refitting*
74    Disconnect the battery negative lead.
75    Disconnect the air hoses from the turbocharger and carburettor, and move them to one side (photos).
76    Remove the air cleaner.
77    Unbolt the heatshield from the bulkhead. Access to the lower bolt is gained by jacking up the front of the car and supporting on axle stands.
78    Unscrew the flange bolts holding the exhaust downpipe elbow to the turbocharger (photo).
79    Unscrew the union nut and remove the oil supply pipe (photo). Loosen the clip and disconnect the oil return hose from the outlet pipe.
80    Disconnect the vacuum hose or hoses from the pressure regulator capsule (photos).
81    Unscrew the mounting nuts or bolts and withdraw the turbocharger from the exhaust manifold. Access is limited to some of the nuts/bolts and a thin section spanner will be required to unscrew them. **Do not** lift the unit by the wastegate control rod.
82    Remove the gasket, then clean the joint faces of the exhaust manifold, turbocharger and downpipe elbow.
83    Refit the turbocharger in reverse order using a new gasket and, if necessary, self-locking mounting nuts.
84    Before starting the engine it is important to prime the oil circuit, as follows. Disconnect the three-pin plug from the ignition module (Fig. 12.19), then operate the starter motor until the oil pressure light goes out. Reconnect the three-pin plug.
85    Start the engine and allow it to idle for several minutes in order to re-establish normal oil flow through the turbocharger.

*Intercooler – removal and refitting*
86    Disconnect the battery negative lead.
87    Remove the HT lead from the ignition module.
88    Disconnect both air hoses from the intercooler.
89    Release the rubber strap from the top of the intercooler and remove the saddle (photo).

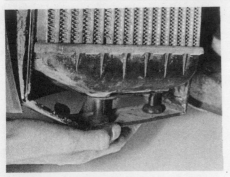

6.94A Removing the intercooler mounting bracket

6.94B Removing the intercooler ducting

6.94C The intercooler removed from the vehicle

6.96 Intercooler thermostat

6.101 Air cleaner and retaining strap

6.102 Removing the air filter element

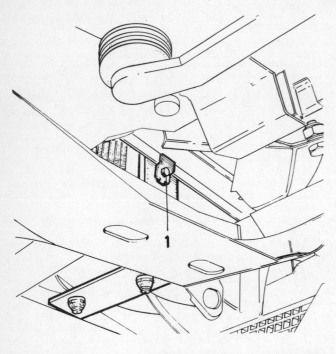

**Fig. 12.20 The intercooler mounting bracket inner bolt (1) and clamp plate (Sec 6)**

90    Jack up the front of the car and support on axle stands. Remove the left-hand front roadwheel.

91    Unbolt the splash guard from under the left-hand front wheel arch (photo). For better access, the front bumper should be released from the body at its left-hand end (with reference to Chapter 11), although this is not essential.

92    Unscrew the bolts securing the intercooler mounting bracket to the body, noting that the inner bolt incorporates a clamp plate.

93    If the bumper has been removed, withdraw the intercooler from the car, together with the mounting bracket and plastic ducting.

94    If the bumper is still in place, unclip the plastic ducting, separate the mounting bracket and ducting from the bottom of the unit, then lower the intercooler from the car. The ducting can then be removed from the car if necessary (photos).

95    Refitting is a reversal of removal, but check that the rubber mounting grommets are in good condition and correctly located in the mounting bracket. Hook the rubber strap in the mounting bracket before refitting the assembly.

*Intercooler thermostat – testing*

96    The intercooler incorporates a thermostatically controlled flap in its header tank, the thermostat being located in the outlet (photo). With the flap closed, no air passes through the cooling fins and there is a direct passageway from the inlet to the outlet. With the flap open, the air is channelled through the cooling fins before passing through the outlet.

97    To test the thermistor, remove the intercooler and immerse the capsule in water at 41 to 45°C (106 to 113°F) for five minutes. The flap should close, blocking air entry to the cooling fins.

98    Repeat the test with the water at 45 to 49°C (113 to 120°F), and the flap should open so that all air passes through the cooling fins.

*Air filter element (Turbo models) – renewal*

99    Disconnect the HT lead from the ignition module and release it from the clips.

100    Disconnect the air hose from the carburettor elbow, release the rubber strap and move the hose to one side.

101    Release the strap from the air cleaner body (photo).

102    Disconnect the turbocharger air inlet hose from the air cleaner. Tilt the air cleaner, then remove the wing nut and cover and extract the air filter element (photo).

103    To completely remove the air cleaner, disconnect the remaining hoses. The unit incorporates an air temperature control flap operated by a thermostat working between 26 and 32°C (79 and 90°F) (photos). The flap, which directs cold air from the front of the car and hot air from the exhaust manifold, can be tested using the same procedure previously

6.103A Disconnecting the air cleaner from the turbocharger hose

6.103B The air temperature control thermostat in the air cleaner

6.103C Air cleaner temperature control flap lever and connecting wire from thermostat

6.106A Fuel filter and pump on Turbo models

6.106B Fuel filter on Turbo models

6.112 Fuel pump on Turbo models

described for the intercooler thermostat, but using the relevant operating temperatures.

104   Wipe clean the inside of the air cleaner and cover before fitting the new air filter element, using a reversal of the removal procedure.

*Fuel filter (Turbo models) – renewal*

105   Chock the front wheels, then jack up the rear of the car and support on axle stands.

106   If available, fit hose clamps to the hose at each end of the fuel filter. Alternatively the hoses will have to be plugged as they are disconnected (photos).

107   Disconnect both hoses.

108   Unscrew the clamp bolt, pull out the clamp and remove the fuel filter.

109   Refitting is a reversal of removal, but make sure that the filter is fitted the correct way round. The direction of flow arrow on the filter body must point to the hose leading to the front of the car.

*Fuel pump (Turbo models) – removal and refitting*

110   Chock the front wheels then jack up the rear of the car and support on axle stands.

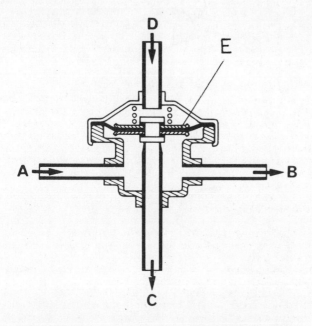

**Fig. 12.21 Diagram of the fuel pressure regulator (Sec 6)**

A   Fuel from electric pump
B   Fuel output to the carburettor
C   Return to fuel tank
D   'Blown' intake air pressure
E   Diaphragm

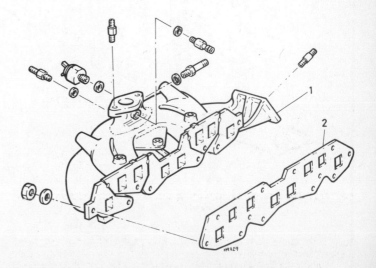

**Fig. 12.22 Inlet and exhaust manifold (1) and gasket (2) on Turbo models (Sec 6)**

6.117 Fuel pressure regulator on Turbo models

6.122 Air pressure check take-off point on the carburettor (Turbo models)

6.123 Safety pressure switch on Turbo models

111   Disconnect the battery negative lead.
112   If available, fit hose clamps to the hoses at each end of the fuel pump. Alternatively the hoses will have to be plugged as they are disconnected (photo).
113   Disconnect both hoses, then disconnect the wires from the two terminals on the pump. Mark the wires for position to ensure correct refitting.
114   Unscrew the clamp bolt, lift the clamp and remove the fuel pump.
115   The fuel pump is sealed and if faulty should be renewed complete.
116   Refitting is a reversal of removal.

## Fuel pressure regulator (Turbo models) – removal and refitting

117   The fuel pressure regulator is located on the right-hand side of the engine compartment on the suspension turret (photo). It controls the fuel pressure by varying the amount of fuel returned to the fuel tank (Fig. 12.21). One side of the diaphragm is subject to the inlet air pressure in the carburettor elbow, assisted by a calibrated spring. The fuel pressure increases until the diaphragm is forced away from the end of the return pipe, so when the inlet air pressure increases this produces a corresponding increase in fuel pressure.
118   To remove the regulator, first disconnect the air hose from the top of the unit.
119   Identify the three fuel hoses for position, then disconnect and plug them.
120   Unbolt the pressure regulator from its mounting bracket.
121   Refitting is a reversal of removal.

## Turbocharger – testing and adjustment

122   All testing and adjustment of the turbocharger should be carried out by a Renault dealer, as special gauges and adaptors are required. The main tests include checking the oil supply pressure, the fuel pressure and the turbocharged air pressure. A take-off point for the air pressure is provided on the carburettor (photo) and any adjustment necessary is made at the rod connecting the vacuum capsule to the wastegate on the turbocharger.
123   If necessary, a further test can be made on the safety pressure switch located in the outlet hose from the turbocharger, but this also requires special equipment (photo).

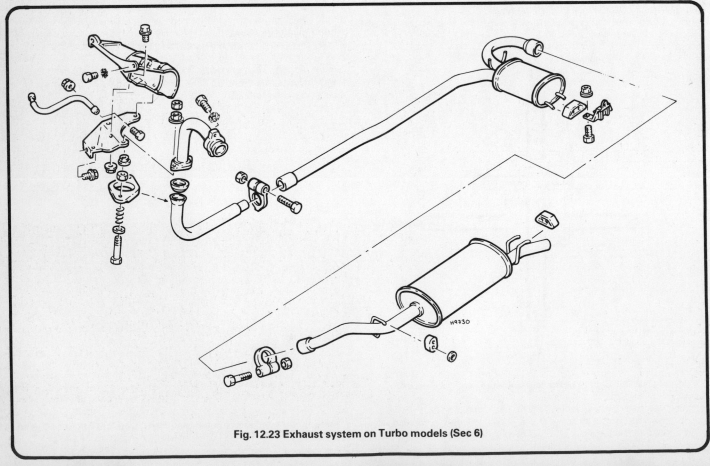

Fig. 12.23 Exhaust system on Turbo models (Sec 6)

6.126A Intermediate muffler outer mounting on Turbo models

6.126B Intermediate muffler inner mounting on Turbo models

6.127 Exhaust system flange with spring-tensioned collar on Turbo models

*Inlet and exhaust manifolds (Turbo models) – removal and refitting*

124   First remove the turbocharger, as previously described, then proceed as described in Chapter 3.

125   Refitting is a reversal of removal, with reference to this Section for the turbocharger.

*Exhaust system (Turbo models) – general*

126   The exhaust system is in four sections with intermediate and tail mufflers. The two front sections are angled, and the intermediate section incorporates an offset muffler supported by two rubber mountings (photos).

127   Checking, removal and refitting procedures are similar to those described in Chapter 3, although the spring-tensioned flange between the two angled front sections is of a different design (photo). The two bolts incorporate locknuts on their threads which can be set to the preload dimension before fitting them in position. This is possible because the holes in the flange are large enough to allow the locknuts to pass through (Fig. 12.24).

128   The flange joint also incorporates an anti-squeak washer, which must always be fitted.

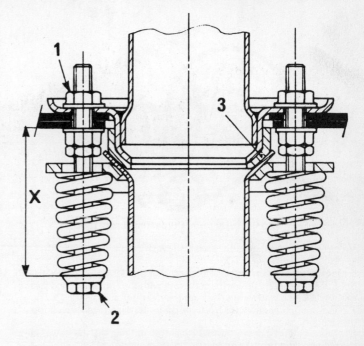

**Fig. 12.24 Exhaust system flange components and spring preload dimensions (Sec 6)**

| 1 | Nut | 3 | Anti-squeak washer |
| 2 | Bolt | | $X = 67.0 \pm 1.0\,mm\ (2.638 \pm 0.04\,in)$ |

*Fault diagnosis – turbocharger*

| Symptom | Reason(s) |
|---|---|
| Noisy operation | Worn bearings |
| | Intake or exhaust leaks |
| | Poor lubrication |
| | Coolant leak |
| Poor acceleration | Air filter clogged |
| | Pressure regulator faulty |
| | Leaks in manifold or ducts |
| Blue smoke in exhaust | Internal oil seals leaking |

**7   Ignition system**

*Contact breaker points – renewal and adjustment*

1   Renault 9 models with the 1108 cc engine may be fitted with an SEV Marchal distributor having cassette points. On this type, the gap (dwell angle) is preset during production and it should be only a matter of changing the cassette to provide the optimum ignition setting. In practice, it is recommended that after the cassette has been renewed, the dwell angle is checked. Any adjustment required can be carried out by inserting a 3.0 mm Allen key through the hole provided in the distributor body.

2   Although a cassette is expensive, when compared with a conventional contact breaker set, it does have the advantage that the spark jumps vertically within the distributor cap. This eliminates any possibility of voltage reduction at the spark plug, as happens with a conventional distributor if worn bushes allow any play in the distributor shaft.

3   To renew the cassette, release the distributor cap and move it to one side.

4   Take off the rotor arm.

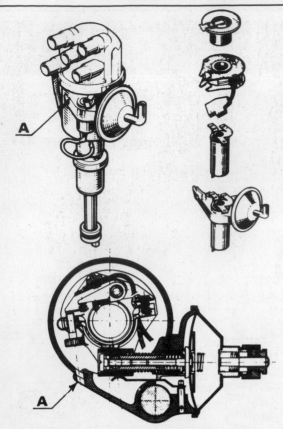

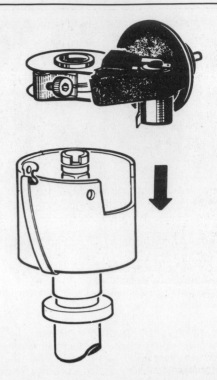

**Fig. 12.26 Fitting cassette into distributor body (Sec 7)**

**Fig. 12.25 Cassette points type distributor (Sec 7)**

*A   Allen key hole*

5   Pull the lead from the spade terminal at the base of the condenser.
6   Pull the cassette upwards, complete with the condenser and plastic mounting block, and remove it from the distributor.
7   Pull the plug connector from the spare terminals located on top of the condenser.
8   Remove and discard the old cassette, and engage the new one in the advance lugs of the condenser plastic mounting block.
9   Make sure that the cassette is the correct way up, with its socket-

headed adjuster screw opposite to the Allen key hole in the distributor body. The cassette is reversible to suit distributors which rotate either clockwise or anti-clockwise.
10   Hold the cassette/mounting block assembly over the distributor ready to fit, but if the rotor cut-out in the top of the distributor shaft is in alignment with the heel (follower) of the contact breaker, rotate the crankshaft slightly to alter the position of the cut-out, otherwise one of the cam peaks may damage the cassette contact heel as the assembly is fitted. Fit the connector plug.
11   Push the cassette/mounting block assembly fully down into the distributor recess. Make sure that the sides of the assembly engage in their grooves, and check that the plastic connecting plug is fully seated with the condenser in a downwards direction.
12   Fit the rotor and distributor cap.
13   Check the dwell angle and timing, as described in Chapter 4 – the specifications are the same as for the Ducellier distributor.

## Distributor rotor arm (1721 cc engines) – general
14   Three different types of rotor arm are fitted to 1721 cc engines. The latest type incorporates an O-ring which engages a groove in the camshaft and requires no locking compound to hold it in place.
15   All replacement rotor arms are of the latest type, and when fitting this type to an earlier camshaft **without** a groove, the rotor arm must be secured using the following procedure.
16   Remove the O-ring from the rotor arm, then thoroughly clean the end of the camshaft using emery cloth if necessary.

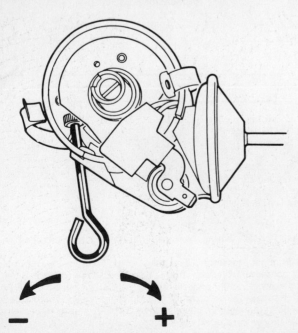

**Fig. 12.27 Adjusting cassette points gap (Sec 7)**

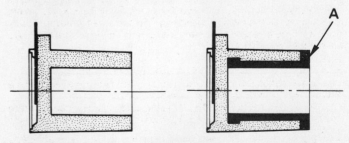

**Fig. 12.28 Early types of distributor rotor arms fitted to 1721 cc engines (Sec 7)**

*A   Metal insert*

7.19 Knock detector on the front of the cylinder head on Turbo models

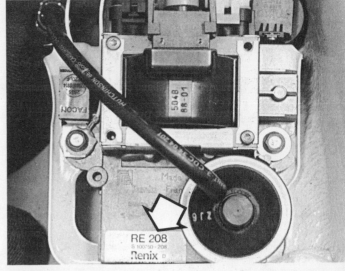

7.24 Module advance curve label – electronic ignition (arrowed)

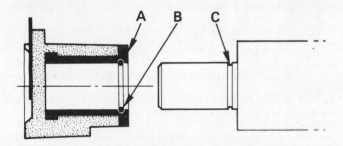

**Fig. 12.29 Latest type of distributor rotor arm fitted to 1721 cc engines (Sec 7)**

A   Metal insert          C   Groove in camshaft
B   O-ring

17   Apply Locktite SCELBOC to the bore and rear face of the rotor arm, then locate it on the camshaft and engage the lug. Hold it firmly in position for 15 seconds, then leave it for 30 minutes to cure.

## Ignition system (Turbo models) – general

18   Turbo models are fitted with an electric ignition system, as described in Chapter 4. The computer module incorporates a speed governor system, which cuts out the ignition at an engine speed of 6200 rpm.
19   Also included on Turbo models is a knock detector, which signals the computer module to retard the ignition timing by 6° in the event of pre-ignition occurring. The unit is secured into the front of the cylinder head near the distributor (photo).
20   To test the knock detector, connect a timing light to the engine then run the engine at idling speed. Direct the timing light on the timing marks, then tap the cylinder head near the knock detector repeatedly using a bronze drift, and check that the ignition timing retards by 6°. Do not tap the knock detector unit.

## Ignition module (electronic ignition) – identification

21   Different computer modules are fitted to different engines, and are of type D or E, which are similar, or type F.
22   Each module has its own pre-set ignition advance curve, which can only be fully tested by a garage with the necessary diagnostic equipment.
23   The ignition timing can be checked, using a stroboscopic timing light (see also Chapter 4, Section 14), using the latest ignition advance figures given in the Specifications at the beginning of this Supplement.
24   The module advance curve reference number is given on a label stuck on to the side or front of the module unit (photo).

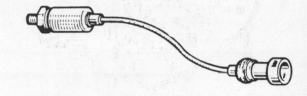

**Fig. 12.30 Knock detector and wiring fitted to Turbo models (Sec 7)**

## 8   Clutch

### Clutch cable self-adjusting mechanism – checking

1   When the self-adjusting mechanism on the clutch pedal is functioning correctly there should be a minimum of 2.0 mm (0.079 in) slack in the cable. To check this dimension, pull out the inner cable near the release fork on the gearbox (Fig. 12.31).

**Fig. 12.31 Checking the clutch cable slack (Sec 8)**

**Fig. 12.32 Later type bi-coloured gearbox identification plate (Sec 9)**

A   Gearbox type          D   Factory of manufacture
B   Gearbox suffix        E   Engine type assembled with
C   Fabrication number         gearbox

*Shaded area is 'two-thirds' colour (see text)*

2   If there is less than the minimum slack in the cable, the self-adjusting mechanism should be checked. Make sure that the serrated quadrant and support arms are free to turn on their respective pivots, and that the spring has not lost its tension. If possible, check the free length of the spring against a new one. Also check that the inner cable is not seizing in the outer cable.

## 9   Manual gearbox

### Gearbox type JB4 or JB5 – description

1   Later models are fitted with the JB4 or JB5 gearbox.
2   These gearboxes are a development of the earlier JB type gearboxes, with modifications. They are lighter in construction, with hollow input and mainshafts, and with lighter differential components and reverse shaft.
3   The overall width of the gearbox has been reduced, and the length of the driveshafts increased as a consequence.
4   Overhaul procedures for the later type gearboxes are basically the same as for the earlier types described in Chapter 6, taking note of the modifications mentioned in this Section.
5   Note also that although most of the modifications apply only to the JB4 and JB5 gearboxes, they may also apply retrospectively to earlier types.

### Gearbox type – identification

6   A colour code is progressively being introduced to ensure correct matching of gearbox and driveshafts. The colours are located on the gearbox identification plate and the outer ends of the driveshafts, and are as follows:

| Gearbox type | Gearbox colour code | Driveshaft colour code Left | Right |
|---|---|---|---|
| JB0, JB1 and MB1 | Red | Yellow/Red | Yellow/Red |
| JB3 (F2N engine) | Black | Yellow/Red | Yellow/Red |
| JB3 (except F2N engine) | Black | Yellow/Red | Yellow/Yellow |
| JB4 and JB5 | Green/Pink | Yellow/Pink | Yellow/Pink |

7   On later gearboxes, the identification plate is bi-coloured, two-thirds of the plate painted with a colour peculiar to each gearbox type (and matching the driveshafts), the remaining one-third painted according to the gearbox suffix number. The new colour markings correspond to the earlier colours as follows:

| Gearbox type | Original colour | 'Two-thirds' colour |
|---|---|---|
| JB0 | Red | Orange |
| JB1 | Red | Red |
| JB2 | Black | Aluminium |
| JB3 | Black | Black |

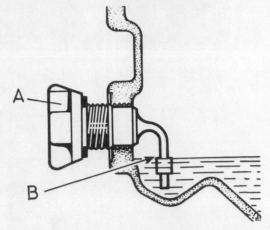

**Fig. 12.33 Plastic gearbox filler plug with dipstick (Sec 9)**

A   Filler plug              B   Dipstick collar

### Gearbox oil (JB4 and JB5) – level checking, draining and refilling

8   When draining and refilling the gearbox oil as described in Chapter 6, Section 3, note that JB4 and JB5 gearboxes have a dipstick incorporated in the filler plug. Also the filler plug is made of plastic, and not steel as previously.
9   The oil level is correct when it is level with the top of the collar on the dipstick.
10   When checking the oil level, the filler should be inserted fully into the filler plug hole, but not screwed in, with the dipstick pointing straight down.
11   Note also that where a gearbox has a modified dipstick, the oil capacity is reduced (see Specifications).

### Differential – modification

12   On later models, a spacer has been introduced between the differential planet wheels. The spacer is secured in position by a spring pin.

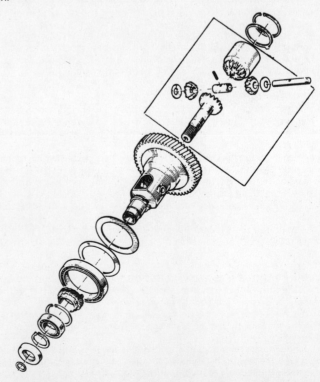

**Fig. 12.34 Spacer and spring pin on later differentials (Sec 9)**

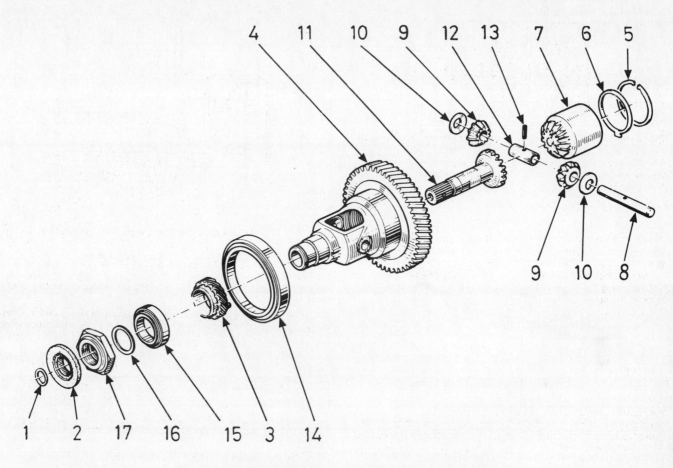

**Fig. 12.35 Later type differential, mounted on taper bearings (Sec 9)**

| | | | | | |
|---|---|---|---|---|---|
| 1 | O-ring | 6 | Shim | 10 | Planet wheel washer |
| 2 | Lip seal | 7 | Spider type sun wheel | 11 | Sun wheel with tail shaft |
| 3 | Speedometer drivegear | 8 | Planet wheel shaft | 12 | Spacer sleeve |
| 4 | Differential housing | 9 | Planet wheels | 13 | Spring pin |
| 5 | Circlip | | | | |

14 Tapered bearing
15 Tapered bearing
16 Adjusting shim
17 Differential nut

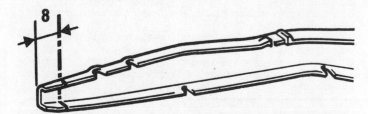

**Fig. 12.36 Cut the plastic oil flow guide as shown when renewing the mechanism casing on early models – dimension in mm (Sec 9)**

13    A further modification is the introduction of taper bearings in place of roller bearings. Note also that the components are secured on the differential housing by a nut and not a circlip as before. The torque loading figure for the differential housing nut is given in the Specifications.

*Oil flow guide – modification*
14    On later models the gearbox oil flow guide is of plastic instead of metal. When renewing the mechanism casing on an early gearbox it will be necessary to cut off approximately 8.0 mm (0.315 in) from the new plastic oil flow guide, otherwise it will be impossible to refit the gearbox rear cover.

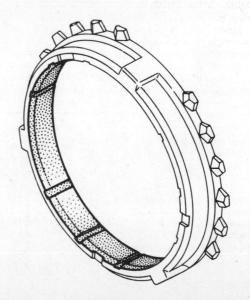

**Fig. 12.37 Later type synchroniser baulk ring with molybdenum disulphide coating (Sec 9)**

Fig. 12.38 Modified shaft protrusion
and circlip groove (Sec 9)

A   Early type
B   Later type
Y = X – 0.2 mm
Insert shows the dished washer

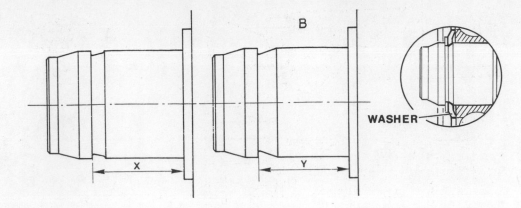

WASHER

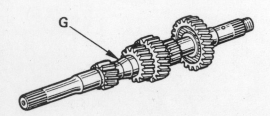

Fig. 12.39 Letter 'G' stamped on modified mainshafts (Sec 9)

## Synchroniser baulk rings – modifications

15    On later models the synchroniser baulk rings incorporate an inner
coating of molybdenum disulphide, and the modified ring is also supplied as a service replacement.
16    When fitting the modified baulk ring Renault recommend that the
inner surface is smeared with 'Molykote M55 + '; obtainable from a
Renault parts stockist.

## Input and mainshaft circlips (JB0 and JB2 gearboxes) – modification

17    When reassembling a gearbox of the above types as described in
Chapter 6, Section 14, paragraph 9, note that the modified profile and
shaft protrusion, and the diameter and width of the dished washer.
18    Fit the correct size washer and circlip according to the shaft fitted.
19    To identify modified shafts, the main shaft has a letter 'G' stamped
as shown in Fig. 12.39.

## Gearbox-to-engine coupling – modification

20    Depending on the coupling method, there are two centring bushes
used in the gearbox-to-engine coupling, one long and one short.
21    From approximately November 1986, both these bushes have
been lengthened, and the cylinder block and clutch housing modified
accordingly.

22    The dimensions of both the old and new bushes are shown in
Fig. 12.40, and it is imperative that the correct bushes of appropriate
length are used.

## Electronic speedometer – general description

23    Some models are fitted with an electronic speedometer, the
sensor for which is incorporated in the differential housing.
24    A sensor ring is mounted on the differential housing, and a pick-up
is mounted on the differential casing.
25    As the sensor ring rotates with the differential, the pick-up senses
the movement and transmits a signal to the speedometer in the
instrument panel.

## Electronic speedometer components – removal and refitting

26    The pick-up is a push fit in the differential casing, and is secured in
place by a spring clip held under one of the differential casing bolts.
Remove the bolt and the clip, and pull out the pick-up unit.
27    Refitting is a reverse of removal, but ensure that the oil seal is in
good condition and apply a little gearbox oil to the seal to ease fitment.
28    The sensor ring can only be removed after the differential has been
dismantled. Note the two methods of securing the sensor ring to the
differential housing.
29    On early types the spacer, spring and sensor can be removed after
the bearing has been pulled off.
30    The spacer used is different for roller and taper bearings, so make
sure the correct spacer is used for the type of bearing.
31    On later types, a spring clip arrangement is used to secure the
sensor ring.
32    To remove the spring clip, prise the tabs out of the groove in the
housing and pull the clip and ring from the housing.
33    Always use a new spring for refitting and tap it back in place using
a suitable piece of large diameter tubing (plastic drainpipe would appear
suitable), ensuring the tabs locate in the groove in the housing.

---

Fig. 12.40 Showing the gearbox-
to-engine coupling and centring
bushes (Sec 9)

**Early**
A = 3.25 to 3.75 mm (0.13 to 0.15 in)
B = 9.5 mm (0.37 in)
C = 23.45 mm (0.92 in)
D = 6.75 to 7.5 mm (0.27 to 0.30 in)
    for short bush, 20.5 mm (0.81 in)
    for long bush
**Later**
5.75 to 6.25 mm (0.23 to 0.25 in)
12.0 mm (0.47 in)
25.9 mm (1.02 in)
Unchanged

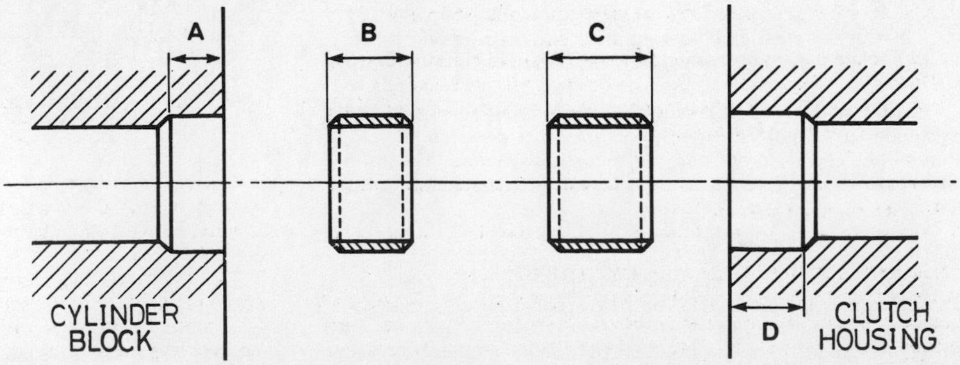

A      B      C

CYLINDER
BLOCK

D      CLUTCH
HOUSING

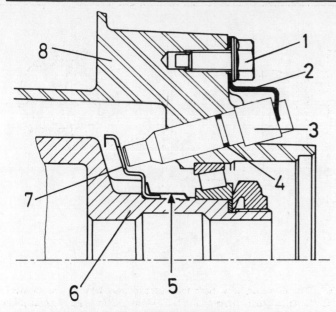

Fig. 12.41 Cutaway view of later type electronic speedometer components (Sec 9)

| | |
|---|---|
| 1 Casing bolt | 5 Spring clip |
| 2 Spring clip | 6 Differential housing |
| 3 Pick-up | 7 Sensor ring |
| 4 Oil seal | 8 Differential casing |

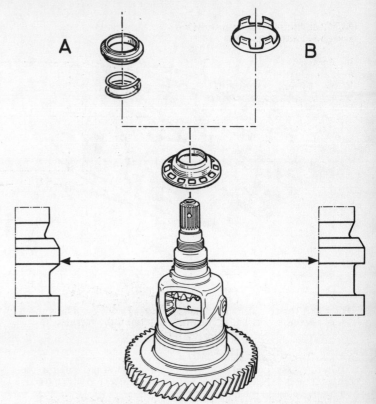

Fig. 12.42 Early (A) and later (B) methods of securing the sensor ring (Sec 9)

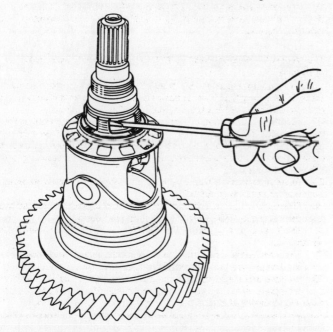

Fig. 12.43 Prising out the tabs on later type spring clips (Sec 9)

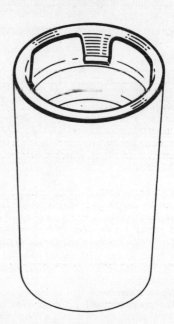

Fig. 12.44 Fitting the spring clip to suitable size piece of tubing (Sec 9)

34  The later type spring cannot be used on earlier differential housings, although the early type spring can be used on later housings.

35  Note also that the air gap between the pick-up and the sensor ring is fixed, and cannot be adjusted.

## 10  Automatic transmission

### *Torque converter driveplate – modification*

1  Where a 227 mm (8.94 in) torque converter is fitted, the diameter of the studs and nuts securing the connector to the driveplate has been increased from 8.0 mm (0.31 in) to 9.0 mm (0.35 in), and the holes in the driveplate increased from 11.0 mm (0.43 in) to 12.0 mm (0.47 in).

2  A torque converter with 8.0 mm studs can be fitted to a driveplate with 12 mm holes, but a torque converter with 9.0 mm studs cannot be fitted to a driveplate with 11.0 mm holes, unless the holes are first drilled out to 12.0 mm.

3  Note that the torque wrench settings for 9.0 and 8.0 mm converter retaining nuts is different (see Specifications).

4  Transmission units with the larger torque converter cannot be removed separately, therefore the engine and transmission must be removed together and separated after removal.

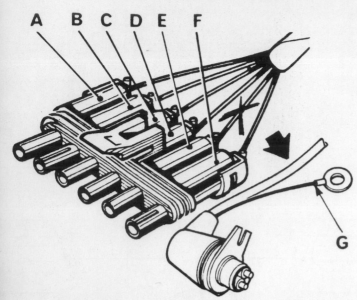

A  B  C  D  E  F

G

Fig. 12.45 The computer module earthing wire is moved from the connector terminal 'E' to the multi-function switch wiring 'G' (Sec 10)

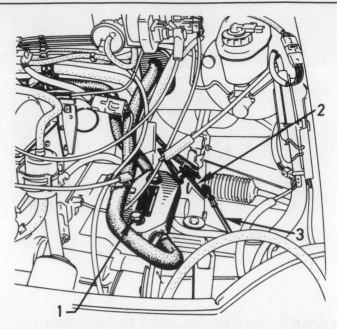

1

2

3

Fig. 12.46 Monobloc oil cooler fitted to the automatic transmission (Sec 10)

1   Oil cooler
2   Selector ballcrank
3   Selector connecting rod

### Computer module – earthing

5   On pre-1985 models, an earthing wire is connected direct to the computer module by means of the multi-plug connector, with the ends of the wire bolted to the transmission.

6   As from 1985, the earthing wire is incorporated in the multi-function switch wiring and the wire end is bolted to the transmission near the switch.

7   If a seven-pin connector is used when the multi-function switch is earthed to the transmission, then the earth lead on the seven-pin connector (coloured yellow or white) should be cut through at the computer end, flush with the sheathing.

8   A poor earth connection will result in the transmission remaining in third gear, or changing gear at random.

### Computer harness components – precautions

9   All automatic transmission harness components must be routed at least 150.0 mm (6.0 in) away from HT electrical sources.

10   All HT cables must be correctly connected and routed, and not in contact with any metal parts.

11   If the above conditions are not met, interference of the automatic transmission control computer may occur.

### Oil cooler – modification

12   On later models, a monobloc oil cooler is fitted to the transmission instead of the tube type fitted in the radiator bottom hose on previous models. The modification was progressively introduced from early 1985.

13   The transmission casing is specially adapted so that the monobloc oil cooler can be bolted directly over the inlet and outlet ports. O-ring seals are located on the ports, and the only pipe connections are the two coolant hoses in the heater return circuit.

14   If the automatic transmission is renewed as a unit, it may not be possible to obtain one with the old type ports, and in this case it will be necessary to fit a new monobloc oil cooler. Check that the O-ring seals are correctly located, and tighten the bolts evenly to the specified torque.

### 11   Driveshafts

#### Left-hand driveshaft bellows retaining plate (automatic transmission models) – description

1   The left-hand driveshaft bellows retaining plate may be of two alternative types. The first type incorporates welded spacers for correct location of the plate, and ordinary bolts should be used to secure this type.

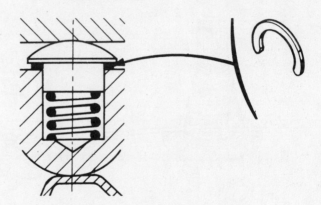

Fig. 12.47 Shim location in the outer constant velocity joint on later models (Sec 11)

2   The second type is **not** fitted with welded spacers, and shouldered bolts should be used to secure this type. Incorrect location will result if ordinary bolts are used.

#### New driveshafts – fitting

3   New driveshafts are supplied with cardboard protectors over the bellows. These protectors must be left in place until fitting is complete, then removed by hand. Do not use sharp-ended tools to remove the protectors, as there is a risk of damaging the bellows.

#### Driveshaft bellows – renewal (general)

4   The rubber bellows at the outboard end of each driveshaft have been superseded by bellows made of a thermoplastic material. These later bellows cannot be expanded to pass over the driveshaft yoke, so the inboard bellows will have to be removed and the driveshaft dismantled as described in Chapter 7, Section 5 or 6, or as follows in this Section.

#### Outer constant velocity joint rubber bellows – renewal

5   On later models, a shim is located beneath the head of the thrust ball in the outer constant velocity joint. The correct shim thickness is determined during manufacture, and no attempt should be made to change it.

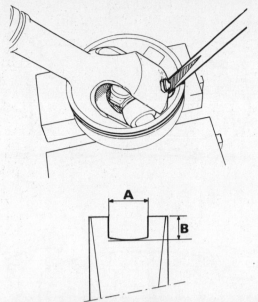

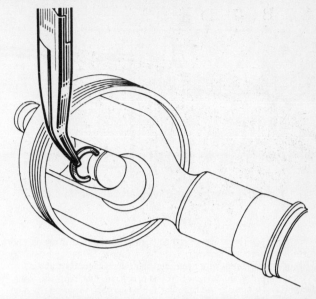

**Fig. 12.48 Use a screwdriver shaped as shown to refit the constant velocity joint starplate (Sec 11)**

$A = 5.0$ mm (0.20 in)     $B = 3.0$ mm (0.12 in)

**Fig. 12.49 Inserting the shim on the thrust ball (Sec 11)**

6    The procedure for removing the outer bellows is basically as given in Chapter 7, Section 4 (bearing in mind the point made in paragraph 4 above, and ignoring references to expanding the bellows). When fitting the new bellows, first assemble the joint without the shim. A screwdriver shaped as shown in Fig. 12.48 will facilitate refitting the starplate.

7    Angle the driveshaft and stub axle in line with one of the starplate arms so that the thrust ball lifts off its seat, then refit the shim; make sure that it does not protrude from the edge of the thrust ball.

8    Pack the joint with the correct quantity of grease, then reposition the bellows and fit the clips. The bellows must be correctly located in the two grooves on later models.

9    Where crimp-type clips are fitted, a crimping tool will be required to tighten them, although pliers may prove satisfactory.

*Right-hand driveshaft inner bellows (later models) – renewal*

10    Two types of driveshaft joint have been used at the right-hand

inner position. The first type is known as GT 62 – the bellows renewal procedure is given in Chapter 7, Section 5. The second type (Fig. 12.50) is known as RC 490, for which the bellows renewal procedure is as follows.

11    Remove the driveshaft (Chapter 7, Section 3).

12    Release the staking which secures the metal casing to the yoke.

13    Cut the bellows retaining clip. Cut open the bellows and remove as much grease as possible.

14    Remove the yoke by tapping the metal casing off it, using a brass or copper drift. Be careful that the rollers do not fall off the trunnions – they must not be interchanged.

15    Remove the circlip (if fitted) which secures the spider to the driveshaft (Fig. 12.51). Make identification marks between the spider and the shaft for use when refitting.

16    Press or pull the spider off the driveshaft – see Chapter 7, Section 5, paragraph 6.

17    Remove the bellows, metal casing and insert. Clean and examine the shaft and spider (Chapter 7, Section 5, paragraphs 8 to 10).

18    To the driveshaft fit a new retaining clip, new bellows, the insert and the metal casing.

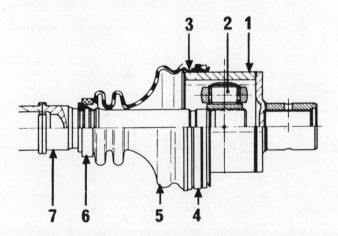

**Fig. 12.50 Sectional view of RC 490 inner constant velocity joint (Sec 11)**

| | | | |
|---|---|---|---|
| 1 | Yoke | 5 | Bellows |
| 2 | Spider | 6 | Clip |
| 3 | Metal cover | 7 | Shaft |
| 4 | Clip | | |

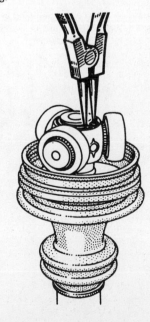

**Fig. 12.51 Removing circlip which retains the spider (Sec 11)**

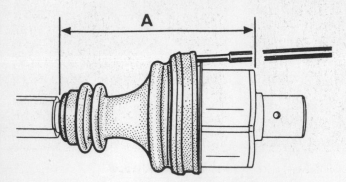

**Fig. 12.52 Venting the driveshaft bellows (Sec 11)**

*A = 156 ± 1 mm*

19    Refit the spider, observing the alignment marks, and press it home.
20    Refit the securing circlip, if one was found. On versions without a circlip, secure the spider by peening the splines in three places.
21    Using the grease supplied in the repair kit, lubricate the yoke, the spider and the inside of the bellows. All the grease must be used.
22    Fit the yoke to the spider. Fit the bellows and insert to the metal casing, then slide the casing onto the yoke. Secure the casing by staking it in three places.
23    Insert a thin blunt instrument, such as a knitting needle, between the end of the bellows and the driveshaft so that air can escape. Move the joint in or out to achieve a dimension 'A' as shown in Fig. 12.52.
24    Without disturbing the joint or the bellows, remove the knitting needle and fit the new retaining clip.
25    Refit the driveshaft (Chapter 7, Section 3).

## 12    Braking system

### *Front disc pads (Bendix) – description and renewal*

1    As from early 1984, Bendix calipers are equipped with offset disc pads, and it is important that these are fitted the correct way round. The calipers have been progressively modified to prevent incorrect fitting of both the offset and previous symmetrical type disc pads, but on unmodified calipers the following procedure should be followed.
2    The inner pads must be fitted with pad wear warning light wires at the top near the caliper bleed screws. The groove in the pad lining will then be offset to the top of the caliper.
3    The outer pads must be fitted with the lining grooves offset to the bottom of the caliper. If the grooves are in line with the inner pad grooves the outer pads must be on the wrong sides of the car.

12.5 Ventilated front brake discs on Turbo models

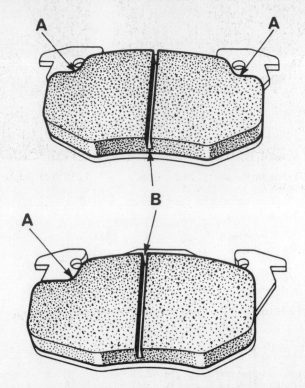

**Fig. 12.53 The differences between symmetrical (top) and offset (bottom) Bendix disc pads (Sec 12)**

A    *Indents*                    B    *Groove in pad lining*

4    Apart from this procedure, renewal of the disc pads remains as given in Chapter 8, Section 3.

### *Front brake disc (Turbo models) – description*

5    On Turbo models, the front brake disc is of the ventilated type (photo). The disc thicknesses are given in the Specifications, and inspection, removal and refitting procedures are as given in Chapter 8.

### *Rear disc brakes (Turbo models) – description*

6    Later Turbo models are equipped with rear disc brakes.
7    The rear disc brake is similar to those fitted to the front, being of single-piston, sliding caliper type.

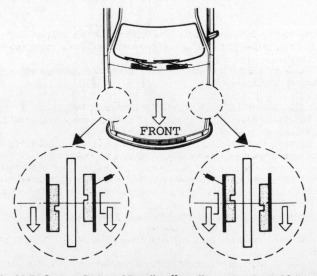

**Fig. 12.54 Correct fitting of Bendix offset disc pads, viewed from the front (Sec 12)**

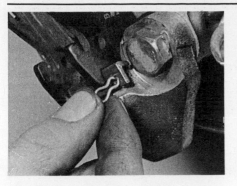

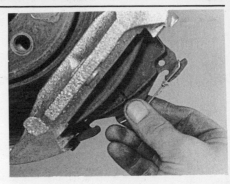

12.12 Removing the spring clip from the retaining key

12.13 Retaining key partly withdrawn

12.14 Removing the pads

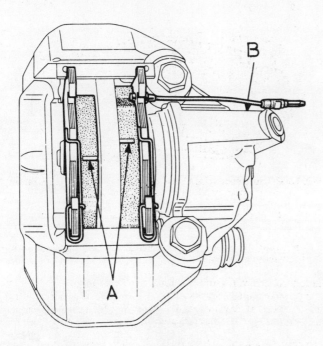

Fig. 12.55 Right-hand caliper fitted with Bendix offset disc pads (Sec 12)

*A   Pad lining grooves*          *B   Bleed screw location*

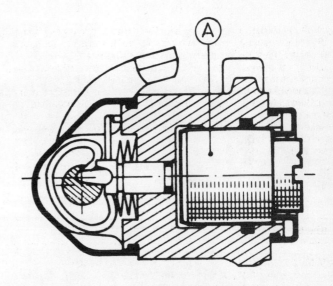

Fig. 12.56 Sectional view of the rear disc brake piston (A) and handbrake lever (Sec 12)

8    The handbrake mechanism is incorporated in the caliper, being direct-acting on the piston and using the disc brake. There is no separate drum brake.
9    The handbrake mechanism also provides for automatic adjustment to compensate for wear.

### Rear disc brake pads – inspection and renewal

10    Proceed as described in Chapter 8, Section 3, paragraphs 1 and 2, then, if the pads need renewing, carry out the following.
11    Remove the brake fluid reservoir cap. Then, using a suitable blunt instrument inserted between the pad and disc carefully push back the piston to give enough play to allow the pads to be removed. Note that pushing the piston back will cause the brake fluid level in the reservoir to rise – anticipate this by syphoning some out. Do not let the fluid drip onto the paintwork.
12    Remove the spring clip from the retaining key (photo).
13    Withdraw the retaining key (photo).
14    Lift out the worn pads, complete with the anti-rattle springs (photo).
15    Take the opportunity to inspect the condition of the piston dust cover, and the gaiters covering the caliper slides. Renew them as necessary.

16    Using a square-shank screwdriver, screw the piston fully inwards until it continues to turn, but does not screw in any further.
17    Position the piston so that the filed mark adjacent to one of the square-section cut-outs is in line with the caliper bleed screw (photo).
18    Fit the anti-rattle springs to the new brake pads (photo).
19    Refit the pads, retaining key and spring clip, and ensure that the anti-rattle springs are located correctly (photo).
20    Check the fluid level in the reservoir, then refit the cap.
21    Operate the brake pedal several times to centralise the caliper, then refit the roadwheel and remove the vehicle from axle stands.

### Rear brake disc – removal, inspection and refitting

22    Remove the brake pads as described earlier.
23    Remove the two caliper bracket retaining bolts and lift off the caliper bracket.
24    Tap off the hub cap, then remove the hub securing nut.
25    Lift off the disc.
26    The disc cannot be re-surfaced, and if heavy scoring and/or corrosion are evident, the disc must be renewed.
27    Removal of the bearings is similar to the procedure given in Chapter 10.
28    Commence refitting by smearing the stub axle with gear oil.
29    Fit the disc/hub assembly, making sure the dust seal is in position on the stub axle, and the circlip securing the bearings is seated correctly in its groove (photos).
30    Fit the washer and hub nut, and tighten to the specified torque (photos).
31    Refit the hub cap, gently tapping it home with a plastic mallet.

12.17 Using a square-shank screwdriver to turn the piston, lining up the filed mark (A) with the bleed screw (B)

12.18 Anti-rattle springs fitted to the brake pads

12.19 Correct location of the anti-rattle springs

12.29A Fitting the dust seal (arrowed) to the stub axle

12.29B Circlip correctly seated in its groove (arrowed)

12.30A Fitting the washer ...

12.30B ... and tightening the nut

12:32A Fitting the caliper bracket ...

12.32B ... and tightening the bolts

12.36 Rigid hydraulic pipeline on the caliper

12.37A Caliper securing bolts (arrowed)

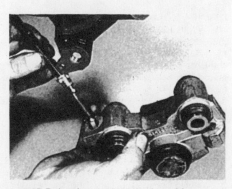

12.37B Releasing the handbrake cable

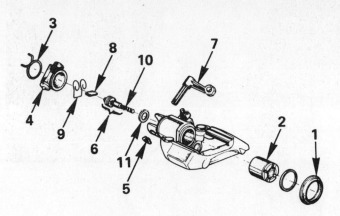

**Fig. 12.57 Exploded view of the rear disc brake caliper (Sec 12)**

| | | | |
|---|---|---|---|
| 1 | Dust seal | 7 | Lever |
| 2 | Piston | 8 | Plunger |
| 3 | Spring clip | 9 | Spring |
| 4 | Dust cover | 10 | Adjuster screw |
| 5 | Circlip | 11 | Large washer |
| 6 | Spring washers | | |

32   Fit the caliper bracket, apply thread-locking fluid to the caliper bracket retaining bolts, then fit the bolts and tighten to the specified torque (photos).
33   Refit the brake pads as described earlier.

*Rear disc brake caliper – removal overhaul and refitting*
34   Before dismantling, obtain an overhaul kit from your Renault dealer, which should contain all the necessary seals and grease required.
35   Remove the brake pads and caliper bracket as described in earlier Sections.
36   Disconnect the rigid hydraulic pipeline on the caliper (photo).
37   Remove the two bolts securing the caliper to the stub axle carrier and lift off the caliper, at the same time releasing the handbrake cable from the lever and the caliper (photos).
38   Place the caliper in a soft-jawed vice.
39   Remove the rubber dust seal from the piston.
40   Unscrew the piston using a square-section screwdriver in the slots in the piston. Once the piston turns freely, eject it from the caliper using compressed air (from a bicycle pump, for example) forced through the hydraulic pipeline hole, having placed a block of wood between the caliper and the piston to prevent damage as the piston is ejected.
41   If the piston is damaged in any way, it must be renewed. Note also that no overhaul of the interior of the caliper piston bore is allowed.
42   Carefully prise the seal from the interior of the caliper piston bore, avoiding scoring the bore surfaces.
43   Remove the dust seals from the caliper slides and remove the slides.
44   Clean all parts in methylated spirit, then inspect them for scoring or corrosion. If any of these conditions exist, the effected component must be renewed.
45   Before reassembly, smear all seals with clean hydraulic fluid.
46   Fit a new seal into the piston bore, ensuring it is seated correctly in its groove.
47   Apply a little hydraulic fluid to the piston bore and piston, then fit the piston into the caliper, initially by hand, then screw it in using the square-section screwdriver once more, until the piston turns without being screwed in.
48   Turn the piston so that the filed mark adjacent to one set of slots in the piston is in line with the bleed nipple on the caliper. This ensures correct bleeding of the caliper, and assembly of the brake pads.
49   Smear the outer edges of the piston with a graphited rubber grease before fitting a new dust seal.
50   Apply graphited rubber grease to the caliper slides, refit them to the caliper and fit the dust seals over their ends.
51   Refit the caliper to the stub axle, feeding the handbrake cable through its bracket on the caliper and into the lever.

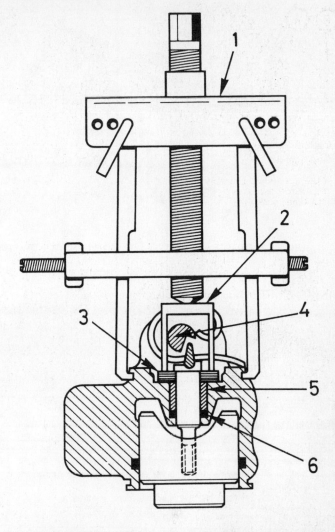

**Fig. 12.58 Special tools required for removing rear disc brake handbrake lever mechanism shown assembled for use (Sec 12)**

| | | | |
|---|---|---|---|
| 1 | Tool B Vi 28-01 (claw extractor) | 4 | Pin and dust guard |
| 2 | Tool Fre 1047 (clamp) | 5 | Bush |
| 3 | Spring washers | 6 | O-ring |

52   Apply thread-locking fluid to the threads of the caliper bolts, then fit and tighten the bolts to the specified torque.
53   Fit and tighten the hydraulic pipeline.
54   Fit the caliper bracket, apply thread-locking fluid to the threads of the bolts, then fit and tighten them to their specified torque.
55   Refit the brake pads, bleed the hydraulic system as described in Chapter 8, Section 15, then refit the roadwheels and remove the vehicle from stands.

*Handbrake (rear disc brake models) – adjustment*
**Note:** *The handbrake must only be adjusted after renewal of the brake pads, handbrake cable or handbrake lever. Adjustment to take up wear should not be necessary.*
56   The vehicle must be jacked and placed on stands and both rear wheels removed.
57   Loosen the locknut on the central compensator, and completely unscrew the adjuster (refer to Chapter 8, Section 16).
58   Check that both cables from the central compensator to the rear brakes are free to move within their outer sheathing.
59   Push both handbrake mechanism operating levers on the rear calipers rearwards as far as they will go.

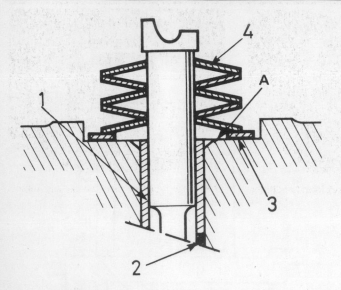

Fig. 12.59 Correct fitting of the bush and spring washers (Sec 12)

1  Bush                4  Spring washers
2  Seal                A  Face
3  Large washer

60    Take up the slack in the cables on the adjuster at the central compensator, so that the nipple on the end of each cable just contacts the operating lever on each caliper, without moving the lever forwards (photo).
61    Continue to tighten the adjuster until the rear brakes are in operation by the time the handbrake lever is pulled up by two notches on the handbrake ratchet.
62    Tighten the locknut on the central compensator adjuster.
63    Refit the roadwheels and remove the vehicle from stands.

### Handbrake mechanism (rear disc brake models) – dismantling and reassembly

64    Dismantling of the handbrake mechanism is a reasonably straight-forward operation, provided that the special tools shown in Fig. 12.51 are available. If this is not the case, then it is recommended that your Renault dealer does the repair work.
65    With the caliper removed and placed in a soft-jawed vice, first pull back the dust cover from the handbrake lever cam. Some covers are secured by a wire clip (photo).
66    Remove the dust seal from the piston and remove the piston as described in earlier paragraphs.
67    Remove the circlip from the end of the lever.
68    Compress the spring washers using the special tools, then remove the lever and dust cover.
69    Lift out the plunger and spring, adjusting screw, large washer and spring washers.
70    The bush can be driven out using a suitable drift, and the O-ring seal extracted from the bore.
71    Clean all parts in methylated spirit, and renew any which show signs of wear. Use a new O-ring seal on reassembly.
72    Lubricate the new seal with clean hydraulic fluid and fit it into position in the bore.
73    Fit the bush, tapping it home with a drift until it is flush with the face 'A' (Fig. 12.59).
74    The remaining sequence is a reversal of removal, assembling the spring washers as shown in Fig. 12.59. Note that although an adjusting screw is mentioned (item 10 in Fig. 12.57), no details of any adjustment were available at the time of writing.
75    Apply high-melting-point grease to the lever, plunger and spring on reassembly.
76    On completion, refit the caliper and adjust the handbrake as previously described.

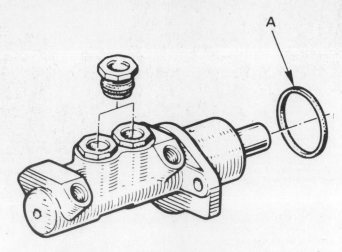

Fig. 12.60 Showing the brake master cylinder on Turbo models, and the seal (A) which must be renewed (Sec 12)

### Brake master cylinder (Turbo models) – general

77    On Turbo models, the brake master cylinder is integral with the brake servo.
78    The seal between the master cylinder and the brake servo must be renewed whenever the two components are separated for repair.

### Brake vacuum servo non-return valve (Turbo models) – general

79    Turbo models are equipped with a valve in the vacuum servo circuit which prevents build up of vacuum pressure when the turbo-charger is in operation.
80    The valve is screwed into the vacuum take-off point on the inlet manifold.
81    Servicing consists of checking that the valve allows air to flow freely in one direction only (towards the manifold) and does not allow air to pass through in the other direction. If this is not the case, the valve must be renewed. Note that a few cases have been reported where the non-return valve was sticking open when the engine was cold, reducing

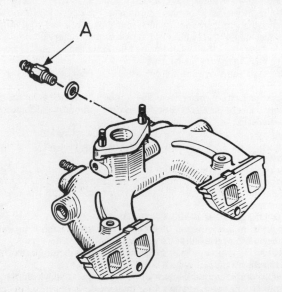

Fig. 12.61 Brake servo non-return valve (A) on Turbo models (Sec 12)

12.60 Handbrake cable fitted to caliper bracket and handbrake lever

1  Cable
2  Bracket on caliper
3  Handbrake operating lever
4  Handbrake cable nipple

12.65 Dust cover pulled back from handbrake lever mechanism

12.88 Later type Bendix rear brake assembly

12.91 Disconnecting the handbrake cable

12.93A Unhook the top spring ...

12.93B ... and withdraw the leading shoe

12.94 Spring and strut engagement in the trailing shoe

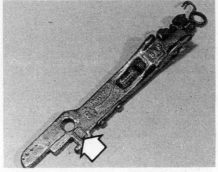

12.96 Right-hand adjuster strut is marked 'D' (arrowed)

12.97 Shoes, springs and strut reassembled

the efficiency of the braking system. A new modified valve has been introduced by Renault to improve the valves performance. Consult your Renault dealer for further information.

### Brake vacuum servo pushrod (Turbo models) – adjustment

82    The adjustment procedure is as described in Chapter 8, Section 23, but note the different dimensions given in the Specifications.

### Fixed brake compensators – general

83    All later models (except 1108 cc engine and Turbo models) are now equipped with fixed brake compensators.
84    These compensators take the place of the pressure regulator valve (see Chapter 8, Section 12) and have the same function.
85    The compensators are integral with each rear wheel cylinder.
86    If a malfunction occurs in either the compensator or wheel cylinder, the complete assembly must be renewed. No overhaul of either component is allowed.

### Rear brake shoes (later Bendix type) – inspection and renewal

87    Remove the brake drum (Chapter 8, Section 6, paragraphs 1 to 9).
88    Note the initial fitted positions of the springs and the adjuster strut (photo).
89    Remove the shoe steady spring cups by depressing them and turning through 90°. Remove the cups, springs and pins.
90    Pull the shoes apart by hand and draw them off the wheel cylinder and bottom pivot. Be careful not to damage the wheel cylinder rubber boots. Allow the springs to draw the shoes together again.
91    Unhook the handbrake cable from the trailing shoe lever and remove the shoes with springs and strut (photo).
92    Remove the bottom spring.
93    Unhook the top spring from the leading shoe and withdraw it from the strut. The adjuster wheel, thread and spring will come away with the shoe (photos).
94    Unhook the springs and the strut from the trailing shoe (photo).
95    If necessary, transfer the handbrake lever from the old trailing shoe to the new one.

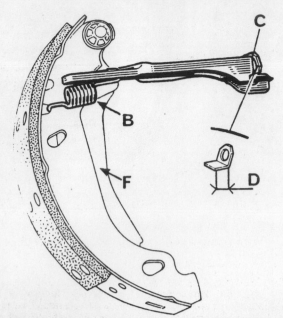

Fig. 12.62 To cure brake drag or noise, renew the spring (B) and
bracket (C) (Sec 12)

D   (Early type) = 12 mm          F   Handbrake lever
D   (Modified type) = 10 mm

96    Clean the adjuster strut, paying particular attention to the wheel
and threads. Note that left-hand and right-hand struts are not interchangeable – they are marked 'G' (gauche) and 'D' (droit) respectively
(photo).
97    Reassemble the shoes, strut and springs (photo).
98    Engage the handbrake cable in the lever. Pull the shoes apart and
fit the assembly to the backplate, again being careful not to damage the
wheel cylinder.
99    Refit the steady pins, springs and cups.
100    Turn the adjuster wheel to expand or contact the strut until the
brake drum will just pass over the shoes.
101    Refit the brake drum (Chapter 8, Section 6, paragraph 26 to 29).

### Rear brakes (later Bendix type) – correction of noise or drag
102    If rear brake drag or noise is a problem on models fitted with the
later type Bendix brakes, renew the handbrake return spring and the
adjuster strut bracket (Fig. 12.62). The latest versions of both these
components have been modified – later springs are yellow or green
where the early ones were white. Later brackets are green where the
early ones were yellow.
103    When excessive heating has occurred as a result of drag, it is
advisable to renew the wheel cylinder and/or hub bearings – consult a
Renault dealer for further advice.

## 13   Electrical system

### Maintenance-free battery – general and charging
1    On some models the maintenance-free battery is very similar in
appearance to the low maintenance type, however the warranty label
fixed to the cell cover describes the battery type. The label must not be
removed within the warranty period, otherwise the manufacturer will
not accept any claim submitted.
2    The maintenance-free period is for four years or 30 000 miles, and
thereafter the electrolyte level should be checked and if necessary
topped-up every two years or 20 000 miles, using the procedure
described in Chapter 9.
3    To check the state of charge of the battery, disconnect the negative
and positive leads, and leave the battery at rest for at least an hour. Then

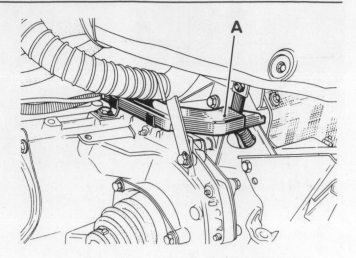

Fig. 12.63 Engine harness protector (A) (Sec 13)

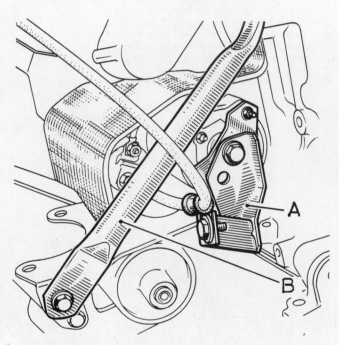

Fig. 12.64 Starter rear support bracket (A) and exhaust downpipe
mounting bar (B) (Sec 13)

use a voltmeter between the terminal posts and check that the reading
is between 12.0 and 12.5 volts.
4    If the reading is less than 12.0 volts, charge the battery at $\frac{1}{10}$th its
capacity for up to five hours (eg 40 amp hr capacity will require 4 amp
charging). The battery leads should then be re-connected (positive first
followed by negative) and any further charging completed by use of the
car. Charging the battery in this way will prevent overcharging and
excessive electrolyte temperatures.

### Integral alternator suppressor – description
5    As from mid-1983 the following alternators were fitted with an
integral radio interference suppressor, and it is important not to fit
additional external suppressors to these alternators.

Ducellier 50 amp No 516 023
Paris-Rhone 50 amp Nos A13 N12 and A13 N29
Paris-Rhone 75 amp No A14 N40

### Starter motor (Turbo models) – removal and refitting
6    Disconnect the battery.
7    Remove the air filter.

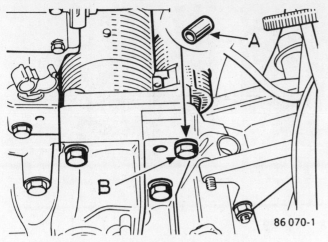

Fig. 12.65 Centring dowel (A) and bolt (B) (Sec 13)

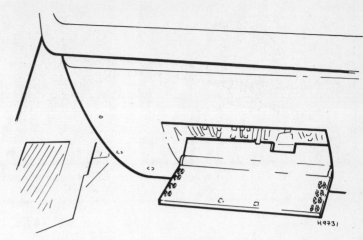

Fig. 12.66 Fusebox lid on pre-1984 Renault 9 models (Sec 13)

8    Remove the hoses for the air scoop.
9    Remove the turbocharger heat shields.
10    Remove the engine electrical harness protector.
11    Undo the three bolts securing the starter.
12    Remove the starter rear support bracket.
13    Disconnect the exhaust downpipe mounting bar.
14    Disconnect the starter leads.
15    Remove the starter, working from behind the front engine right-hand roadwheel.
16    Refit in reverse order, ensuring the centring dowel is fitted to the starter mounting bolt hole (Fig. 12.65).

*Fuses and relays – general*
17    On pre-1984 Renault 9 models, access to the fuses is by opening the fusebox lid located below the glovebox. The festoon type fuses are located between metal terminals. When renewing a fuse check that the terminals are clean and that the fuse is held firmly in position.
18    Details of fuse and relay locations for 1985 models are shown in the accompanying illustrations.
19    On later models, two relays are located behind the radiator grille, clipped to the front panel (photo).
20    The left-hand relay is for air horn and the right-hand relay for the foglamps, where this equipment is fitted.

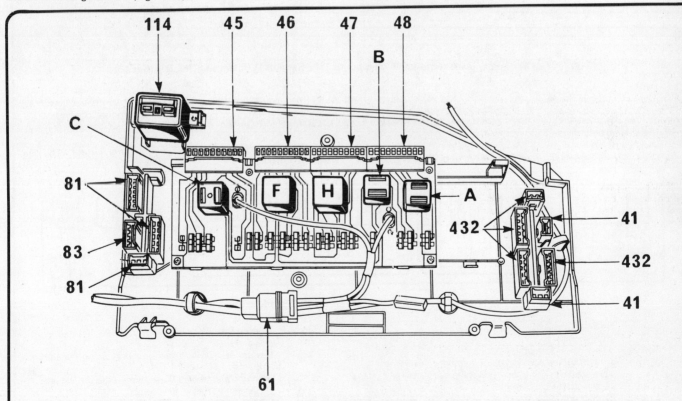

Fig. 12.67 Accessory plate component location for 1985 Renault 9 and 11 models except 11 'Electronic' (Sec 13)

| | | | |
|---|---|---|---|
| A | Headlamps dipped beam relay (Renault 11 only) | F | Flasher unit |
| B | Heated rear window relay (Renault 11 only) | H | Lights-on reminder buzzer |
| C | After ignition switch relay | 41 | RH front door courtesy light switch |
| | | 45 | to 48 Front wiring harness multi-plug sockets |

| | |
|---|---|
| 61 | Connector before ignition switch |
| 81 | Rear wiring harness multi-plug sockets |

| | |
|---|---|
| 83 | Heater motor multi-plug socket |
| 114 | Windscreen wiper timer relay |
| 432 | Facia wiring harness multi-plug sockets |

13.19 Air horn relay (A) and foglamp relay (B) located behind the radiator grille

13.22 Removing the plastic cover from the rear of the headlamp unit

13.23 Electrical connector on the bulb

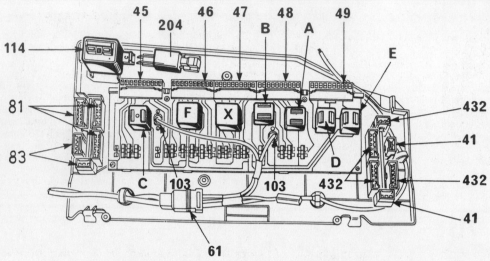

Fig. 12.68 Accessory plate component location for 1985 Renault 11 'Electronic' models (Sec 13)

A   Headlight dipped beam relay
B   Heater rear window relay
C   After ignition switch relay (not used on models without electric door locks)
D   Rear foglight relay
E   Rear window wiper relay (not used on models without electric door locks)
F   Flasher unit
X   Not fitted
41   RH front door courtesy light switch

45 to 49   Front wiring harness multi-plug sockets
61   Connector before ignition switch
81   Rear wiring harness multi-plug sockets
83   Heater motor multi-plug socket
103   Feeds to accessory plate
114   Windscreen wiper timer relay
204   Starter
432   Facia wiring harness multi-plug sockets

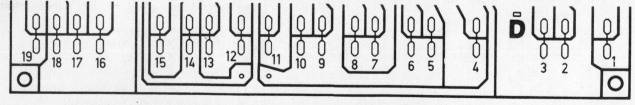

Fig. 12.69 Fuse locations and ratings for 1985 models (Sec 13)

| Fuse | No | Rating Circuit(s) |
|---|---|---|
| 1 | 7.5A | Rear foglights |
| 2 | 7.5A | Wiper 'park' function |
| 3 | 15A | Clock/luggage compartment lighting, cigar lighter ('Electronic') with door locking, infra-red locking |
| 4 | 20A | Rear window demister |
| 5 | 10A | Wipers and washers |
| 6 | 7.5A | Reversing lights, windscreen wiper timer |
| 7 | 5A | RH side and rear lights, instrument lighting |
| 8 | 5A | LH side and rear lights, facia lighting |
| 9 | 3A | (Except 'Electronic') Instrument panel |
| | 5A | ('Electronic') Instrument panel |
| 10 | 10A | Stop-lights ('Electronic') with door locking |
| 10 | 15A | Stop-lights, cigar lighter |

| Fuse | No | Rating Circuit(s) |
|---|---|---|
| 11 | 10A | Flasher unit |
| 12 | 10A | Heater blower (bottom range only on non-'Electronic' models) |
| 13 | 3A | (Except 'Electronic') Radio, computer, driving aid |
| | 10A | ('Electronic') Radio, driving aid |
| 14 | 2A | Automatic transmission (where applicable) |
| 15 | 15A | Door locking (where applicable) |
| 16 | 25A | Air conditioning and sunroof where applicable, heater blower top range on non-'Electronic' models |
| 17 | 25A | LH window and rear view mirror where applicable |
| 18 | 25A | RH window |
| 19 | | Not used |

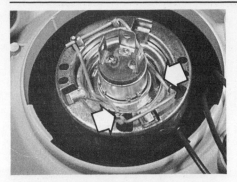

13.24 Release the wire clip by depressing it in the direction of the arrows

13.25 Bulb partly withdrawn

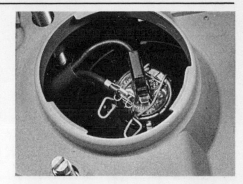

13.29 Electrical connector on the driving lamp

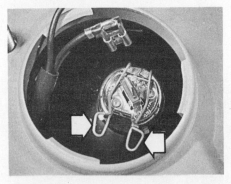

13.30 Release the spring clip by depressing it in the direction of the arrows

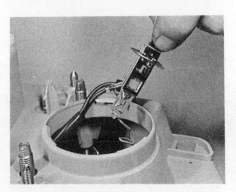

13.31 Removing the bulb

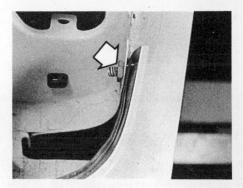

13.35 Nut securing the outer edge of the trim strip (arrowed)

## Headlamps (Renault 9 models, 1985 on) – description

21   Renault 9 models are fitted with four headlamps. The headlamps are the same as those fitted to Renault 11 models, as described in Chapter 9.

## Headlamp unit (1986 on) – bulb renewal

22   Remove the plastic cover from the back of the headlamp unit (photo).
23   Pull of the electrical connector (photo).
24   Release the wire clip securing the bulb (photo).
25   Lift out the bulb (photo).
26   Refitting is a reversal of removal.

## Driving lamp (1986 on) – bulb renewal

27   On some models, the driving lamp is integral with the headlamp unit.
28   Remove the cover from the rear of the unit.
29   Disconnect the electrical connector (photo).
30   Release the spring clip (photo).
31   Remove the bulb (photo).
32   Refitting is a reversal of removal.

## Headlamp unit (1986 on) – removal and refitting

33   Remove the radiator grille as described in Section 15.
34   Remove the front indicator lamp unit as described later in this Section.
35   Remove the nut securing the outer edge of the trim strip under the headlamp unit (photo).
36   Disconnect the electrical connectors from the headlamp unit. On models with integral driving lights, disconnect the headlamp unit at the main connector after lifting up the plastic cover (photo).
37   Where fitted, disconnect the remote headlamp adjuster cable at the balljoint by turning it approximately a quarter of a turn, and pulling it to disengage the socket (photos).
38   Remove the four headlamp securing nuts (photo).
39   Lift out the headlamp unit (photo).
40   Remove the trim strip by depressing the plastic clips along the lower edge of the unit (photo).

41   The glass lens can be removed from the reflector assembly by removing the clips and prising off the lens (photo). The lens is sealed to the reflector with mastic, so it may prove difficult to remove, and breakage of the glass would be the probable outcome. Note that, even if the glass lens is already broken, there would seem little point in attempting to separate it from the reflector, since the lens is not available separately as a spare part.
42   Refitting is a reversal of removal, and on completion, have the headlamp beam adjusted by a garage with the necessary equipment.

## Front sidelight bulb (1986 on) – renewal

43   The front sidelight bulbholder is a push fit in the headlamp unit reflector.
44   Pull the holder from the headlamp unit.
45   The bulb is a bayonet fix in the holder.
46   Refit in the reverse order.

## Front direction indicator bulb (1986 on) – renewal

47   The bulbholder is tucked away under the front wing.
48   Disconnect the electrical connector and twist the bulbholder anti-clockwise to remove it (photo).
49   The bulb is a bayonet fix in the holder.
50   Refit in reverse order.

## Front direction indicator light unit (1986 on) – removal and refitting

51   Disconnect the electrical lead from the rear of the unit.
52   Disengage the securing spring from the plastic bracket by pulling it rearwards (photo).
53   Ease the unit forwards, disengaging the plastic clips from the headlamp unit (photo).
**Note**: *It will be easier on some models to loosen the headlamp retaining nuts somewhat to give a little play.*
54   Refit in reverse order, ensuring the plastic clips engage with the headlamp unit.

13.36 Plastic cover (arrowed) over the electrical connection on models with integral driving lamps

13.37A Remote headlamp adjuster balljoint (arrowed) ...

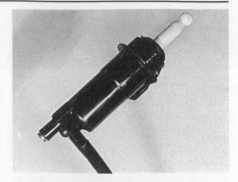

13.37B ... the balljoint removed ...

13.37C ... and the adjuster on the headlamp

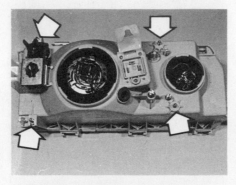

13.38 Headlamp securing nuts (arrowed) headlamp removed for clarity

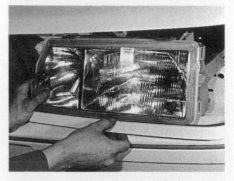

13.39 Removing a headlamp unit

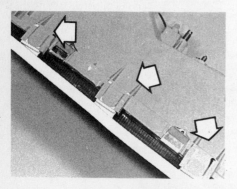

13.40 Trim strip plastic clips (arrowed)

13.41 Removing a headlamp lens retaining clip

13.48 Removing a bulbholder from a direction indicator lamp unit (unit removed for clarity)

13.52 Direction indicator lamp securing spring

13.53 Easing the direction indicator lamp unit forwards

13.55 Bulbholder removed from the side repeater lamp

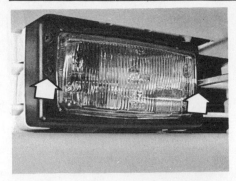

13.59 Removing the screws from the front foglamp (arrowed)

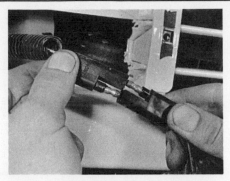

13.60 Disconnecting the front foglamp lead

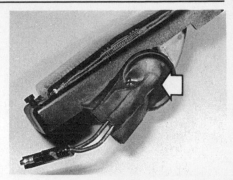

13.61 Pull back the rubber cover (arrowed)

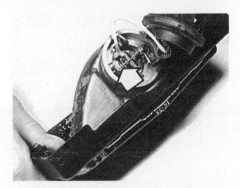

13.62A Unhook the wire clip (arrowed) ...

13.62B ... and lift out the bulbholder

13.64 Foglamp beam adjusting screw (arrowed)

13.70 Release the spring clip by depressing in the direction of the arrows

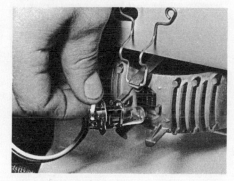

13.71A Pull out the bulb ...

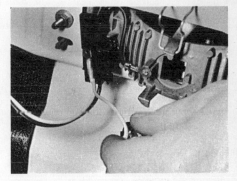

13.71B ... and disconnect the lead

## Direction indicator side repeater lamp – removal, bulb renewal and refitting

55    Using a piece of rag to protect the paintwork, prise the lamp unit from the front wing with a screwdriver. It is held by plastic clips (photo).
56    Turn and pull the bulbholder from the rear of the unit.
57    The bulb is a push fit in the holder.
58    If the lens is broken, it may be necessary to obtain a complete unit, as the lens is sealed to the body with adhesive mastic.

## Front foglamp (1986 on) – removal, bulb renewal and refitting

59    Remove the two screws securing the unit to the front bumper (photo). The third screw is for beam adjustment.
60    Pull the lamp assembly forwards, and then disconnect the lead (photo).
61    Pull back the rubber cover from the bulbholder (photo).
62    Unhook the wire clip and lift out the bulbholder (photos).
63    The bulb is a push fit in the holder.
64    To remove the lamp trim, undo the adjusting screw completely, and then unclip the trim from the lamp unit (photo). As with other lamp units, the lens is sealed to the unit by adhesive mastic.
65    Refit in reverse order.

## Rear lamp units (1986 on) – general

66    The procedure for bulb renewal, and removal and refitting of the lamp units, is as described in Chapter 9, Sections 32 and 33.
67    Note, however, that on Renault 11 models, the red plastic trim rail which houses the foglamp unit must be removed first, to allow room for the rear lamp clusters to be removed.

## Rear foglamp (Renault 11 models, 1986 on) – bulb renewal, removal and refitting

68    The foglamp is housed in the rear valance, integral with the red plastic trim rail.
69    To renew the bulb, extract the plastic retainers inside the luggage area securing the interior trim panel, and lower the panel.
70    Release the spring clip on the bulbholder (photo).
71    Pull out the bulb, and disconnect the single wire connector from the connector at the side of the lamp unit (photos).
72    Fitting of a new bulb is a reverse of this procedure.
73    To remove the complete assembly, remove the five nuts securing the red plastic trim rail to the rear valance (photo). These are all accessible from inside the luggage area, under the trim panel.
74    Disconnect the lead from the connector to the left of the lamp unit (photo).

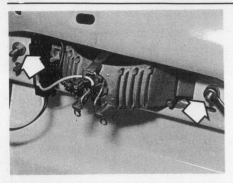

13.73 Removing the nuts (arrowed) which secure the rail

13.74 Disconnect the rear foglamp lead

13.75 Two nuts (arrowed) secure the lamp unit to the rail

13.79 Disconnect the rear number plate lamp connector

13.80 Lens assembly separated from the body to show the bulbholder

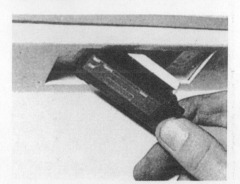

13.81 Refitting the lamp unit

13.84 Dim-dip system resistor

13.87 Air horn compressor

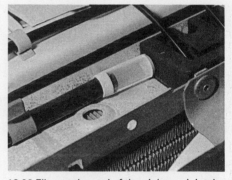

13.92 Filter at the end of the air horn air intake tube

75   Lift off the trim rail and remove the two nuts securing the lamp unit to the rail (photo).
76   Refitting is a reverse of removal.
77   If it is intended to fit an extra foglamp unit to a vehicle (a single foglamp is standard), then a heavier supply lead should be fitted to cope with the increase in current.

### Rear number plate lamp (1986 on) – bulb renewal
78   Prise the unit from the bumper.
79   Disconnect the electrical connector (photo).
80   Prise the lens assembly from the body. The bulb is of the festoon type, held between two spring contacts (photo).
81   Snap the unit back into place after reconnecting the electrical lead (photo).

### Dim-dip lighting system – general
82   From 1987, all models are equipped with a dim-dip lighting system.
83   This system operates the headlamp on reduced intensity dipped beam when the sidelights are switched on and the engine is running. The intention is to prevent driving with sidelights only switched on.
84   The dim-dip relay is located on the accessory plate, and a resistor is mounted in the right-hand scuttle above the inner wing (photo).

85   The system is a legal requirement on all UK models manufactured after April 1st 1987.

### Air horn – general
86   Some models are fitted with an electric air horn.
87   The motor which compresses the air is bolted to the front cross-member, low down in the engine bay (photo).
88   To remove the motor, first disconnect the electrical leads.
89   Remove the nut from the motor securing bracket.
90   Disconnect the air tubes and lift out the motor.
91   Refit in reverse order.
92   Periodically, check and clean the air filter on the end of the inlet air tube, which is clipped to the front panel above the radiator (photo).

### Electro-mechanical door locks – general
93   In the event of failure of the electro-mechanical door locks, the source of trouble could be bad earthing. First check the printed circuit earth terminal of the remote control receiver, located over the interior mirror, by removing the moulding.
94   Further check the earthing of the timer, located on the centre console beneath the radio. The timer is only fitted to Renault 11 models and 1984-on Renault 9 models, and its purpose is to limit the operation of the door locks to 3 seconds. Earlier models had a thermal cut-out, as briefly described in Chapter 9.

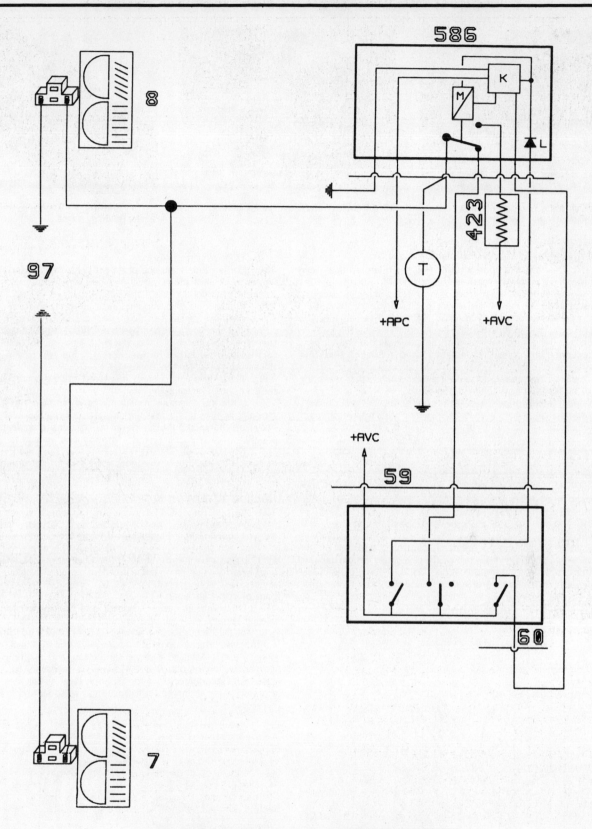

**Fig. 12.70 Wiring diagram for dim-dip lighting system (Sec 13)**

| | | | | | | |
|---|---|---|---|---|---|---|
| 7 | LH headlight unit | 97 | Earth | + | AVC + Before ignition | L | Relay (586) diode |
| 8 | RH headlight unit | 423 | Dipped beam headlight | + | APC + After ignition | M | Relay (586) coil |
| 59 | Headlight and direction | | intensity reducing resistor | K | Relay (586) electronic | T | Dipped beam headlight |
| | indicator control switch | 586 | Dipped beam headlight | | circuit | | "on" warning light |
| 60 | Direction indicator control | | intensity reducing relay | | | | |
| | switch | | | | | | |

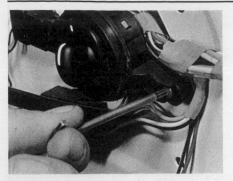

13.98 Removing the Torx type screw securing the switch to the door skin

13.100 Switch retaining clips (arrowed)

13.101 Refitting the switch to the door – screw guide arrowed

## Electrically operated rear view mirror – general

95    Some models are equipped with electrically operated rear view mirrors, controlled by a switch mounted in the driver's door interior trim panel. The switch operates the mirrors on both sides of the vehicle.

96    Removal and refitting of the mirror is similar to the procedure given for the standard mirror in Chapter 11, Section 34, but additionally the wiring must be disconnected at the connector.

97    To remove the control switch, first remove the door interior trim panel as described in Chapter 11, Section 21 and in Section 15 of this Supplement.

98    Remove the Torx type screw securing the switch to the inner door skin (photo), and prise the switch from the door.

99    Disconnect the electrical leads at the connector.

100    The switch can be removed from the outer body by releasing the spring clips (photo).

101    Refit in the reverse order, ensuring the switch is clipped into the inner door skin, and the screw guide is located in the hole (photo).

## 'Normalar' cruise control – description

102    Certain Renault 9 models may be equipped with 'Normalar' cruise control. The system is activated by a main switch on the facia, then top speed and cruising speed selected by switches in the centre of the steering wheel. LED indicators on the speedometer show the speeds selected.

103    The cruise control unit automatically controls the throttle on the carburettor, although this may be overridden in certain circumstances. At the time of publication, no information was available regarding the removal and refitting of the control unit, or of any possible adjustments.

## Trip computer – general

104    Some models are equipped with a trip computer instead of the digital clock, and the removal and refitting procedure is as given in Chapter 9, Section 21.

105    The computer is supplied with information from four separate sensors. A flow sensor is fitted in the fuel supply line to the carburettor to monitor fuel used. A speed sensor is fitted in the speedometer cable to monitor speed and distance covered. A thermistor at the front of the car monitors the outside temperature. The fuel tank gauge unit monitors the amount of fuel in the fuel tank.

106    The time is permanently displayed when the special functions of the computer are not being used.

107    If the trip computer malfunctions, it can be set to a fault-finding mode. However, this is best carried out by a Renault dealer. Work by the home mechanic should be limited to checking electrical connections and wiring.

108    Note that, because of the speed sensor, the speedometer cable is in two sections, but the connections to the instrument panel and transmission are the same as for the single cable.

## Renault 11 'Electronic' models – general

109    Certain Renault 11 models are equipped with an 'Electronic' package, comprising a liquid crystal display (LCD) instrument panel with a digital speedometer. Engine speed, water temperature, oil level and oil pressure are all of the graphic bar display type, and a trip computer is also incorporated in the instrument panel on some models. Besides the visual warnings given on the instrument panel, a voice synthesizer also announces warnings for items such as a drop in oil pressure, worn brake pads or a door left open.

110    On some 'Electronic' models, the right-hand steering column combination switch for the windscreen and headlamp wipers and washers also incorporates a remote control unit for the radio. The control unit uses a computer-search system to select the best frequency for listening to a particular station, and this is useful on long journeys when frequency changes may be necessary.

111    The steering column combination switch stalk also incorporates a message repetition key for repeating messages made by the voice synthesizer.

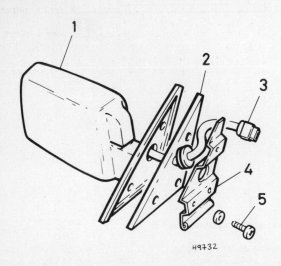

Fig. 12.71 Electrically operated external rear view mirror (Sec 13)

| 1 | Mirror body | 4 | Bracket |
| 2 | Gasket | 5 | Bolt |
| 3 | Multi-plug | | |

Fig. 12.72 Speed sensor fitted in the speedometer cable for the trip computer (Sec 13)

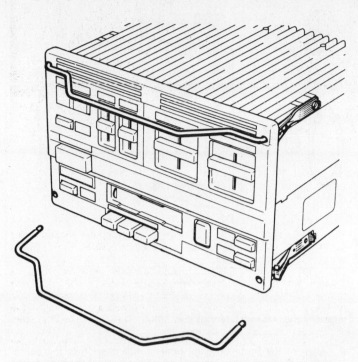

Fig. 12.73 Using dowel rods to release the audio set retaining clips (Sec 13)

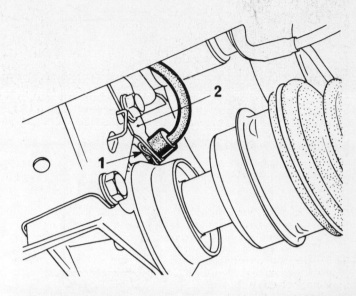

Fig. 12.74 Speed sensor location on Renault 11 'Electronic' models (Sec 13)

1  Clip                    2  Holding bracket

112    A cruise control system is fitted, which is similar to that described for Renault 9 models in paragraphs 102 and 103.
113    The speedometer is controlled electronically by a sensor located on the transmission final drive casing. A module in the instrument panel receives signals from the sensor, and activates the digital read-out and stage motor for the odometer.
114    A light bulb defect warning system is also incorporated, and the control unit is located near the fusebox.
115    In the event of malfunction of the electronic components or circuits a Renault dealer should be consulted. Work by the home mechanic should be limited to checking electrical connections and wiring.
116    Removal and refitting of the instrument panel is similar to that described in Chapter 9.

### Audio set (Renault 11 'Electronic' models) – removal and refitting
117    Disconnect the battery negative terminal.
118    Insert dowel rod into the holes at the corners of the audio set facia in order to release the retaining clips (Fig. 12.73).
119    Withdraw the audio set and disconnect the multi-plugs, earth wire and aerial.
120    Refitting is a reversal of removal.

### Speed sensor (Renault 11 'Electronic' models) – removal and refitting
121    Jack up the front of the car and support on axle stands. Apply the handbrake.
122    Extract the clip, then withdraw the sensor from the right-hand side of the transmission just above the driveshaft. If necessary, prevent any oil from running out by blocking the hole with a piece of cloth.
123    Refitting is a reversal of removal, but make sure that the sensor is fully engaged with the holding bracket. Top up the transmission oil if necessary.

### Wiring diagrams – general
124    It should be noted that, owing to the extremely large number of wiring diagrams produced for this range of vehicles, space restrictions prevent more than a typical selection being included.
125    For most practical purposes, the Renault 9 is very similar to the Renault 11. Owners of later Renault 9 models may therefore find the wiring diagrams for the Renault 11 of some use.

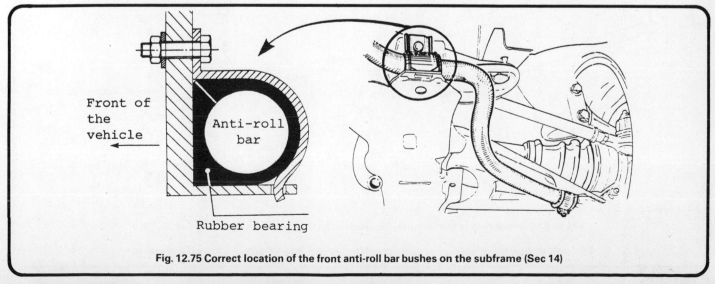

Fig. 12.75 Correct location of the front anti-roll bar bushes on the subframe (Sec 14)

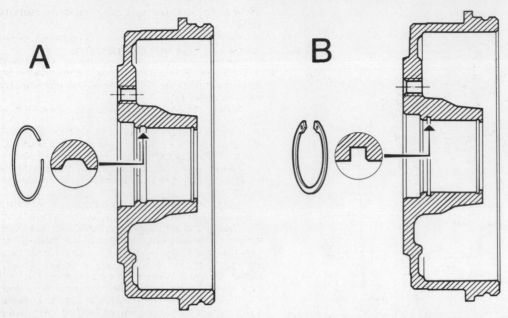

**Fig. 12.76 Early (A) and later (B) methods of retaining the rear hub bearings (Sec 14)**

## 14   Suspension and steering

### Front anti-roll bar bushes – modification
1    On early models the front anti-roll bar bushes are of polyurethane, which can cause a grating noise under certain operating conditions. To prevent this, later models are fitted with rubber brushes.

2    Most of the noise on early models emanates from the central bushes on the front subframe, so if a problem exists these bushes only should be renewed. The bushes can be fitted more easily if first dipped in soapy water. They should be located as shown in Fig. 12.75.

### Rear hub bearings – renewal
3    On models manufactured before May 1983, the rear hub bearing is

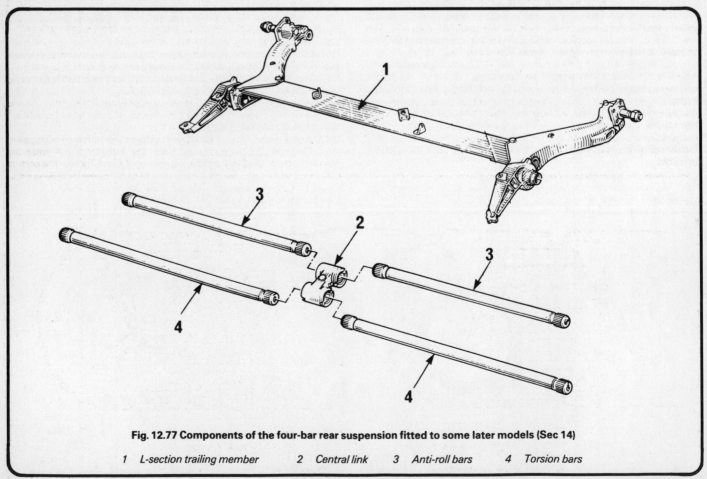

**Fig. 12.77 Components of the four-bar rear suspension fitted to some later models (Sec 14)**

| 1   *L-section trailing member* | 2   *Central link* | 3   *Anti-roll bars* | 4   *Torsion bars* |

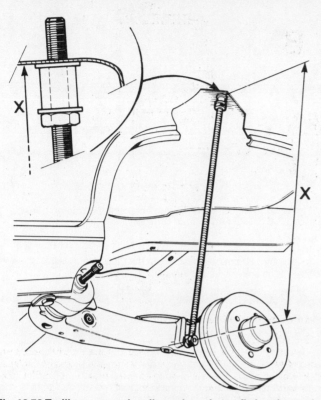

**Fig. 12.78 Trailing arm setting dimension when refitting the torsion bars (Sec 14)**

*For dimension X, see Specifications*

retained by a spring ring, however from this date onwards a conventional circlip is used. As the groove contour in the hub varies, it is important that the correct clip is fitted, as shown in Fig. 12.68.

### Four-bar rear suspension – description

4    Renault 11 Turbo models manufactured after June 1985, and 1721 cc models manufactured after October 1986, are equipped with a four-bar rear suspension, as shown in Fig. 12.77. The two rear axle trailing arms are connected by an L-section member and the torsion bars and anti-roll bars are connected together by a central link. Note that the rear of the car must **not** be raised using a jack beneath the L-section member.

### Rear axle (four-bar rear suspension) – removal and refitting

5    Chock the front wheels, then jack up the rear of the car and support on axle stands. Remove the rear wheels.
6    Remove the intermediate and rear sections of the exhaust system.
7    Disconnect the lower mountings of the rear shock absorbers, with reference to Chapter 10, then slowly lower the trailing arms until they hang unsupported.
8    Remove the brake drums, shoes and backplates, with reference to Chapter 8.
9    Disconnect the handbrake cables and the hydraulic brake lines from the rear axle, with reference to Chapter 8. If available, use brake hose clamps on the flexible hoses to prevent loss of fluid.
10    Remove the rear seat cushion and mouldings to gain access to the trailing arm mounting bracket nuts. Have an assistant hold the nuts from above.
11    Support the rear axle with a trolley jack, then unscrew the mounting bracket bolts and lower the assembly to the ground.
12    Refitting is a reversal of removal, but bleed the brake hydraulic system and adjust the handbrake, as described in Chapter 8. Providing that the torsion bars and anti-roll bars have not been disturbed, no adjustment should be necessary. However, the underbody height should be checked, as described later in this Section. If either of the torsion bars has been removed, carry out the following procedure.
13    Pull out both of the torsion bars so that they are disconnected from the mounting brackets and central link, then position the trailing arms to give the dimension shown in Fig. 12.78. If threaded adjustment rods are unavailable, use trolley jacks or axle stands. Disconnect the shock absorbers to make the adjustment easier.
14    Apply molybdenum disulphide grease to the splines of the torsion bars, then insert one while turning it to find the point where both sets of splines enter freely. Similarly insert the other bar on the remaining side. When fitted, the drill marks on the outer ends of the torsion bars should be in the same relative position or within a maximum of two splines difference.
15    Reconnect the shock absorbers, refit the wheels and lower the car to the ground.

### Rear axle (four-bar rear suspension) – dismantling and reassembly

16    With the rear axle removed, extract the torsion bars from each side using a slide hammer screwed into the end of the bars. If the Renault tool (Fig. 12.80) is not available, use a suitable bolt and claw lever, identify each torsion bar for its correct side.
17    Mark the anti-roll bars in relation to the central link and also identify them side for side, then extract them using the method described in paragraph 16. Recover the central link.
18    If necessary remove the mounting brackets from the trailing arms.
19    Clean all the components, then examine them for wear and damage. Check the L-section member for distortion. Renew the compo-

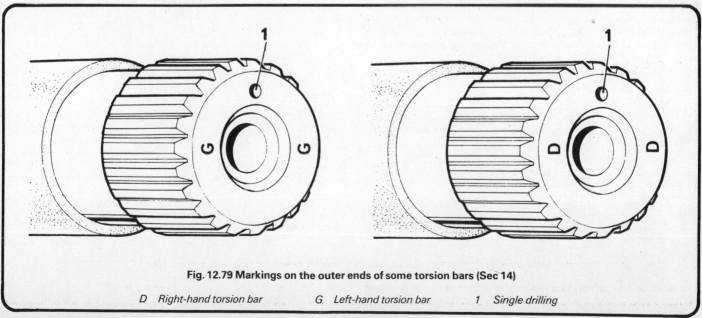

**Fig. 12.79 Markings on the outer ends of some torsion bars (Sec 14)**

D   *Right-hand torsion bar*          G   *Left-hand torsion bar*          1   *Single drilling*

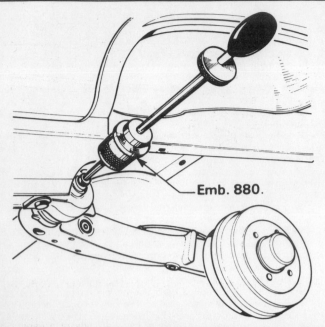

**Fig. 12.80 Using the Renault slide hammer tool to remove a torsion bar (Sec 14)**

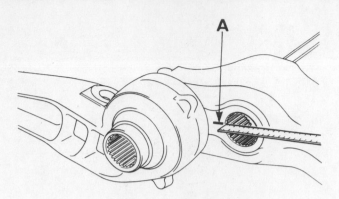

**Fig. 12.81 Mark the trailing arms between the torsion bar and anti-roll bar centres (Sec 14)**

nents as necessary. Note that the bars are different for each side of the car – the left-hand bars should have two drillings or the letter 'G' on their outer ends, whilst the right-hand bars should have three drillings or the letter 'D'.

20   Before commencing reassembly, apply molybdenum disulphide grease to the splines on the bars and in the trailing arms. Also grease the trailing arm bearings and mounting bracket splines.

21   Refit the mounting brackets on the trailing arms, then position the rear axle upside down on a flat surface with the L-section member on blocks of wood so that the mounting brackets are free.

22   Using a rule, mark each trailing arm as shown in Fig. 12.81 between the centre points of the torsion bar and anti-roll bar. The marks should be in the hollow between two splines.

23   Using a mallet, insert one anti-roll bar with its end drilling in line with the mark made in paragraph 22.

24   Fit the central link on the inner end of the anti-roll bar so that it is parallel to the L-section member.

25   Insert the remaining anti-roll bar from the other side with its end drilling in line with the mark made in paragraph 22.

26   The following procedure must be completed to ensure that the central link does not touch the L-section members during the flexing of the rear suspension. First measure the amount of play of the central link (Fig. 12.83). If it is less than 2.0 mm (0.079 in) all well and good, but if it is more, refer to the following table to determine how many splines the

central link must be moved away from the L-section member. Remove just one of the anti-roll bars to reposition the central link.

| Play measured (mm) | No of splines to move |
|---|---|
| 2 to 4 | 1 |
| 5 to 6 | 2 |
| 7 to 8 | 3 |
| 9 to 10 | 4 |
| 11 to 12 | 5 |
| 13 to 14 | 6 |
| 15 to 16 | 7 |
| 17 to 18 | 8 |
| 19 to 20 | 9 |

27   Use a G-clamp to position the central link parallel to the L-section member, then refit the torsion bars while turning them to find the point where both sets of splines enter freely. Remove the G-clamp after completion.

*Vehicle underbody height – general*

28   In order to standardise checking methods with other Renault models, the H5 measurement is now taken from the centre point of the torsion bar, and not from the rearmost bolt of the suspension mounting bracket, as before (see also Chapter 10, Section 25).

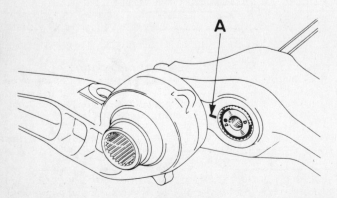

**Fig. 12.82 Fit the anti-roll bars with the drilling in line with the mark 'A' (Sec 14)**

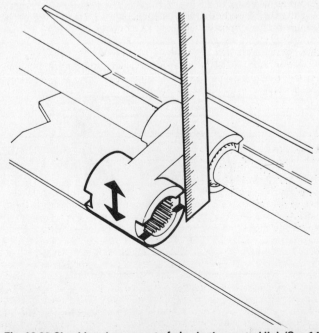

**Fig. 12.83 Checking the amount of play in the central link (Sec 14)**

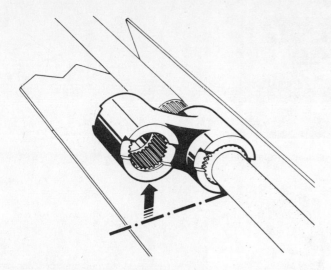

Fig. 12.84 Repositioning the central link away from the L-section member (Sec 14)

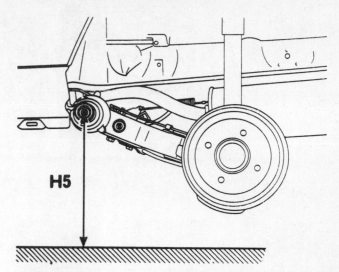

Fig. 12.85 The revised H5 checking point for the rear underbody height (Sec 14)

29   Note, however, that some of the dimensions given in the Specifications of this Supplement still relate to the earlier point of measurement.
30   The difference between the right- and left-hand sides of the same axle must not exceed 10.0 mm (0.39 in), and the driver's side must always be the higher.
31   Where a minus dimension is given, it means that the floor frame is higher then the wheel centre in relation to the ground.
32   After any alteration to underbody height, the brake pressure regulating valve and headlamp beam must be adjusted.

*Vehicle underbody height (four-bar rear suspension models) – adjustment*
33   If the rear underbody height is incorrect, first carry out the torsion bar setting procedure described in paragraphs 13 to 15.
34   If the difference between the left and right sides exceeds the maximum amount given in paragraph 30, the anti-roll bars must be adjusted. To do this, both torsion bars and the anti-roll bar on the **lower** side must be removed, after marking them for position, then, with both trailing arms positioned at the same height, the anti-roll bar must be refitted so that the splines enter freely. Refit the torsion bars in the same positions as removed.
35   If the rear underbody height is once again incorrect, the torsion bars must both be repositioned by equal amounts as required.

*Steering wheel retaining nut – torque wrench setting*
36   As from August 1983 the self-locking steering wheel retaining nut is replaced by a normal thin section nut, and the torque wrench setting is reduced, as given in the Specifications.

## 15   Bodywork and fittings

*Minor body damage – repair*
**Plastic components**
1   With the use of more and more plastic body components by the vehicle manufacturers (eg bumpers, spoilers, and in some cases major body panels), rectification of more serious damage to such items has become a matter of either entrusting repair work to a specialist in this field, or renewing complete components. Repair of such damage by the DIY owner is not really feasible owing to the cost of the equipment and materials required for effecting such repairs. The basic technique involves making a groove along the line of the crack in the plastic using a rotary burr in a power drill. The damaged part is then welded back together by using a hot air gun to heat up and fuse a plastic filler rod into the groove. Any excess plastic is then removed and the area rubbed down to a smooth finish. It is important that a filler rod of the correct

plastic is used, as body components can be made of a variety of different types (eg polycarbonate, ABS, polypropylene).
2   If the owner is renewing a complete component himself, or if he has repaired it with epoxy filler, he will be left with the problem of finding a suitable paint for finishing which is compatible with the type of plastic used. At one time the use of a universal paint was not possible owing to the complex range of plastics encountered in body component applications. Standard paints, generally speaking, will not bond to plastic, or rubber satisfactorily, but Holts Professional Spraymatch paints to match any plastic or rubber finish can be obtained from dealers. However, it is now possible to obtain a plastic body parts finishing kit which consists of a pre-primer treatment, a primer and coloured top coat.
3   Full instructions are normally supplied with a kit, but basically the method of use is to first apply the pre-primer to the component concerned and allow it to dry for up to 30 minutes. Then the primer is applied and left to dry for about an hour before finally applying the special coloured top coat. The result is a correctly coloured component where the paint will flex with the plastic or rubber, a property that standard paint does not normally possess.

*Bodywork and fittings – general*
4   Many of the bodywork components and fittings are secured by splined or Torx type screws (photo).
5   It is therefore essential that a good set of different sized splined and Torx type drive keys be obtained when working on these vehicles.

*Bonnet – removal and refitting*
6   On later models, the bonnet has an additional restraining wire riveted to the bonnet and the front wing valance.
7   When the bonnet has to be completely removed (eg for engine removal), one or other of the rivets must be drilled out, and a nut and bolt substituted in its place.

*Radiator grille (1986 on) – removal and refitting*
8   Remove the two Torx type screws from the front of the grille (photo).
9   Open the bonnet and remove the three Torx type screws from the top edge of the grille, then disengage the plastic clips (photo).
10   Close the bonnet and remove the grille.
11   Refit in reverse order, ensuring the plastic clips at the top of the grille engage in the slots correctly.

*Tailgate support struts (Renault 11 models) – general*
12   As from late 1983 the tailgate support struts incorporate improved internal sealing, and must be fitted with the cylinder end at the body. Struts manufactured prior to this date must still be fitted with the cylinder end at the tailgate.

15.4 Torx type screw and key

15.8 Radiator grille retaining screw

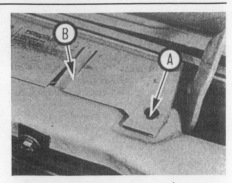
15.9 Screw (A) and clip (B) on the top edge of the grille

15.14A Removing the trim panel from the armrest on later models

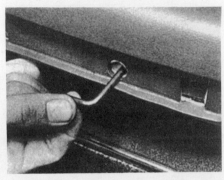
15.14B Removing the armrest screws

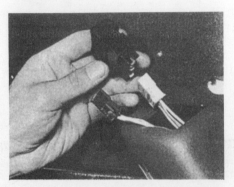
15.15 Disconnecting the electric window switches

15.16 Removing the electric mirror switch surround

15.18 Disengaging a hinged rear window tongue from its slot

15.21 Bumper attachment locations on the front bumper (bumper removed for clarity)

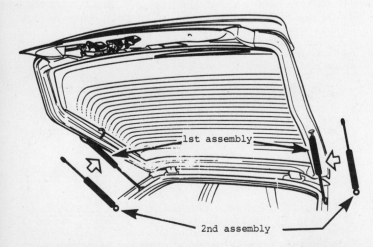
Fig. 12.86 Correct fitting of the tailgate support struts (Sec 15)

13   To identify the struts, the later type are marked with a circle the same colour as the manufacturer's name, and are supplied by Socalfran (reference number 210121) or Sacks-Stabilus (reference number 158453).

*Front door interior trim panel (later models) – removal and refitting*
14   When removing a front door interior trim panel (as described in Chapter 11, Section 21) on later models, the door armrest screws are located underneath a trim panel which clips in place (photos).
15   Where fitted, disconnect the electric window switches before removing the armrest (photo).
16   Before removing the trim panel, prise out the electric rear view mirror switch surround, if fitted (photo).

*Hinged opening rear side windows – general*
17   Some Renault 11 models have hinged opening rear side windows.
18   To remove the windows, release the locking catch, pull the window outwards **slightly** at the rear end, at the same time disengaging the tongues from their slots at the front edge (photo).
19   Refit in reverse order.

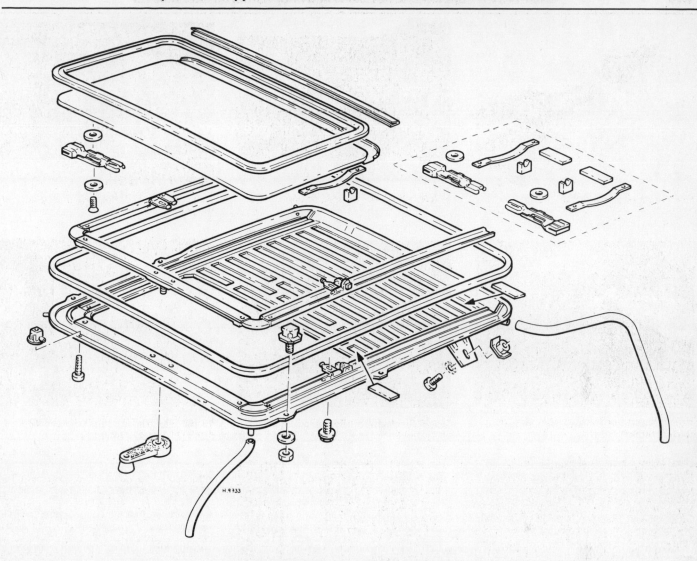

**Fig. 12.87 Exploded view of the sunroof (Sec 15)**

## Bumpers (1986-on) – removal and refitting
**Front**
20   Disconnect or remove the front foglamps as described in Section 13.
21   Working from underneath the front wing, remove the securing nut and screw from each side of the bumper (photo).
22   Remove the two bolts from the bumper lower front edge (photo).
23   Pull the bumper out at each side to disengage the stud from the bracket on the bodywork, at the same time easing the bumper forwards to release the box section formers, which give the bumper rigidity (photos).
**Rear**
24   The procedure is similar to that described for the front bumper, but the rear bumper is secured by two bolts at each side.
25   The bolts are accessible from underneath on the right-hand side, and from inside the luggage area on the left-hand side after pulling back the sound-deadening material (photos).
26   Before removing the bumper, disconnect or remove the number plate lamps as described in Section 13.
**Front and rear**
27   Refitting is a reversal of removal.

## Sunroof – general
28   Certain models are equipped with a sunroof of the sliding, manual control type. The sunroof requires no maintenance. However, the accompanying illustration (Fig. 12.87) is provided to assist those wishing to carry out work on the assembly.

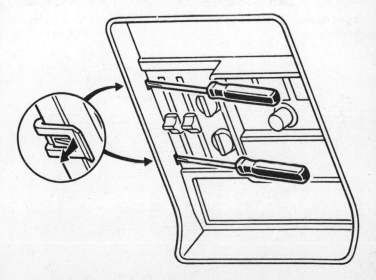

**Fig. 12.88 Removing the heater control panel on Renault 9 models (Sec 15)**

15.22 One of the two bolts at the front of the bumper

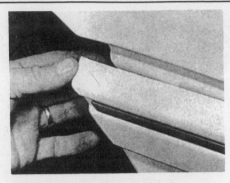

15.23A Prising out the edge of the bumper

15.23B The bumper partly removed

15.23C Showing the rear of the bumper and the box sections

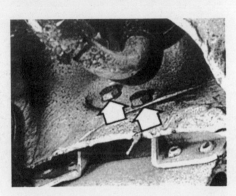

15.25A Rear bumper securing bolts (arrowed) on the right-hand side ...

15.25B ... and those on the left-hand side, inside the luggage area

## Heater control panel (Renault 9 models) – removal and refitting

29   To remove the heater control panel on Renault 9 models, first disconnect the battery negative lead then, using two screwdrivers through the slots in the surround, prise up the tabs to release them. The control panel can then be pressed in from the facia and the cables and wiring disconnected.

30   Refitting is a reversal of removal. Pull the control panel until the tabs click into place over the shoulders.

# General guide to use of wiring diagrams

*See particularly the note at the bottom of this page*

Example:

Or as shown in the diagram on the right:
Unit 40 (L.H. door pillar switch) with
wire 133-N-2-41 connected to Unit 41.

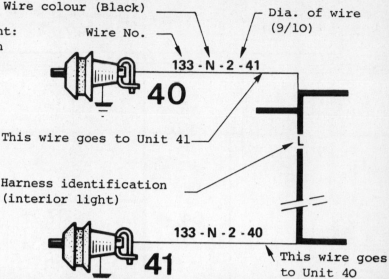

Wire colour (Black)

Wire No.

Dia. of wire (9/10)

133 - N - 2 - 41

This wire goes to Unit 41

Harness identification (interior light)

Wire 133 is seen again connected to
Unit 41 (R.H. door pillar switch) but
this time it is numbered: 133-N-2-40.

133 - N - 2 - 40

This wire goes to Unit 40

## Wire identification and diagram explanation

*Each wire is identified by a number followed by a letter(s) indicating its colour, a number giving its diameter and finally a number giving the unit destination. Where the end of a wire is of a different colour to the original basic colour, two colour codes are given. Example Or/N Orange basic colour but Black end.*

## Colour code

| B, Bl or BE | Blue | MA | Brown |
|---|---|---|---|
| Bc or BA | White | N or NO | Black |
| Be or BJ | Beige | Or, O or OR | Orange |
| C or CY | Clear | R or RG | Red |
| G or GR | Grey | S or SA | Pink |
| J or JA | Yellow | V, VE or VT | Green |
| M | Maroon for pre 1985 models, Brown for 1985 Renault 11 Electronic models with electric door locking | Vi or VI | Violet |

## Wire diameters

| No | mm | No | mm |
|---|---|---|---|
| 1 | 0.7 | 7 | 2.5 |
| 2 | 0.9 | 8 | 3.0 |
| 3 | 1.0 | 9 | 4.5 |
| 4 | 1.2 or 1.4 | 10 | 5.0 or 5.1 |
| 5 | 1.6 | 11 | 7.0 |
| 6 | 2.0 or 2.1 | 12 | 8.0 |

## Harness identification (where applicable)

| A | Engine front | L | Interior lamp door pillar switches | P | Door locks |
|---|---|---|---|---|---|
| B | Engine rear | M | Windscreen wiper/washer | R | Engine |
| K | Starter | | | Y | Dashboard (facia) |

## Unit locations

Some of the wiring diagrams are arranged in a grid system with columns 1 to 9 running vertically and zones A to D horizontally. The grid location of the various components is given in the diagram key, where applicable, after the component description.

## General

The wiring diagrams are as supplied by the vehicle manufacturers. Note that some of the accessories and options listed are not applicable to UK models.

Note: *Owing to the extremely large number of diagrams produced for this range of vehicles, it has only been possible to include a typical selection.*

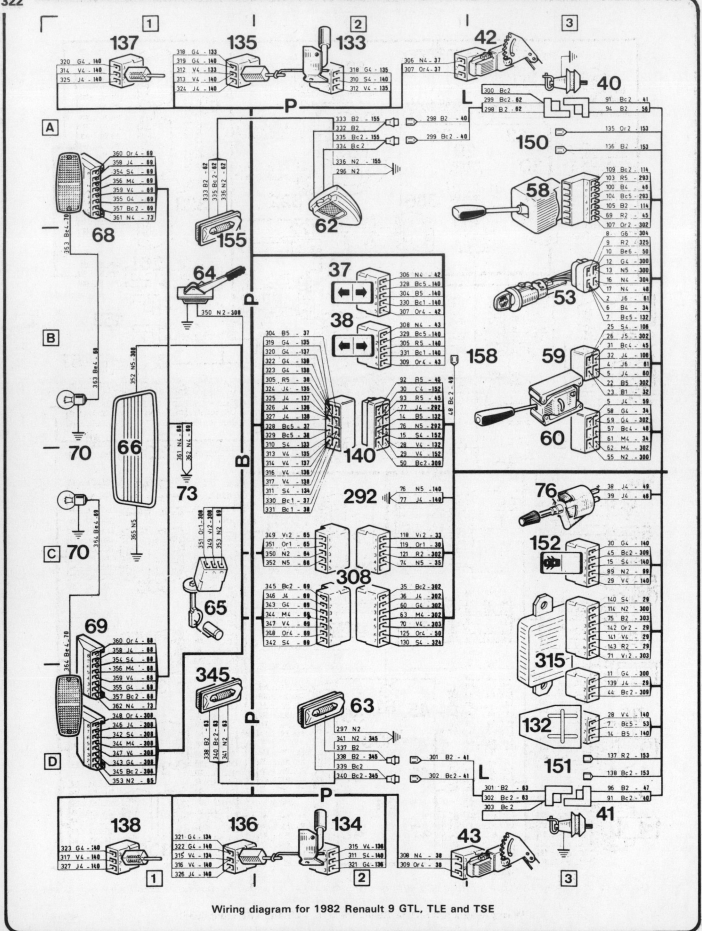

Wiring diagram for 1982 Renault 9 GTL, TLE and TSE

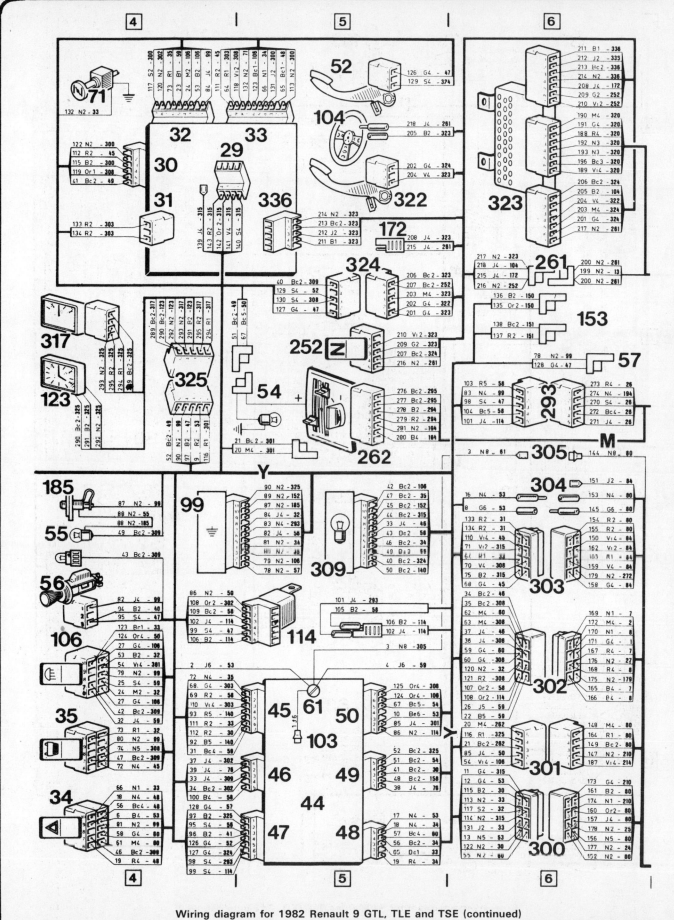

**Wiring diagram for 1982 Renault 9 GTL, TLE and TSE (continued)**

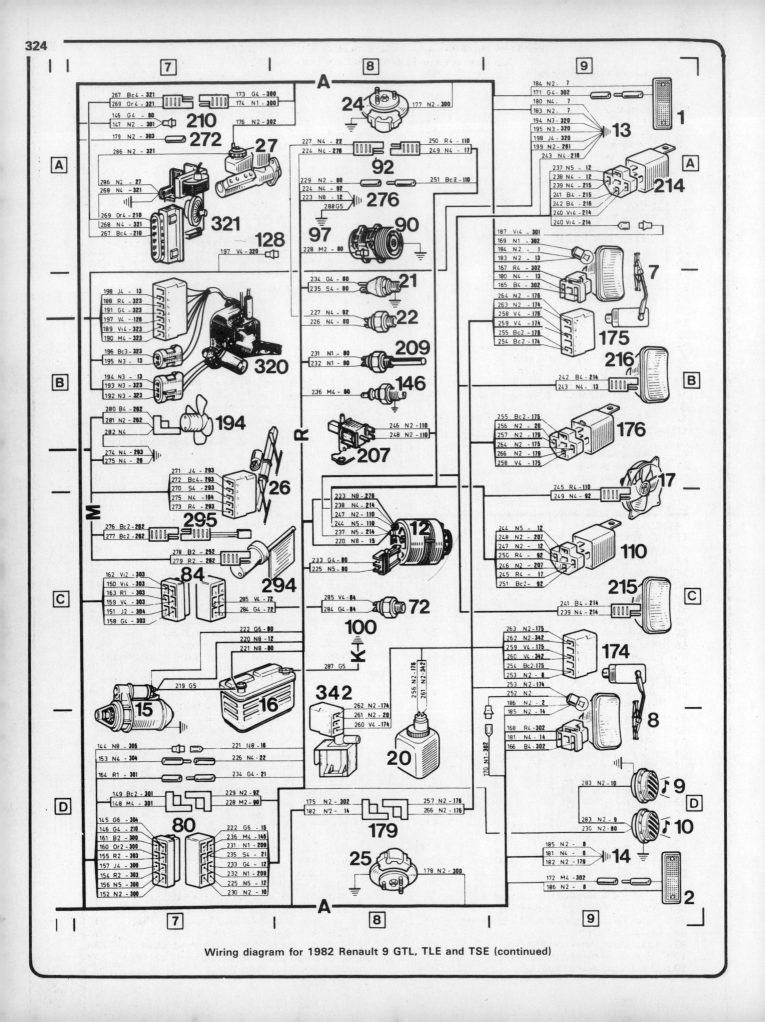

Wiring diagram for 1982 Renault 9 GTL, TLE and TSE (continued)

| | | |
|---|---|---|
| 1 | LH front direction indicator | A9 |
| 2 | RH front direction indicator | D9 |
| 7 | LH headlamp | A9 |
| 8 | RH headlamp | D9 |
| 9 | LH horn | D9 |
| 10 | RH horn | D9 |
| 12 | Alternator | C8 |
| 13 | LH side earth | A9 |
| 14 | RH side earth | D9 |
| 15 | Starter | D7 |
| 16 | Battery | D7 |
| 17 | Engine cooling fan motor | B9 |
| 20 | Electric windscreen washer pump | B8 |
| 21 | Oil pressure switch | B8 |
| 22 | Thermal switch on radiator | B8 |
| 24 | LH front brake | A8 |
| 25 | RH front brake | D8 |
| 26 | Windscreen wiper plate | B7 |
| 27 | Brake master cylinder | A7 |
| 29 | Instrument panel | A4 |
| 30 | Connector No 1 – Instrument panel | A4 |
| 31 | Connector No 2 – Instrument panel | B4 |
| 32 | Connector No 3 – Instrument panel | A4 |
| 33 | Connector No 4 – Instrument panel | A5 |
| 34 | 'Hazard' warning light switch | D4 |
| 35 | Rear screen demister switch | D4 |
| 37 | LH window switch | B2 |
| 38 | RH window switch | B2 |
| 40 | LH door pillar switch | A3 |
| 41 | RH door pillar switch | D3 |
| 42 | LH window motor | A3 |
| 43 | RH window motor | D3 |
| 44 | Accessories plate | D5 |
| 45 | Junction block – front harness to accessories plate | D5 |
| 46 | Junction block – front harness to accessories plate | D5 |
| 47 | Junction block – front harness to accessories plate | D5 |
| 48 | Junction block – front harness to accessories plate | D5 |
| 49 | Junction block – front harness to accessories plate | D5 |
| 50 | Junction block – front harness to accessories plate | D5 |
| 52 | Stop-lights switch | A5 |
| 53 | Ignition/starter – anti-theft switch | B3 |
| 54 | Heater controls illumination | B5 |
| 55 | Glove compartment light | C4 |
| 56 | Cigar lighter | C4 |
| 57 | Feed to radio | B6 |
| 58 | Windscreen wiper/washer switch | A3 |
| 59 | Combination lighting switch | B3 |
| 60 | Direction indicators switch | C3 |
| 61 | (+) feed before ignition/starter switch | D5 |
| 62 | LH interior light | A2 |
| 63 | RH interior light | D2 |
| 64 | Handbrake 'On' warning light switch | B1 |
| 65 | Fuel gauge tank unit | C1 |
| 66 | Rear screen demister | C1 |
| 68 | LH rear light assembly | A1 |
| 69 | RH rear light assembly | C1 |
| 70 | Number plate lights | B1 |
| 71 | Choke 'On' warning light switch | A4 |
| 72 | Reversing lights switch | C8 |
| 73 | Rear lights earth | C1 |
| 76 | Instrument panel lighting rheostat | C3 |
| 80 | Junction block – front harness to engine harness | D7 |
| 84 | Junction – front harness to gearbox | C7 |
| 90 | Wire junction – air conditioning EM clutch | A8 |
| 92 | Wire junction – optional air conditioning | A8 |
| 97 | Bodyshell earth | A8 |
| 99 | Dashboard (facia) earth | C5 |
| 100 | Inner wing panel gusset earth | C8 |
| 103 | Feed to accessories plate | D5 |

| | | |
|---|---|---|
| 104 | Wire junction – steering wheel switches (Normalur) | A5 |
| 106 | Rear foglamp switch | D4 |
| 110 | Engine cooling fan motor relay | C9 |
| 114 | Windscreen wiper/washer timer | C5 |
| 123 | Clock | B4 |
| 128 | Kick-down switch | A7 |
| 132 | Inertia switch | D3 |
| 133 | LH front door switch | A2 |
| 134 | RH front door switch | D2 |
| 135 | LH front door lock solenoid | A2 |
| 136 | RH front door lock solenoid | D2 |
| 137 | LH rear door lock solenoid | A1 |
| 138 | RH rear door lock solenoid | D1 |
| 140 | Junction block – electromagnetic locks harness | B2 |
| 146 | Thermal switch | B8 |
| 150 | LH speaker | A3 |
| 151 | RH speaker | D3 |
| 152 | Central electro-magnetic door locks switch | C3 |
| 153 | Speaker wires | B6 |
| 155 | LH rear interior light | A1 |
| 158 | Automatic transmission selector illumination | B3 |
| 172 | Impulse generator | B5 |
| 174 | RH headlight wiper/washer | C9 |
| 175 | LH headlight wiper/washer | B9 |
| 176 | Headlight wiper/washer timer relay | B9 |
| 179 | Wire junction – windscreen washer/headlamp washer pump | D8 |
| 185 | Glove compartment light switch | C4 |
| 194 | Junction block – engine cooling fan motor wiring | B7 |
| 207 | Anti-stall solenoid valve | B8 |
| 209 | Engine oil level indicator sensor | B8 |
| 210 | Junction block – engine front harness and AEI harness | A7 |
| 214 | Front foglamps relay | A9 |
| 215 | RH front foglamp | C9 |
| 216 | LH front foglamp | B9 |
| 252 | 'Normalur' cruise control switch | B5 |
| 261 | Wire junction – 'Normalur' cruise control | B6 |
| 262 | Heater and air conditioning control | B5 |
| 272 | Throttle butterfly switch | A7 |
| 276 | Engine earth | A8 |
| 292 | Steering column – bracket earth | C2 |
| 293 | Wire junction – windscreen wiper harness | B6 |
| 294 | Air conditioning recycling flap | C7 |
| 295 | Air conditioning air temperature sensor | C7 |
| 300 | Connector No 1 – dashboard (facia) harness to engine front harness | D6 |
| 301 | Connector No 2 – dashboard (facia) harness to engine front harness | D6 |
| 302 | Connector No 3 – dashboard (facia) harness to engine front harness | D6 |
| 303 | Connector No 4 – dashboard (facia) harness to engine front harness | C6 |
| 304 | Connector No 5 – dashboard (facia) harness to engine front harness | C6 |
| 305 | Connector No 6 – dashboard (facia) harness to engine front harness | C6 |
| 308 | Connector – Dashboard (facia) harness to rear harness | C2 |
| 309 | Rear lights junction plate | C4 |
| 315 | Econometer computer | C3 |
| 317 | Oil pressure gauge | B4 |
| 320 | 'Normalur' cruise control servo | B7 |
| 321 | Wire junction – AEI module | A7 |
| 322 | Clutch pedal switch | A5 |
| 323 | 'Normalur' cruise control computer | A6 |
| 324 | Wire junction – 'Normalur' cruise control and dashboard (facia) harness | B4 |
| 325 | Wire junction – clock | B4 |
| 336 | Connector No 5 – Instrument panel | B5 |
| 342 | Headlight wiper/washers solenoid valve | D8 |
| 345 | RH rear interior light | D1 |

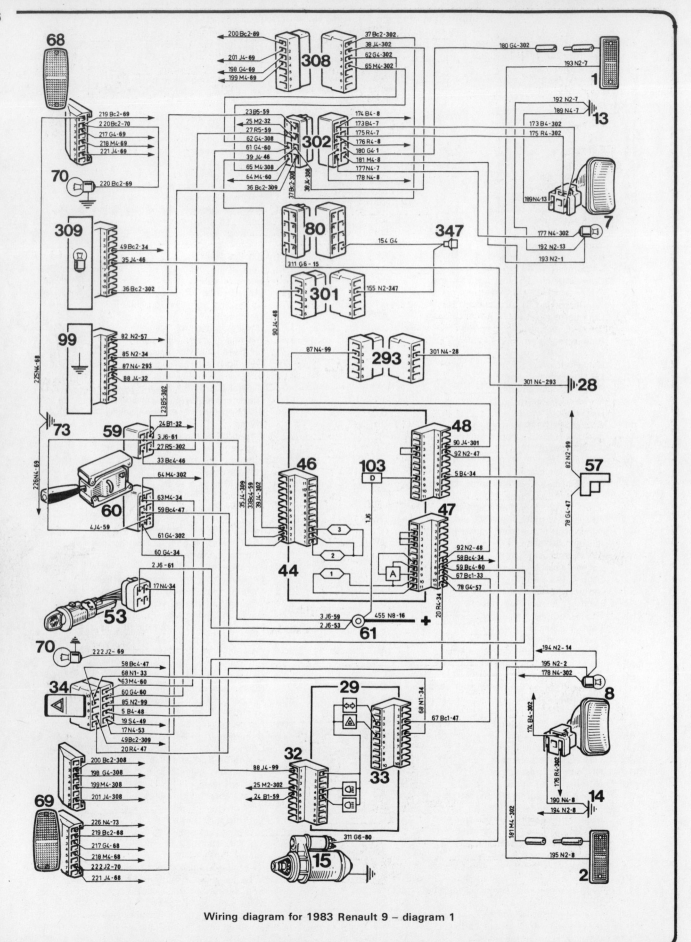

**Wiring diagram for 1983 Renault 9 – diagram 1**

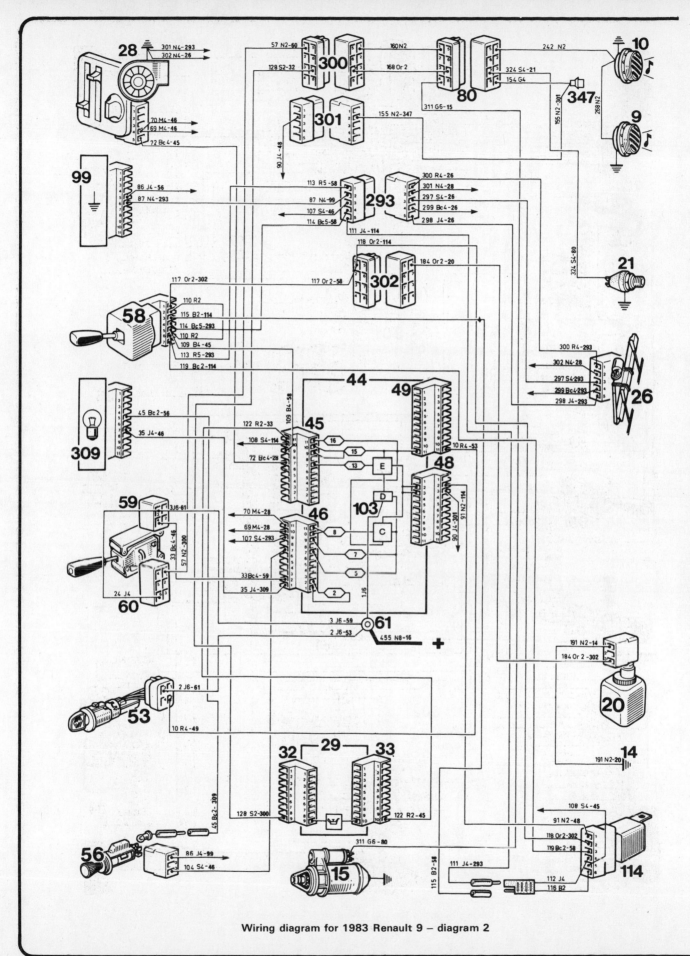

**Wiring diagram for 1983 Renault 9 – diagram 2**

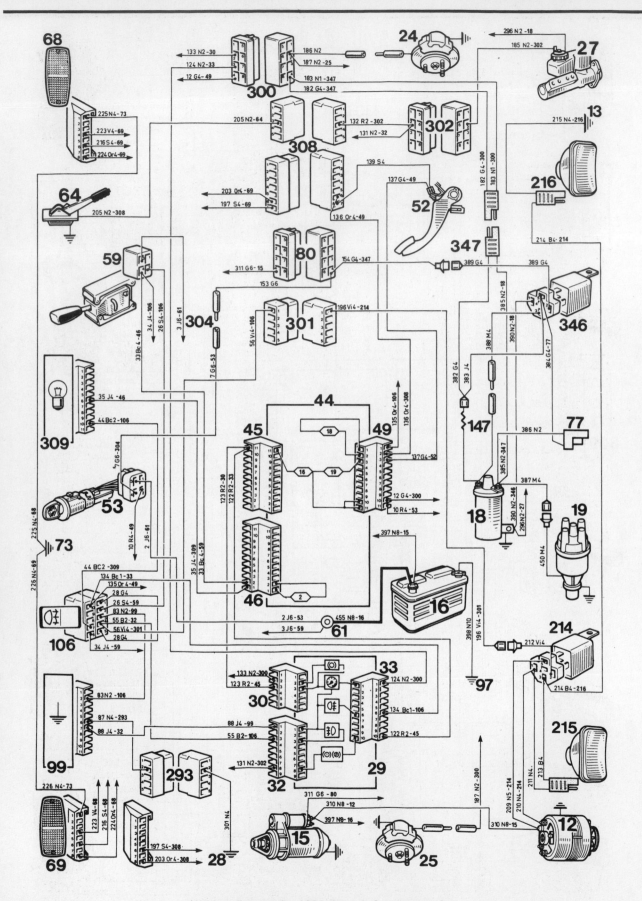

**Wiring diagram for 1983 Renault 9 – diagram 3**

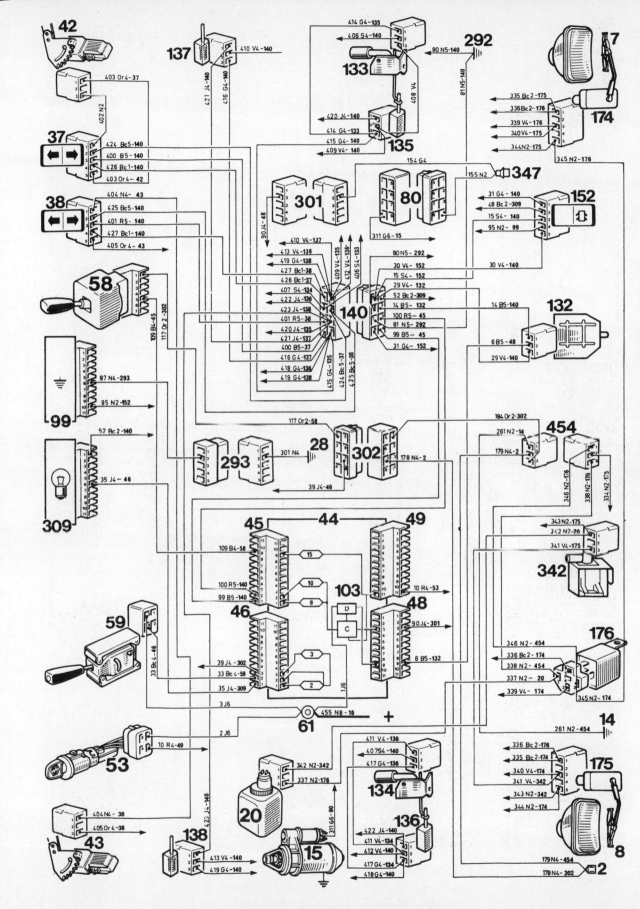

**Wiring diagram for 1983 Renault 9 – diagram 4**

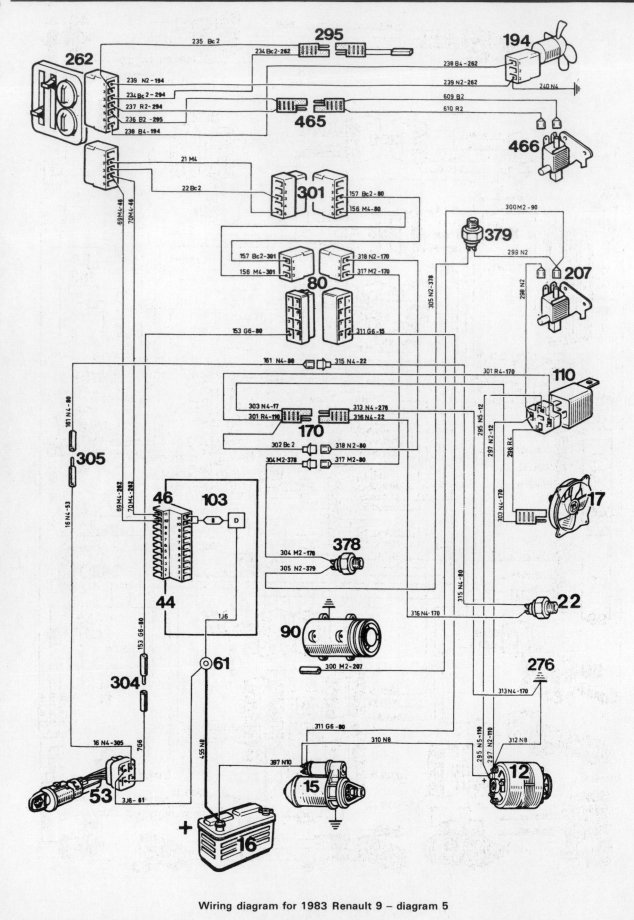

Wiring diagram for 1983 Renault 9 – diagram 5

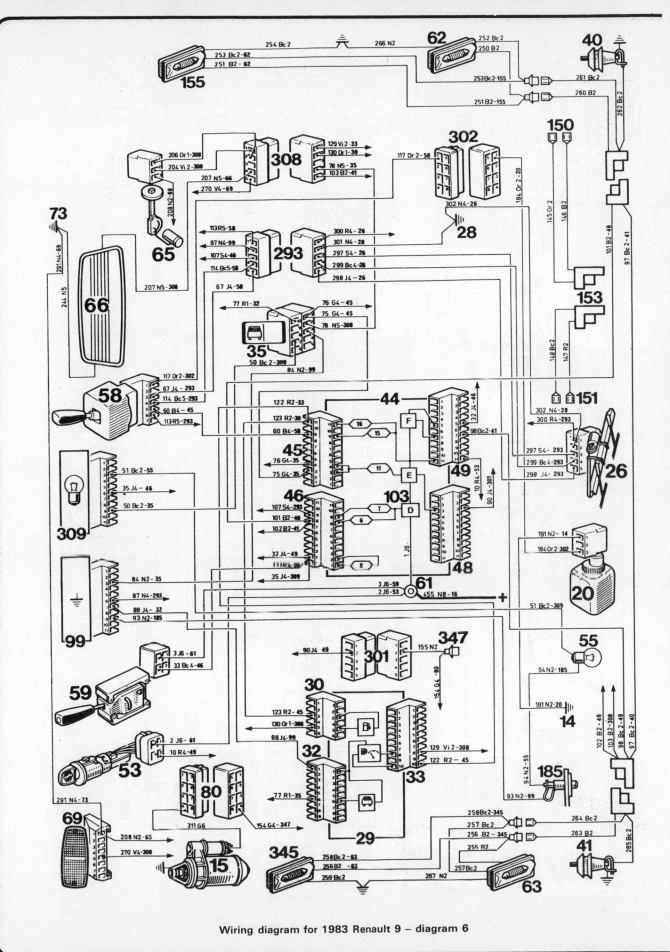

Wiring diagram for 1983 Renault 9 – diagram 6

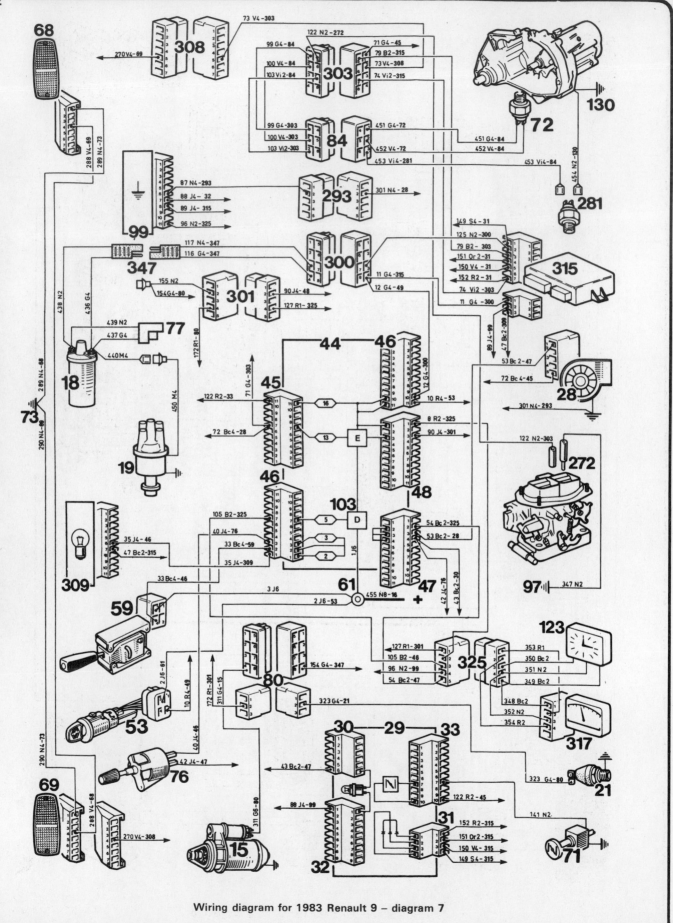

**Wiring diagram for 1983 Renault 9 – diagram 7**

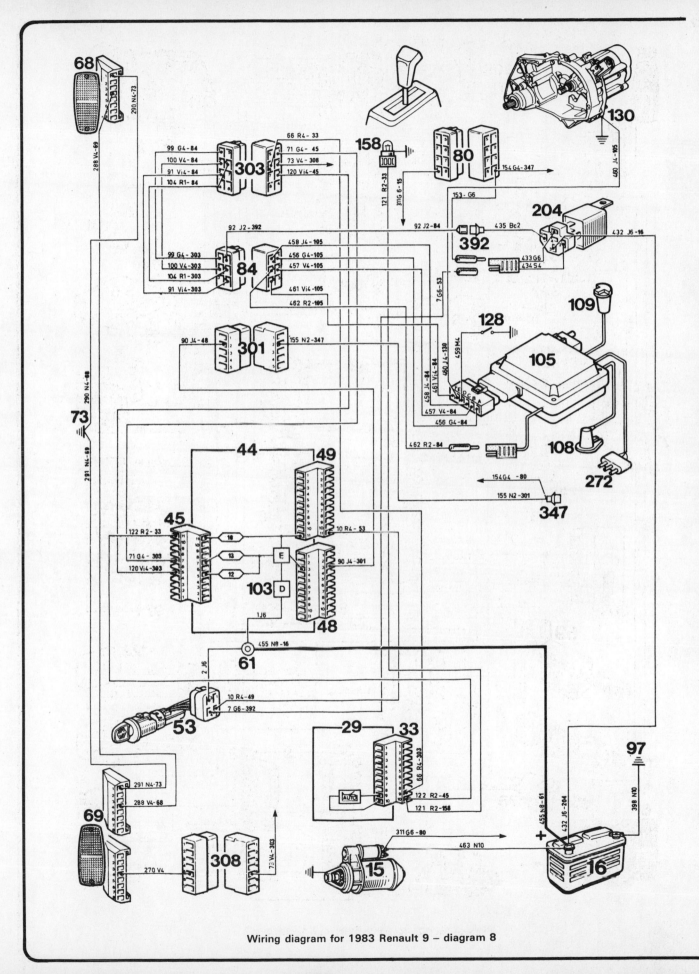

**Wiring diagram for 1983 Renault 9 – diagram 8**

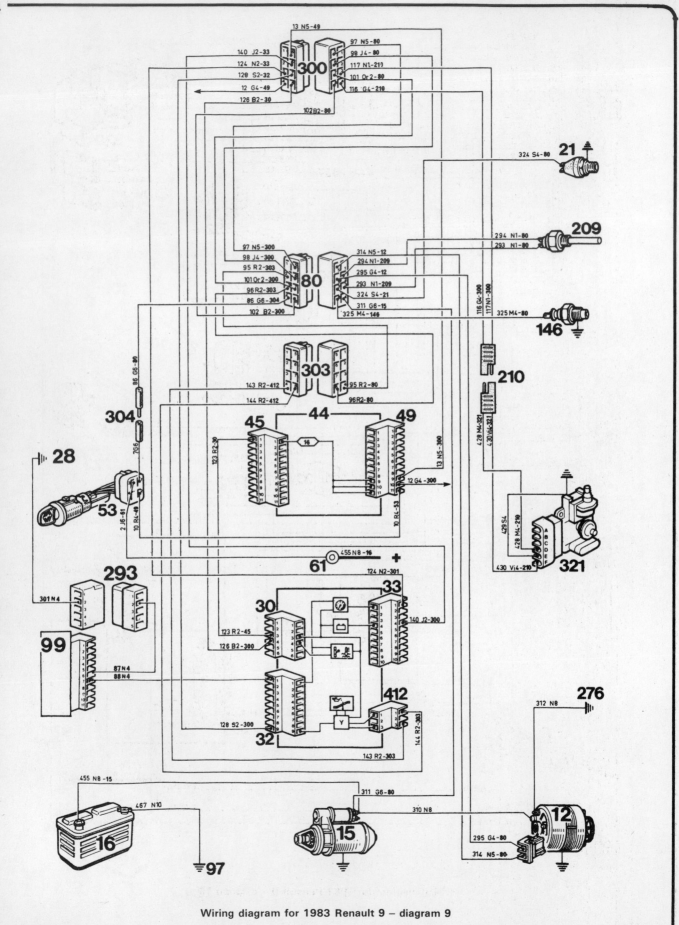

**Wiring diagram for 1983 Renault 9 – diagram 9**

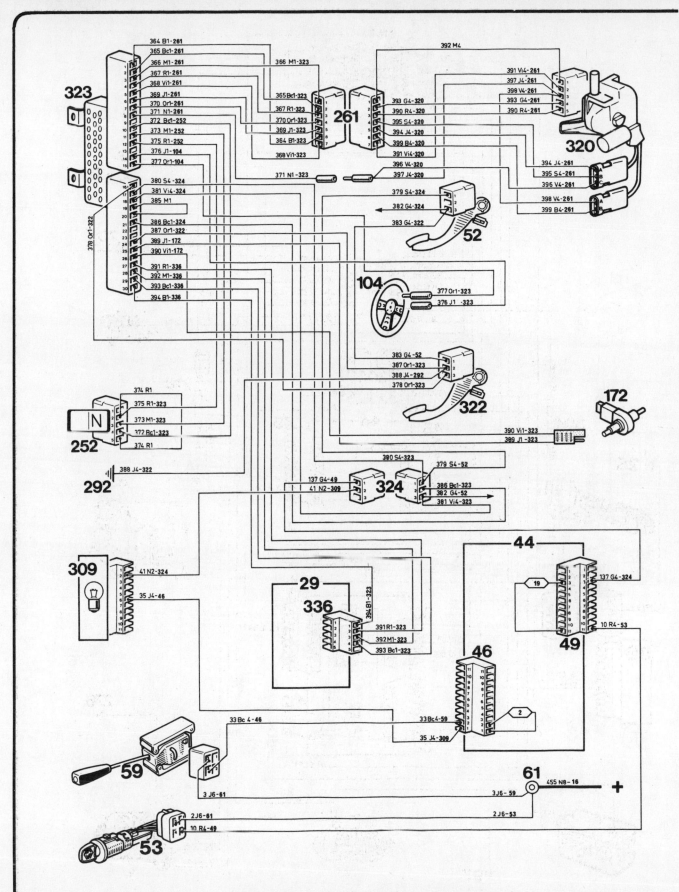

**Wiring diagram for 1983 Renault 9 – diagram 10**

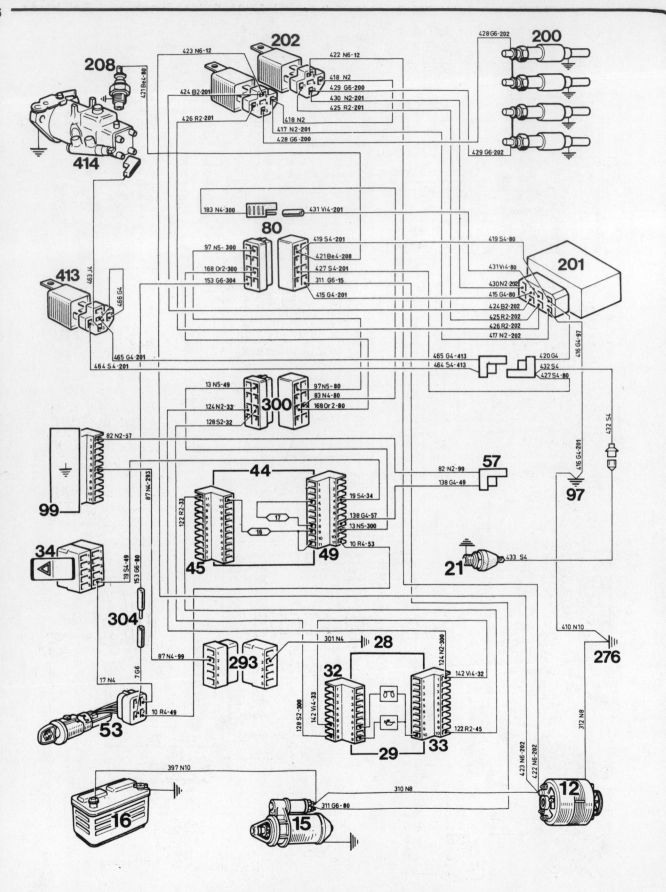

**Wiring diagram for 1983 Renault 9 – diagram 11**

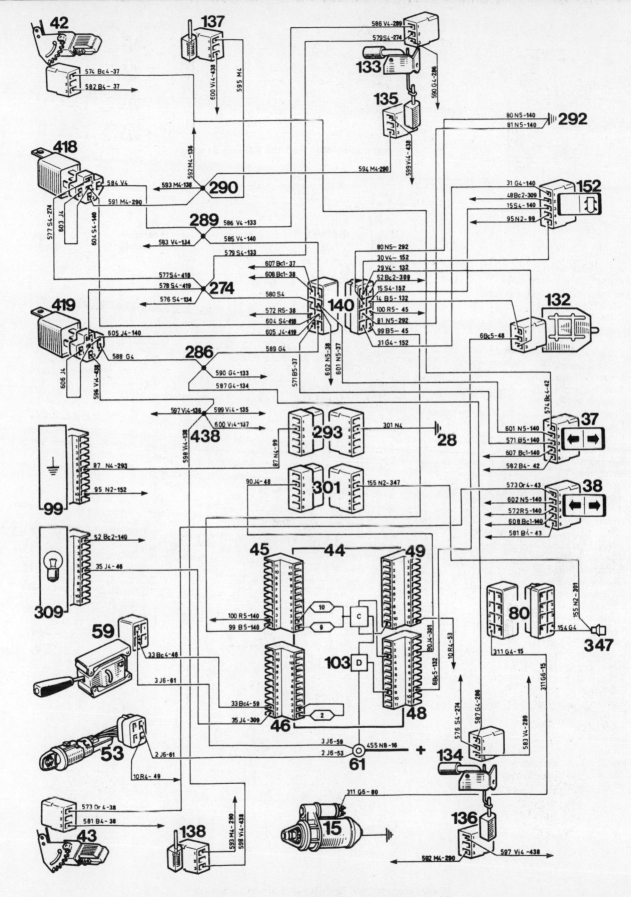

Wiring diagram for 1983 Renault 9 – diagram 12

## Key to wiring diagrams for 1983 Renault 9 models

*Depending on the item required, the diagram relating to that item is given below*

| | All models | Bottom range models | Mid range models | Top range models |
|---|---|---|---|---|
| AEI ignition | 9 | – | – | – |
| Air conditioning | – | – | – | 5 |
| Automatic transmission | 8 | – | – | – |
| Brake pad wear warning light | 3 | – | – | – |
| Charging circuit | 9 | – | – | – |
| Choke | 7 | – | – | – |
| Cigar lighter | 2 | – | – | – |
| Clock | 7 | – | – | – |
| Conventional ignition | 7 | – | – | – |
| Cooling fan motor | 5 | – | – | – |
| Direction indicators | – | 1 | 1 | 1 |
| Door locks (electro-magnetic) | – | – | – | 4 |
| Door locks (electric) | – | – | – | 12 |
| Econometer | – | 7 | – | – |
| Extreme cold ignition | 3 | – | – | – |
| Front interior lights | 6 | – | – | – |
| Front foglights | – | – | – | 3 |
| Fuel gauge | 6 | – | – | – |
| Handbrake | 3 | – | – | – |
| Headlight dipped beams | – | 1 | 1 | 1 |
| Headlight main beams | – | 1 | 1 | 1 |
| Headlight wiper/washers | 4 | – | – | – |
| Heating/ventilating | 2 | – | – | – |
| Horn | – | 2 | 2 | 2 |
| Instrument panel illumination | 7 | – | – | – |
| Nivocode | 3 | – | – | – |
| Normalur cruise control | – | – | – | 10 |
| Oil level indicator | 9 | – | – | – |
| Oil pressure indicator | – | – | – | 7 |
| Oil pressure switch | 2 | – | – | – |
| Radio | – | 1 | 1 | 11 |
| Rear foglight | 3 | – | – | – |
| Rear interior lights | 6 | – | – | – |
| Rear screen demister | 6 | – | – | – |
| Reversing lights | 7 | – | – | – |
| Selector lever illumination | 8 | – | – | – |
| Sidelights | – | 1 | 1 | 1 |
| Speakers | 6 | – | – | – |
| Starter | 3 | – | – | – |
| Stoplights | 3 | – | – | – |
| Temperature switch | 9 | – | – | – |
| Window winders (to November 1982) | – | – | – | 4 |
| Window winders (December 1982 on) | – | – | – | 12 |
| Windscreen wiper/washer | – | 6 | – | – |
| Windscreen wiper/washer with timer | – | – | 2 | 2 |

**Key to wiring diagrams for 1983 Renault 9 – all models**

*For information on use and colour code see page 321*

1   LH sidelight and/or direction indicator
2   RH sidelight and/or direction indicator
7   LH headlamp
8   RH headlamp
9   LH horn
10  RH horn
12  Alternator
13  LH front earth
14  RH front earth
15  Starter
16  Battery
17  Engine cooling fan motor
18  Ignition coil (or mounting)
19  Distributor
20  Windscreen washer pump
21  Oil pressure switch
22  Thermal switch on radiator
24  LH front brake
25  RH front brake
26  Windscreen wiper motor
27  Nivocode or ICP (pressure drop indicator)
28  Heating/ventilating fan motor
29  Instrument panel
30  Connector No 1 – Instrument panel
31  Connector No 2 – Instrument panel
32  Connector No 3 – Instrument panel
33  Connector No 4 – Instrument panel
34  'Hazard' warning lights switch
35  Rear screen demister switch
37  LH window switch
38  RH window switch
40  LH front door pillar switch
41  RH front door pillar switch
42  LH window motor
43  RH window motor
44  Accessories plate or fusebox
45  Junction block – front harness – accessories plate
46  Junction block – front harness – accessories plate
47  Junction block – front harness – accessories plate
48  Junction block – front harness – accessories plate
49  Junction block – front harness – accessories plate
52  Stop-lights switch

53  Ignition/starter – anti-theft switch
55  Glove compartment illumination
56  Cigar lighter
57  Feed to car radio
58  Windscreen wiper/washer switch
59  Lighting and direction indicators switch
60  Direction indicators switch or connector
61  (+) feed before ignition/starter switch
62  LH interior light
63  RH interior light
64  Handbrake switch
65  Fuel gauge tank unit
66  Rear screen demister
68  LH rear light assembly
69  RH rear light assembly
70  Number plate lights
71  Choke 'On' warning light switch
72  Reversing lights switch
73  Rear light assembly earth
74  Flasher unit
76  Instrument panel lighting rheostat
77  Wire junction – diagnostic socket
80  Junction block – front and engine harnesses
84  Junction block – front and automatic transmission harnesses
90  Wire junction – air conditioning compressor
97  Bodyshell earth
99  Dashboard (facia) earth
103 Feed to accessories plate
104 Junction – Steering wheel tracks
105 Automatic transmission computer
106 Rear foglamp switch
108 Multi-function switch
110 Engine cooling fan motor relay
114 Windscreen wiper timer relay
123 Clock
128 Kick-down switch
130 Automatic transmission earth
132 Inertia switch
133 LH front door lock switch
134 RH front door lock switch
135 LH front door lock solenoid

## Key to wiring diagrams for 1983 Renault 9 – all models (continued)

136 RH front door lock solenoid
137 LH rear door lock solenoid
138 RH rear door lock solenoid
140 Junction – electro-magnetic door locks harness
146 Temperature or thermal switch
147 Ignition coil resistance
150 LH front door speaker
151 RH front door speaker
152 Electro-magnetic locks central switch
153 Speaker wires
155 Rear or LH rear interior light
158 Automatic transmission selector illumination
170 Wire junction – air conditioning harness
172 Impulse generator
174 RH headlamp wiper motor
175 LH headlamp wiper motor
176 Headlamp wipers timer relay
185 Glove compartment light switch
194 Connection No 1 – cooled air blower fan
195 Idle cut-out
200 Heater plus
201 Heater plugs control box
202 Heater plugs relay
204 Starter relay
207 Anti-stall solenoid valve
208 Fuel cut-off solenoid
209 Engine oil level indicator
210 Wire junction – AEI harness
214 Front foglamps relay
215 RH front foglamp
216 LH front foglamp
252 'Normalur' switch
261 Junction – 'Normalur' harness
262 Air conditioning and heater controls
272 Throttle butterfly switch
273 Flowmeter
274 Wire joint No 1
276 Engine earth
278 Carburettor
281 Top gear switch
284 Electrical start relay
286 Wire joint No 2
289 Wire joint No 3

290 Wire joint No 4
292 Steering column bracket earth
293 Junction – windscreen wiper harness
295 Air conditioning air temperature sensor
300 Connector No 1 – dashboard (facia) and front harnesses
301 Connector No 2 – dashboard (facia) and front harnesses
302 Connector No 3 – dashboard (facia) and front harnesses
303 Connector No 4 – dashboard (facia) and front harnesses
304 Connector No 5 – dashboard (facia) and front harnesses
305 Connector No 6 – dashboard (facia) and front harnesses
308 Junction – dashboard (facia) and rear harnesses
309 Sidelights terminal
315 Econometer computer
317 Oil pressure gauge
320 'Normalur' servo motor
321 AEI module
322 Declutching switch
323 'Normalur' computer
324 Junction – 'Normalur' and dashboard (facia)
325 Junction – clock wiring
336 Connector No 5 – instrument panel
340 'Driving Aid' computer
342 Headlamp washers solenoid valve
345 RH rear interior light
347 Junction – ignition coil harness
353 Thermal switch – 15°C
378 Air conditioning hp sensor
379 Air conditioning lp sensor
392 Wire junction – starter relay
393 Battery cut-out
411 Direction indicators control box
412 Connection No 6 – instrument panel
413 Advance corrector relay
414 Advance corrector
415 Wire junction – front foglamps harness
418 'Door open' relay
419 'Door closed' relay
438 Wire joint No 5
454 Wire junction – engine front harness to headlight wiper/washer harness
459 Anti-pollution solenoid valve
465 Wire junction – recycling flap solenoid valve
466 Recycling flap solenoid valve

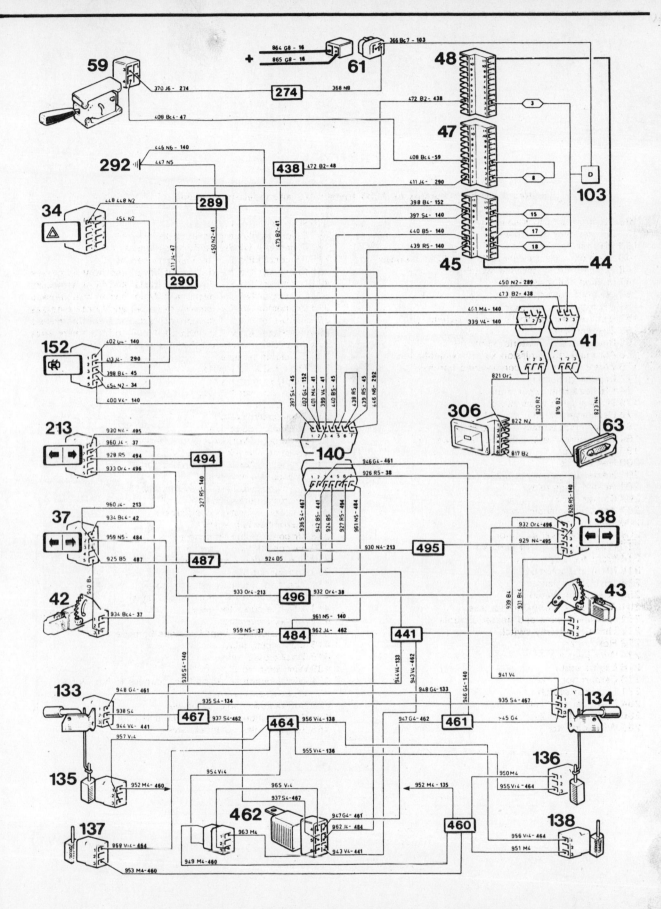

Wiring diagram for 1984 Renault 11 (Renault 9 similar) – diagram 1

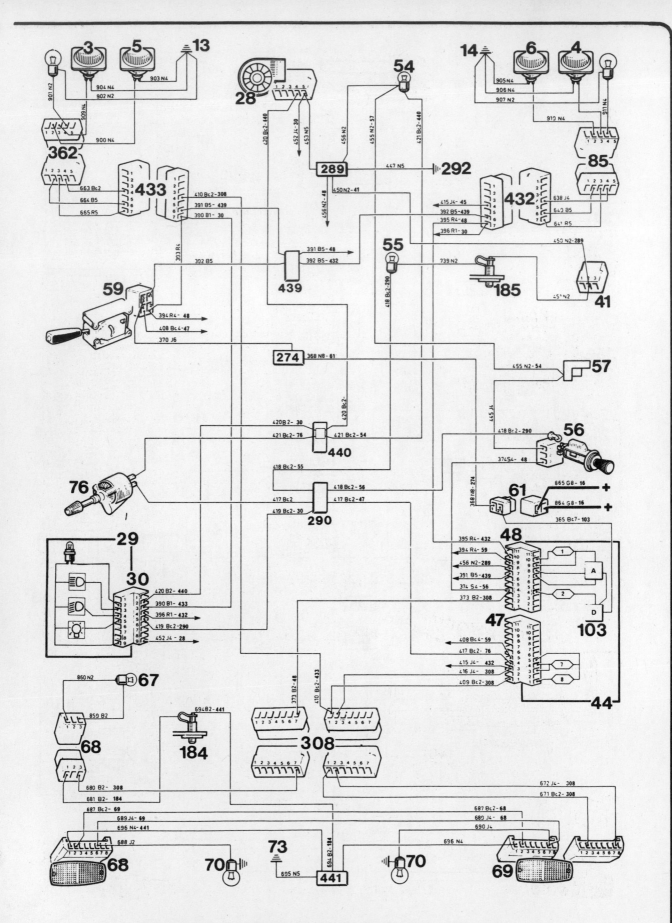

**Wiring diagram for 1984 Renault 11 (Renault 9 similar) – diagram 2**

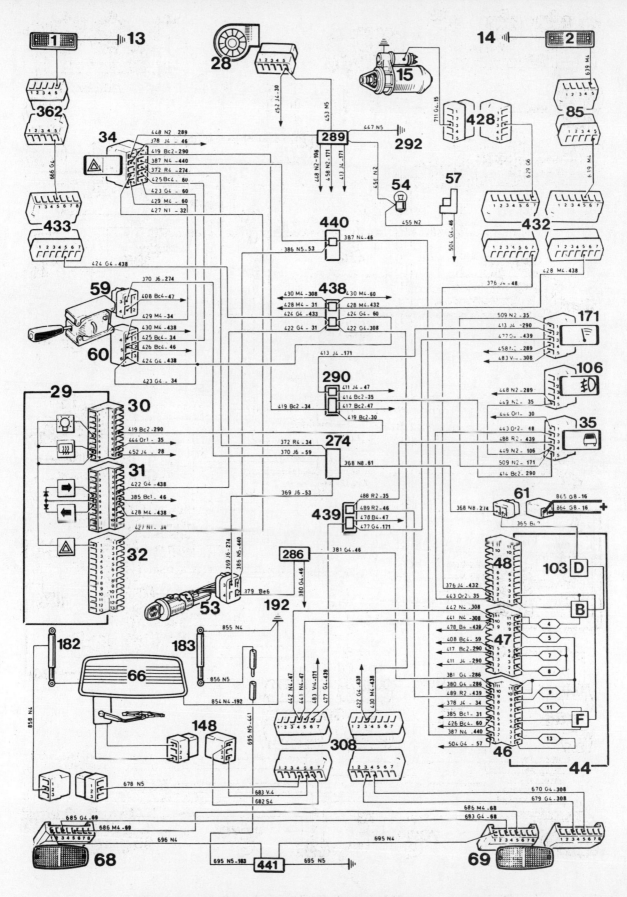

**Wiring diagram for 1984 Renault 11 (Renault 9 similar) – diagram 3**

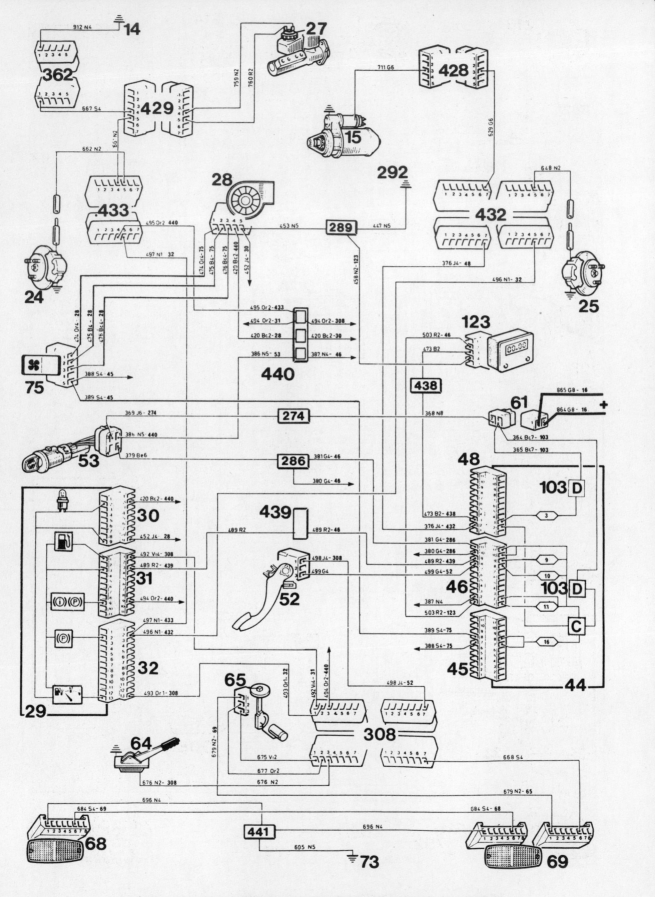

**344**

Wiring diagram for 1984 Renault 11 (Renault 9 similar) – diagram 4

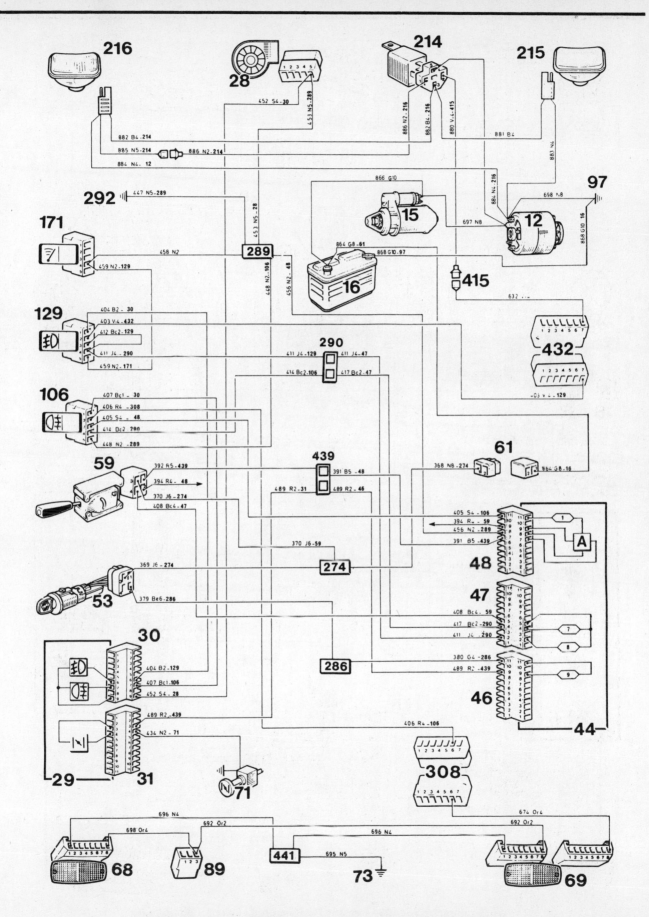

Wiring diagram for 1984 Renault 11 (Renault 9 similar) – diagram 5

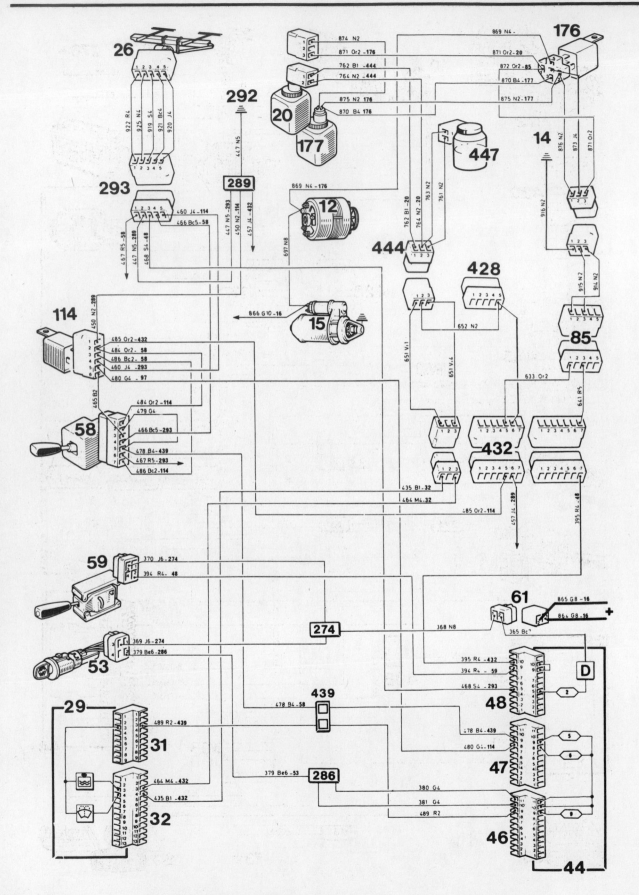

**Wiring diagram for 1984 Renault 11 (Renault 9 similar) – diagram 6**

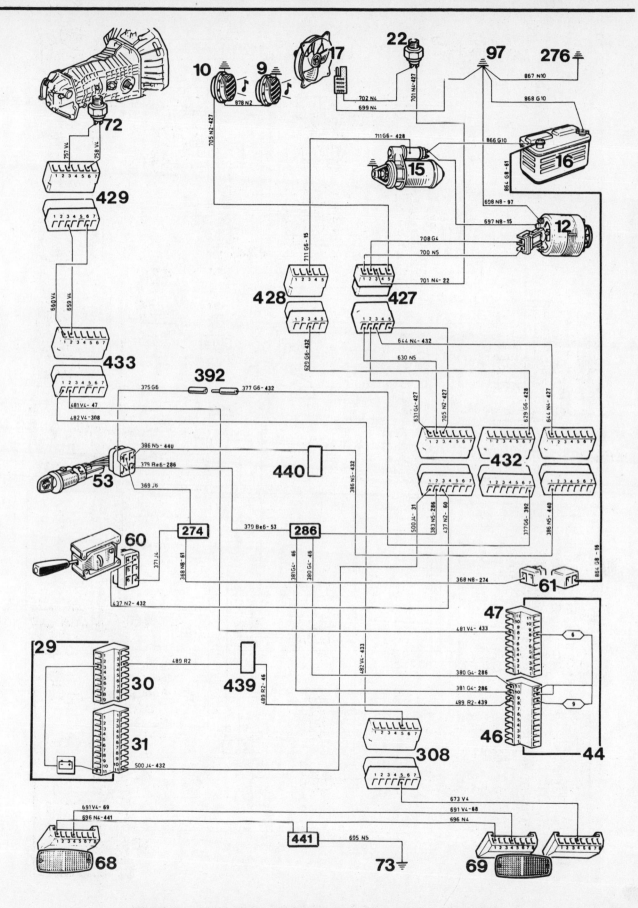

**Wiring diagram for 1984 Renault 11 (Renault 9 similar) – diagram 7**

348

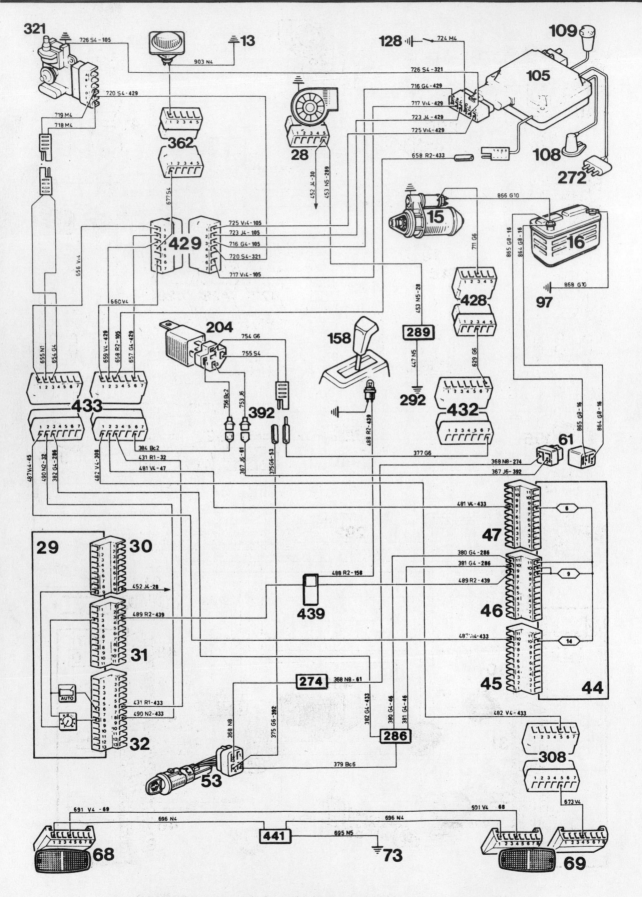

Wiring diagram for 1984 Renault 11 (Renault 9 similar) – diagram 8

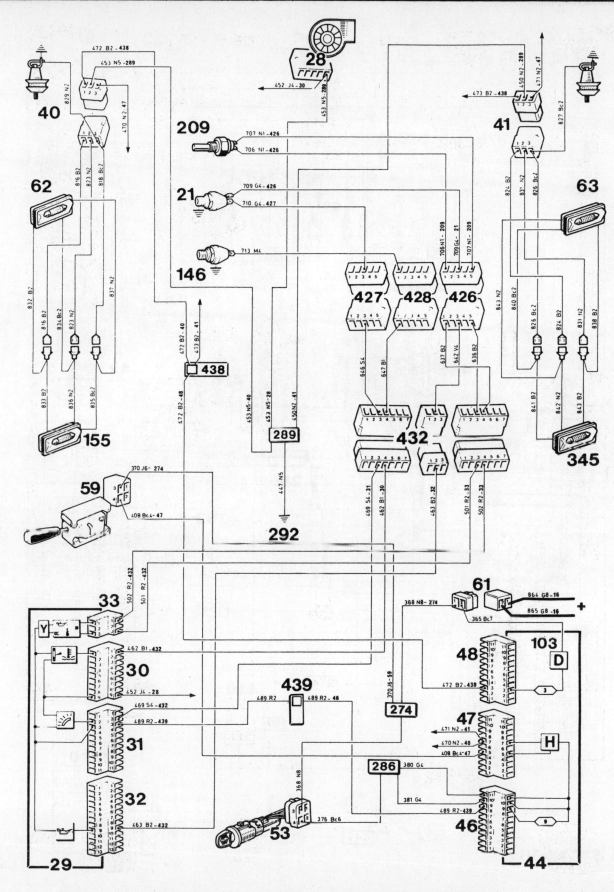

**Wiring diagram for 1984 Renault 11 (Renault 9 similar) – diagram 9**

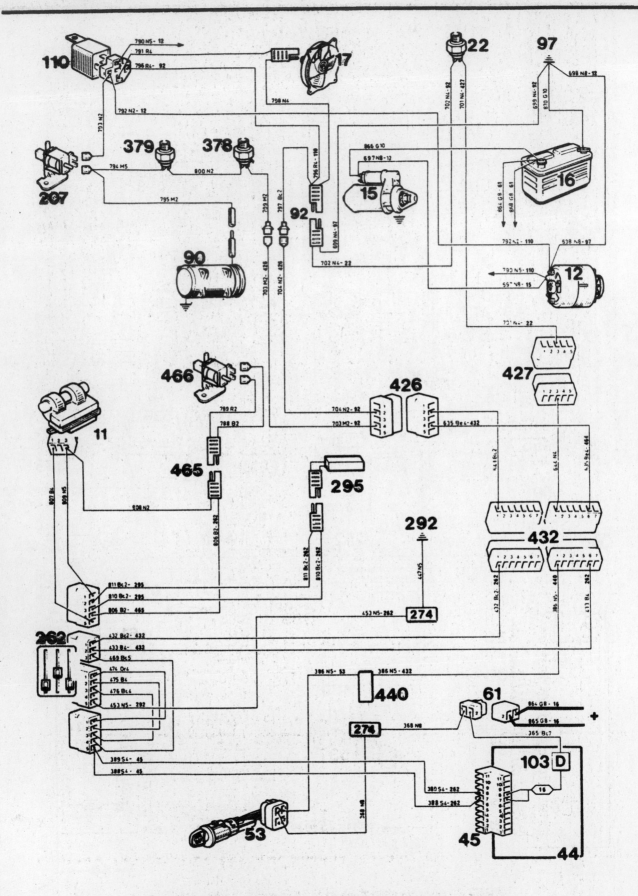

**Wiring diagram for 1984 Renault 11 (Renault 9 similar) – diagram 10**

351

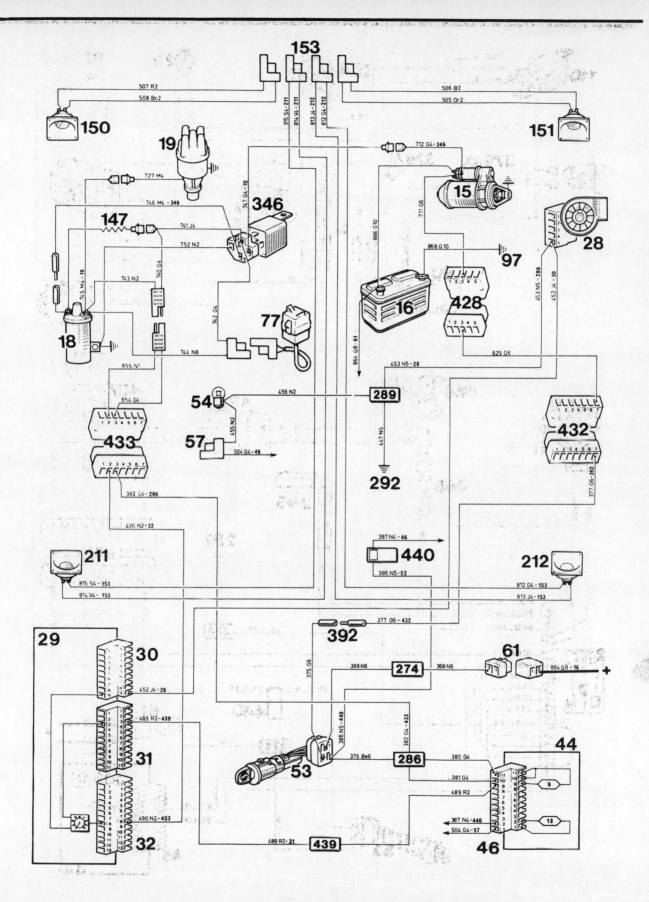

**Wiring diagram for 1984 Renault 11 (Renault 9 similar) – diagram 11**

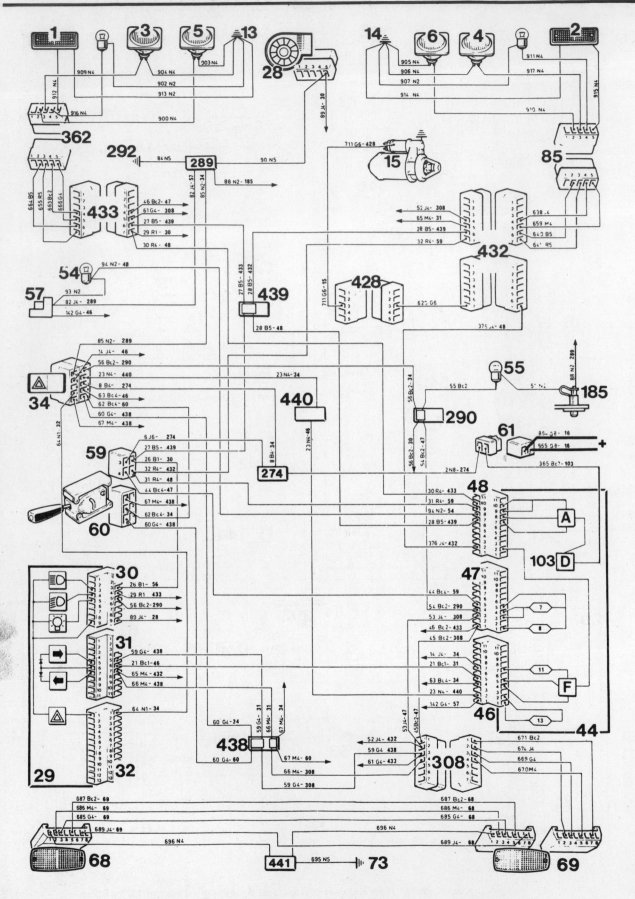

**Wiring diagram for 1984 Renault 11 (Renault 9 similar) – diagram 12**

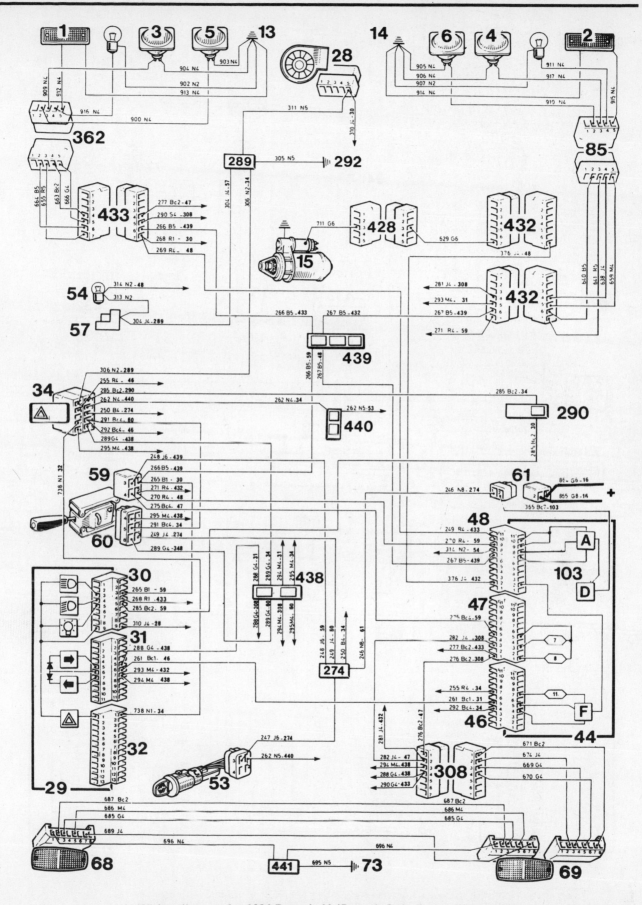

**Wiring diagram for 1984 Renault 11 (Renault 9 similar) – diagram 13**

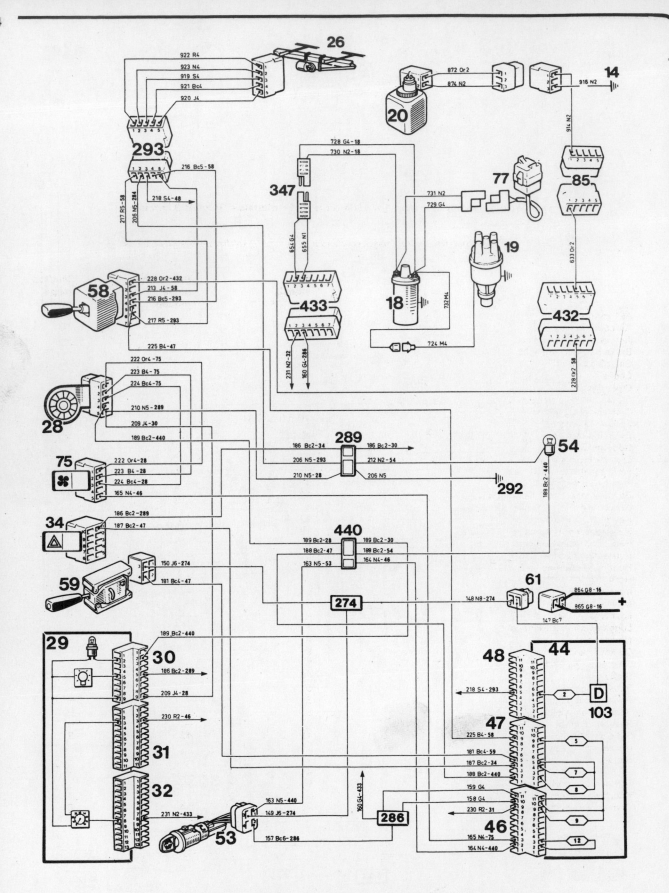

Wiring diagram for 1984 Renault 11 (Renault 9 similar) – diagram 14

### Key to wiring diagrams for 1984 Renault 11 models – Renault 9 similar

*Depending on the item required, the diagram relating to that item is given below*

| | All models | Bottom/mid range models | Mid/top range models |
|---|---|---|---|
| AEI ignition | – | – | 8 |
| Air conditioning | – | – | 10 |
| Automatic transmission | 8 | – | – |
| Brake pad warning light | 4 | – | – |
| Charging circuit | 7 | – | – |
| Choke | 5 | – | – |
| Cigar lighter | 2 | – | – |
| Clock | 4 | – | – |
| Conventional ignition | – | 14 | – |
| Cooling fan motor | 7 | – | – |
| Direction indicators | 12 | 13 | 3 |
| Door locks | – | – | 1 |
| Extreme cold ignition | 11 | – | – |
| Front foglights | 5 | – | – |
| Fuel gauge | 4 | – | – |
| Glove compartment illumination | 12 | – | 2 |
| Handbrake | 4 | – | – |
| Headlight dipped beams | 12 | 13 | 2 |
| Headlight main beams | 12 | 13 | 2 |
| Headlight wiper/washers | 6 | – | – |
| Heater controls illumination | 2 | – | – |
| Heating/ventilating | – | 14 | 4 |
| Horn | – | 7 | 7 |
| Interior lights | 9 | – | – |
| Low coolant | – | – | 6 |
| Low washer fluid | – | – | 6 |
| Luggage compartment light | 2 | – | – |
| Nivocode | 4 | – | – |
| Oil level indicator | 9 | – | – |
| Oil pressure switch | 9 | – | – |
| Radio | 12 | 3 | 3 |
| Rear foglight | 5 | – | – |
| Rear screen demister | 3 | – | – |
| Rear screen wiper | 3 | – | – |
| Reversing lights | 7 | – | – |
| Sidelights | 12 | 13 | 2 |
| Speakers | 11 | – | – |
| Starter | 7 | – | – |
| Stoplights | 4 | – | – |
| Temperature switch | 9 | – | – |
| Window winders | – | – | 1 |
| Windscreen wiper/washer | – | 14 | 6 |

**356**

**Key to wiring diagram for 1984 Renault 11 (Renault 9 similar) – all models**

*For information on use and colour code see page 321*

| | | | |
|---|---|---|---|
| 1 | LH sidelight and/or direction indicator | 53 | Ignition/starter – anti-theft switch |
| 2 | RH sidelight and/or direction indicator | 54 | Heating/ventilating controls illumination |
| 3 | LH dipped beam headlamp | 55 | Glove compartment light |
| 4 | RH dipped beam headlamp | 56 | Cigar lighter |
| 5 | RH main beam headlamp | 57 | Feed to car radio |
| 6 | LH main beam headlamp | 58 | Windscreen wiper/washer switch |
| 9 | LH horn | 59 | Lighting and direction indicators switch |
| 10 | RH horn | 60 | Direction indicator switch or connector |
| 11 | Air conditioning blower | 61 | Feed terminal before ignition/starter switch |
| 12 | Alternator | 62 | LH interior light |
| 13 | LH earth | 63 | RH interior light |
| 14 | RH earth | 64 | Handbrake 'On' warning light switch |
| 15 | Starter | 65 | Fuel gauge tank unit |
| 16 | Battery | 66 | Rear screen demister |
| 17 | Engine cooling fan motor | 67 | Luggage compartment light |
| 18 | Ignition coil (or mounting) | 68 | LH rear light assembly |
| 19 | Distributor | 69 | RH rear light assembly |
| 20 | Windscreen washer pump | 70 | Number plate lights |
| 21 | Oil pressure switch | 71 | Choke 'On' warning light |
| 22 | Fan motor No 1 activating thermal switch | 72 | Reversing lights switch |
| 24 | LH front brake | 73 | Rear light assemblies earth |
| 25 | RH front brake | 75 | Heating/ventilating fan switch |
| 26 | Windscreen wiper motor | 76 | Instrument panel and warning lights rheostat |
| 27 | Nivocode or ICP (pressure drop indicator) | 77 | Diagnostic socket |
| 28 | Heating/ventilating fan motor | 80 | Junction block – engine harness |
| 29 | Instrument panel | 85 | Junction block – RH headlamp harness |
| 30 | Connector No 1 – instrument panel | 90 | Air conditioning compressor |
| 31 | Connector No 2 – instrument panel | 92 | Wire junction – air conditioning harness (engine end) |
| 32 | Connector No 3 – instrument panel | 103 | Feed to accessories plate |
| 33 | Connector No 4 – instrument panel | 105 | Automatic transmission computer |
| 34 | 'Hazard' warning lights switch | 106 | Rear foglamp switch |
| 35 | Rear screen demister switch | 108 | Multi-function switch |
| 37 | LH window switch | 109 | Speed sensor |
| 38 | RH window switch | 114 | Windscreen wiper timer relay |
| 40 | LH front door pillar switch | 123 | Clock |
| 41 | RH front door pillar switch | 128 | Kick-down switch |
| 42 | LH window motor | 129 | Front foglamp switch |
| 43 | RH window motor | 133 | LH front door lock switch |
| 44 | Accessories plate or fusebox | 134 | RH front door lock switch |
| 45 | Junction block – front harness – accessories plate | 135 | LH front door solenoid |
| 46 | Junction block – front harness – accessories plate | 136 | RH front door solenoid |
| 47 | Junction block – front harness – accessories plate | 137 | LH rear door solenoid |
| 48 | Junction block – front harness – accessories plate | 138 | RH rear door solenoid |
| 52 | Stop-lights switch | 146 | Temperature or thermal switch |

**Key to wiring diagram for 1984 Renault 11 (Renault 9 similar) – all models (continued)**

147 Ignition coil resistance
148 Tailgate or luggage compartment fixed contact
150 LH front door speaker
151 RH front door speaker
152 Central door locking switch
153 Radio speaker wires
155 Rear or LH rear interior light
158 Automatic transmission selector illumination
171 Rear screen wiper/washer switch
172 Impulse generator
177 Headlamp washers pump
182 Tailgate RH counterbalance
183 Tailgate LH counterbalance
184 Luggage compartment light switch
185 Glove compartment light switch
192 Tailgate earth
195 Idling cut-out
200 Heater plugs
201 Air pre-heating box
204 Starter relay
207 Anti-stall solenoid valve
208 Diesel fuel cut-off solenoid
209 Oil level indicator sensor
211 Speaker in RH rear panel
212 Speaker in LH rear panel
213 LH window switch for passenger's side (LHD)
214 Relay No 1 – additional driving lights
215 RH front foglamp
216 LH front foglamp
248 Relay No 2 – additional driving lights
262 Heating and air conditioning control panel
272 Throttle spindle switch
273 Flowmeter
274 Wire junction No 1
278 Carburettor
284 Cold start relay
286 Wire junction No 2
289 Wire junction No 3
290 Wire junction No 4
292 Steering column bracket earth
293 Junction – windscreen wiper wiring
295 Air conditioning air sensor

306 Remote control door unlocking device – 'PLIP'
308 Junction No 2 – rear harness
321 AEI module
340 Car-borne computer for 'Driving Aid'
345 RH rear interior light
347 Junction – ignition coil harness
353 Thermal switch 15°C
362 Junction – LH headlamp harness
378 Air conditioning high pressure detector
379 Air conditioning low pressure detector
392 Junction – starter relay harness
411 Dual control direction indicators control box (LHD)
413 Advance corrector relay
414 Advance corrector
415 Connector – additional front lights harness
426 Junction No 1 – side-member and engine harnesses
427 Junction No 2 – side-member and engine harnesses
428 Junction No 3 – side-member and engine harnesses
429 Window switch support plate
432 Junction – dashboard and RH side-member harnesses
433 Junction – dashboard and LH side-member harnesses
438 Wire junction No 5
439 Wire junction No 6
440 Wire junction No 7
441 Wire junction No 8
444 Junction – 'low' coolant harness
447 Coolant level detector
451 Junction – engine harness and advance corrector wiring
459 Anti-pollution solenoid valve
460 Wire junction No 9
461 Wire junction No 10
462 Door locking timer relay
464 Wire junction No 11
465 Junction – Recycling flap solenoid valve wiring
466 Recycling flap solenoid valve
467 Splicing No 12
484 Splicing No 13
487 Splicing No 14
494 Connection No 15
495 Connection No 16
496 Connection No 17
497 Connection No 18

**Key to typical wiring diagram for 1985 and later Renault 11 – Renault 9 similar**

*Depending on the item required, the diagram relating to that item is given below*

| | | | |
|---|---|---|---|
| Brake pad wear warning light | 9 | Min coolant level | 6 |
| Car radio | 9 | Min windscreen washer fluid level | 6 |
| Charging circuit | 3 | Nivocode | 9 |
| Choke flap | 4 | Oil level probe | 4 |
| Cigar lighter | 5 | Oil pressure gauge | 4 |
| Clock | 9 | Oil pressure switch | 3 |
| Direction indicator lights | 1 | Rear foglight | 2 |
| Door, tailgate and bonnet opening switches | 9 | Rear screen demister | 2 |
| Engine cooling fan motor | 3 | Rear screen wiper | 2 |
| Flowmeter | 8 | Reversing lights | 5 |
| Fuel gauge | 8 | Side and rear lights | 1 |
| Glove compartment lighting | 7 | Speakers | 9 |
| Handbrake | 8 | Speedometer | 4 |
| Hazard warning lights | 1 | Starter | 3 |
| Headlight dipped beam | 1 | Stop-lights | 5 |
| Headlight main beam | 1 | Switches lighting | 7 |
| Headlight washers | 6 | Temperature sensor | 8 |
| Heating | 7 | Temperature switch | 3 |
| Horn | 3 | Trip computer | 8 |
| Ignition | 4 | Voice synthesizer repeater (wire No 362) | 4 |
| Interior lights | 5 | Windscreen washer/wiper | 6 |
| Luggage compartment lighting | 2 | | |

**Key to typical wiring diagram for 1985 and later Renault 11 – Renault 9 similar**

| | | | |
|---|---|---|---|
| 1 | LH sidelight and/or direction indicator | 47 | Junction block – front harness – accessories plate |
| 2 | RH sidelight and/or direction indicator | 48 | Junction block – front harness – accessories plate |
| 3 | LH dipped beam headlight | 49 | Junction block – front harness – accessories plate |
| 4 | RH dipped beam headlight | 52 | Stop-lights switch |
| 5 | RH main beam headlight | 53 | Ignition starter anti-theft switch |
| 9 | LH horn | 54 | Heating/ventilating controls illumination |
| 10 | RH horn | 55 | Glove compartment light |
| 12 | Alternator | 56 | Cigar lighter |
| 13 | LH earth | 57 | Feed to car radio |
| 14 | RH earth | 58 | Windscreen wiper/washer switch |
| 15 | Starter | 59 | Lighting and direction indicators switch |
| 16 | Battery | 60 | Direction indicator switch or connector |
| 17 | Engine cooling fan motor | 61 | Terminal before ignition switch |
| 20 | Windscreen washer pump | 62 | LH interior light |
| 21 | Oil pressure switch | 63 | RH interior light |
| 22 | Fan motor No 1 activating thermal switch | 64 | Handbrake "On" warning light switch |
| 24 | LH front brake | 65 | Fuel gauge tank unit |
| 25 | RH front brake | 66 | Rear screen demister |
| 26 | Windscreen wiper motor | 67 | Luggage compartment light |
| 27 | Nivocode or ICP (pressure drop indicator) | 68 | LH rear light assembly |
| 29 | Instrument panel | 69 | RH rear light assembly |
| 30 | Connector No 1 – instrument panel | 70 | Number plate lights |
| 31 | Connector No 2 – instrument panel | 71 | Choke "On" warning light |
| 32 | Connector No 3 – instrument panel | 72 | Reversing lights switch |
| 33 | Connector No 4 – instrument panel | 75 | Heating ventilating fan switch |
| 34 | Hazard warning lights switch | 76 | Instrument panel and warning lights rheostat |
| 40 | LH front door pillar switch | 78 | Rear screen wiper motor |
| 41 | RH front door pillar switch | 81 | Juntion block – rear harness No 1 |
| 44 | Accessories plate or fusebox | 83 | Junction block – heating/ventilating motor harness |
| 45 | Junction block – front harness – accessories plate | 84 | Junction block – gearbox/automatic transmission harness |
| 46 | Junction block – front harness – accessories plate | | |

**Key to typical wiring diagram for 1985 and later Renault 11 – Renault 9 similar (continued)**

| | | | |
|---|---|---|---|
| 85 | Junction block – RH headlight harness | 332 | LH rear door switch |
| 89 | Rear foglight | 333 | RH rear door switch |
| 97 | Bodyshell earth | 341 | External air temperature sensor |
| 103 | Feed to accessories plate | 345 | RH rear interior light |
| 109 | Speed sensor | 362 | Junction – LH headlight harness |
| 113 | Fuel preheater | 382 | Connector – driver's door harness |
| 114 | Windscreen wiper timer relay | 427 | Junction No 2 sidemember and engine harnesses |
| 115 | Connector – temperature sensor harness | 430 | Bonnet closing switch |
| 123 | Clock | 431 | Spoken message speaker |
| 128 | Kick down switch | 432 | Harness junction – dashboard to RH front |
| 146 | Temperature or thermal switch | 433 | Harness junction – dashboard to LH front |
| 148 | Tailgate or luggage compartment fixed contact | 436 | Mileage module |
| 150 | LH front door speaker | 437 | Spoken message module |
| 151 | RH front door speaker | 438 | Wire junction No 5 |
| 153 | Radio speaker wires | 439 | Wire junction No 6 |
| 155 | Rear or LH rear interior light | 440 | Wire junction No 7 |
| 171 | Rear screen wiper/washer switch | 441 | Wire junction No 8 |
| 176 | Headlight wipers timer relay | 447 | Coolant level detector |
| 177 | Headlight washers pump | 460 | Wire junction No 9 |
| 182 | Tailgate RH counterbalance | 461 | Wire junction No 10 |
| 183 | Tailgate LH counterbalance | 463 | Instrument lighting rheostat relay |
| 184 | Luggage compartment light switch | 464 | Wire junction No 11 |
| 185 | Glove compartment light switch | 467 | Splicing No 12 |
| 102 | Tailgate earth | 476 | Windscreen washer liquid level sensor |
| 209 | Oil level indicator sensor | 484 | Splicing No 13 |
| 210 | Junction – AEI harness | 487 | Splicing No 14 |
| 273 | Flowmeter | 494 | Connection No 15 |
| 274 | Wire junction No 1 | 495 | Connection No 16 |
| 276 | Engine earth | 496 | Connection No 17 |
| 286 | Wire junction No 2 | 497 | Connection No 18 |
| 289 | Wire junction No 3 | 498 | Connection No 19 |
| 290 | Wire junction No 4 | 499 | Connection No 20 |
| 292 | Steering column bracket earth | 500 | Connection No 21 |
| 293 | Junction – windscreen wiper wiring | 501 | Connection No 22 |
| 311 | Connector – passenger door harness | 502 | Connection No 23 |
| 321 | AEI module | 539 | Junction – flowmeter harness |
| 329 | Bulb monitor control box | 557 | Junction – LH rear door harness |
| 330 | LH front door switch | 558 | Junction – RH rear door harness |
| 331 | RH front door switch | | |

*For information for use and colour code see page 322*

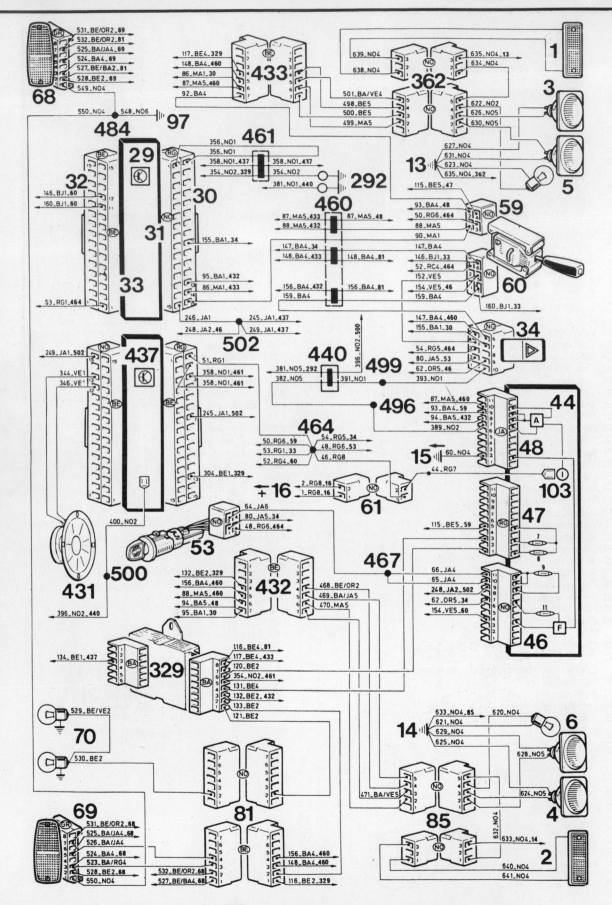

Typical wiring diagram for 1985 and later Renault 11 (Renault 9 similar) – diagram 1

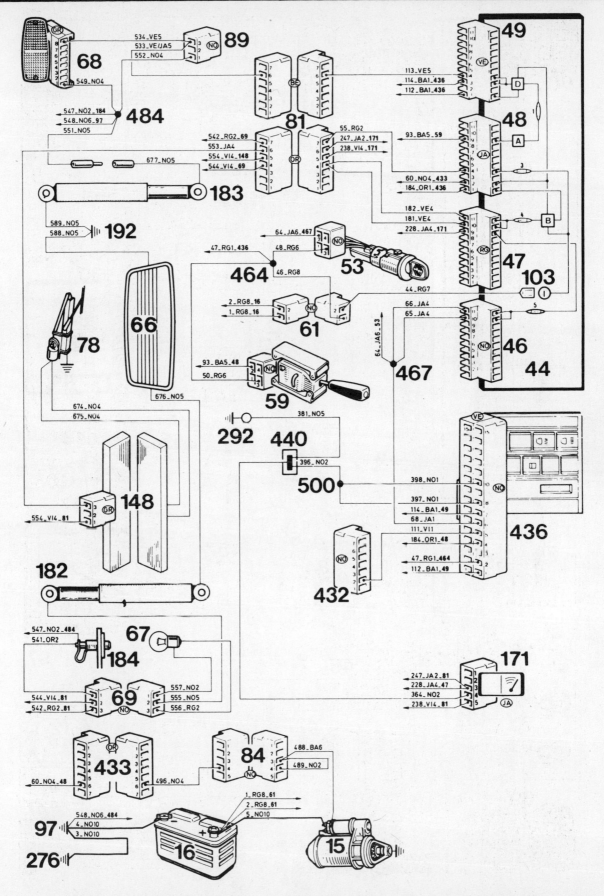

Typical wiring diagram for 1985 and later Renault 11 (Renault 9 similar) – diagram 2

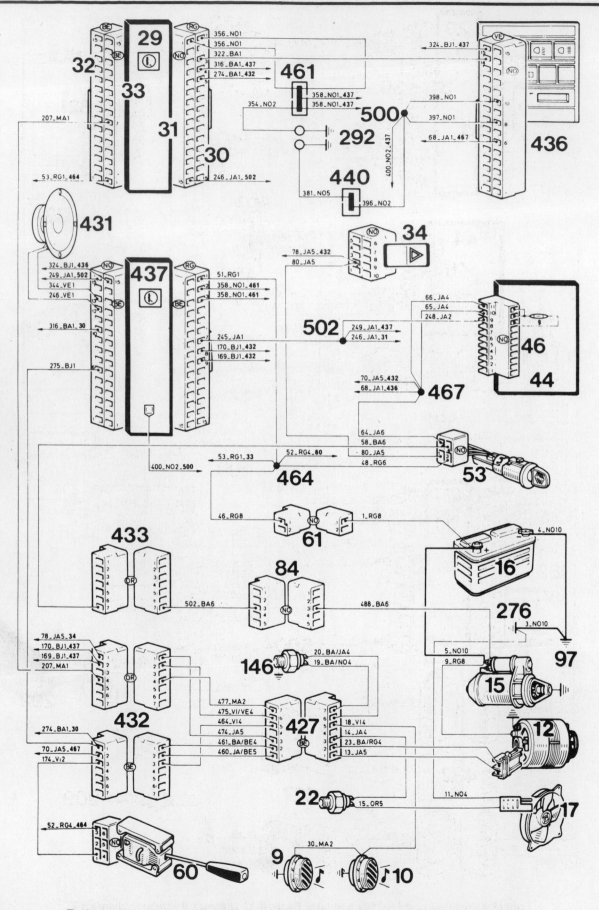

Typical wiring diagram for 1985 and later Renault 11 (Renault 9 similar) – diagram 3

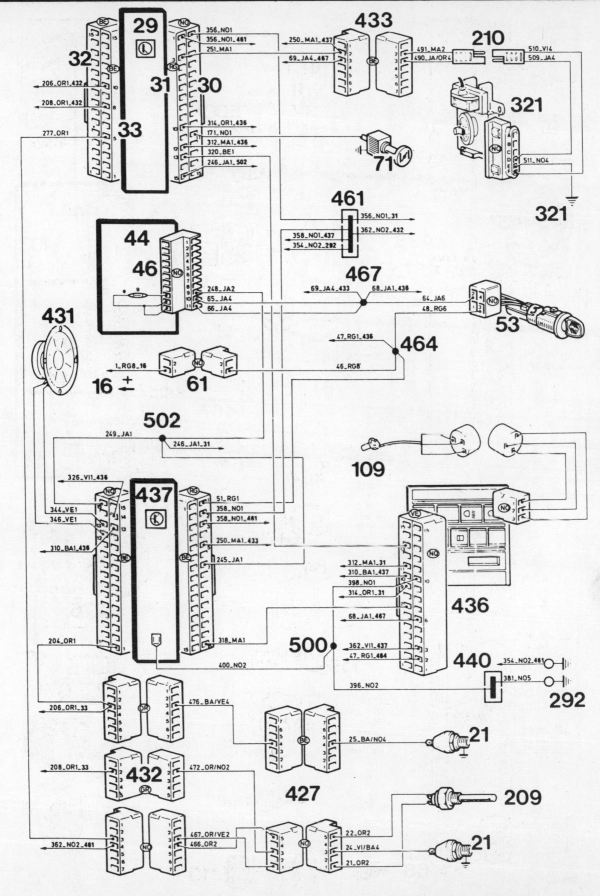

Typical wiring diagram for 1985 and later Renault 11 (Renault 9 similar) – diagram 4

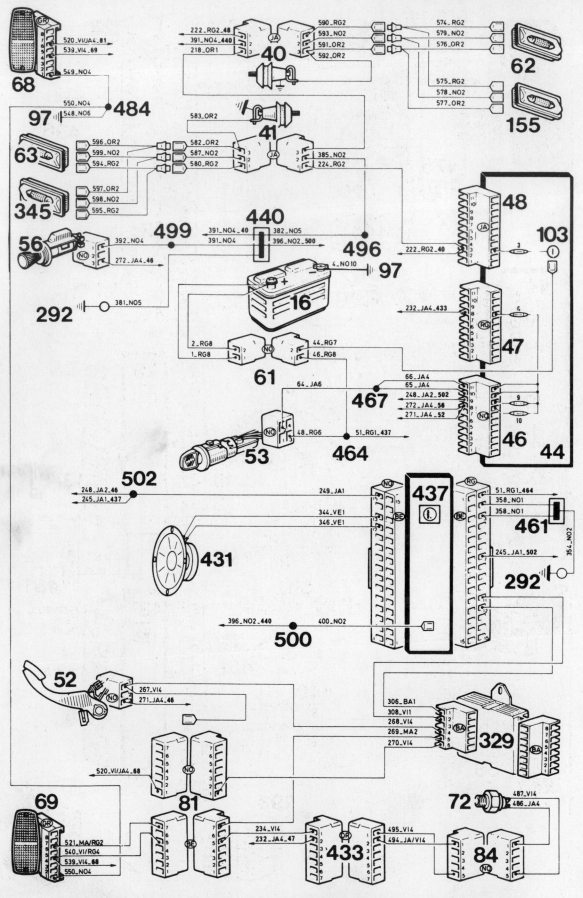

**Typical wiring diagram for 1985 and later Renault 11 (Renault 9 similar) – diagram 5**

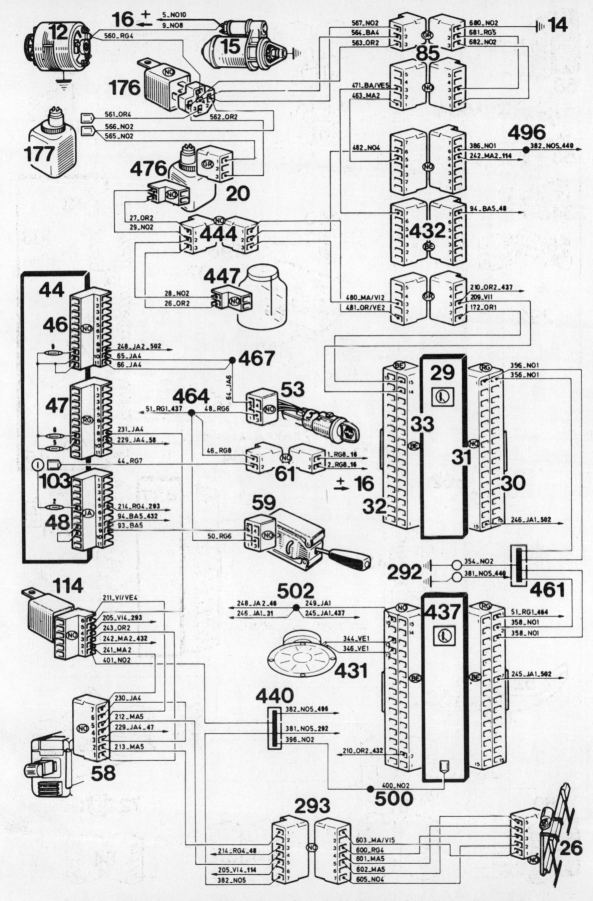

Typical wiring diagram for 1985 and later Renault 11 (Renault 9 similar) – diagram 6

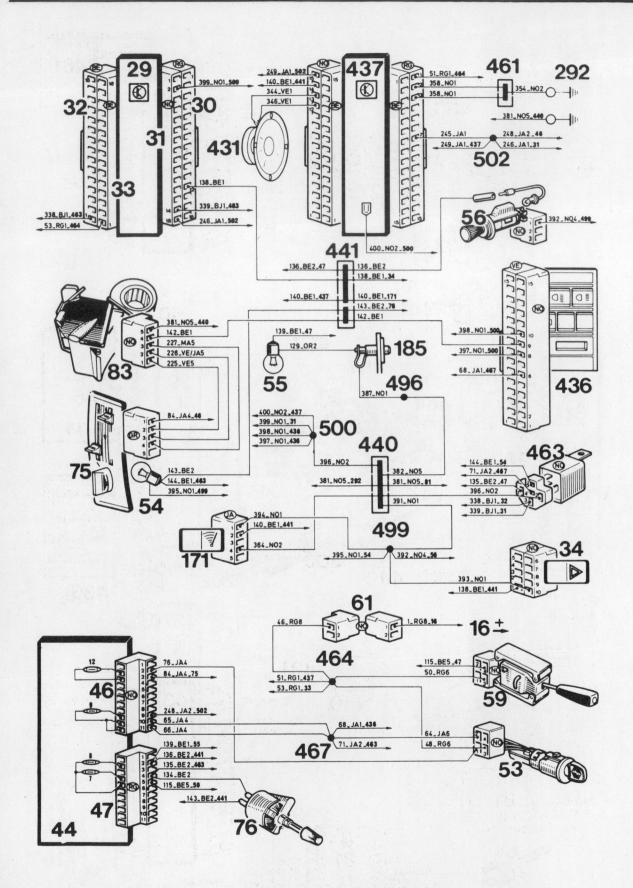

Typical wiring diagram for 1985 and later Renault 11 (Renault 9 similar) – diagram 7

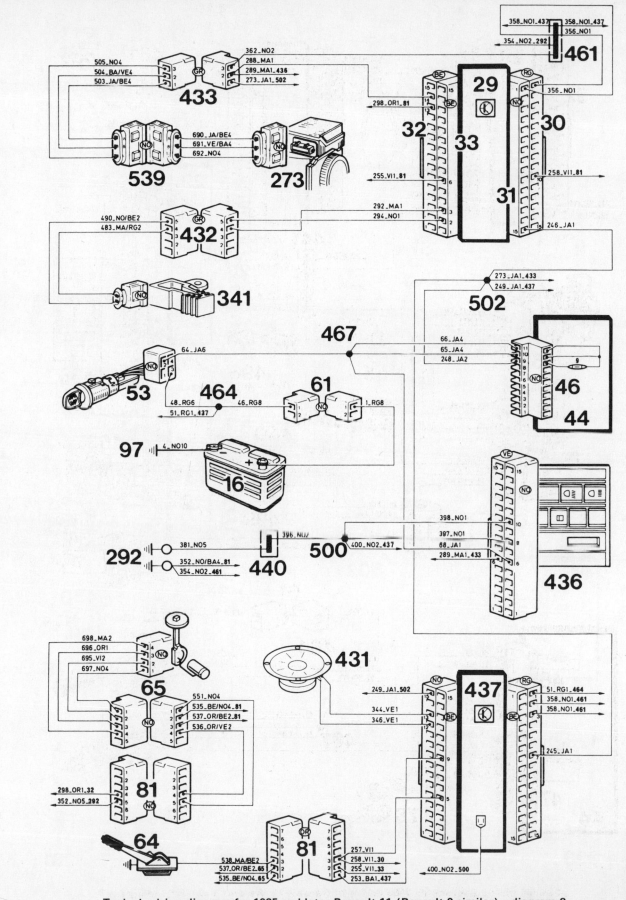

Typical wiring diagram for 1985 and later Renault 11 (Renault 9 similar) – diagram 8

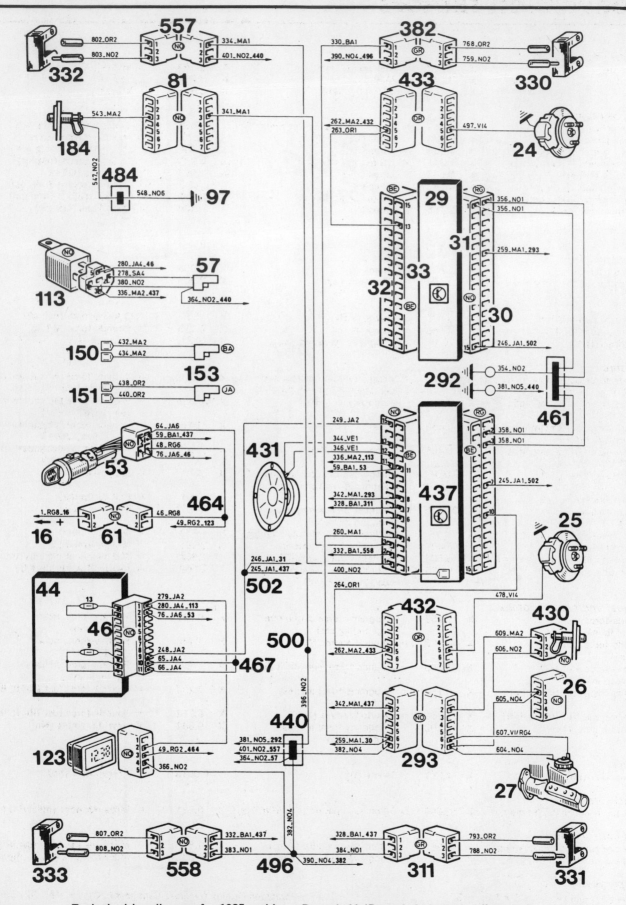

Typical wiring diagram for 1985 and later Renault 11 (Renault 9 similar) – diagram 9

# Conversion factors

## Length (distance)

| | | | | | |
|---|---|---|---|---|---|
| Inches (in) | X | 25.4 | = Millimetres (mm) | X 0.0394 | = Inches (in) |
| Feet (ft) | X | 0.305 | = Metres (m) | X 3.281 | = Feet (ft) |
| Miles | X | 1.609 | = Kilometres (km) | X 0.621 | = Miles |

## Volume (capacity)

| | | | | | |
|---|---|---|---|---|---|
| Cubic inches (cu in; in³) | X | 16.387 | = Cubic centimetres (cc; cm³) | X 0.061 | = Cubic inches (cu in; in³) |
| Imperial pints (Imp pt) | X | 0.568 | = Litres (l) | X 1.76 | = Imperial pints (Imp pt) |
| Imperial quarts (Imp qt) | X | 1.137 | = Litres (l) | X 0.88 | = Imperial quarts (Imp qt) |
| Imperial quarts (Imp qt) | X | 1.201 | = US quarts (US qt) | X 0.833 | = Imperial quarts (Imp qt) |
| US quarts (US qt) | X | 0.946 | = Litres (l) | X 1.057 | = US quarts (US qt) |
| Imperial gallons (Imp gal) | X | 4.546 | = Litres (l) | X 0.22 | = Imperial gallons (Imp gal) |
| Imperial gallons (Imp gal) | X | 1.201 | = US gallons (US gal) | X 0.833 | = Imperial gallons (Imp gal) |
| US gallons (US gal) | X | 3.785 | = Litres (l) | X 0.264 | = US gallons (US gal) |

## Mass (weight)

| | | | | | |
|---|---|---|---|---|---|
| Ounces (oz) | X | 28.35 | = Grams (g) | X 0.035 | = Ounces (oz) |
| Pounds (lb) | X | 0.454 | = Kilograms (kg) | X 2.205 | = Pounds (lb) |

## Force

| | | | | | |
|---|---|---|---|---|---|
| Ounces-force (ozf; oz) | X | 0.278 | = Newtons (N) | X 3.6 | = Ounces-force (ozf; oz) |
| Pounds-force (lbf; lb) | X | 4.448 | = Newtons (N) | X 0.225 | = Pounds-force (lbf; lb) |
| Newtons (N) | X | 0.1 | = Kilograms-force (kgf; kg) | X 9.81 | = Newtons (N) |

## Pressure

| | | | | | |
|---|---|---|---|---|---|
| Pounds-force per square inch (psi; lbf/in²; lb/in²) | X | 0.070 | = Kilograms-force per square centimetre (kgf/cm²; kg/cm²) | X 14.223 | = Pounds-force per square inch (psi; lbf/in²; lb/in²) |
| Pounds-force per square inch (psi; lbf/in²; lb/in²) | X | 0.068 | = Atmospheres (atm) | X 14.696 | = Pounds-force per square inch (psi; lbf/in²; lb/in²) |
| Pounds-force per square inch (psi; lbf/in²; lb/in²) | X | 0.069 | = Bars | X 14.5 | = Pounds-force per square inch (psi; lbf/in²; lb/in²) |
| Pounds-force per square inch (psi; lbf/in²; lb/in²) | X | 6.895 | = Kilopascals (kPa) | X 0.145 | = Pounds-force per square inch (psi; lbf/in²; lb/in²) |
| Kilopascals (kPa) | X | 0.01 | = Kilograms-force per square centimetre (kgf/cm²; kg/cm²) | X 98.1 | = Kilopascals (kPa) |
| Millibar (mbar) | X | 100 | = Pascals (Pa) | X 0.01 | = Millibar (mbar) |
| Millibar (mbar) | X | 0.0145 | = Pounds-force per square inch (psi; lbf/in²; lb/in²) | X 68.947 | = Millibar (mbar) |
| Millibar (mbar) | X | 0.75 | = Millimetres of mercury (mmHg) | X 1.333 | = Millibar (mbar) |
| Millibar (mbar) | X | 0.401 | = Inches of water (inH₂O) | X 2.491 | = Millibar (mbar) |
| Millimetres of mercury (mmHg) | X | 0.535 | = Inches of water (inH₂O) | X 1.868 | = Millimetres of mercury (mmHg) |
| Inches of water (inH₂O) | X | 0.036 | = Pounds-force per square inch (psi; lbf/in²; lb/in²) | X 27.68 | = Inches of water (inH₂O) |

## Torque (moment of force)

| | | | | | |
|---|---|---|---|---|---|
| Pounds-force inches (lbf in; lb in) | X | 1.152 | = Kilograms-force centimetre (kgf cm; kg cm) | X 0.868 | = Pounds-force inches (lbf in; lb in) |
| Pounds-force inches (lbf in; lb in) | X | 0.113 | = Newton metres (Nm) | X 8.85 | = Pounds-force inches (lbf in; lb in) |
| Pounds-force inches (lbf in; lb in) | X | 0.083 | = Pounds-force feet (lbf ft; lb ft) | X 12 | = Pounds-force inches (lbf in; lb in) |
| Pounds-force feet (lbf ft; lb ft) | X | 0.138 | = Kilograms-force metres (kgf m; kg m) | X 7.233 | = Pounds-force feet (lbf ft; lb ft) |
| Pounds-force feet (lbf ft; lb ft) | X | 1.356 | = Newton metres (Nm) | X 0.738 | = Pounds-force feet (lbf ft; lb ft) |
| Newton metres (Nm) | X | 0.102 | = Kilograms-force metres (kgf m; kg m) | X 9.804 | = Newton metres (Nm) |

## Power

| | | | | | |
|---|---|---|---|---|---|
| Horsepower (hp) | X | 745.7 | = Watts (W) | X 0.0013 | = Horsepower (hp) |

## Velocity (speed)

| | | | | | |
|---|---|---|---|---|---|
| Miles per hour (miles/hr; mph) | X | 1.609 | = Kilometres per hour (km/hr; kph) | X 0.621 | = Miles per hour (miles/hr; mph) |

## Fuel consumption*

| | | | | | |
|---|---|---|---|---|---|
| Miles per gallon, Imperial (mpg) | X | 0.354 | = Kilometres per litre (km/l) | X 2.825 | = Miles per gallon, Imperial (mpg) |
| Miles per gallon, US (mpg) | X | 0.425 | = Kilometres per litre (km/l) | X 2.352 | = Miles per gallon, US (mpg) |

## Temperature

Degrees Fahrenheit = (°C x 1.8) + 32

Degrees Celsius (Degrees Centigrade; °C) = (°F - 32) x 0.56

*It is common practice to convert from miles per gallon (mpg) to litres/100 kilometres (l/100km), where mpg (Imperial) x l/100 km = 282 and mpg (US) x l/100 km = 235

# Index